Elementary Linear Algebra

SEVENTH EDITION

Ron Larson

The Pennsylvania State University / The Behrend College

BROOKS/COLE
CENGAGE Learning

Australia • Brazil • Japan • Korea • Mexico • Singapore • Spain • United Kingdom • United States

BROOKS/COLE
CENGAGE Learning

ISBN-13: 978-1-133-36538-9
ISBN-10: 1-133-36538-8

Brooks/Cole
20 Channel Center Street
Boston, MA 02210
USA

Cengage Learning is a leading provider of customized learning solutions with office locations around the globe, including Singapore, the United Kingdom, Australia, Mexico, Brazil, and Japan. Locate your local office at: **www.cengage.com/global**

Cengage Learning products are represented in Canada by Nelson Education, Ltd.

To learn more about Brooks/Cole, visit **www.cengage.com/brookscole**

Purchase any of our products at your local college store or at our preferred online store **www.cengagebrain.com**

Printed in the United States of America
1 2 3 4 5 6 7 16 15 14 13 12

CONTENTS

C H A P T E R 1
Systems of Linear Equations

C H A P T E R 1
Systems of Linear Equations

Section 1.1 Introduction to Systems of Linear Equations

2. Because the term xy cannot be rewritten as $ax + by$ for any real numbers a and b, the equation cannot be written in the form $a_1x + a_2y = b$. So, this equation is *not* linear in the variables x and y.

4. Because the terms x^2 and y^2 cannot be rewritten as $ax + by$ for any real numbers a and b, the equation cannot be written in the form $a_1x + a_2y = b$. So, this equation is *not* linear in the variables x and y.

6. Because the equation is in the form $a_1x + a_2y = b$, it *is* linear in the variables x and y.

8. Choosing y as the free variable, let $y = t$ and obtain

$$3x - \tfrac{1}{2}t = 9$$
$$3x = 9 + \tfrac{1}{2}t$$
$$x = 3 + \tfrac{1}{6}t.$$

So, you can describe the solution set as $x = 3 + \tfrac{1}{6}t$ and $y = t$, where t is any real number.

10. Choosing x_2 and x_3 as free variables, let $x_3 = t$ and $x_2 = s$ and obtain $13x_1 - 26x + 39t = 13$.

Dividing this equation by 13 you obtain

$$x_1 - 2s + 3t = 1$$
$$x_1 = 1 + 2s - 3t.$$

So, you can describe the solution set as $x_1 = 1 + 2s - 3t$, $x_2 = s$, and $x_3 = t$, where t and s are any real numbers.

12.

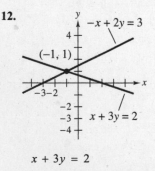

$$x + 3y = 2$$
$$-x + 2y = 3$$

Adding the first equation to the second equation produces a new second equation, $5y = 5$ or $y = 1$.
So, $x = 2 - 3y = 2 - 3(1)$, and the solution is: $x = -1$, $y = 1$. This is the point where the two lines intersect.

14.

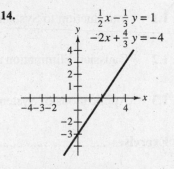

The two lines coincide.

Multiplying the first equation by 2 produces a new first equation.

$$x - \tfrac{2}{3}y = 2$$
$$-2x + \tfrac{4}{3}y = -4$$

Adding 2 times the first equation to the second equation produces a new second equation.

$$x - \tfrac{2}{3}y = 2$$
$$0 = 0$$

Choosing $y = t$ as the free variable, you obtain

$x = \tfrac{2}{3}t + 2$. So, you can describe the solution set as $x = \tfrac{2}{3}t + 2$ and $y = t$, where t is any real number.

16.

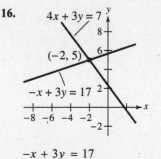

$$-x + 3y = 17$$
$$4x + 3y = 7$$

Subtracting the first equation from the second equation produces a new second equation, $5x = -10$ or $x = -2$.
So, $4(-2) + 3y = 7$ or $y = 5$, and the solution is:
$x = -2$, $y = 5$. This is the point where the two lines intersect.

18.

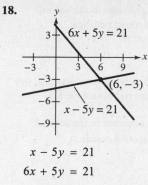

$x - 5y = 21$

$6x + 5y = 21$

Adding the first equation to the second equation produces a new second equation, $7x = 42$ or $x = 6$.

So, $6 - 5y = 21$ or $y = -3$, and the solution is: $x = 6$, $y = -3$. This is the point where the two lines intersect.

20.

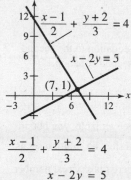

$$\frac{x - 1}{2} + \frac{y + 2}{3} = 4$$

$$x - 2y = 5$$

Multiplying the first equation by 6 produces a new first equation.

$3x + 2y = 23$

$x - 2y = 5$

Adding the first equation to the second equation produces a new second equation, $4x = 28$ or $x = 7$.

So, $7 - 2y = 5$ or $y = 1$, and the solution is: $x = 7$, $y = 1$. This is the point where the two lines intersect.

22.

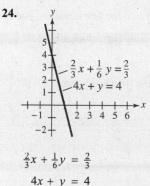

$0.2x - 0.5y = -27.8$

$0.3x + 0.4y = 68.7$

Multiplying the first equation by 40 and the second equation by 50 produces new equations.

$8x - 20y = -1112$

$15x + 20y = 3435$

Adding the first equation to the second equation produces a new second equation, $23x = 2323$ or $x = 101$.

So, $8(101) - 20y = -1112$ or $y = 96$, and the solution is: $x = 101$, $y = 96$. This is the point where the two lines intersect.

24.

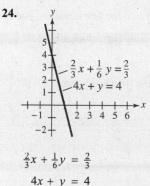

$\frac{2}{3}x + \frac{1}{6}y = \frac{2}{3}$

$4x + y = 4$

Adding 6 times the first equation to the second equation produces a new second equation, $0 = 0$. Choosing $x = t$ as the free variable, you obtain $y = 4 - 4t$. So, you can describe the solution as $x = t$ and $y = 4 - 4t$, where t is any real number.

26. From Equation 2 you have $x_2 = 3$. Substituting this value into Equation 1 produces $2x_1 - 12 = 6$ or $x_1 = 9$. So, the system has exactly one solution: $x_1 = 9$ and $x_2 = 3$.

28. From Equation 3 you conclude that $z = 2$. Substituting this value into Equation 2 produces $2y + 2 = 6$ or $y = 2$. Finally, substituting $y = 2$ and $z = 2$ into Equation 1, you obtain $x - 2 = 4$ or $x = 6$. So, the system has exactly one solution: $x = 6$, $y = 2$, and $z = 2$.

30. From the second equation you have $x_2 = 0$. Substituting this value into Equation 1 produces $x_1 + x_3 = 0$. Choosing x_3 as the free variable, you have $x_3 = t$ and obtain $x_1 + t = 0$ or $x_1 = -t$. So, you can describe the solution set as $x_1 = -t$, $x_2 = 0$, and $x_3 = t$.

32. (a)

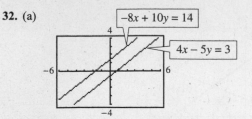

$-8x + 10y = 14$

$4x - 5y = 3$

(b) This system is inconsistent, because you see two parallel lines on the graph of the system.

34. (a)

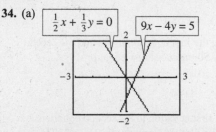

$\frac{1}{2}x + \frac{1}{3}y = 0$

$9x - 4y = 5$

(b) Two lines corresponding to two equations intersect at a point, so this system is consistent.

(c) The solution is approximately $x = \frac{1}{3}$ and $y = -\frac{1}{2}$.

(d) Adding -18 times the second equation to the first equation, you obtain $-10y = 5$ or $y = -\frac{1}{2}$.

Substituting $y = -\frac{1}{2}$ into the first equation, you obtain $9x = 3$ or $x = \frac{1}{3}$. The solution is: $x = \frac{1}{3}$ and $y = -\frac{1}{2}$.

(e) The solutions in (c) and (d) are the same.

36. (a)

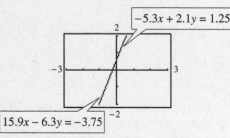

$-5.3x + 2.1y = 1.25$

$15.9x - 6.3y = -3.75$

(b) Because each equation has the same line as a graph, there are infinitely many solutions.

(c) All solutions of this system lie on the line $y = \frac{53}{21}x + \frac{25}{42}$. So let $x = t$, then the solution set is $x = t$, $y = \frac{53}{21}t + \frac{25}{42}$, where t is any real number.

(d) Adding 3 times the first equation to the second equation you obtain

$-5.3x + 2.1y = 1.25$

$0 = 0.$

Choosing $x = t$ as the free variable, you obtain $2.1y = 5.3t + 1.25$ or $21y = 53t + 12.5$ or $y = \frac{53}{21}t + \frac{25}{42}$. So, you can describe the solution set as $x = t$, $y = \frac{53}{21}t + \frac{25}{42}$, where t is any real number.

(e) The solutions in (c) and (d) are the same.

38. Adding -2 times the first equation to the second equation produces a new second equation.

$3x + 2y = 2$

$0 = 10$

Because the second equation is a false statement, the original system of equations has no solution.

40. Adding -6 times the first equation to the second equation produces a new second equation.

$x_1 - 2x_2 = 0$

$14x_2 = 0$

Now, using back-substitution, the system has exactly one solution: $x_1 = 0$ and $x_2 = 0$.

42. Multiplying the first equation by $\frac{3}{2}$ produces a new first equation.

$x_1 + \frac{1}{4}x_2 = 0$

$4x_1 + x_2 = 0$

Adding -4 times the first equation to the second equation produces a new second equation.

$x_1 + \frac{1}{4}x_2 = 0$

$0 = 0$

Choosing $x_2 = t$ as the free variable, you obtain $x_1 = -\frac{1}{4}t$. So you can describe the solution set as $x_1 = -\frac{1}{4}t$ and $x_2 = t$, where t is any real number.

44. To begin, change the form of the first equation.

$\frac{x_1}{3} + \frac{x_2}{2} = -\frac{5}{6}$

$3x_1 - x_2 = -2$

Multiplying the first equation by 3 yields a new first equation.

$x_1 + \frac{3}{2}x_2 = -\frac{5}{2}$

$3x_1 - x_2 = -2$

Adding -3 times the first equation to the second equation produces a new second equation.

$x_1 + \frac{3}{2}x_2 = -\frac{5}{2}$

$-\frac{11}{2}x_2 = \frac{11}{2}$

Multiplying the second equation by $-\frac{2}{11}$ yields a new second equation.

$x_1 + \frac{3}{2}x_2 = -\frac{5}{2}$

$x_2 = -1$

Now, using back-substitution, the system has exactly one solution: $x_1 = -1$ and $x_2 = -1$.

46. Multiplying the first equation by 20 and the second equation by 100 produces a new system.

$$x_1 - 0.6x_2 = 4.2$$
$$7x_1 + 2x_2 = 17$$

Adding -7 times the first equation to the second equation produces a new second equation.

$$x_1 - 0.6x_2 = 4.2$$
$$6.2x_2 = -12.4$$

Now, using back-substitution, the system has exactly one solution: $x_1 = 3$ and $x_2 = -2$.

48. Adding the first equation to the second equation yields a new second equation.

$$x + y + z = 2$$
$$4y + 3z = 10$$
$$4x + y = 4$$

Adding -4 times the first equation to the third equation yields a new third equation.

$$x + y + z = 2$$
$$4y + 3z = 10$$
$$-3y - 4z = -4$$

Dividing the second equation by 4 yields a new second equation.

$$x + y + z = 2$$
$$y + \tfrac{3}{4}z = \tfrac{5}{2}$$
$$-3y - 4z = -4$$

Adding 3 times the second equation to the third equation yields a new third equation.

$$x + y + z = 2$$
$$y + \tfrac{3}{4}z = \tfrac{5}{2}$$
$$-\tfrac{7}{4}z = \tfrac{7}{2}$$

Multiplying the third equation by $-\tfrac{4}{7}$ yields a new third equation.

$$x + y + z = 2$$
$$y + \tfrac{3}{4}z = \tfrac{5}{2}$$
$$z = -2$$

Now, using back-substitution the system has exactly one solution: $x = 0$, $y = 4$, and $z = -2$.

50. Interchanging the first and third equations yields a new system.

$$x_1 - 11x_2 + 4x_3 = 3$$
$$2x_1 + 4x_2 - x_3 = 7$$
$$5x_1 - 3x_2 + 2x_3 = 3$$

Adding -2 times the first equation to the second equation yields a new second equation.

$$x_1 - 11x_2 + 4x_3 = 3$$
$$26x_2 - 9x_3 = 1$$
$$5x_1 - 3x_2 + 2x_3 = 3$$

Adding -5 times the first equation to the third equation yields a new third equation.

$$x_1 - 11x_2 + 4x_3 = 3$$
$$26x_2 - 9x_3 = 1$$
$$52x_2 - 18x_3 = -12$$

At this point, you realize that Equations 2 and 3 cannot both be satisfied. So, the original system of equations has no solution.

52. Adding -4 times the first equation to the second equation and adding -2 times the first equation to the third equation produces new second and third equations.

$$x_1 + 4x_3 = 13$$
$$-2x_2 - 15x_3 = -45$$
$$-2x_2 - 15x_3 = -45$$

The third equation can be disregarded because it is the same as the second one. Choosing x_3 as a free variable and letting $x_3 = t$, you can describe the solution as

$$x_1 = 13 - 4t$$
$$x_2 = \tfrac{45}{2} - \tfrac{15}{2}t$$
$$x_3 = t, \text{ where } t \text{ is any real number.}$$

54. Adding -3 times the first equation to the second equation produces a new second equation.

$$x_1 - 2x_2 + 5x_3 = 2$$
$$8x_2 - 16x_3 = -8$$

Dividing the second equation by 8 yields a new second equation.

$$x_1 - 2x_2 + 5x_3 = 2$$
$$x_2 - 2x_3 = -1$$

Adding 2 times the second equation to the first equation yields a new first equation.

$$x_1 + x_3 = 0$$
$$x_2 - 2x_3 = -1$$

Letting $x_3 = t$ be the free variable, you can describe the solution as $x_1 = -t$, $x_2 = 2t - 1$, and $x_3 = t$, where t is any real number.

56. Adding -2 times the first equation to the fourth equation, yields

$$
\begin{aligned}
x_1 \qquad\qquad\quad + 3x_4 &= 4 \\
2x_2 - x_3 - x_4 &= 0 \\
3x_2 \qquad\;\; - 2x_4 &= 1 \\
-x_2 + 4x_3 - 6x_4 &= -3.
\end{aligned}
$$

Multiplying the fourth equation by -1, and interchanging it with the second equation, yields

$$
\begin{aligned}
x_1 \qquad\qquad\quad + 3x_4 &= 4 \\
x_2 - 4x_3 + 6x_4 &= 3 \\
3x_2 \qquad\;\; - 2x_4 &= 1 \\
2x_2 - x_3 - x_4 &= 0.
\end{aligned}
$$

Adding -3 times the second equation to the third, and -2 times the second equation to the fourth, produces

$$
\begin{aligned}
x_1 \qquad\qquad\quad + 3x_4 &= 4 \\
x_2 - 4x_3 + 6x_4 &= 3 \\
12x_3 - 20x_4 &= -8 \\
7x_3 - 13x_4 &= -6.
\end{aligned}
$$

Dividing the third equation by 12 yields

$$
\begin{aligned}
x_1 \qquad\qquad\quad + 3x_4 &= 4 \\
x_2 - 4x_3 + 6x_4 &= 3 \\
x_3 - \tfrac{5}{3}x_4 &= -\tfrac{2}{3} \\
7x_3 - 13x_4 &= -6.
\end{aligned}
$$

Adding -7 times the third equation to the fourth yields

$$
\begin{aligned}
x_1 \qquad\qquad\quad + 3x_4 &= 4 \\
x_2 - 4x_3 + 6x_4 &= 3 \\
x_3 - \tfrac{5}{3}x_4 &= -\tfrac{2}{3} \\
\tfrac{4}{3}x_4 &= \tfrac{4}{3}.
\end{aligned}
$$

Using back-substitution, the original system has exactly one solution: $x_1 = 1$, $x_2 = 1$, $x_3 = 1$, and $x_4 = 1$.

Answers may vary slightly for Exercises 58–60.

58. Using a computer software program or graphing utility, you obtain $x = 0.8$, $y = 1.2$, $z = -2.4$.

60. Using a computer software program or graphing utility, you obtain

$$x = 6.8813,\ y = -163.3111,\ z = -210.2915,$$
$$w = -59.2913.$$

62. $x = y = z = 0$ is clearly a solution.

Dividing the first equation by 2 produces

$$
\begin{aligned}
x + \tfrac{3}{2}y \qquad\;\; &= 0 \\
4x + 3y - z &= 0 \\
8x + 3y + 3z &= 0.
\end{aligned}
$$

Adding -4 times the first equation to the second equation, and -8 times the first equation to the third, yields

$$
\begin{aligned}
x + \tfrac{3}{2}y \qquad\;\; &= 0 \\
-3y - z &= 0 \\
-9y + 3z &= 0.
\end{aligned}
$$

Adding -3 times the second equation to the third equation yields

$$
\begin{aligned}
x + \tfrac{3}{2}y \qquad\;\; &= 0 \\
-3y - z &= 0 \\
6z &= 0.
\end{aligned}
$$

Using back-substitution, you conclude there is exactly one solution: $x = y = z = 0$.

64. $x = y = z = 0$ is clearly a solution.

Dividing the first equation by 12 yields

$$
\begin{aligned}
x + \tfrac{5}{12}y + \tfrac{1}{12}z &= 0 \\
12x + 4y - z &= 0.
\end{aligned}
$$

Adding -12 times the first equation to the second yields

$$
\begin{aligned}
x + \tfrac{5}{12}y + \tfrac{1}{12}z &= 0 \\
-y - 2z &= 0.
\end{aligned}
$$

Letting $z = t$ be the free variable, you can describe the solution as $x = \tfrac{3}{4}t$, $y = -2t$, and $z = t$, where t is any real number.

66. Let $x = $ the speed of the plane that leaves first and $y = $ the speed of the plane that leaves second.

$$
\begin{aligned}
y - x &= 80 && \text{Equation 1} \\
2x + \tfrac{3}{2}y &= 3200 && \text{Equation 2}
\end{aligned}
$$

$$
\begin{aligned}
-2x + 2y &= 160 \\
\underline{2x + \tfrac{3}{2}y} &= \underline{3200} \\
\tfrac{7}{2}y &= 3360 \\
y &= 960
\end{aligned}
$$

$$
\begin{aligned}
960 - x &= 80 \\
x &= 880
\end{aligned}
$$

Solution: First plane: 880 kilometers per hour; second plane: 960 kilometers per hour

68. (a) False. Any system of linear equations is either consistent, which means it has a unique solution, or infinitely many solutions; or inconsistent, which means it has no solution. This result is stated on page 5 of the text, and will be proved later in Theorem 2.5.

(b) True. See definition on page 6 of the text.

(c) False. Consider the following system of three linear equations with two variables.

$$2x + y = -3$$
$$-6x - 3y = 9$$
$$x = 1.$$

The solution to this system is: $x = 1$, $y = -5$.

70. Because $x_1 = t$ and $x_2 = s$, you can write $x_3 = 3 + s - t = 3 + x_2 - x_1$. One system could be

$$x_1 - x_2 + x_3 = 3$$
$$-x_1 + x_2 - x_3 = -3$$

Letting $x_3 = t$ and $x_2 = s$ be the free variables, you can describe the solution as $x_1 = 3 + s - t$, $x_2 = s$, and $x_3 = t$, where t and s are any real numbers.

72. Substituting $A = \dfrac{1}{x}$ and $B = \dfrac{1}{y}$ into the original system yields

$$2A + 3B = 0$$
$$3A - 4B = -\dfrac{25}{6}.$$

Reduce the system to row-echelon form.

$$8A + 12B = 0$$
$$9A - 12B = -\dfrac{25}{2}$$
$$8A + 12B = 0$$
$$17A = -\dfrac{25}{2}$$

So, $A = -\dfrac{25}{34}$ and $B = \dfrac{25}{51}$. Because $A = \dfrac{1}{x}$ and $B = \dfrac{1}{y}$, the solution of the original system of equations

is: $x = -\dfrac{34}{25}$ and $y = \dfrac{51}{25}$.

74. Substituting $A = \dfrac{1}{x}$, $B = \dfrac{1}{y}$, and $C = \dfrac{1}{z}$ into the original system yields

$$2A + B - 2C = 5$$
$$3A - 4B = -1$$
$$2A + B + 3C = 0.$$

Reduce the system to row-echelon form.

$$2A + B - 2C = 5$$
$$3A - 4B = -1$$
$$5C = -5$$
$$3A - 4B = -1$$
$$-11B + 6C = -17$$
$$5C = -5$$

So, $C = -1$. Using back-substitution, $-11B + 6(-1) = -17$, or $B = 1$ and $3A - 4(1) = -1$, or $A = 1$. Because $A = 1/x$, $B = 1/y$, and $C = 1/z$, the solution of the original system of equations is: $x = 1$, $y = 1$, and $z = -1$.

76. Multiplying the first equation by $\sin \theta$ and the second by $\cos \theta$ produces

$$(\sin \theta \cos \theta)x + (\sin^2 \theta)y = \sin \theta$$
$$-(\sin \theta \cos \theta)x + (\cos^2 \theta)y = \cos \theta.$$

Adding these two equations yields

$$(\sin^2 \theta + \cos^2 \theta)y = \sin \theta + \cos \theta$$
$$y = \sin \theta + \cos \theta.$$

So,

$(\cos \theta)x + (\sin \theta)y = (\cos \theta)x + \sin \theta(\sin \theta + \cos \theta) = 1$ and

$$x = \frac{(1 - \sin^2 \theta - \sin \theta \cos \theta)}{\cos \theta} = \frac{(\cos^2 \theta - \sin \theta \cos \theta)}{\cos \theta} = \cos \theta - \sin \theta.$$

Finally, the solution is $x = \cos \theta - \sin \theta$ and $y = \cos \theta + \sin \theta$.

78. Interchange the two equations and row reduce.

$$x - \tfrac{3}{2}y = -6$$
$$kx + y = 4$$

$$x - \tfrac{3}{2}y = -6$$
$$\left(\tfrac{3}{2}k + 1\right)y = 4 + 6k$$

So, if $k = -\tfrac{2}{3}$, there will be an infinite number of solutions.

80. Reduce the system.

$$x + ky = 2$$
$$\left(1 - k^2\right)y = 4 - 2k$$

If $k = \pm 1$, there will be no solution.

82. Interchange the first two equations and row reduce.

$$x + \quad y + \quad z = 0$$
$$ky + 2kz = 4k$$
$$-3y - \quad z = 1$$

If $k = 0$, then there is an infinite number of solutions. Otherwise,

$$x + y + \quad z = 0$$
$$y + 2z = 4$$
$$5z = 13.$$

Because this system has exactly one solution, the answer is all $k \neq 0$.

84. Reducing the system to row-echelon form produces

$$x + \quad 5y + \quad z = 0$$
$$y - \quad 2z = 0$$
$$(a - 10)y + (b - 2)z = c$$

$$x + 5y + \quad z = 0$$
$$y - 2z = 0$$
$$(2a + b - 22)z = c.$$

So, you see that

(a) if $2a + b - 22 \neq 0$, then there is exactly one solution.

(b) if $2a + b - 22 = 0$ and $c = 0$, then there is an infinite number of solutions.

(c) if $2a + b - 22 = 0$ and $c \neq 0$, there is no solution.

86. If $c_1 = c_2 = c_3 = 0$, then the system is consistent because $x = y = 0$ is a solution.

88. Multiplying the first equation by c, and the second by a, produces

$$acx + bcy = ec$$
$$acx + day = af.$$

Subtracting the second equation from the first yields

$$acx + bcy = ec$$
$$(ad - bc)y = af - ec.$$

So, there is a unique solution if $ad - bc \neq 0$.

90.

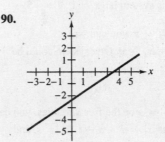

The two lines coincide.

$$2x - 3y = 7$$
$$0 = 0$$

Letting $y = t$, $x = \dfrac{7 + 3t}{2}$.

The graph does not change.

92.
$$21x - 20y = \quad 0$$
$$13x - 12y = 120$$

Subtracting 5 times the second equation from 3 times the first equation produces a new first equation, $-2x = -600$, or $x = 300$. So, $21(300) - 20y = 0$ or $y = 315$, and the solution is: $x = 300$, $y = 315$. The graphs are misleading because they appear to be parallel, but they actually intersect at $(300, 315)$.

Section 1.2   Gaussian Elimination and Gauss-Jordan Elimination

2. Because the matrix has 4 rows and 1 column, it has size 4×1.

4. Because the matrix has 1 row and 1 column, it has size 1×1.

6. Because the matrix has 1 row and 5 columns, it has size 1×5.

8. $\begin{bmatrix} 3 & -1 & -4 \\ -4 & 3 & 7 \end{bmatrix} \Rightarrow \begin{bmatrix} 3 & -1 & -4 \\ 5 & 0 & -5 \end{bmatrix}$

Add 3 times Row 1 to Row 2.

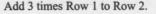

10. $\begin{bmatrix} -1 & -2 & 3 & -2 \\ 2 & -5 & 1 & -7 \\ 5 & 4 & -7 & 6 \end{bmatrix} \Rightarrow \begin{bmatrix} -1 & -2 & 3 & -2 \\ 0 & -9 & 7 & -11 \\ 0 & -6 & 8 & -4 \end{bmatrix}$

Add 2 times Row 1 to Row 2.

Add 5 times Row 1 to Row 3.

12. Because the matrix is in reduced row-echelon form, you can convert back to a system of linear equations

$x_1 = 2$

$x_2 = 3.$

14. Because the matrix is in row-echelon form, you can convert back to a system of linear equations

$x_1 + 2x_2 + x_3 = 0$

$x_3 = -1.$

Using back-substitution, you have $x_3 = -1$. Letting $x_2 = t$ be the free variable, you can describe the solution as $x_1 = 1 - 2t$, $x_2 = t$, and $x_3 = -1$, where t is any real number.

16. Gaussian elimination produces the following.

$\begin{bmatrix} 2 & 1 & 1 & 0 \\ 1 & -2 & 1 & -2 \\ 1 & 0 & 1 & 0 \end{bmatrix} \Rightarrow \begin{bmatrix} 1 & 0 & 1 & 0 \\ 1 & -2 & 1 & -2 \\ 2 & 1 & 1 & 0 \end{bmatrix}$

$\Rightarrow \begin{bmatrix} 1 & 0 & 1 & 0 \\ 0 & -2 & 0 & -2 \\ 2 & 1 & 1 & 0 \end{bmatrix} \Rightarrow \begin{bmatrix} 1 & 0 & 1 & 0 \\ 0 & 1 & 0 & 1 \\ 2 & 1 & 1 & 0 \end{bmatrix}$

$\Rightarrow \begin{bmatrix} 1 & 0 & 1 & 0 \\ 0 & 1 & 0 & 1 \\ 0 & 1 & -1 & 0 \end{bmatrix} \Rightarrow \begin{bmatrix} 1 & 0 & 1 & 0 \\ 0 & 1 & 0 & 1 \\ 0 & 0 & 1 & 1 \end{bmatrix}$

Because the matrix is in row-echelon form, convert back to a system of linear equations.

$x_1 \quad + x_3 = 0$

$\quad x_2 \quad = 1$

$\quad\quad x_3 = 1$

By back-substitution, $x_1 = -x_3 = -1$. So, the solution is: $x_1 = -1$, $x_2 = 1$, and $x_3 = 1$.

18. Because the fourth row of this matrix corresponds to the equation $0 = 2$, there is no solution to the linear system.

20. Because the leading 1 in the first row is not farther to the left than the leading 1 in the second row, the matrix is *not* in row-echelon form.

22. The matrix satisfies all three conditions in the definition of row-echelon form. However, because the third column does not have zeros above the leading 1 in the third row, the matrix is *not* in reduced row-echelon form.

24. The matrix satisfies all three conditions in the definition of row-echelon form. Moreover, because each column that has a leading 1 (columns one and four) has zeros elsewhere, the matrix *is* in reduced row-echelon form.

26. The augmented matrix for this system is

$\begin{bmatrix} 2 & 6 & 16 \\ -2 & -6 & -16 \end{bmatrix}.$

Use Gauss-Jordan elimination as follows.

$\begin{bmatrix} 2 & 6 & 16 \\ -2 & -6 & -16 \end{bmatrix} \Rightarrow \begin{bmatrix} 1 & 3 & 8 \\ -2 & -6 & -16 \end{bmatrix} \Rightarrow \begin{bmatrix} 1 & 3 & 8 \\ 0 & 0 & 0 \end{bmatrix}$

Converting back to a system of linear equations, you have

$x + 3y = 8.$

Choosing $y = t$ as the free variable, you can describe the solution as $x = 8 - 3t$ and $y = t$, where t is any real number.

28. The augmented matrix for this system is

$\begin{bmatrix} 2 & -1 & -0.1 \\ 3 & 2 & 1.6 \end{bmatrix}.$

Gaussian elimination produces the following.

$\begin{bmatrix} 2 & -1 & -0.1 \\ 3 & 2 & 1.6 \end{bmatrix} \Rightarrow \begin{bmatrix} 1 & -\frac{1}{2} & -\frac{1}{20} \\ 3 & 2 & \frac{8}{5} \end{bmatrix}$

$\Rightarrow \begin{bmatrix} 1 & -\frac{1}{2} & -\frac{1}{20} \\ 0 & \frac{7}{2} & \frac{7}{4} \end{bmatrix}$

$\Rightarrow \begin{bmatrix} 1 & -\frac{1}{2} & -\frac{1}{20} \\ 0 & 1 & \frac{1}{2} \end{bmatrix} \Rightarrow \begin{bmatrix} 1 & 0 & \frac{1}{5} \\ 0 & 1 & \frac{1}{2} \end{bmatrix}$

Converting back to a system of equations, the solution is:

$x = \frac{1}{5}$ and $y = \frac{1}{2}.$

30. The augmented matrix for this system is

$\begin{bmatrix} 1 & 2 & 0 \\ 1 & 1 & 6 \\ 3 & -2 & 8 \end{bmatrix}.$

Gaussian elimination produces the following.

$\begin{bmatrix} 1 & 2 & 0 \\ 1 & 1 & 6 \\ 3 & -2 & 8 \end{bmatrix} \Rightarrow \begin{bmatrix} 1 & 2 & 0 \\ 0 & -1 & 6 \\ 0 & -8 & 8 \end{bmatrix}$

$\Rightarrow \begin{bmatrix} 1 & 2 & 0 \\ 0 & 1 & -6 \\ 0 & -8 & 8 \end{bmatrix} \Rightarrow \begin{bmatrix} 1 & 2 & 0 \\ 0 & 1 & -6 \\ 0 & 0 & -40 \end{bmatrix}$

Because the third row corresponds to the equation $0 = -40$, you conclude that the system has no solution.

32. The augmented matrix for this system is

$$\begin{bmatrix} 2 & -1 & 3 & 24 \\ 0 & 2 & -1 & 14 \\ 7 & -5 & 0 & 6 \end{bmatrix}.$$

Gaussian elimination produces the following.

$$\begin{bmatrix} 2 & -1 & 3 & 24 \\ 0 & 2 & -1 & 14 \\ 7 & -5 & 0 & 6 \end{bmatrix} \Rightarrow \begin{bmatrix} 1 & -\frac{1}{2} & \frac{3}{2} & 12 \\ 0 & 2 & -1 & 14 \\ 7 & -5 & 0 & 6 \end{bmatrix} \Rightarrow \begin{bmatrix} 1 & -\frac{1}{2} & \frac{3}{2} & 12 \\ 0 & 2 & -1 & 14 \\ 0 & -\frac{3}{2} & -\frac{21}{2} & -78 \end{bmatrix} \Rightarrow \begin{bmatrix} 1 & -\frac{1}{2} & \frac{3}{2} & 12 \\ 0 & 1 & -\frac{1}{2} & 7 \\ 0 & 0 & -\frac{45}{4} & -\frac{135}{2} \end{bmatrix}$$

Back-substitution now yields

$x_3 = 6$

$x_2 = 7 + \frac{1}{2}x_3 = 7 + \frac{1}{2}(6) = 10$

$x_1 = 12 - \frac{3}{2}x_3 + \frac{1}{2}x_2 = 12 - \frac{3}{2}(6) + \frac{1}{2}(10) = 8.$

So, the solution is: $x_1 = 8$, $x_2 = 10$, and $x_3 = 6$.

34. The augmented matrix for this system is

$$\begin{bmatrix} 1 & 1 & -5 & 3 \\ 1 & 0 & -2 & 1 \\ 2 & -1 & -1 & 0 \end{bmatrix}.$$

Subtracting the first row from the second row yields a new second row.

$$\begin{bmatrix} 1 & 1 & -5 & 3 \\ 0 & -1 & 3 & -2 \\ 2 & -1 & -1 & 0 \end{bmatrix}$$

Adding -2 times the first row to the third row yields a new third row.

$$\begin{bmatrix} 1 & 1 & -5 & 3 \\ 0 & -1 & 3 & -2 \\ 0 & -3 & 9 & -6 \end{bmatrix}$$

Multiplying the second row by -1 yields a new second row.

$$\begin{bmatrix} 1 & 1 & -5 & 3 \\ 0 & 1 & -3 & 2 \\ 0 & -3 & 9 & -6 \end{bmatrix}$$

Adding 3 times the second row to the third row yields a new third row.

$$\begin{bmatrix} 1 & 1 & -5 & 3 \\ 0 & 1 & -3 & 2 \\ 0 & 0 & 0 & 0 \end{bmatrix}$$

Adding -1 times the second row to the first row yields a new first row.

$$\begin{bmatrix} 1 & 0 & -2 & 1 \\ 0 & 1 & -3 & 2 \\ 0 & 0 & 0 & 0 \end{bmatrix}$$

Converting back to a system of linear equations produces

$x_1 \quad - 2x_3 = 1$

$\quad x_2 - 3x_3 = 2.$

Finally, choosing $x_3 = t$ as the free variable, you can describe the solution as $x_1 = 1 + 2t$, $x_2 = 2 + 3t$, and $x_3 = t$, where t is any real number.

36 The augmented matrix for this system is

$$\begin{bmatrix} 1 & 2 & 1 & 8 \\ -3 & -6 & -3 & -21 \end{bmatrix}.$$

Gaussian elimination produces the following matrix.

$$\begin{bmatrix} 1 & 2 & 1 & 8 \\ 0 & 0 & 0 & 3 \end{bmatrix}$$

Because the second row corresponds to the equation $0 = 3,$ there is no solution to the original system.

38. The augmented matrix for this system is

$$\begin{bmatrix} 2 & 1 & -1 & 2 & -6 \\ 3 & 4 & 0 & 1 & 1 \\ 1 & 5 & 2 & 6 & -3 \\ 5 & 2 & -1 & -1 & 3 \end{bmatrix}.$$

Gaussian elimination produces the following.

$$\begin{bmatrix} 1 & 5 & 2 & 6 & -3 \\ 3 & 4 & 0 & 1 & 1 \\ 2 & 1 & -1 & 2 & -6 \\ 5 & 2 & -1 & -1 & 3 \end{bmatrix} \Rightarrow \begin{bmatrix} 1 & 5 & 2 & 6 & -3 \\ 0 & -11 & -6 & -17 & 10 \\ 0 & -9 & -5 & -10 & 0 \\ 0 & -23 & -11 & -31 & 18 \end{bmatrix} \Rightarrow \begin{bmatrix} 1 & 5 & 2 & 6 & -3 \\ 0 & 1 & \frac{6}{11} & \frac{17}{11} & -\frac{10}{11} \\ 0 & -9 & -5 & -10 & 0 \\ 0 & -23 & -11 & -31 & 18 \end{bmatrix}$$

$$\Rightarrow \begin{bmatrix} 1 & 5 & 2 & 6 & -3 \\ 0 & 1 & \frac{6}{11} & \frac{17}{11} & -\frac{10}{11} \\ 0 & 0 & -\frac{1}{11} & \frac{43}{11} & -\frac{90}{11} \\ 0 & 0 & \frac{17}{11} & \frac{50}{11} & -\frac{32}{11} \end{bmatrix} \Rightarrow \begin{bmatrix} 1 & 5 & 2 & 6 & -3 \\ 0 & 1 & \frac{6}{11} & \frac{17}{11} & -\frac{10}{11} \\ 0 & 0 & 1 & -43 & 90 \\ 0 & 0 & \frac{17}{11} & \frac{50}{11} & -\frac{32}{4} \end{bmatrix}$$

$$\Rightarrow \begin{bmatrix} 1 & 5 & 2 & 6 & -3 \\ 0 & 1 & \frac{6}{11} & \frac{17}{11} & -\frac{10}{11} \\ 0 & 0 & 1 & -43 & 90 \\ 0 & 0 & 0 & \frac{781}{11} & -\frac{1562}{11} \end{bmatrix} \Rightarrow \begin{bmatrix} 1 & 5 & 2 & 6 & -3 \\ 0 & 1 & \frac{6}{11} & \frac{17}{11} & -\frac{10}{11} \\ 0 & 0 & 1 & -43 & 90 \\ 0 & 0 & 0 & 1 & -2 \end{bmatrix}$$

Back-substitution now yields

$w = -2$

$z = 90 + 43w = 90 + 43(-2) = 4$

$y = -\frac{10}{11} - \frac{6}{11}(z) - \frac{17}{11}(w) = -\frac{10}{11} - \frac{6}{11}(4) - \frac{17}{11}(-2) = 0$

$x = -3 - 5y - 2z - 6w = -3 - 5(0) - 2(4) - 6(-2) = 1.$

So, the solution is: $x = 1,\ y = 0,\ z = 4,$ and $w = -2.$

40. Using a computer software program or graphing utility, you obtain

$x_1 = 1$

$x_2 = -1$

$x_3 = 2$

$x_4 = 0$

$x_5 = -2$

$x_6 = 1.$

42. The corresponding equations are

$x_1 \qquad = 0$

$\qquad x_2 + x_3 = 0.$

Choosing $x_4 = t$ and $x_3 = t$ as the free variables, you can describe the solution as $x_1 = 0,\ x_2 = -s,\ x_3 = s,$ and $x_4 = t,$ where s and t are any real numbers.

44. The corresponding equations are all $0 = 0.$ So, there are three free variables. So, $x_1 = t,\ x_2 = s,$ and $x_3 = r,$ where $t,\ s,$ and r are any real numbers.

46. x = number of $1 bills

y = number of $5 bills

z = number of $10 bills

w = number of $20 bills

$x + 5y + 10z + 20w = 95$

$x + y + z + w = 26$

$y - 4z = 0$

$x - 2y = -1$

$$\begin{bmatrix} 1 & 5 & 10 & 20 & 95 \\ 1 & 1 & 1 & 1 & 26 \\ 0 & 1 & -4 & 0 & 0 \\ 1 & -2 & 0 & 0 & -1 \end{bmatrix} \Rightarrow \begin{bmatrix} 1 & 0 & 0 & 0 & 15 \\ 0 & 1 & 0 & 0 & 8 \\ 0 & 0 & 1 & 0 & 2 \\ 0 & 0 & 0 & 1 & 1 \end{bmatrix}$$

$x = 15$

$y = 8$

$z = 2$

$w = 1$

The server has 15 $1 bills, 8 $5 bills, 2 $10 bills, and one $20 bill.

48. (a) If A is the *augmented* matrix of a system of linear equations, then the number of equations in this system is three (because it is equal to the number of rows of the augmented matrix). The number of variables is two because it is equal to the number of columns of the augmented matrix minus one.

(b) Using Gaussian elimination on the augmented matrix of a system, you have the following.

$$\begin{bmatrix} 2 & -1 & 3 \\ -4 & 2 & k \\ 4 & -2 & 6 \end{bmatrix} \Rightarrow \begin{bmatrix} 2 & -1 & 3 \\ 0 & 0 & k+6 \\ 0 & 0 & 0 \end{bmatrix}$$

This system is consistent if and only if $k + 6 = 0$, so $k = -6$.

If A is the *coefficient* matrix of a system of linear equations, then the number of equations is three, because it is equal to the number of rows of the coefficient matrix. The number of variables is also three, because it is equal to the number of columns of the coefficient matrix.

Using Gaussian elimination on A you obtain the following coefficient matrix of an equivalent system.

$$\begin{bmatrix} 1 & -\frac{1}{2} & \frac{3}{2} \\ 0 & 0 & k+6 \\ 0 & 0 & 0 \end{bmatrix}$$

Because the homogeneous system is always consistent, the homogeneous system with the coefficient matrix A is consistent for any value of k.

50. Using Gaussian elimination on the augmented matrix, you have the following.

$$\begin{bmatrix} 1 & 1 & 0 & 0 \\ 0 & 1 & 1 & 0 \\ 1 & 0 & 1 & 0 \\ a & b & c & 0 \end{bmatrix} \Rightarrow \begin{bmatrix} 1 & 1 & 0 & 0 \\ 0 & 1 & 1 & 0 \\ 0 & -1 & 1 & 0 \\ 0 & (b-a) & c & 0 \end{bmatrix} \Rightarrow \begin{bmatrix} 1 & 1 & 0 & 0 \\ 0 & 1 & 1 & 0 \\ 0 & 0 & 2 & 0 \\ 0 & 0 & (a-b+c) & 0 \end{bmatrix} \Rightarrow \begin{bmatrix} 1 & 1 & 0 & 0 \\ 0 & 1 & 1 & 0 \\ 0 & 0 & 1 & 0 \\ 0 & 0 & 0 & 0 \end{bmatrix}$$

From this row reduced matrix you see that the original system has a unique solution.

52. Because the system composed of Equations 1 and 2 is consistent, but has a free variable, this system must have an infinite number of solutions.

54. Use Gauss-Jordan elimination as follows.

$$\begin{bmatrix} 1 & 2 & 3 \\ 4 & 5 & 6 \\ 7 & 8 & 9 \end{bmatrix} \Rightarrow \begin{bmatrix} 1 & 2 & 3 \\ 0 & -3 & -6 \\ 0 & -6 & -12 \end{bmatrix} \Rightarrow \begin{bmatrix} 1 & 2 & 3 \\ 0 & 1 & 2 \\ 0 & 0 & 0 \end{bmatrix} \Rightarrow \begin{bmatrix} 1 & 0 & -1 \\ 0 & 1 & 2 \\ 0 & 0 & 0 \end{bmatrix}$$

56. Begin by finding all possible first rows

$$[0 \;\; 0 \;\; 0], [0 \;\; 0 \;\; 1], [0 \;\; 1 \;\; 0], [0 \;\; 1 \;\; a], [1 \;\; 0 \;\; 0], [1 \;\; 0 \;\; a], [1 \;\; a \;\; b], [1 \;\; a \;\; 0],$$

where a and b are nonzero real numbers. For each of these examine the possible remaining rows.

$$
\begin{bmatrix} 0 & 0 & 0 \\ 0 & 0 & 0 \\ 0 & 0 & 0 \end{bmatrix},
\begin{bmatrix} 0 & 0 & 1 \\ 0 & 0 & 0 \\ 0 & 0 & 0 \end{bmatrix},
\begin{bmatrix} 0 & 1 & 0 \\ 0 & 0 & 0 \\ 0 & 0 & 0 \end{bmatrix},
\begin{bmatrix} 0 & 1 & 0 \\ 0 & 0 & 1 \\ 0 & 0 & 0 \end{bmatrix},
\begin{bmatrix} 0 & 1 & a \\ 0 & 0 & 0 \\ 0 & 0 & 0 \end{bmatrix},
$$

$$
\begin{bmatrix} 1 & 0 & 0 \\ 0 & 0 & 0 \\ 0 & 0 & 0 \end{bmatrix},
\begin{bmatrix} 1 & 0 & 0 \\ 0 & 1 & 0 \\ 0 & 0 & 0 \end{bmatrix},
\begin{bmatrix} 1 & 0 & 0 \\ 0 & 1 & 0 \\ 0 & 0 & 1 \end{bmatrix},
\begin{bmatrix} 1 & 0 & 0 \\ 0 & 0 & 1 \\ 0 & 0 & 0 \end{bmatrix},
\begin{bmatrix} 1 & 0 & 0 \\ 0 & 1 & a \\ 0 & 0 & 0 \end{bmatrix},
$$

$$
\begin{bmatrix} 1 & a & 0 \\ 0 & 0 & 0 \\ 0 & 0 & 0 \end{bmatrix},
\begin{bmatrix} 1 & a & 0 \\ 0 & 0 & 1 \\ 0 & 0 & 0 \end{bmatrix},
\begin{bmatrix} 1 & a & b \\ 0 & 0 & 0 \\ 0 & 0 & 0 \end{bmatrix},
\begin{bmatrix} 1 & 0 & a \\ 0 & 0 & 0 \\ 0 & 0 & 0 \end{bmatrix},
\begin{bmatrix} 1 & 0 & a \\ 0 & 1 & 0 \\ 0 & 0 & 0 \end{bmatrix}
$$

58. (a) False. A 4×7 matrix has 4 rows and 7 columns.

(b) True. Reduced row-echelon form of a given matrix is unique while row-echelon form is not. (See also exercise 64 of this section.)

(c) True. See Theorem 1.1 on page 21.

(d) False. Multiplying a row by a *nonzero* constant is one of the elementary row operations. However, multiplying a row of a matrix by a constant $c = 0$ is *not* an elementary row operation. (This would change the system by eliminating the equation corresponding to this row.)

60. No, the row-echelon form is not unique. For instance, $\begin{bmatrix} 1 & 2 \\ 0 & 1 \end{bmatrix}$ and $\begin{bmatrix} 1 & 0 \\ 0 & 1 \end{bmatrix}$. The reduced row-echelon form is unique.

62. First, you need $a \neq 0$ or $c \neq 0$. If $a \neq 0$, then you have

$$
\begin{bmatrix} a & b \\ c & d \end{bmatrix} \Rightarrow
\begin{bmatrix} a & b \\ 0 & -\dfrac{cb}{a} + b \end{bmatrix} \Rightarrow
\begin{bmatrix} a & b \\ 0 & ad - bc \end{bmatrix}.
$$

So, $ad - bc = 0$ and $b = 0$, which implies that $d = 0$. If $c \neq 0$, then you interchange rows and proceed.

$$
\begin{bmatrix} a & b \\ c & d \end{bmatrix} \Rightarrow
\begin{bmatrix} c & d \\ 0 & -\dfrac{ad}{c} + b \end{bmatrix} \Rightarrow
\begin{bmatrix} c & d \\ 0 & ad - bc \end{bmatrix}
$$

Again, $ad - bc = 0$ and $d = 0$, which implies that $b = 0$. In conclusion, $\begin{bmatrix} a & b \\ c & d \end{bmatrix}$ is row-equivalent to $\begin{bmatrix} 1 & 0 \\ 0 & 0 \end{bmatrix}$ if and only if $b = d = 0$, and $a \neq 0$ or $c \neq 0$.

64. Row reduce the augmented matrix for this system.

$$
\begin{bmatrix} \lambda - 1 & 2 & 0 \\ 1 & \lambda & 0 \end{bmatrix} \Rightarrow
\begin{bmatrix} 1 & \lambda & 0 \\ \lambda - 1 & 2 & 0 \end{bmatrix} \Rightarrow
\begin{bmatrix} 1 & \lambda & 0 \\ 0 & (-\lambda^2 + \lambda + 2) & 0 \end{bmatrix}
$$

To have a nontrivial solution you must have

$$\lambda^2 - \lambda - 2 = 0$$
$$(\lambda - 2)(\lambda + 1) = 0.$$

So, if $\lambda = -1$ or $\lambda = 2$, the system will have nontrivial solutions.

66. Answers will vary. *Sample answer:* Because the third row consists of all zeros, choose a third equation that is a multiple of one of the other two equations.

$$x + 3z = -2$$
$$y + 4z = 1$$
$$2y + 8z = 2$$

68. A matrix is in reduced row-echelon form if every column that has a leading 1 has zeros in every position above and below its leading 1. A matrix in row-echelon form may have any real numbers above the leading 1's.

Section 1.3   Applications of Systems of Linear Equations

2. (a) Because there are three points, choose a second-degree polynomial, $p(x) = a_0 + a_1 x + a_2 x^2$. Then substitute $x = 0, 2,$ and 4 into $p(x)$ and equate the results to $y = 0, -2,$ and 0, respectively.

$$a_0 + a_1(0) + a_2(0)^2 = a_0 \qquad\qquad = 0$$

$$a_0 + a_1(2) + a_2(2)^2 = a_0 + 2a_1 + 4a_2 = -2$$

$$a_0 + a_1(4) + a_2(4)^2 = a_0 + 4a_1 + 16a_2 = 0$$

Use Gauss-Jordan elimination on the augmented matrix for this system.

$$\begin{bmatrix} 1 & 0 & 0 & 0 \\ 1 & 2 & 4 & -2 \\ 1 & 4 & 16 & 0 \end{bmatrix} \Rightarrow \begin{bmatrix} 1 & 0 & 0 & 0 \\ 0 & 1 & 0 & -2 \\ 0 & 0 & 1 & \frac{1}{2} \end{bmatrix}$$

So, $p(x) = -2x + \frac{1}{2}x^2$.

(b)

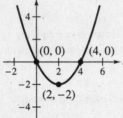

4. (a) Because there are three points, choose a second-degree polynomial, $p(x) = a_0 + a_1 x + a_2 x^2$. Then substitute $x = 2, 3,$ and 4 into $p(x)$ and equate the results to $y = 4, 4,$ and 4, respectively.

$$a_0 + a_1(2) + a_2(2)^2 = a_0 + 2a_1 + 4a_2 = 4$$

$$a_0 + a_1(3) + a_2(3)^2 = a_0 + 3a_1 + 9a_2 = 4$$

$$a_0 + a_1(4) + a_2(4)^2 = a_0 + 4a_1 + 16a_2 = 4$$

Use Gauss-Jordan elimination on the augmented matrix for this system.

$$\begin{bmatrix} 1 & 2 & 4 & 4 \\ 1 & 3 & 9 & 4 \\ 1 & 4 & 16 & 4 \end{bmatrix} \Rightarrow \begin{bmatrix} 1 & 0 & 0 & 4 \\ 0 & 1 & 0 & 0 \\ 0 & 0 & 1 & 0 \end{bmatrix}$$

So, $p(x) = 4$.

(b)

6. (a) Because there are four points, choose a third-degree polynomial, $p(x) = a_0 + a_1x + a_2x^2 + a_3x^3$. Then substitute $x = 0, 1, 2,$ and 3 into $p(x)$ and equate the results to $y = 42, 0, -40,$ and $-72,$ respectively.

$$a_0 + a_1(0) + a_2(0)^2 + a_3(0)^3 = a_0 \qquad\qquad\qquad = 42$$
$$a_0 + a_1(1) + a_2(1)^2 + a_3(1)^3 = a_0 + a_1 \ + a_2 \ + a_3 \ = 0$$
$$a_0 + a_1(2) + a_2(2)^2 + a_3(2)^3 = a_0 + 2a_1 + 4a_2 + 8a_3 \ = -40$$
$$a_0 + a_1(3) + a_2(3)^2 + a_3(3)^2 = a_0 + 3a_1 + 9a_2 + 27a_3 = -72$$

Use Gauss-Jordan elimination on the augmented matrix for this system.

$$\begin{bmatrix} 1 & 0 & 0 & 0 & 42 \\ 1 & 1 & 1 & 1 & 0 \\ 1 & 2 & 4 & 8 & -40 \\ 1 & 3 & 9 & 27 & -72 \end{bmatrix} \Rightarrow \begin{bmatrix} 1 & 0 & 0 & 0 & 42 \\ 0 & 1 & 0 & 0 & -41 \\ 0 & 0 & 1 & 0 & -2 \\ 0 & 0 & 0 & 1 & 1 \end{bmatrix}$$

So, $p(x) = 42 - 41x - 2x^2 + x^3$.

(b)

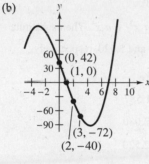

8. (a) Because there are five points, choose a fourth-degree polynomial, $p(x) = a_0 + a_1x + a_2x^2 + a_3x^3 + a_4x^4$. Then substitute $x = -4, 0, 4, 6,$ and 8 into $p(x)$ and equate the results to $y = 18, 1, 0, 28,$ and 135, respectively.

$$a_0 + a_1(-4) + a_2(-4)^2 + a_3(-4)^3 + a_4(-4)^4 = a_0 - 4a_1 + 16a_2 \qquad\qquad 64u_3 + \ 256a_4 = 18$$
$$a_0 + a_1(0) \ + a_2(0)^2 + a_3(0)^3 + a_4(0)^4 = a_0 \qquad\qquad\qquad\qquad\qquad\qquad = 1$$
$$a_0 + a_1(4) \ + u_2(4)^2 + a_3(4)^3 + a_4(4)^4 = a_0 + 4a_1 + 16a_2 + \ 64a_3 + \ 256a_4 - 0$$
$$a_0 + a_1(6) \ + a_2(6)^2 + a_3(6)^3 + a_4(6)^4 = a_0 + 6a_1 + 36a_2 + 216a_3 + 1296a_4 = 28$$
$$a_0 + a_1(8) \ + a_2(8)^2 + a_3(8)^3 + a_4(8)^4 = a_0 + 8a_1 + 64a_2 + 512a_3 + 4096a_4 = 135$$

Use Gauss-Jordan elimination on the augmented matrix for this system.

$$\begin{bmatrix} 1 & -4 & 16 & -64 & 256 & 18 \\ 1 & 0 & 0 & 0 & 0 & 1 \\ 1 & 4 & 16 & 64 & 256 & 0 \\ 1 & 6 & 36 & 216 & 1296 & 28 \\ 1 & 8 & 64 & 512 & 4096 & 135 \end{bmatrix} \Rightarrow \begin{bmatrix} 1 & 0 & 0 & 0 & 0 & 1 \\ 0 & 1 & 0 & 0 & 0 & \frac{3}{4} \\ 0 & 0 & 1 & 0 & 0 & -\frac{1}{2} \\ 0 & 0 & 0 & 1 & 0 & -\frac{3}{16} \\ 0 & 0 & 0 & 0 & 1 & \frac{1}{16} \end{bmatrix}$$

So, $p(x) = 1 + \frac{3}{4}x - \frac{1}{2}x^2 - \frac{3}{16}x^3 + \frac{1}{16}x^4 = \frac{1}{16}\left(16 + 12x - 8x^2 - 3x^3 + x^4\right)$.

(b)

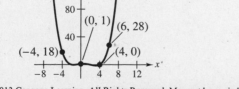

10. Assume that the equation of the ellipse is $x^2 + ax + by^2 + cy - d = 0$. Because each of the given points lies on the ellipse, you have the following linear equations.

$$(-5)^2 + a(-5) + b(1)^2 + c(1) - d = -5a + b + c - d + 25 = 0$$

$$(-3)^2 + a(-3) + b(2)^2 + c(2) - d = -3a + 4b + 2c - d + 9 = 0$$

$$(-1)^2 + a(-1) + b(1)^2 + c(1) - d = -a + b + c - d + 1 = 0$$

$$(-3)^2 + a(-3) + b(0)^2 + c(0) - d = -3a - d + 9 = 0$$

Use Gauss-Jordan elimination on the system.

$$\begin{bmatrix} -5 & 1 & 1 & -1 & -25 \\ -3 & 4 & 2 & -1 & -9 \\ -1 & 1 & 1 & -1 & -1 \\ -3 & 0 & 0 & -1 & -9 \end{bmatrix} \Rightarrow \begin{bmatrix} 1 & 0 & 0 & 0 & 6 \\ 0 & 1 & 0 & 0 & 4 \\ 0 & 0 & 1 & 0 & -8 \\ 0 & 0 & 0 & 1 & -9 \end{bmatrix}$$

So, the equation of the ellipse is $x^2 + 6x + 4y^2 - 8y + 9 = 0$ or $\dfrac{(x+3)^2}{4} + \dfrac{(y-1)^2}{1} = 1$.

12. (a) Because there are four points, choose a third-degree polynomial, $p(x) = a_0 + a_1 x + a_2 x^2 + a_3 x^3$. Then substitute $x = 1, 1.189, 1.316,$ and 1.414 into $p(x)$ and equate the results to $y = 1, 1.587, 2.080,$ and 2.520, respectively.

$$a_0 + a_1(1) + a_2(1)^2 + a_3(1)^3 = a_0 + a_1 + a_2 + a_3 = 1$$

$$a_0 + a_1(1.189) + a_2(1.189)^2 + a_3(1.189)^3 \approx a_0 + 1.189a_1 + 1.414a_2 + 1.681a_3 = 1.587$$

$$a_0 + a_1(1.316) + a_2(1.316)^2 + a_3(1.316)^3 \approx a_0 + 1.316a_1 + 1.732a_2 + 2.279a_3 = 2.080$$

$$a_0 + a_1(1.414) + a_2(1.414)^2 + a_3(1.414)^3 \approx a_0 + 1.414a_1 + 1.999a_2 + 2.827a_3 = 2.520$$

Use Gauss-Jordan elimination on the augmented matrix for this system.

$$\begin{bmatrix} 1 & 1 & 1 & 1 & 1 \\ 1 & 1.189 & 1.414 & 1.681 & 1.587 \\ 1 & 1.316 & 1.732 & 2.279 & 2.080 \\ 1 & 1.414 & 1.999 & 2.827 & 2.520 \end{bmatrix} \Rightarrow \begin{bmatrix} 1 & 0 & 0 & 0 & -0.095 \\ 0 & 1 & 0 & 0 & 0.103 \\ 0 & 0 & 1 & 0 & 0.405 \\ 0 & 0 & 0 & 1 & 0.587 \end{bmatrix}$$

So, $p(x) \approx -0.095 + 0.103x + 0.405x^2 + 0.587x^3$.

(b)

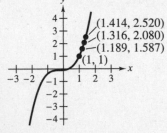

(1.414, 2.520)
(1.316, 2.080)
(1.189, 1.587)
(1, 1)

14. Choosing a second-degree polynomial approximation $p(x) = a_0 + a_1 x + a_2 x^2$, substitute $x = 1, 2,$ and 4 into $p(x)$ and equate the results to $y = 0, 1,$ and 2, respectively.

$$a_0 + a_1 + a_2 = 0$$

$$a_0 + 2a_1 + 4a_2 = 1$$

$$a_0 + 4a_1 + 16a_2 = 2$$

The solution to this system is $a_0 = -\frac{4}{3}$, $a_1 = \frac{3}{2}$, and $a_2 = -\frac{1}{6}$.

So, $p(x) = -\frac{4}{3} + \frac{3}{2}x - \frac{1}{6}x^2$.

Finally, to estimate $\log_2 3$, calculate $p(3) = -\frac{4}{3} + \frac{3}{2}(3) - \frac{1}{6}(3)^2 = \frac{5}{3}$.

16. Assume that the equation of the ellipse is $ax^2 + cy^2 + dx + ey + f = 0$. Because each of the given points lies on the ellipse, you have the following linear equations.

$$a(-5)^2 + c(1)^2 + d(-5) + e(1) + f = 25a + c - 5d + e + f = 0$$
$$a(-3)^2 + c(2)^2 + d(-3) + e(2) + f = 9a + 4c - 3d + 2e + f = 0$$
$$a(-1)^2 + c(1)^2 + d(-1) + e(1) + f = a + c - d + e + f = 0$$
$$a(-3)^2 + c(0)^2 + d(-3) + e(0) + f = 9a - 3d + f = 0$$

Use Gauss-Jordan elimination on the system.

$$\begin{bmatrix} 25 & 1 & -5 & 1 & 1 & 0 \\ 9 & 4 & -3 & 2 & 1 & 0 \\ 1 & 1 & -1 & 1 & 1 & 0 \\ 9 & 0 & -3 & 0 & 1 & 0 \end{bmatrix} \Rightarrow \begin{bmatrix} 1 & 0 & 0 & 0 & -\frac{1}{9} & 0 \\ 0 & 1 & 0 & 0 & -\frac{4}{9} & 0 \\ 0 & 0 & 1 & 0 & -\frac{2}{3} & 0 \\ 0 & 0 & 0 & 1 & \frac{8}{9} & 0 \end{bmatrix}$$

Letting $f = t$ be the free variable, you have $a = \frac{1}{9}t$, $c = \frac{4}{9}t$, $d = \frac{2}{3}t$, $e = -\frac{8}{9}t$, and $f = t$, where t is any real number.

18. (a) Letting $z = \dfrac{x - 1940}{10}$, the four data points are $(0, 132)$, $(1, 151)$, $(2, 179)$, and $(3, 203)$.

Let $p(z) = a_0 + a_1 z + a_2 z^2 + a_3 z^3$. Substituting the points into $p(z)$ produces the following system of linear equations.

$$a_0 + a_1(0) + a_2(0)^2 + a_3(0)^3 = a_0 = 132$$
$$a_0 + a_1(1) + a_2(1)^2 + a_3(1)^3 = a_0 + a_1 + a_2 + a_3 = 151$$
$$a_0 + a_1(2) + a_2(2)^2 + a_3(2)^3 = a_0 + 2a_1 + 4a_2 + 8a_3 = 179$$
$$a_0 + a_1(3) + a_2(3)^2 + a_3(3)^3 = a_0 + 3a_1 + 9a_2 + 27a_3 = 203$$

Form the augmented matrix

$$\begin{bmatrix} 1 & 0 & 0 & 0 & 132 \\ 1 & 1 & 1 & 1 & 151 \\ 1 & 2 & 4 & 8 & 179 \\ 1 & 3 & 9 & 27 & 203 \end{bmatrix}$$

and use Gauss-Jordan elimination to obtain the equivalent reduced row-echelon matrix

$$\begin{bmatrix} 1 & 0 & 0 & 0 & 132 \\ 0 & 1 & 0 & 0 & \frac{61}{6} \\ 0 & 0 & 1 & 0 & 11 \\ 0 & 0 & 0 & 1 & -\frac{13}{6} \end{bmatrix}.$$

So, the cubic polynomial is $p(z) = 132 + \dfrac{61}{6}z + 11z^2 - \dfrac{13}{6}z^3$.

Because $z = \dfrac{x - 1940}{10}$, $p(x) = 132 + \dfrac{61}{6}\left(\dfrac{x - 1940}{10}\right) + 11\left(\dfrac{x - 1940}{10}\right)^2 - \dfrac{13}{6}\left(\dfrac{x - 1940}{10}\right)^3$.

(b) To estimate the population in 1980, let $x = 1980$. $p(1980) = 132 + \dfrac{61}{6}(4) + 11(4)^2 - \dfrac{13}{6}(4)^3 = 210$ million, which is less than the actual population of 227 million.

20. (a) Letting $z = x - 2000$, the five points are $(2, 244.5), (3, 256.3), (4, 285.2), (5, 312.4)$, and $(6, 345.0)$.

Let $p(z) = a_0 + a_1 z + a_2 z^2 + a_3 z^3 + a_4 z^4$.

$$a_0 + a_1(2) + a_2(2)^2 + a_3(2)^3 + a_4(2)^4 = a_0 + 2a_1 + 4a_2 + 8a_3 + 16a_4 = 244.5$$
$$a_0 + a_1(3) + a_2(3)^2 + a_3(3)^3 + a_4(3)^4 = a_0 + 3a_1 + 9a_2 + 27a_3 + 81a_4 = 256.3$$
$$a_0 + a_1(4) + a_2(4)^2 + a_3(4)^3 + a_4(4)^4 = a_0 + 4a_1 + 16a_2 + 64a_3 + 256a_4 = 285.2$$
$$a_0 + a_1(5) + a_2(5)^2 + a_3(5)^3 + a_4(5)^4 = a_0 + 5a_1 + 25a_2 + 125a_3 + 625a_4 = 312.4$$
$$a_0 + a_1(6) + a_2(6)^2 + a_3(6)^3 + a_4(6)^4 = a_0 + 6a_1 + 36a_2 + 216a_3 + 1296a_4 = 345.0$$

(b) Use Gauss-Jordan elimination to solve the system.

$$\begin{bmatrix} 1 & 2 & 4 & 8 & 16 & 244.5 \\ 1 & 3 & 9 & 27 & 81 & 256.3 \\ 1 & 4 & 16 & 64 & 256 & 285.2 \\ 1 & 5 & 25 & 125 & 625 & 312.4 \\ 1 & 6 & 36 & 216 & 1296 & 345.0 \end{bmatrix} \Rightarrow \begin{bmatrix} 1 & 0 & 0 & 0 & 0 & \frac{4769}{10} \\ 0 & 1 & 0 & 0 & 0 & -\frac{33{,}433}{120} \\ 0 & 0 & 1 & 0 & 0 & \frac{27{,}209}{240} \\ 0 & 0 & 0 & 1 & 0 & -\frac{2189}{120} \\ 0 & 0 & 0 & 0 & 1 & \frac{259}{240} \end{bmatrix}$$

So, $p(z) = \dfrac{4769}{10} - \dfrac{33{,}433}{120}z + \dfrac{27{,}209}{240}z^2 - \dfrac{2189}{120}z^3 + \dfrac{259}{240}z^4$.

Letting $z = x - 2000$, $p(x) = \dfrac{4769}{10} - \dfrac{33{,}433}{120}(x - 2000) + \dfrac{27{,}209}{240}(x - 2000)^2 - \dfrac{2189}{120}$

$(x - 2000)^3 + \dfrac{259}{240}(x - 2000)^4$.

To determine the reasonableness of the model for years after 2006, compare the predicted values for 2007–2009 to the actual values.

x	2007	2008	2009
$p(x)$	416	584.3	934.7
Actual	374.5	401.2	405.0

The predicted values are not close to the actual values.

22. Let

$$p_1(x) = a_0 + a_1 x + a_2 x^2 + \cdots + a_{n-1} x^{n-1} \text{ and}$$
$$p_2(x) = b_0 + b_1 x + b_2 x^2 + \cdots + b_{n-1} x^{n-1}$$

be two different polynomials that pass through the n given points. The polynomial

$$p_1(x) - p_2(x) = (a_0 - b_0) + (a_1 - b_1)x + (a_2 - b_2)x^2 + \cdots + (a_{n-1} - b_{n-1})x^{n-1}$$

is zero for these n values of x. So, $a_0 = b_0$, $a_1 = b_1$, $a_2 = b_2$, ..., $a_{n-1} = b_{n-1}$.

Therefore, there is only one polynomial function of degree $n - 1$ (or less) whose graph passes through n points in the plane with distinct x-coordinates.

24. Let $p(x) = a_0 + a_1x + a_2x^2$ be the equation of the parabola. Because the parabola passes through the points $(0, 1)$ and $\left(\frac{1}{2}, \frac{1}{2}\right)$, you have

$$a_0 + a_1(0) + a_2(0)^2 = a_0 \qquad\qquad = 1$$
$$a_0 + a_1\left(\tfrac{1}{2}\right) + a_2\left(\tfrac{1}{2}\right)^2 = a_0 + \tfrac{1}{2}a_1 + \tfrac{1}{4}a_2 = \tfrac{1}{2}.$$

Because $p(x)$ has a horizontal tangent at $\left(\frac{1}{2}, \frac{1}{2}\right)$, the derivative of $p(x)$, $p'(x) = a_1 + 2a_2x$, equals zero when $x = \frac{1}{2}$. So, you have a third linear equation

$$a_1 + 2a_2\left(\tfrac{1}{2}\right) = a_1 + a_2 = 0.$$

Use Gauss-Jordan elimination on the augmented matrix for this linear system.

$$\begin{bmatrix} 1 & 0 & 0 & 1 \\ 1 & \frac{1}{2} & \frac{1}{4} & \frac{1}{2} \\ 0 & 1 & 1 & 0 \end{bmatrix} \Rightarrow \begin{bmatrix} 1 & 0 & 0 & 1 \\ 0 & 1 & 0 & -2 \\ 0 & 0 & 1 & 2 \end{bmatrix}$$

So, $p(x) = 1 - 2x + 2x^2$.

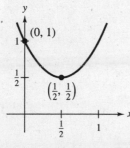

26. Choose a fourth-degree polynomial and substitute $x = 1, 2, 3,$ and 4 into

$$p(x) = a_0 + a_1x + a_2x^2 + a_3x^3 + a_4x^4.$$ However, when you substitute $x = 3$ into $p(x)$ and equate it to $y = 2$ and $y = 3$ you get the contradictory equations

$$a_0 + 3a_1 + 9a_2 + 27a_3 + 81a_4 = 2$$
$$a_0 + 3a_1 + 9a_2 + 27a_3 + 81a_4 = 3$$

and must conclude that the system containing these two equations will have no solution. Also, y is not a function of x because the x-value of 3 is repeated. By similar reasoning, you cannot choose

$$p(y) = b_0 + b_1y + b_2y^2 + b_3y^3 + b_4y^4$$ because $y = 1$ corresponds to both $x = 1$ and $x = 2$.

28. (a) Each of the network's four junctions gives rise to a linear equation as shown below.

$$\textbf{input} = \textbf{output}$$
$$300 = x_1 + x_2$$
$$x_1 + x_3 = x_4 + 150$$
$$x_2 + 200 = x_3 + x_5$$
$$x_4 + x_5 = 350$$

Rearrange these equations, form the augmented matrix, and use Gauss-Jordan elimination.

$$\begin{bmatrix} 1 & 1 & 0 & 0 & 0 & 300 \\ 1 & 0 & 1 & -1 & 0 & 150 \\ 0 & 1 & -1 & 0 & -1 & -200 \\ 0 & 0 & 0 & 1 & 1 & 350 \end{bmatrix} \Rightarrow \begin{bmatrix} 1 & 0 & 1 & 0 & 1 & 500 \\ 0 & 1 & -1 & 0 & -1 & -200 \\ 0 & 0 & 0 & 1 & 1 & 350 \\ 0 & 0 & 0 & 0 & 0 & 0 \end{bmatrix}$$

Letting $x_5 = t$ and $x_3 = s$ be the free variables, you have

$$x_1 = 500 - s - t$$
$$x_2 = -200 + s + t$$
$$x_3 = s$$
$$x_4 = 350 - t$$
$$x_5 = t,$$ where t and s are any real numbers.

(b) If $x_2 = 200$ and $x_3 = 50$, then you have $s = 50$ and $t = 350$.

So, the solution is: $x_1 = 100$, $x_2 = 200$, $x_3 = 50$, $x_4 = 0$, and $x_5 = 350$.

(c) If $x_2 = 150$ and $x_3 = 0$, then you have $s = 0$ and $t = 350$.

So, the solution is: $x_1 = 150$, $x_2 = 150$, $x_3 = 0$, $x_4 = 0$, and $x_5 = 350$.

30. (a) Each of the network's four junctions gives rise to a linear equation as shown below.

$$\text{input} = \text{output}$$

$$400 + x_2 = x_1$$
$$x_1 + x_3 = x_4 + 600$$
$$300 = x_2 + x_3 + x_5$$
$$x_4 + x_5 = 100$$

Rearrange these equations, form the augmented matrix, and use Gauss-Jordan elimination.

$$\begin{bmatrix} 1 & -1 & 0 & 0 & 0 & 400 \\ 1 & 0 & 1 & -1 & 0 & 600 \\ 0 & 1 & 1 & 0 & 1 & 300 \\ 0 & 0 & 0 & 1 & 1 & 100 \end{bmatrix} \Rightarrow \begin{bmatrix} 1 & 0 & 1 & 0 & 1 & 700 \\ 0 & 1 & 1 & 0 & 1 & 300 \\ 0 & 0 & 0 & 1 & 1 & 100 \\ 0 & 0 & 0 & 0 & 0 & 0 \end{bmatrix}$$

Letting $x_5 = t$ and $x_3 = s$ be the free variables, you can describe the solution as

$$x_1 = 700 - s - t$$
$$x_2 = 300 - s - t$$
$$x_3 = s$$
$$x_4 = 100 - t$$
$$x_5 = t, \text{ where } t \text{ and } s \text{ are any real numbers.}$$

(b) If $x_3 = 0$ and $x_5 = 100$, then the solution is: $x_1 = 600$, $x_2 = 200$, $x_3 = 0$, $x_4 = 0$, and $x_5 = 100$.

(c) If $x_3 = x_5 = 100$, then the solution is: $x_1 = 500$, $x_2 = 100$, $x_3 = 100$, $x_4 = 0$, and $x_5 = 100$.

32. Applying Kirchoff's first law to three of the four junctions produces

$$I_1 + I_3 = I_2$$
$$I_1 + I_4 = I_2$$
$$I_3 + I_6 = I_5$$

and applying the second law to the three paths produces

$$R_1 I_1 + R_2 I_2 = 3I_1 + 2I_2 = 14$$
$$R_2 I_2 + R_4 I_4 + R_5 I_5 + R_3 I_3 = 2I_2 + 2I_4 + I_5 + 4I_3 = 25$$
$$R_5 I_5 + R_6 I_6 = I_5 + I_6 = 8.$$

Rearrange these equations, form the augmented matrix, and use Gauss-Jordan elimination.

$$\begin{bmatrix} 1 & -1 & 1 & 0 & 0 & 0 & 0 \\ 1 & -1 & 0 & 1 & 0 & 0 & 0 \\ 0 & 0 & 1 & 0 & -1 & 1 & 0 \\ 3 & 2 & 0 & 0 & 0 & 0 & 14 \\ 0 & 2 & 4 & 2 & 1 & 0 & 25 \\ 0 & 0 & 0 & 0 & 1 & 1 & 8 \end{bmatrix} \Rightarrow \begin{bmatrix} 1 & 0 & 0 & 0 & 0 & 0 & 2 \\ 0 & 1 & 0 & 0 & 0 & 0 & 4 \\ 0 & 0 & 1 & 0 & 0 & 0 & 2 \\ 0 & 0 & 0 & 1 & 0 & 0 & 2 \\ 0 & 0 & 0 & 0 & 1 & 0 & 5 \\ 0 & 0 & 0 & 0 & 0 & 1 & 3 \end{bmatrix}$$

So, the solution is: $I_1 = 2$, $I_2 = 4$, $I_3 = 2$, $I_4 = 2$, $I_5 = 5$, and $I_6 = 3$.

34. (a) For a set of n points with distinct x-values, substitute the points into the polynomial

$p(x) = a_0 + a_1 x + \cdots + a_{n-1} x^{n-1}$. This creates a system of linear equations in $a_0, a_1, \cdots a_{n-1}$. Solving the system gives values for the coefficients a_n, and the resulting polynomial fits the original points.

(b) In a network, the total flow into a junction is equal to the total flow out of a junction. So, each junction determines an equation, and the set of equations for all the junctions in a network forms a linear system. In an electrical network, Kirchhoff's Laws are used to determine additional equations for the system.

36. $T_1 = \dfrac{50 + 25 + T_2 + T_3}{4}$

$T_2 = \dfrac{50 + 25 + T_1 + T_4}{4}$

$T_3 = \dfrac{25 + 0 + T_1 + T_4}{4}$ $\Rightarrow$

$T_4 = \dfrac{25 + 0 + T_2 + T_3}{4}$

$$\begin{aligned} 4T_1 - T_2 - T_3 &= 75 \\ -T_1 + 4T_2 \qquad - T_4 &= 75 \\ -T_1 \qquad + 4T_3 - T_4 &= 25 \\ -T_2 - T_3 + 4T_4 &= 25 \end{aligned}$$

Use Gauss-Jordan elimination to solve this system.

$$\begin{bmatrix} 4 & -1 & -1 & 0 & 75 \\ -1 & 4 & 0 & -1 & 75 \\ -1 & 0 & 4 & -1 & 25 \\ 0 & -1 & -1 & 4 & 25 \end{bmatrix} \Rightarrow \begin{bmatrix} 1 & 0 & 0 & 0 & 31.25 \\ 0 & 1 & 0 & 0 & 31.25 \\ 0 & 0 & 1 & 0 & 18.75 \\ 0 & 0 & 0 & 1 & 18.75 \end{bmatrix}$$

So, $T_1 = 31.25°C$, $T_2 = 31.25°C$, $T_3 = 18.75°C$, and $T_4 = 18.75°C$.

38. $\dfrac{3x^2 - 7x - 12}{(x + 4)(x - 4)^2} = \dfrac{A}{x + 4} + \dfrac{B}{x - 4} + \dfrac{C}{(x - 4)^2}$

$3x^2 - 7x - 12 = A(x - 4)^2 + B(x + 4)(x - 4) + C(x + 4)$

$3x^2 - 7x - 12 = Ax^2 - 8Ax + 16A + Bx^2 - 16B + Cx + 4C$

$3x^2 - 7x - 12 = (A + B)x^2 + (-8A + C)x + 16A - 16B + 4C$

So, $\quad A + B \qquad = 3$

$-8A \qquad + C = -7$

$16A - 16B + 4C = -12.$

Use Gauss-Jordan elimination to solve the system.

$$\begin{bmatrix} 1 & 1 & 0 & 3 \\ -8 & 0 & 1 & -7 \\ 16 & -16 & 4 & -12 \end{bmatrix} \Rightarrow \begin{bmatrix} 1 & 0 & 0 & 1 \\ 0 & 1 & 0 & 2 \\ 0 & 0 & 1 & 1 \end{bmatrix}$$

The solution is: $A = 1$, $B = 2$, and $C = 1$.

So, $\dfrac{3x^2 - 7x - 12}{(x + 4)(x - 4)^2} = \dfrac{1}{x + 4} + \dfrac{2}{x - 4} + \dfrac{1}{(x - 4)^2}$

40. Use Gauss-Jordan elimination to solve the system.

$$\begin{bmatrix} 0 & 2 & 2 & -2 \\ 2 & 0 & 1 & -1 \\ 2 & 1 & 0 & 100 \end{bmatrix} \Rightarrow \begin{bmatrix} 1 & 0 & 0 & 25 \\ 0 & 1 & 0 & 50 \\ 0 & 0 & 1 & -51 \end{bmatrix}$$

So, $x = 25$, $y = 50$, and $\lambda = -51$.

Review Exercises for Chapter 1

2. Because the equation cannot be written in the form $a_1x + a_2y = b$, it is *not* linear in the variables x and y.

4. Because the equation is in the form $a_1x + a_2y = b$, it *is* linear in the variables x and y.

6. Because the equation is in the form $a_1x + a_2y = b$, it *is* linear in the variables x and y.

8. Choosing x_2 and x_3 as the free variables and letting $x_2 = s$ and $x_3 = t$, you have

$3x_1 + 2s - 4t = 0$

$3x_1 = -2s + 4t$

$x_1 = \frac{1}{3}(-2s + 4t).$

10. Row reduce the augmented matrix for this system.

$$\begin{bmatrix} 1 & 1 & -1 \\ 3 & 2 & 0 \end{bmatrix} \Rightarrow \begin{bmatrix} 1 & 1 & -1 \\ 0 & -1 & 3 \end{bmatrix} \Rightarrow \begin{bmatrix} 1 & 1 & -1 \\ 0 & 1 & -3 \end{bmatrix} \Rightarrow \begin{bmatrix} 1 & 0 & 2 \\ 0 & 1 & -3 \end{bmatrix}$$

Converting back to a linear system, the solution is $x = 2$ and $y = -3$.

12. Rearrange the equations, form the augmented matrix, and row reduce.

$$\begin{bmatrix} 1 & -1 & 3 \\ 4 & -1 & 10 \end{bmatrix} \Rightarrow \begin{bmatrix} 1 & -1 & 3 \\ 0 & 3 & -2 \end{bmatrix} \Rightarrow \begin{bmatrix} 1 & -1 & 3 \\ 0 & 1 & -\frac{2}{3} \end{bmatrix} \Rightarrow \begin{bmatrix} 1 & 0 & \frac{7}{3} \\ 0 & 1 & -\frac{2}{3} \end{bmatrix}.$$

Converting back to a linear system, you obtain the solution $x = \frac{7}{3}$ and $y = -\frac{2}{3}$.

14. Rearrange the equations, form the augmented matrix, and row reduce.

$$\begin{bmatrix} 4 & 1 & 0 \\ -1 & 1 & 0 \end{bmatrix} \Rightarrow \begin{bmatrix} 1 & -1 & 0 \\ 4 & 1 & 0 \end{bmatrix} \Rightarrow \begin{bmatrix} 1 & -1 & 0 \\ 0 & 5 & 0 \end{bmatrix} \Rightarrow \begin{bmatrix} 1 & 0 & 0 \\ 0 & 1 & 0 \end{bmatrix}.$$

Converting back to a linear system, the solution is $x = y = 0$.

16. Row reduce the augmented matrix for this system.

$$\begin{bmatrix} 40 & 30 & 24 \\ 20 & 15 & -14 \end{bmatrix} \Rightarrow \begin{bmatrix} 1 & \frac{3}{4} & \frac{3}{5} \\ 20 & 15 & -14 \end{bmatrix} \Rightarrow \begin{bmatrix} 1 & \frac{3}{4} & \frac{3}{5} \\ 0 & 0 & -26 \end{bmatrix}$$

Because the second row corresponds to the false statement $0 = -26$, the system has no solution.

18. Use Gauss-Jordan elimination on the augmented matrix.

$$\begin{bmatrix} \frac{1}{3} & \frac{4}{7} & 3 \\ 2 & 3 & 15 \end{bmatrix} \Rightarrow \begin{bmatrix} 1 & 0 & -3 \\ 0 & 1 & 7 \end{bmatrix}$$

So, the solution is: $x = -3$, $y = 7$.

20. Multiplying both equations by 100 and forming the augmented matrix produces

$$\begin{bmatrix} 20 & -10 & 7 \\ 40 & -50 & -1 \end{bmatrix}.$$

Gauss-Jordan elimination yields the following.

$$\begin{bmatrix} 1 & -\frac{1}{2} & \frac{7}{20} \\ 40 & -50 & -1 \end{bmatrix} \Rightarrow \begin{bmatrix} 1 & -\frac{1}{2} & \frac{7}{20} \\ 0 & -30 & -15 \end{bmatrix}$$

$$\Rightarrow \begin{bmatrix} 1 & -\frac{1}{2} & \frac{7}{20} \\ 0 & 1 & \frac{1}{2} \end{bmatrix} \Rightarrow \begin{bmatrix} 1 & 0 & \frac{3}{5} \\ 0 & 1 & \frac{1}{2} \end{bmatrix}$$

So, the solution is: $x = \frac{3}{5}$ and $y = \frac{1}{2}$.

22. Because the matrix has 3 rows and 2 columns, it has size 3×2.

24. This matrix corresponds to the system

$$x_1 + 2x_2 + 3x_3 = 0$$
$$0 = 1.$$

Because the second equation is impossible, the system has no solution.

26. The matrix satisfies all three conditions in the definition of row-echelon form. Because each column that has a leading 1 (columns 1 and 4) has zeros elsewhere, the matrix is in reduced row-echelon form.

28. The matrix satisfies all three conditions in the definition of row-echelon form. Because each column that has a leading 1 (columns 2 and 3) has zeros elsewhere, the matrix is in reduced row-echelon form.

30. Use Gauss-Jordan elimination on the augmented matrix.

$$\begin{bmatrix} 2 & 3 & 1 & 10 \\ 2 & -3 & -3 & 22 \\ 4 & -2 & 3 & -2 \end{bmatrix} \Rightarrow \begin{bmatrix} 1 & 0 & 0 & 5 \\ 0 & 1 & 0 & 2 \\ 0 & 0 & 1 & -6 \end{bmatrix}$$

So, the solution is: $x = 5$, $y = 2$, and $z = -6$.

32. Use the Gauss-Jordan elimination on the augmented matrix.

$$\begin{bmatrix} 2 & 1 & 2 & 4 \\ 2 & 2 & 0 & 5 \\ 2 & -1 & 6 & 2 \end{bmatrix} \Rightarrow \begin{bmatrix} 1 & 0 & 2 & \frac{3}{2} \\ 0 & 1 & -2 & 1 \\ 0 & 0 & 0 & 0 \end{bmatrix}$$

Choosing $z = t$ as the free variable, you can describe the solution as $x = \frac{3}{2} - 2t$, $y = 1 + 2t$, and $z = t$, where t is any real number.

34. Use Gauss-Jordan elimination on the augmented matrix.

$$\begin{bmatrix} 2 & 0 & 6 & -9 \\ 3 & -2 & 11 & -16 \\ 3 & -1 & 7 & -11 \end{bmatrix} \Rightarrow \begin{bmatrix} 1 & 0 & 0 & -\frac{3}{4} \\ 0 & 1 & 0 & 0 \\ 0 & 0 & 1 & -\frac{5}{4} \end{bmatrix}$$

So, the solution is: $x = -\frac{3}{4}$, $y = 0$, and $z = -\frac{5}{4}$.

36. Use Gauss-Jordan elimination on the augmented matrix.

$$\begin{bmatrix} 2 & 5 & -19 & 34 \\ 3 & 8 & -31 & 54 \end{bmatrix} \Rightarrow \begin{bmatrix} 1 & 0 & 3 & 2 \\ 0 & 1 & -5 & 6 \end{bmatrix}$$

Choosing $x_3 = t$ as the free variable, you can describe the solution as $x_1 = 2 - 3t$, $x_2 = 6 + 5t$, and $x_3 = t$, where t is any real number.

38. Use Gauss-Jordan elimination on the augmented matrix.

$$\begin{bmatrix} 1 & 5 & 3 & 0 & 0 & 14 \\ 0 & 4 & 2 & 5 & 0 & 3 \\ 0 & 0 & 3 & 8 & 6 & 16 \\ 2 & 4 & 0 & 0 & -2 & 0 \\ 2 & 0 & -1 & 0 & 0 & 0 \end{bmatrix} \Rightarrow \begin{bmatrix} 1 & 0 & 0 & 0 & 0 & 2 \\ 0 & 1 & 0 & 0 & 0 & 0 \\ 0 & 0 & 1 & 0 & 0 & 4 \\ 0 & 0 & 0 & 1 & 0 & -1 \\ 0 & 0 & 0 & 0 & 1 & 2 \end{bmatrix}$$

So, the solution is: $x_1 = 2$, $x_2 = 0$, $x_3 = 4$, $x_4 = -1$, and $x_5 = 2$.

40. Using a graphing utility, the augmented matrix reduces to

$$\begin{bmatrix} 1 & 5 & 0 & 0 \\ 0 & 0 & 1 & 0 \\ 0 & 0 & 0 & 1 \\ 0 & 0 & 0 & 0 \end{bmatrix}.$$

The system is inconsistent, so there is no solution.

42. Using a graphing utility, the augmented matrix reduces to

$$\begin{bmatrix} 1 & 0 & 0 & 1.5 & 0 \\ 0 & 1 & 0 & 0.5 & 0 \\ 0 & 0 & 1 & 0.5 & 0 \end{bmatrix}.$$

Choosing $w = t$ as the free variable, you can describe the solution as $x = -1.5t$, $y = -0.5t$, $z = -0.5t$, $w = t$, where t is any real number.

44. Use Gauss-Jordan elimination on the augmented matrix.

$$\begin{bmatrix} 2 & 4 & -7 & 0 \\ 1 & -3 & 9 & 0 \end{bmatrix} \Rightarrow \begin{bmatrix} 1 & 0 & \frac{3}{2} & 0 \\ 0 & 1 & -\frac{5}{2} & 0 \end{bmatrix}$$

Letting $x_3 = t$ be the free variable, you have $x_1 = -\frac{3}{2}t$, $x_2 = \frac{5}{2}t$, and $x_3 = t$, where t is any real number.

46. Use Gauss-Jordan elimination on the augmented matrix.

$$\begin{bmatrix} 1 & 3 & 5 & 0 \\ 1 & 4 & \frac{1}{2} & 0 \end{bmatrix} \Rightarrow \begin{bmatrix} 1 & 0 & \frac{37}{2} & 0 \\ 0 & 1 & -\frac{9}{2} & 0 \end{bmatrix}$$

Choosing $x_3 = t$ as the free variable, you can describe the solution as $x_1 = -\frac{37}{2}t$, $x_2 = \frac{9}{2}t$, and $x_3 = t$, where t is any real number.

48. Use Gaussian elimination on the augmented matrix.

$$\begin{bmatrix} 1 & -1 & 2 & 0 \\ -1 & 1 & -1 & 0 \\ 1 & k & 1 & 0 \end{bmatrix} \Rightarrow \begin{bmatrix} 1 & -1 & 2 & 0 \\ 0 & 0 & 1 & 0 \\ 0 & (k+1) & -1 & 0 \end{bmatrix}$$

$$\Rightarrow \begin{bmatrix} 1 & -1 & 2 & 0 \\ 0 & (k+1) & -1 & 0 \\ 0 & 0 & 1 & 0 \end{bmatrix}$$

So, there will be exactly one solution (the trivial solution $x = y = z = 0$) if and only if $k \neq -1$.

50. Form the augmented matrix for the system.

$$\begin{bmatrix} 2 & -1 & 1 & a \\ 1 & 1 & 2 & b \\ 0 & 3 & 3 & c \end{bmatrix}$$

Use Gaussian elimination to reduce the matrix to row-echelon form.

$$\begin{bmatrix} 1 & -\frac{1}{2} & \frac{1}{2} & \frac{a}{2} \\ 1 & 1 & 2 & b \\ 0 & 3 & 3 & c \end{bmatrix} \Rightarrow \begin{bmatrix} 1 & -\frac{1}{2} & -\frac{1}{2} & \frac{a}{2} \\ 0 & \frac{3}{2} & \frac{3}{2} & \frac{2b-a}{2} \\ 0 & 3 & 3 & c \end{bmatrix}$$

$$\Rightarrow \begin{bmatrix} 1 & -\frac{1}{2} & \frac{1}{2} & \frac{a}{2} \\ 0 & 1 & 1 & \frac{2b-a}{3} \\ 0 & 3 & 3 & c \end{bmatrix}$$

$$\Rightarrow \begin{bmatrix} 1 & -\frac{1}{2} & \frac{1}{2} & \frac{a}{2} \\ 0 & 1 & 1 & \frac{2b-a}{3} \\ 0 & 0 & 0 & c-2b+a \end{bmatrix}$$

(a) If $c - 2b + a \neq 0$, then the system has no solution.

(b) The system cannot have one solution.

(c) If $c - 2b + a = 0$, then the system has infinitely many solutions.

52. Find all possible first rows, where a and b are nonzero real numbers.

$$\begin{bmatrix} 0 & 0 & 0 \end{bmatrix}, \begin{bmatrix} 0 & 0 & 1 \end{bmatrix}, \begin{bmatrix} 0 & 1 & 0 \end{bmatrix}, \begin{bmatrix} 0 & 1 & a \end{bmatrix}, \begin{bmatrix} 1 & 0 & 0 \end{bmatrix}, \begin{bmatrix} 1 & a & 0 \end{bmatrix}, \begin{bmatrix} 1 & a & b \end{bmatrix}, \begin{bmatrix} 1 & 0 & a \end{bmatrix}$$

For each of these, examine the possible second rows.

$$\begin{bmatrix} 0 & 0 & 0 \\ 0 & 0 & 0 \end{bmatrix}, \begin{bmatrix} 0 & 0 & 1 \\ 0 & 0 & 0 \end{bmatrix}, \begin{bmatrix} 0 & 1 & 0 \\ 0 & 0 & 0 \end{bmatrix}, \begin{bmatrix} 0 & 1 & 0 \\ 0 & 0 & 1 \end{bmatrix},$$

$$\begin{bmatrix} 0 & 1 & a \\ 0 & 0 & 0 \end{bmatrix}, \begin{bmatrix} 1 & 0 & 0 \\ 0 & 0 & 0 \end{bmatrix}, \begin{bmatrix} 1 & 0 & 0 \\ 0 & 1 & 0 \end{bmatrix}, \begin{bmatrix} 1 & 0 & 0 \\ 0 & 0 & 1 \end{bmatrix}, \begin{bmatrix} 1 & 0 & 0 \\ 0 & 1 & a \end{bmatrix},$$

$$\begin{bmatrix} 1 & a & 0 \\ 0 & 0 & 0 \end{bmatrix}, \begin{bmatrix} 1 & a & 0 \\ 0 & 0 & 1 \end{bmatrix}, \begin{bmatrix} 1 & a & b \\ 0 & 0 & 0 \end{bmatrix}, \begin{bmatrix} 1 & 0 & a \\ 0 & 0 & 0 \end{bmatrix}, \begin{bmatrix} 1 & 0 & a \\ 0 & 1 & 0 \end{bmatrix}$$

54. Use Gaussian elimination on the augmented matrix.

$$\begin{bmatrix} (\lambda + 2) & -2 & 3 & 0 \\ -2 & (\lambda - 1) & 6 & 0 \\ 1 & 2 & \lambda & 0 \end{bmatrix} \Rightarrow \begin{bmatrix} 1 & 2 & \lambda & 0 \\ 0 & \lambda + 3 & 6 + 2\lambda & 0 \\ 0 & -2\lambda - 6 & -\lambda^2 - 2\lambda + 3 & 0 \end{bmatrix} \Rightarrow \begin{bmatrix} 1 & 2 & \lambda & 0 \\ 0 & \lambda + 3 & 6 + 2\lambda & 0 \\ 0 & 0 & (\lambda^2 - 2\lambda - 15) & 0 \end{bmatrix}$$

So, you need $\lambda^2 - 2\lambda - 15 = (\lambda - 5)(\lambda + 3) = 0$, which implies $\lambda = 5$ or $\lambda = -3$.

56. (a) True. A homogeneous system of linear equations is always consistent, because there is always a trivial solution, *i.e.*, when all variables are equal to zero. See Theorem 1.1 on page 21.

(b) False. Consider, for example, the following system (with three variables and two equations).

$$x + y - z = 2$$
$$-2x - 2y + 2z = 1.$$

It is easy to see that this system has *no* solution.

58. From the following chart, you obtain a system of equations.

	A	B	C
Mixture X	$\frac{1}{5}$	$\frac{2}{5}$	$\frac{2}{5}$
Mixture Y	0	0	1
Mixture Z	$\frac{1}{3}$	$\frac{1}{3}$	$\frac{1}{3}$
Desired Mixture	$\frac{6}{27}$	$\frac{8}{27}$	$\frac{13}{27}$

$$\left.\begin{array}{l} \frac{1}{5}x + \frac{1}{3}z = \frac{6}{27} \\ \frac{2}{5}x + \frac{1}{3}z = \frac{8}{27} \end{array}\right\} x = \frac{10}{27}, z = \frac{12}{27}$$

$$\frac{2}{5}x + y + \frac{1}{3}z = \frac{13}{27} \Rightarrow y = \frac{5}{27}$$

To obtain the desired mixture, use 10 gallons of spray X, 5 gallons of spray Y, and 12 gallons of spray Z.

60. $\dfrac{3x^2 + 3x - 2}{(x + 1)^2(x - 1)} = \dfrac{A}{x + 1} + \dfrac{B}{x - 1} + \dfrac{C}{(x + 1)^2}$

$$3x^2 + 3x - 2 = A(x + 1)(x - 1) + B(x + 1)^2 + C(x - 1)$$
$$3x^2 + 3x - 2 = Ax^2 - A + Bx^2 + 2Bx + B + Cx - C$$
$$3x^2 + 3x - 2 = (A + B)x^2 + (2B + C)x - A + B - C$$

So, $A + B = 3$
$$2B + C = 3$$
$$-A + B - C = -2.$$

Use Gauss-Jordan elimination to solve the system.

$$\begin{bmatrix} 1 & 1 & 0 & 3 \\ 0 & 2 & 1 & 3 \\ -1 & 1 & -1 & -2 \end{bmatrix} \Rightarrow \begin{bmatrix} 1 & 0 & 0 & 2 \\ 0 & 1 & 0 & 1 \\ 0 & 0 & 1 & 1 \end{bmatrix}$$

The solution is: $A = 2$, $B = 1$, and $C = 1$.

So, $\dfrac{3x^2 + 3x - 2}{(x + 1)^2(x - 1)} = \dfrac{2}{x + 1} + \dfrac{1}{x - 1} + \dfrac{1}{(x + 1)^2}$.

62. (a) Because there are four points, choose a third-degree polynomial, $p(x) = a_0 + a_1x + a_2x^2 + a_3x^3$.

By substituting the values at each point into this equation, you obtain the system

$$a_0 - a_1 + a_2 - a_3 = -1$$
$$a_0 \qquad\qquad\qquad = 0$$
$$a_0 + a_1 + a_2 + a_3 = 1$$
$$a_0 + 2a_1 + 4a_2 + 8a_3 = 4.$$

Use Gauss-Jordan elimination on the augmented matrix.

$$\begin{bmatrix} 1 & -1 & 1 & -1 & -1 \\ 1 & 0 & 0 & 0 & 0 \\ 1 & 1 & 1 & 1 & 1 \\ 1 & 2 & 4 & 8 & 4 \end{bmatrix} \Rightarrow \begin{bmatrix} 1 & 0 & 0 & 0 & 0 \\ 0 & 1 & 0 & 0 & \frac{2}{3} \\ 0 & 0 & 1 & 0 & 0 \\ 0 & 0 & 0 & 1 & \frac{1}{3} \end{bmatrix}$$

So, $p(x) = \frac{2}{3}x + \frac{1}{3}x^3$.

(b)

64. Substituting the points, $(1, 0)$, $(2, 0)$, $(3, 0)$, and $(4, 0)$ into the polynomial $p(x)$ yields the system

$$a_0 + a_1 + a_2 + a_3 = 0$$
$$a_0 + 2a_1 + 4a_2 + 8a_3 = 0$$
$$a_0 + 3a_1 + 9a_2 + 27a_3 = 0$$
$$a_0 + 4a_1 + 16a_2 + 64a_3 = 0.$$

Gaussian elimination shows that the only solution is $a_0 = a_1 = a_2 = a_3 = 0$.

66. $s = \frac{1}{2}at^2 + v_0 t + s_0$

(a) When $t = 1$: $s = 134$: $\frac{1}{2}a(1)^2 + v_0(1) + s_0 = 134 \Rightarrow a + 2v_0 + 2s_0 = 268$

When $t = 2$: $s = 86$: $\frac{1}{2}a(2)^2 + v_0(2) + s_0 = 86 \Rightarrow 2a + 2v_0 + s_0 = 86$

When $t = 3$: $s = 6$: $\frac{1}{2}a(3)^2 + v_0(3) + s_0 = 6 \Rightarrow 9a + 6v_0 + 2s_0 = 12$

Use Gaussian elimination to solve the system.

$$
\begin{aligned}
a + 2v_0 + 2s_0 &= 268 \\
2a + 2v_0 + s_0 &= 86 \\
9a + 6v_0 + 2s_0 &= 12
\end{aligned}
$$

$$
\begin{aligned}
a + 2v_0 + 2s_0 &= 268 \\
-2v_0 - 3s_0 &= -450 \quad & (-2)\text{Eq.1} + \text{Eq.2} \\
-12v_0 - 16s_0 &= -2400 \quad & (-9)\text{Eq.1} + \text{Eq.3}
\end{aligned}
$$

$$
\begin{aligned}
a + 2v_0 + 2s_0 &= 268 \\
-2v_0 - 3s_0 &= 450 \\
3v_0 + 4s_0 &= 600 \quad & \left(-\tfrac{1}{4}\right)\text{Eq.3}
\end{aligned}
$$

$$
\begin{aligned}
a + 2v_0 + 2s_0 &= 268 \\
-2v_0 - 3s_0 &= -450 \\
-s_0 &= -150 \quad & 3\text{Eq.2} + 2\text{Eq.3}
\end{aligned}
$$

$$-s_0 = -150 \Rightarrow s_0 = 150$$
$$-2v_0 - 3(150) = -450 \Rightarrow v_0 = 0$$
$$a + 2(0) + 2(150) = 268 \Rightarrow a = -32$$

The position equation is $s = \frac{1}{2}(-32)t^2 + (0)t + 150$, or $s = -16t^2 + 150$.

68. (a) First find the equations corresponding to each node in the network.

       input = output

$$
\begin{aligned}
x_1 + 200 &= x_2 + x_4 \\
x_6 + 100 &= x_1 + x_3 \\
x_2 + x_3 &= x_5 + 300 \\
x_4 + x_5 &= x_6
\end{aligned}
$$

Rearranging this system and forming the augmented matrix, you have

$$
\begin{bmatrix}
1 & -1 & 0 & -1 & 0 & 0 & -200 \\
1 & 0 & 1 & 0 & 0 & -1 & 100 \\
0 & 1 & 1 & 0 & -1 & 0 & 300 \\
0 & 0 & 0 & 1 & 1 & -1 & 0
\end{bmatrix}.
$$

The equivalent reduced row-echelon matrix is

$$
\begin{bmatrix}
1 & 0 & 1 & 0 & 0 & -1 & 100 \\
0 & 1 & 1 & 0 & -1 & 0 & 300 \\
0 & 0 & 0 & 1 & 1 & -1 & 0 \\
0 & 0 & 0 & 0 & 0 & 0 & 0
\end{bmatrix}.
$$

Choosing $x_3 = r$, $x_5 = s$, and $x_6 = t$ as the free variables, you obtain

$$
\begin{aligned}
x_1 &= 100 - r + t \\
x_2 &= 300 - r + s \\
x_4 &= -s + t,
\end{aligned}
$$

where r, s, and t are any real numbers.

(b) When $x_3 = 100 = r$, $x_5 = 50 = s$, and $x_6 = 50 = t$, you have

$$
\begin{aligned}
x_1 &= 100 - 100 + 50 = 50 \\
x_2 &= 300 - 100 + 50 = 250 \\
x_4 &= -50 + 50 = 0.
\end{aligned}
$$

Project Solutions for Chapter 1

1 Graphing Linear Equations

1. $\begin{bmatrix} 2 & -1 & 3 \\ a & b & 6 \end{bmatrix} \Rightarrow \begin{bmatrix} 1 & -\frac{1}{2} & \frac{3}{2} \\ 0 & b + \frac{1}{2}a & 6 - \frac{3}{2}a \end{bmatrix}$

   (a) Unique solution if $b + \frac{1}{2}a \neq 0$. For instance, $a = b = 2$.

   (b) Infinite number of solutions if $b + \frac{1}{2}a = 6 - \frac{3}{2}a = 0 \Rightarrow a = 4$ and $b = -2$.

   (c) No solution if $b + \frac{1}{2}a = 0$ and $6 - \frac{3}{2}a \neq 0 \Rightarrow a \neq 4$ and $b = -\frac{1}{2}a$. For instance, $a = 2$, $b = -1$.

   (d)

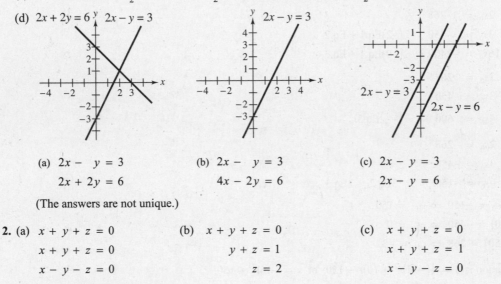

(a) $2x - y = 3$	(b) $2x - y = 3$	(c) $2x - y = 3$
$2x + 2y = 6$	$4x - 2y = 6$	$2x - y = 6$

   (The answers are not unique.)

2. (a) $x + y + z = 0$
      $x + y + z = 0$
      $x - y - z = 0$

   (b) $x + y + z = 0$
      $y + z = 1$
      $z = 2$

   (c) $x + y + z = 0$
      $x + y + z = 1$
      $x - y - z = 0$

   (The answers are not unique.)

   There are other configurations, such as three mutually parallel planes or three planes that intersect pairwise in lines.

2 Underdetermined and Overdetermined Systems of Equations

1. Yes, $x + y = 2$ is a consistent underdetermined system.

2. Yes,

   $x + y = 2$
   $2x + 2y = 4$
   $3x + 3y = 6$

   is a consistent, overdetermined system.

3. Yes,

   $x + y + z = 1$
   $x + y + z = 2$

   is an inconsistent underdetermined system.

4. Yes,

   $x + y = 1$
   $x + y = 2$
   $x + y = 3$

   is an inconsistent underdetermined system.

5. In general, a linear system with more equations than variables would probably be inconsistent. Here is an intuitive reason: Each variable represents a degree of freedom, while each equation gives a condition that in general reduces number of degrees of freedom by one. If there are more equations (conditions) than variables (degrees of freedom), then there are too many conditions for the system to be consistent. So you expect such a system to be inconsistent in general. But, as Exercise 2 shows, this is not always true.

6. In general, a linear system with more variables than equations would probably be consistent. As in Exercise 5, the intuitive explanation is as follows. Each variable represents a degree of freedom, and each equation represents a condition that takes away one degree of freedom. If there are more variables than equations, in general, you would expect a solution. But, as Exercise 3 shows, this is not always true.

CHAPTER 2
Matrices

CHAPTER 2
Matrices

Section 2.1   Operations with Matrices

2. $x = 13, y = 12$

4.
$$x + 2 = 2x + 6 \qquad 2y = 18$$
$$-4 = x \qquad\qquad y = 9$$

$$2x = -8 \qquad\quad y + 2 = 11$$
$$x = -4 \qquad\qquad y = 9$$

6. (a) $A + B = \begin{bmatrix} 1 & 2 \\ 2 & 1 \end{bmatrix} + \begin{bmatrix} -3 & -2 \\ 4 & 2 \end{bmatrix} = \begin{bmatrix} 1-3 & 2-2 \\ 2+4 & 1+2 \end{bmatrix} = \begin{bmatrix} -2 & 0 \\ 6 & 3 \end{bmatrix}$

(b) $A - B = \begin{bmatrix} 1 & 2 \\ 2 & 1 \end{bmatrix} - \begin{bmatrix} -3 & -2 \\ 4 & 2 \end{bmatrix} = \begin{bmatrix} 1+3 & 2+2 \\ 2-4 & 1-2 \end{bmatrix} = \begin{bmatrix} 4 & 4 \\ -2 & -1 \end{bmatrix}$

(c) $2A = 2\begin{bmatrix} 1 & 2 \\ 2 & 1 \end{bmatrix} = \begin{bmatrix} 2(1) & 2(2) \\ 2(2) & 2(1) \end{bmatrix} = \begin{bmatrix} 2 & 4 \\ 4 & 2 \end{bmatrix}$

(d) $2A - B = \begin{bmatrix} 2 & 4 \\ 4 & 2 \end{bmatrix} - \begin{bmatrix} -3 & -2 \\ 4 & 2 \end{bmatrix} = \begin{bmatrix} 5 & 6 \\ 0 & 0 \end{bmatrix}$

(e) $B + \frac{1}{2}A = \begin{bmatrix} -3 & -2 \\ 4 & 2 \end{bmatrix} + \frac{1}{2}\begin{bmatrix} 1 & 2 \\ 2 & 1 \end{bmatrix} = \begin{bmatrix} -3 & -2 \\ 4 & 2 \end{bmatrix} + \begin{bmatrix} \frac{1}{2} & 1 \\ 1 & \frac{1}{2} \end{bmatrix} = \begin{bmatrix} -\frac{5}{2} & -1 \\ 5 & \frac{5}{2} \end{bmatrix}$

8. (a) $A + B = \begin{bmatrix} 2 & 1 & 1 \\ -1 & -1 & 4 \end{bmatrix} + \begin{bmatrix} 2 & -3 & 4 \\ -3 & 1 & -2 \end{bmatrix} = \begin{bmatrix} 2+2 & 1-3 & 1+4 \\ -1-3 & -1+1 & 4-2 \end{bmatrix} = \begin{bmatrix} 4 & -2 & 5 \\ -4 & 0 & 2 \end{bmatrix}$

(b) $A - B = \begin{bmatrix} 2 & 1 & 1 \\ -1 & -1 & 4 \end{bmatrix} - \begin{bmatrix} 2 & -3 & 4 \\ -3 & 1 & -2 \end{bmatrix} = \begin{bmatrix} 2-2 & 1+3 & 1-4 \\ -1+3 & -1-1 & 4+2 \end{bmatrix} = \begin{bmatrix} 0 & 4 & -3 \\ 2 & -2 & 6 \end{bmatrix}$

(c) $2A = 2\begin{bmatrix} 2 & 1 & 1 \\ -1 & -1 & 4 \end{bmatrix} = \begin{bmatrix} 2(2) & 2(1) & 2(1) \\ 2(-1) & 2(-1) & 2(4) \end{bmatrix} = \begin{bmatrix} 4 & 2 & 2 \\ -2 & -2 & 8 \end{bmatrix}$

(d) $2A - B = \begin{bmatrix} 4 & 2 & 2 \\ -2 & -2 & 8 \end{bmatrix} - \begin{bmatrix} 2 & -3 & 4 \\ -3 & 1 & -2 \end{bmatrix} = \begin{bmatrix} 2 & 5 & -2 \\ 1 & -3 & 10 \end{bmatrix}$

(e) $B + \frac{1}{2}A = \begin{bmatrix} 2 & -3 & 4 \\ -3 & 1 & -2 \end{bmatrix} + \frac{1}{2}\begin{bmatrix} 2 & 1 & 1 \\ -1 & -1 & 4 \end{bmatrix} = \begin{bmatrix} 2 & -3 & 4 \\ -3 & 1 & -2 \end{bmatrix} + \begin{bmatrix} 1 & \frac{1}{2} & \frac{1}{2} \\ -\frac{1}{2} & -\frac{1}{2} & 2 \end{bmatrix} = \begin{bmatrix} 3 & -\frac{5}{2} & \frac{9}{2} \\ -\frac{7}{2} & \frac{1}{2} & 0 \end{bmatrix}$

10. (a) $A + B = \begin{bmatrix} 2 & 3 & 4 \\ 0 & 1 & -1 \\ 2 & 0 & 1 \end{bmatrix} + \begin{bmatrix} 0 & 6 & 2 \\ 4 & 1 & 0 \\ -1 & 2 & 4 \end{bmatrix} = \begin{bmatrix} 2+0 & 3+6 & 4+2 \\ 0+4 & 1+1 & -1+0 \\ 2+(-1) & 0+2 & 1+4 \end{bmatrix} = \begin{bmatrix} 2 & 9 & 6 \\ 4 & 2 & -1 \\ 1 & 2 & 5 \end{bmatrix}$

(b) $A - B = \begin{bmatrix} 2 & 3 & 4 \\ 0 & 1 & -1 \\ 2 & 0 & 1 \end{bmatrix} - \begin{bmatrix} 0 & 6 & 2 \\ 4 & 1 & 0 \\ -1 & 2 & 4 \end{bmatrix} = \begin{bmatrix} 2-0 & 3-6 & 4-2 \\ 0-4 & 1-1 & -1-0 \\ 2-(-1) & 0-2 & 1-4 \end{bmatrix} = \begin{bmatrix} 2 & -3 & 2 \\ -4 & 0 & -1 \\ 3 & -2 & -3 \end{bmatrix}$

(c) $2A = 2\begin{bmatrix} 2 & 3 & 4 \\ 0 & 1 & -1 \\ 2 & 0 & 1 \end{bmatrix} = \begin{bmatrix} 2(2) & 2(3) & 2(4) \\ 2(0) & 2(1) & 2(-1) \\ 2(2) & 2(0) & 2(1) \end{bmatrix} = \begin{bmatrix} 4 & 6 & 8 \\ 0 & 2 & -2 \\ 4 & 0 & 2 \end{bmatrix}$

(d) $2A - B = 2\begin{bmatrix} 2 & 3 & 4 \\ 0 & 1 & -1 \\ 2 & 0 & 1 \end{bmatrix} - \begin{bmatrix} 0 & 6 & 2 \\ 4 & 1 & 0 \\ -1 & 2 & 4 \end{bmatrix} = \begin{bmatrix} 4 & 6 & 8 \\ 0 & 2 & -2 \\ 4 & 0 & 2 \end{bmatrix} - \begin{bmatrix} 0 & 6 & 2 \\ 4 & 1 & 0 \\ -1 & 2 & 4 \end{bmatrix} = \begin{bmatrix} 4 & 0 & 6 \\ -4 & 1 & -2 \\ 5 & -2 & -2 \end{bmatrix}$

(e) $B + \frac{1}{2}A = \begin{bmatrix} 0 & 6 & 2 \\ 4 & 1 & 0 \\ -1 & 2 & 4 \end{bmatrix} + \frac{1}{2}\begin{bmatrix} 2 & 3 & 4 \\ 0 & 1 & -1 \\ 2 & 0 & 1 \end{bmatrix} = \begin{bmatrix} 0 & 6 & 2 \\ 4 & 1 & 0 \\ -1 & 2 & 4 \end{bmatrix} + \begin{bmatrix} 1 & \frac{3}{2} & 2 \\ 0 & \frac{1}{2} & -\frac{1}{2} \\ 1 & 0 & \frac{1}{2} \end{bmatrix} = \begin{bmatrix} 1 & \frac{15}{2} & 4 \\ 4 & \frac{3}{2} & -\frac{1}{2} \\ 0 & 2 & \frac{9}{2} \end{bmatrix}$

12. (a) $A + B$ is not possible. A and B have different sizes.

(b) $A - B$ is not possible. A and B have different sizes.

(c) $2A = 2\begin{bmatrix} 3 \\ 2 \\ -1 \end{bmatrix} = \begin{bmatrix} 6 \\ 4 \\ -2 \end{bmatrix}$

(d) $2A - B$ is not possible. A and B have different sizes.

(e) $B + \frac{1}{2}A$ is not possible. A and B have different sizes.

14. (a) $c_{23} = 5a_{23} + 2b_{23} = 5(2) + 2(11) = 32$

(b) $c_{32} = 5a_{32} + 2b_{32} = 5(1) + 2(4) = 13$

16. Simplifying the right side of the equation produces

$$\begin{bmatrix} w & x \\ y & x \end{bmatrix} = \begin{bmatrix} -4 + 2y & 3 + 2w \\ 2 + 2z & -1 + 2x \end{bmatrix}.$$

By setting corresponding entries equal to each other, you obtain four equations.

$$\begin{aligned} w &= -4 + 2y \\ x &= 3 + 2w \\ y &= 2 + 2z \\ x &= -1 + 2x \end{aligned} \Rightarrow \begin{cases} -2y + w = -4 \\ x - 2w = 3 \\ y - 2z = 2 \\ x = 1 \end{cases}$$

The solution to this linear system is:

$x = 1$, $y = \frac{3}{2}$, $z = -\frac{1}{4}$, and $w = -1$.

18. (a) $AB = \begin{bmatrix} 2 & -2 \\ -1 & 4 \end{bmatrix}\begin{bmatrix} 4 & 1 \\ 2 & -2 \end{bmatrix} = \begin{bmatrix} 2(4) + (-2)(2) & 2(1) + (-2)(-2) \\ -1(4) + 4(2) & -1(1) + 4(-2) \end{bmatrix} = \begin{bmatrix} 4 & 6 \\ 4 & -9 \end{bmatrix}$

(b) $BA = \begin{bmatrix} 4 & 1 \\ 2 & -2 \end{bmatrix}\begin{bmatrix} 2 & -2 \\ -1 & 4 \end{bmatrix} = \begin{bmatrix} 4(2) + 1(-1) & 4(-2) + 1(4) \\ 2(2) + (-2)(-1) & 2(-2) + (-2)(4) \end{bmatrix} = \begin{bmatrix} 7 & -4 \\ 6 & -12 \end{bmatrix}$

20. (a) $AB = \begin{bmatrix} 1 & -1 & 7 \\ 2 & -1 & 8 \\ 3 & 1 & -1 \end{bmatrix}\begin{bmatrix} 1 & 1 & 2 \\ 2 & 1 & 1 \\ 1 & -3 & 2 \end{bmatrix} = \begin{bmatrix} 1(1) + (-1)(2) + 7(1) & 1(1) + (-1)(1) + 7(-3) & 1(2) + (-1)(1) + 7(2) \\ 2(1) + (-1)(2) + 8(1) & 2(1) + (-1)(1) + 8(-3) & 2(2) + (-1)(1) + 8(2) \\ 3(1) + 1(2) + (-1)(1) & 3(1) + 1(1) + (-1)(-3) & 3(2) + 1(1) + (-1)(2) \end{bmatrix} = \begin{bmatrix} 6 & -21 & 15 \\ 8 & -23 & 19 \\ 4 & 7 & 5 \end{bmatrix}$

(b) $BA = \begin{bmatrix} 1 & 1 & 2 \\ 2 & 1 & 1 \\ 1 & -3 & 2 \end{bmatrix}\begin{bmatrix} 1 & -1 & 7 \\ 2 & -1 & 8 \\ 3 & 1 & -1 \end{bmatrix} = \begin{bmatrix} 1(1) + 1(2) + 2(3) & 1(-1) + 1(-1)1 + 2(1) & 1(7) + 1(8) + 2(-1) \\ 2(1) + 1(2) + 1(3) & 2(-1) + 1(-1) + 1(1) & 2(7) + 1(8) + 1(-1) \\ 1(1) + (-3)(2) + 2(3) & 1(-1) + (-3)(-1) + 2(1) & 1(7) + (-3)(8) + 2(-1) \end{bmatrix} = \begin{bmatrix} 9 & 0 & 13 \\ 7 & -2 & 21 \\ 1 & 4 & -19 \end{bmatrix}$

22. (a) $AB = \begin{bmatrix} 3 & 2 & 1 \\ -3 & 0 & 4 \\ 4 & -2 & -4 \end{bmatrix}\begin{bmatrix} 1 & 2 \\ 2 & -1 \\ 1 & -2 \end{bmatrix} = \begin{bmatrix} 3(1) + 2(2) + 1(1) & 3(2) + 2(-1) + 1(-2) \\ -3(1) + 0(2) + 4(1) & -3(2) + 0(-1) + 4(-2) \\ 4(1) + (-2)(2) + (-4)(1) & 4(2) + (-2)(-1) + (-4)(-2) \end{bmatrix} = \begin{bmatrix} 8 & 2 \\ 1 & -14 \\ -4 & 18 \end{bmatrix}$

(b) BA is not defined because B is 3×2 and A is 3×3.

24. (a) $AB = \begin{bmatrix} -1 \\ 2 \\ -2 \\ 1 \end{bmatrix}\begin{bmatrix} 2 & 1 & 3 & 2 \end{bmatrix} = \begin{bmatrix} -1(2) & -1(1) & -1(3) & -1(2) \\ 2(2) & 2(1) & 2(3) & 2(2) \\ -2(2) & -2(1) & -2(3) & -2(2) \\ 1(2) & 1(1) & 1(3) & 1(2) \end{bmatrix} = \begin{bmatrix} -2 & -1 & -3 & -2 \\ 4 & 2 & 6 & 4 \\ -4 & -2 & -6 & -4 \\ 2 & 1 & 3 & 2 \end{bmatrix}$

(b) $BA = \begin{bmatrix} 2 & 1 & 3 & 2 \end{bmatrix}\begin{bmatrix} -1 \\ 2 \\ -2 \\ 1 \end{bmatrix} = \begin{bmatrix} 2(-1) + 1(2) + 3(-2) + 2(1) \end{bmatrix} = \begin{bmatrix} -4 \end{bmatrix}$

26. (a) AB is not defined because A is 2×2 and B is 3×2.

(b) $BA = \begin{bmatrix} 2 & 1 \\ 1 & 3 \\ 2 & -1 \end{bmatrix} \begin{bmatrix} 2 & -3 \\ 5 & 2 \end{bmatrix} = \begin{bmatrix} 2(2) + 1(5) & 2(-3) + 1(2) \\ 1(2) + 3(5) & 1(-3) + 3(2) \\ 2(2) + (-1)(5) & 2(-3) + (-1)(2) \end{bmatrix} = \begin{bmatrix} 9 & -4 \\ 17 & 3 \\ -1 & -8 \end{bmatrix}$

28. (a) $AB = \begin{bmatrix} 2 & 1 & 2 \\ 3 & -1 & -2 \\ -2 & 1 & -2 \end{bmatrix} \begin{bmatrix} 4 & 0 & 1 & 3 \\ -1 & 2 & -3 & -1 \\ -2 & 1 & 4 & 3 \end{bmatrix}$

$= \begin{bmatrix} 2(4) + 1(-1) + 2(-2) & 2(0) + 1(2) + 2(1) & 2(1) + 1(-3) + 2(4) & 2(3) + 1(-1) + 2(3) \\ 3(4) + (-1)(-1) + (-2)(-2) & 3(0) + (-1)(2) + (-2)(1) & 3(1) + (-1)(-3) + (-2)(4) & 3(3) + (-1)(-1) + (-2)(3) \\ -2(4) + 1(-1) + (-2)(-2) & -2(0) + 1(2) + (-2)(1) & -2(1) + 1(-3) + (-2)(4) & -2(3) + 1(-1) + (-2)(3) \end{bmatrix}$

$= \begin{bmatrix} 3 & 4 & 7 & 11 \\ 17 & -4 & -2 & 4 \\ -5 & 0 & -13 & -13 \end{bmatrix}$

(b) BA is not defined because B is 3×4 and A is 3×3.

30. (a) AB is not defined because A is 2×5 and B is 2×2.

(b) $BA = \begin{bmatrix} 1 & 6 \\ 4 & 2 \end{bmatrix} \begin{bmatrix} 1 & 0 & 3 & -2 & 4 \\ 6 & 13 & 8 & -17 & 20 \end{bmatrix}$

$= \begin{bmatrix} 1(1) + 6(6) & 1(0) + 6(13) & 1(3) + 6(8) & 1(-2) + 6(-17) & 1(4) + 6(20) \\ 4(1) + 2(6) & 4(0) + 2(13) & 4(3) + 2(8) & 4(-2) + 2(-17) & 4(4) + 2(20) \end{bmatrix}$

$= \begin{bmatrix} 37 & 78 & 51 & -104 & 124 \\ 16 & 26 & 28 & -42 & 56 \end{bmatrix}$

32. $C + E$ is not defined because C and E have different sizes.

34. $-4A$ is defined and has size 3×4 because A has size 3×4.

36. BE is defined. Because B has size 3×4 and E has size 4×3, the size of BE is 3×3.

38. $2D + C$ is defined and has size 4×2 because $2D$ and C have size 4×2.

40. As a system of linear equations, $Ax = 0$ is

$x_1 + 2x_2 + x_3 + 3x_4 = 0$
$x_1 - x_2 \qquad + x_4 = 0.$
$\qquad x_2 - x_3 + 2x_4 = 0$

Use Gauss-Jordan elimination on the augmented matrix for this system.

$\begin{bmatrix} 1 & 2 & 1 & 3 & 0 \\ 1 & -1 & 0 & 1 & 0 \\ 0 & 1 & -1 & 2 & 0 \end{bmatrix} \Rightarrow \begin{bmatrix} 1 & 0 & 0 & 2 & 0 \\ 0 & 1 & 0 & 1 & 0 \\ 0 & 0 & 1 & -1 & 0 \end{bmatrix}$

Choosing $x_4 = t$, the solution is

$x_1 = -2t, x_2 = -t, x_3 = t,$ and $x_4 = t,$ where t is any real number.

42. In matrix form $Ax = b$, the system is

$\begin{bmatrix} 2 & 3 \\ 1 & 4 \end{bmatrix} \begin{bmatrix} x_1 \\ x_2 \end{bmatrix} = \begin{bmatrix} 5 \\ 10 \end{bmatrix}.$

Use Gauss-Jordan elimination on the augmented matrix.

$\begin{bmatrix} 2 & 3 & 5 \\ 1 & 4 & 10 \end{bmatrix} \Rightarrow \begin{bmatrix} 1 & 0 & -2 \\ 0 & 1 & 3 \end{bmatrix}$

So, the solution is $\begin{bmatrix} x_1 \\ x_2 \end{bmatrix} = \begin{bmatrix} -2 \\ 3 \end{bmatrix}.$

44. In matrix form $Ax = b$, the system is

$\begin{bmatrix} -4 & 9 \\ 1 & -3 \end{bmatrix} \begin{bmatrix} x_1 \\ x_2 \end{bmatrix} = \begin{bmatrix} -13 \\ 12 \end{bmatrix}.$

Use Gauss-Jordan elimination on the augmented matrix.

$\begin{bmatrix} -4 & 9 & -13 \\ 1 & -3 & 12 \end{bmatrix} \Rightarrow \begin{bmatrix} 1 & 0 & -23 \\ 0 & 1 & -\frac{35}{3} \end{bmatrix}$

So, the solution is $\begin{bmatrix} x_1 \\ x_2 \end{bmatrix} = \begin{bmatrix} -23 \\ -\frac{35}{3} \end{bmatrix}.$

46. In matrix form $A\mathbf{x} = \mathbf{b}$, the system is

$$\begin{bmatrix} 1 & 1 & -3 \\ -1 & 2 & 0 \\ 1 & -1 & 1 \end{bmatrix} \begin{bmatrix} x_1 \\ x_2 \\ x_3 \end{bmatrix} = \begin{bmatrix} -1 \\ 1 \\ 2 \end{bmatrix}.$$

Use Gauss-Jordan elimination on the augmented matrix.

$$\begin{bmatrix} 1 & 1 & -3 & -1 \\ -1 & 2 & 0 & 1 \\ 1 & -1 & 1 & 2 \end{bmatrix} \Rightarrow \begin{bmatrix} 1 & 0 & 0 & 2 \\ 0 & 1 & 0 & \frac{3}{2} \\ 0 & 0 & 1 & \frac{3}{2} \end{bmatrix}$$

So, the solution is $\begin{bmatrix} x_1 \\ x_2 \\ x_3 \end{bmatrix} = \begin{bmatrix} 2 \\ \frac{3}{2} \\ \frac{3}{2} \end{bmatrix}.$

48. In matrix form $A\mathbf{x} = \mathbf{b}$, the system is

$$\begin{bmatrix} 1 & -1 & 4 \\ 1 & 3 & 0 \\ 0 & -6 & 5 \end{bmatrix} \begin{bmatrix} x_1 \\ x_2 \\ x_3 \end{bmatrix} = \begin{bmatrix} 17 \\ -11 \\ 40 \end{bmatrix}.$$

Use Gauss-Jordan elimination on the augmented matrix.

$$\begin{bmatrix} 1 & -1 & 4 & 17 \\ 1 & 3 & 0 & -11 \\ 0 & -6 & 5 & 40 \end{bmatrix} \Rightarrow \begin{bmatrix} 1 & 0 & 0 & 4 \\ 0 & 1 & 0 & -5 \\ 0 & 0 & 1 & 2 \end{bmatrix}$$

So, the solution is $\begin{bmatrix} x_1 \\ x_2 \\ x_3 \end{bmatrix} = \begin{bmatrix} 4 \\ -5 \\ 2 \end{bmatrix}.$

50. The augmented matrix row reduces as follows.

$$\begin{bmatrix} 1 & 2 & 4 & 1 \\ -1 & 0 & 2 & 3 \\ 0 & 1 & 3 & 2 \end{bmatrix} \Rightarrow \begin{bmatrix} 1 & 0 & -2 & -3 \\ 0 & 1 & 3 & 2 \\ 0 & 0 & 0 & 0 \end{bmatrix}$$

There are an infinite number of solutions. For example, $x_3 = 0, x_2 = 2, x_1 = -3.$

So, $\mathbf{b} = \begin{bmatrix} 1 \\ 3 \\ 2 \end{bmatrix} = -3 \begin{bmatrix} 1 \\ -1 \\ 0 \end{bmatrix} + 2 \begin{bmatrix} 2 \\ 0 \\ 1 \end{bmatrix} + 0 \begin{bmatrix} 4 \\ 2 \\ 3 \end{bmatrix}.$

52. The augmented matrix row reduces as follows.

$$\begin{bmatrix} -3 & 5 & -22 \\ 3 & 4 & 4 \\ 4 & -8 & 32 \end{bmatrix} \Rightarrow \begin{bmatrix} 1 & -3 & 10 \\ 0 & 9 & -18 \\ 0 & -4 & 8 \end{bmatrix}$$

$$\Rightarrow \begin{bmatrix} 1 & -3 & 10 \\ 0 & 1 & -2 \\ 0 & 1 & -2 \end{bmatrix} \Rightarrow \begin{bmatrix} 1 & 0 & 4 \\ 0 & 1 & -2 \\ 0 & 0 & 0 \end{bmatrix}.$$

So,

$$\begin{bmatrix} -22 \\ 4 \\ 32 \end{bmatrix} = 4 \begin{bmatrix} -3 \\ 3 \\ 4 \end{bmatrix} + (-2) \begin{bmatrix} 5 \\ 4 \\ -8 \end{bmatrix}.$$

54. Expanding the left side of the equation produces

$$\begin{bmatrix} 2 & -1 \\ 3 & -2 \end{bmatrix} A = \begin{bmatrix} 2 & -1 \\ 3 & -2 \end{bmatrix} \begin{bmatrix} a_{11} & a_{12} \\ a_{21} & a_{22} \end{bmatrix}$$

$$= \begin{bmatrix} 2a_{11} - a_{21} & 2a_{12} - a_{22} \\ 3a_{11} - 2a_{21} & 3a_{12} - 2a_{22} \end{bmatrix} = \begin{bmatrix} 1 & 0 \\ 0 & 1 \end{bmatrix}$$

and you obtain the system

$$\begin{array}{rcl} 2a_{11} - a_{21} & = & 1 \\ 2a_{12} - a_{22} & = & 0 \\ 3a_{11} - 2a_{21} & = & 0 \\ 3a_{12} - 2a_{22} & = & 1. \end{array}$$

Solving by Gauss-Jordan elimination yields

$a_{11} = 2, a_{12} = -1, a_{21} = 3,$ and $a_{22} = -2.$

So, you have $A = \begin{bmatrix} 2 & -1 \\ 3 & -2 \end{bmatrix}.$

56. Expanding the left side of the matrix equation produces

$$\begin{bmatrix} a & b \\ c & d \end{bmatrix} \begin{bmatrix} 2 & 1 \\ 3 & 1 \end{bmatrix} = \begin{bmatrix} 2a + 3b & a + b \\ 2c + 3d & c + d \end{bmatrix} = \begin{bmatrix} 3 & 17 \\ 4 & -1 \end{bmatrix}.$$

You obtain two systems of linear equations (one involving a and b and the other involving c and d).

$$\begin{array}{rcl} 2a + 3b & = & 3 \\ a + b & = & 17, \end{array}$$

and

$$\begin{array}{rcl} 2c + 3d & = & 4 \\ c + d & = & -1. \end{array}$$

Solving by Gauss-Jordan elimination yields

$a = 48, b = -31, c = -7,$ and $d = 6.$

58. $AA = \begin{bmatrix} 2 & 0 & 0 \\ 0 & -3 & 0 \\ 0 & 0 & 0 \end{bmatrix} \begin{bmatrix} 2 & 0 & 0 \\ 0 & -3 & 0 \\ 0 & 0 & 0 \end{bmatrix} = \begin{bmatrix} 4 & 0 & 0 \\ 0 & 9 & 0 \\ 0 & 0 & 0 \end{bmatrix}$

60. $AB = \begin{bmatrix} 3 & 0 & 0 \\ 0 & -5 & 0 \\ 0 & 0 & 0 \end{bmatrix} \begin{bmatrix} -7 & 0 & 0 \\ 0 & 4 & 0 \\ 0 & 0 & 12 \end{bmatrix}$

$$= \begin{bmatrix} 3(-7) + 0 + 0 & 0 + 0 + 0 & 0 + 0 + 0 \\ 0 + 0 + 0 & 0 + (-5)4 + 0 & 0 + 0 + 0 \\ 0 + 0 + 0 & 0 + 0 + 0 & 0 + 0 + 0 \end{bmatrix}$$

$$= \begin{bmatrix} -21 & 0 & 0 \\ 0 & -20 & 0 \\ 0 & 0 & 0 \end{bmatrix}.$$

Similarly,

$$BA = \begin{bmatrix} -21 & 0 & 0 \\ 0 & -20 & 0 \\ 0 & 0 & 0 \end{bmatrix}.$$

62. (a) $AB = \begin{bmatrix} a_{11} & 0 & 0 \\ 0 & a_{22} & 0 \\ 0 & 0 & a_{33} \end{bmatrix}\begin{bmatrix} b_{11} & b_{12} & b_{13} \\ b_{21} & b_{22} & b_{23} \\ b_{31} & b_{32} & b_{33} \end{bmatrix} = \begin{bmatrix} a_{11}b_{11} & a_{11}b_{12} & a_{11}b_{13} \\ a_{22}b_{21} & a_{22}b_{22} & a_{22}b_{23} \\ a_{33}b_{31} & a_{33}b_{32} & a_{33}b_{33} \end{bmatrix}$

The ith row of B has been multiplied by a_{ii}, the ith diagonal entry of A.

(b) $BA = \begin{bmatrix} b_{11} & b_{12} & b_{13} \\ b_{21} & b_{22} & b_{23} \\ b_{31} & b_{32} & b_{33} \end{bmatrix}\begin{bmatrix} a_{11} & 0 & 0 \\ 0 & a_{22} & 0 \\ 0 & 0 & a_{33} \end{bmatrix} = \begin{bmatrix} a_{11}b_{11} & a_{22}b_{12} & a_{33}b_{13} \\ a_{11}b_{21} & a_{22}b_{22} & a_{33}b_{23} \\ a_{11}b_{31} & a_{22}b_{32} & a_{33}b_{33} \end{bmatrix}$

The ith column of B has been multiplied by a_{ii}, the ith diagonal entry of A.

(c) If $a_{11} = a_{22} = a_{33}$, then $AB = a_{11}B = BA$.

64. The trace is the sum of the elements on the main diagonal.

$1 + 1 + 1 = 3$

66. The trace is the sum of the elements on the main diagonal.

$1 + 0 + 2 + (-3) = 0$

68. Let $AB = [c_{ij}]$, where $c_{ij} = \sum_{k=1}^{n} a_{ik}b_{kj}$. Then, $Tr(AB) = \sum_{i=1}^{n} c_{ii} = \sum_{i=1}^{n}\left(\sum_{k=1}^{n} a_{ik}b_{ki}\right)$.

Similarly, if $BA = [d_{ij}]$, $d_{ij} = \sum_{k=1}^{n} b_{ik}a_{kj}$. Then $Tr(BA) = \sum_{i=1}^{n} d_{ii} = \sum_{i=1}^{n}\left(\sum_{k=1}^{n} b_{ik}a_{ki}\right) = Tr(AB)$.

70. $AB = \begin{bmatrix} \cos\alpha & -\sin\alpha \\ \sin\alpha & \cos\alpha \end{bmatrix}\begin{bmatrix} \cos\beta & -\sin\beta \\ \sin\beta & \cos\beta \end{bmatrix}\begin{bmatrix} \cos\alpha\cos\beta - \sin\alpha\sin\beta & \cos\alpha(-\sin\beta) - \sin\alpha\cos\beta \\ \sin\alpha\cos\beta + \cos\alpha\sin\beta & \sin\alpha(-\sin\beta) + \cos\alpha\cos\beta \end{bmatrix}$

$BA = \begin{bmatrix} \cos\beta & -\sin\beta \\ \sin\beta & \cos\beta \end{bmatrix}\begin{bmatrix} \cos\alpha & -\sin\alpha \\ \sin\alpha & \cos\alpha \end{bmatrix}\begin{bmatrix} \cos\beta\cos\alpha - \sin\beta\sin\alpha & \cos\beta(-\sin\alpha) - \sin\beta\cos\alpha \\ \sin\beta\cos\alpha + \cos\beta\sin\alpha & \sin\beta(-\sin\alpha) + \cos\beta\cos\alpha \end{bmatrix}$

So, you see that $AB = BA = \begin{bmatrix} \cos(\alpha+\beta) & -\sin(\alpha+\beta) \\ \sin(\alpha+\beta) & \cos(\alpha+\beta) \end{bmatrix}$.

72. Let $A = \begin{bmatrix} a_{11} & a_{12} \\ a_{21} & a_{22} \end{bmatrix}$ and $B = \begin{bmatrix} b_{11} & b_{12} \\ b_{21} & b_{22} \end{bmatrix}$.

Then the matrix equation $AB - BA = \begin{bmatrix} 1 & 0 \\ 0 & 1 \end{bmatrix}$ is equivalent to

$\begin{bmatrix} a_{11} & a_{12} \\ a_{21} & a_{22} \end{bmatrix}\begin{bmatrix} b_{11} & b_{12} \\ b_{21} & b_{22} \end{bmatrix} - \begin{bmatrix} b_{11} & b_{12} \\ b_{21} & b_{22} \end{bmatrix}\begin{bmatrix} a_{11} & a_{12} \\ a_{21} & a_{22} \end{bmatrix} = \begin{bmatrix} 1 & 0 \\ 0 & 1 \end{bmatrix}$.

This equation implies that

$a_{11}b_{11} + a_{12}b_{21} - b_{11}a_{11} - b_{12}a_{21} = a_{12}b_{21} - b_{12}a_{21} = 1$

$a_{21}b_{12} + a_{22}b_{22} - b_{21}a_{12} - b_{22}a_{22} = a_{21}b_{12} - b_{21}a_{12} = 1$

which is impossible. So, the original equation has no solution.

74. Assume that A is an $m \times n$ matrix and B is a $p \times q$ matrix. Because the product AB is defined, you know that $n = p$. Moreover, because AB is square, you know that $m = q$. Therefore, B must be of order $n \times m$, which implies that the product BA is defined.

76. Let rows s and t be identical in the matrix A. So, $a_{sj} = a_{tj}$ for $j = 1, \ldots, n$. Let $AB = [c_{ij}]$, where

$c_{ij} = \sum_{k=1}^{n} a_{ik}b_{kj}$. Then, $c_{sj} = \sum_{k=1}^{n} a_{sk}b_{kj}$, and $c_{tj} = \sum_{k=1}^{n} a_{tk}b_{kj}$. Because $a_{sk} = a_{tk}$ for $k = 1, \ldots, n$, rows s and t of AB are the same.

78. (a) No, the matrices have different sizes.

(b) No, the matrices have different sizes.

(c) Yes; No, BA is undefined.

80. $1.2\begin{bmatrix} 70 & 50 & 25 \\ 35 & 100 & 70 \end{bmatrix} = \begin{bmatrix} 84 & 60 & 30 \\ 42 & 120 & 84 \end{bmatrix}$

82. (a) Multiply the matrix for 2009 by $\frac{1}{3070}$. This produces a matrix giving the information as percents of the total population.

$$A = \tfrac{1}{3070} \begin{bmatrix} 12{,}399 & 35{,}137 & 7747 \\ 16{,}047 & 41{,}902 & 8888 \\ 27{,}959 & 70{,}751 & 14{,}608 \\ 5791 & 13{,}716 & 2616 \\ 12{,}352 & 31{,}381 & 5712 \end{bmatrix} \approx \begin{bmatrix} 4.04 & 11.45 & 2.52 \\ 5.23 & 13.65 & 2.90 \\ 9.11 & 23.05 & 4.76 \\ 1.89 & 4.47 & 0.85 \\ 4.02 & 10.22 & 1.86 \end{bmatrix}$$

Multiply the matrix for 2015 by $\frac{1}{3220}$. This produces a matrix giving the information as percents of the total population.

$$B = \tfrac{1}{3220} \begin{bmatrix} 12{,}441 & 35{,}289 & 8835 \\ 16{,}363 & 42{,}250 & 9955 \\ 29{,}373 & 73{,}496 & 17{,}572 \\ 6015 & 14{,}231 & 3337 \\ 12{,}826 & 33{,}292 & 7086 \end{bmatrix} \approx \begin{bmatrix} 3.86 & 10.96 & 2.74 \\ 5.08 & 13.12 & 3.09 \\ 9.12 & 22.82 & 5.46 \\ 1.87 & 4.42 & 1.04 \\ 3.98 & 10.34 & 2.20 \end{bmatrix}$$

(b) $B - A = \begin{bmatrix} 3.86 & 10.96 & 2.74 \\ 5.08 & 13.12 & 3.09 \\ 9.12 & 22.82 & 5.46 \\ 1.87 & 4.42 & 1.04 \\ 3.98 & 10.34 & 2.20 \end{bmatrix} - \begin{bmatrix} 4.04 & 11.45 & 2.52 \\ 5.23 & 13.65 & 2.90 \\ 9.11 & 23.05 & 4.76 \\ 1.89 & 4.47 & 0.85 \\ 4.02 & 10.22 & 1.86 \end{bmatrix} = \begin{bmatrix} -0.18 & -0.49 & 0.22 \\ -0.15 & -0.53 & 0.19 \\ 0.01 & -0.23 & 0.70 \\ -0.02 & -0.05 & 0.19 \\ -0.04 & 0.12 & 0.34 \end{bmatrix}$

(c) The 65+ age group is projected to show relative growth from 2009 to 2015 over all regions because its column in $B - A$ contains all positive percents.

84. $AB = \left[\begin{array}{cc|cc} 0 & 0 & 1 & 0 \\ 0 & 0 & 0 & 1 \\ \hline -1 & 0 & 0 & 0 \\ 0 & -1 & 0 & 0 \end{array}\right]\left[\begin{array}{cc|cc} 1 & 2 & 3 & 4 \\ 5 & 6 & 7 & 8 \\ \hline 1 & 2 & 3 & 4 \\ 5 & 6 & 7 & 8 \end{array}\right] = \left[\begin{array}{cc|cc} 1 & 2 & 3 & 4 \\ 5 & 6 & 7 & 8 \\ \hline -1 & -2 & -3 & -4 \\ -5 & -6 & -7 & -8 \end{array}\right]$

86. (a) True. The number of elements in a row of the first matrix must be equal to the number of elements in a column of the second matrix. See page 43 of the text.

(b) True. See page 45 of the text.

Section 2.2 Properties of Matrix Operations

2. $\begin{bmatrix} 6 & 8 \\ -1 & 0 \end{bmatrix} + \begin{bmatrix} 0 & 5 \\ -3 & -1 \end{bmatrix} + \begin{bmatrix} -11 & -7 \\ 2 & -1 \end{bmatrix} = \begin{bmatrix} 6 + 0 + (-11) & 8 + 5 + (-7) \\ -1 + (-3) + 2 & 0 + (-1) + (-1) \end{bmatrix} = \begin{bmatrix} -5 & 6 \\ -2 & -2 \end{bmatrix}$

4. $\tfrac{1}{2}\left(\begin{bmatrix} 5 & -2 & 4 & 0 \end{bmatrix} + \begin{bmatrix} 14 & 6 & -18 & 9 \end{bmatrix}\right) = \tfrac{1}{2}\begin{bmatrix} 5 + 14 & -2 + 6 & 4 + (-18) & 0 + 9 \end{bmatrix} = \tfrac{1}{2}\begin{bmatrix} 19 & 4 & -14 & 9 \end{bmatrix} = \begin{bmatrix} \frac{19}{2} & 2 & -7 & \frac{9}{2} \end{bmatrix}$

6. $-1\begin{bmatrix} 4 & 11 \\ -2 & -1 \\ 9 & 3 \end{bmatrix} + \tfrac{1}{6}\left(\begin{bmatrix} -5 & -1 \\ 3 & 4 \\ 0 & 13 \end{bmatrix} + \begin{bmatrix} 7 & 5 \\ -9 & -1 \\ 6 & -1 \end{bmatrix}\right) = \begin{bmatrix} -4 & -11 \\ 2 & 1 \\ -9 & -3 \end{bmatrix} + \tfrac{1}{6}\begin{bmatrix} -5 + 7 & -1 + 5 \\ 3 + (-9) & 4 + (-1) \\ 0 + 6 & 13 + (-1) \end{bmatrix}$

$= \begin{bmatrix} -4 & -11 \\ 2 & 1 \\ -9 & -3 \end{bmatrix} + \tfrac{1}{6}\begin{bmatrix} 2 & 4 \\ -6 & 3 \\ 6 & 12 \end{bmatrix} = \begin{bmatrix} -4 & -11 \\ 2 & 1 \\ -9 & -3 \end{bmatrix} + \begin{bmatrix} \frac{1}{3} & \frac{2}{3} \\ -1 & \frac{1}{2} \\ 1 & 2 \end{bmatrix}$

$= \begin{bmatrix} -4 + \frac{1}{3} & -11 + \frac{2}{3} \\ 2 + (-1) & 1 + \frac{1}{2} \\ -9 + 1 & -3 + 2 \end{bmatrix} = \begin{bmatrix} -\frac{11}{3} & -\frac{31}{3} \\ 1 & \frac{3}{2} \\ -8 & -1 \end{bmatrix}$

8. $A + B = \begin{bmatrix} 1 & 2 \\ 3 & 4 \end{bmatrix} + \begin{bmatrix} 0 & 1 \\ -1 & 2 \end{bmatrix} = \begin{bmatrix} 1 & 3 \\ 2 & 6 \end{bmatrix}$

10. $(a + b)B = \left(3 + (-4)\right)\begin{bmatrix} 0 & 1 \\ -1 & 2 \end{bmatrix} = (-1)\begin{bmatrix} 0 & 1 \\ -1 & 2 \end{bmatrix} = \begin{bmatrix} 0 & -1 \\ 1 & -2 \end{bmatrix}$

12. $(ab)0 = (3)(-4)\begin{bmatrix} 0 & 0 \\ 0 & 0 \end{bmatrix} = (-12)\begin{bmatrix} 0 & 0 \\ 0 & 0 \end{bmatrix} = \begin{bmatrix} 0 & 0 \\ 0 & 0 \end{bmatrix}$

14. (a) $X = 3A - 2B$

$= \begin{bmatrix} -6 & -3 \\ 3 & 0 \\ 9 & -12 \end{bmatrix} - \begin{bmatrix} 0 & 6 \\ 4 & 0 \\ -8 & -2 \end{bmatrix}$

$= \begin{bmatrix} 6 & -9 \\ -1 & 0 \\ 17 & -10 \end{bmatrix}$

(b) $2X = 2A - B$

$2X = \begin{bmatrix} -4 & -2 \\ 2 & 0 \\ 6 & -8 \end{bmatrix} - \begin{bmatrix} 0 & 3 \\ 2 & 0 \\ -4 & -1 \end{bmatrix}$

$2X = \begin{bmatrix} -4 & -5 \\ 0 & 0 \\ 10 & -7 \end{bmatrix}$

$X = \begin{bmatrix} -2 & -\frac{5}{2} \\ 0 & 0 \\ 5 & -\frac{7}{2} \end{bmatrix}$

(c) $2X + 3A = B$

$2X + \begin{bmatrix} -6 & -3 \\ 3 & 0 \\ 9 & -12 \end{bmatrix} = \begin{bmatrix} 0 & 3 \\ 2 & 0 \\ -4 & -1 \end{bmatrix}$

$2X = \begin{bmatrix} 6 & 6 \\ -1 & 0 \\ -13 & 11 \end{bmatrix}$

$X = \begin{bmatrix} 3 & 3 \\ -\frac{1}{2} & 0 \\ -\frac{13}{2} & \frac{11}{2} \end{bmatrix}$

(d) $2A + 4B = -2X$

$\begin{bmatrix} -4 & -2 \\ 2 & 0 \\ 6 & -8 \end{bmatrix} + \begin{bmatrix} 0 & 12 \\ 8 & 0 \\ -16 & -4 \end{bmatrix} = -2X$

$\begin{bmatrix} -4 & 10 \\ 10 & 0 \\ -10 & -12 \end{bmatrix} = -2X$

$\begin{bmatrix} 2 & -5 \\ -5 & 0 \\ 5 & 6 \end{bmatrix} = X$

16. $C(BC) = \begin{bmatrix} 0 & 1 \\ -1 & 0 \end{bmatrix}\left(\begin{bmatrix} 1 & 3 \\ -1 & 2 \end{bmatrix}\begin{bmatrix} 0 & 1 \\ -1 & 0 \end{bmatrix}\right)$

$= \begin{bmatrix} 0 & 1 \\ -1 & 0 \end{bmatrix}\begin{bmatrix} -3 & 1 \\ -2 & -1 \end{bmatrix} = \begin{bmatrix} -2 & -1 \\ 3 & -1 \end{bmatrix}$

18. $B(C + O) = \begin{bmatrix} 1 & 3 \\ -1 & 2 \end{bmatrix}\left(\begin{bmatrix} 0 & 1 \\ -1 & 0 \end{bmatrix} + \begin{bmatrix} 0 & 0 \\ 0 & 0 \end{bmatrix}\right)$

$= \begin{bmatrix} 1 & 3 \\ -1 & 2 \end{bmatrix}\begin{bmatrix} 0 & 1 \\ -1 & 0 \end{bmatrix} = \begin{bmatrix} -3 & 1 \\ -2 & -1 \end{bmatrix}$

20. $B(cA) = \begin{bmatrix} 1 & 3 \\ -1 & 2 \end{bmatrix}\left((-2)\begin{bmatrix} 1 & 2 & 3 \\ 0 & 1 & -1 \end{bmatrix}\right)$

$= \begin{bmatrix} 1 & 3 \\ -1 & 2 \end{bmatrix}\begin{bmatrix} -2 & -4 & -6 \\ 0 & -2 & 2 \end{bmatrix} = \begin{bmatrix} -2 & -10 & 0 \\ 2 & 0 & 10 \end{bmatrix}$

22. (a) $(AB)C = \left(\begin{bmatrix} -4 & 2 \\ 1 & -3 \end{bmatrix}\begin{bmatrix} 1 & -5 & 0 \\ -2 & 3 & 3 \end{bmatrix}\right)\begin{bmatrix} -3 & 4 \\ 0 & 1 \\ -1 & 1 \end{bmatrix}$

$= \begin{bmatrix} -8 & 26 & 6 \\ 7 & -14 & -9 \end{bmatrix}\begin{bmatrix} -3 & 4 \\ 0 & 1 \\ -1 & 1 \end{bmatrix}$

$= \begin{bmatrix} 18 & 0 \\ -12 & 5 \end{bmatrix}$

(b) $A(BC) = \begin{bmatrix} -4 & 2 \\ 1 & -3 \end{bmatrix}\left(\begin{bmatrix} 1 & -5 & 0 \\ -2 & 3 & 3 \end{bmatrix}\begin{bmatrix} -3 & 4 \\ 0 & 1 \\ -1 & 1 \end{bmatrix}\right)$

$= \begin{bmatrix} -4 & 2 \\ 1 & -3 \end{bmatrix}\begin{bmatrix} -3 & -1 \\ 3 & -2 \end{bmatrix}$

$= \begin{bmatrix} 18 & 0 \\ -12 & 5 \end{bmatrix}$

24. $AB = \begin{bmatrix} \frac{1}{4} & \frac{1}{2} \\ \frac{1}{2} & \frac{1}{2} \end{bmatrix}\begin{bmatrix} \frac{1}{2} & \frac{1}{2} \\ \frac{1}{2} & \frac{1}{4} \end{bmatrix} = \begin{bmatrix} \frac{3}{8} & \frac{1}{4} \\ \frac{1}{2} & \frac{3}{8} \end{bmatrix}$

$BA = \begin{bmatrix} \frac{1}{2} & \frac{1}{2} \\ \frac{1}{2} & \frac{1}{4} \end{bmatrix}\begin{bmatrix} \frac{1}{4} & \frac{1}{2} \\ \frac{1}{2} & \frac{1}{2} \end{bmatrix} = \begin{bmatrix} \frac{3}{8} & \frac{1}{2} \\ \frac{1}{4} & \frac{3}{8} \end{bmatrix} \neq AB$

26. $AC = \begin{bmatrix} 1 & 2 & 3 \\ 0 & 5 & 4 \\ 3 & -2 & 1 \end{bmatrix}\begin{bmatrix} 0 & 0 & 0 \\ 0 & 0 & 0 \\ 4 & -2 & 3 \end{bmatrix} = \begin{bmatrix} 12 & -6 & 9 \\ 16 & -8 & 12 \\ 4 & -2 & 3 \end{bmatrix}$

$= \begin{bmatrix} 4 & -6 & 3 \\ 5 & 4 & 4 \\ -1 & 0 & 1 \end{bmatrix}\begin{bmatrix} 0 & 0 & 0 \\ 0 & 0 & 0 \\ 4 & -2 & 3 \end{bmatrix} = BC$

But $A \neq B$.

28. $AB = \begin{bmatrix} 2 & 4 \\ 2 & 4 \end{bmatrix}\begin{bmatrix} 1 & -2 \\ -\frac{1}{2} & 1 \end{bmatrix} = \begin{bmatrix} 0 & 0 \\ 0 & 0 \end{bmatrix} = O$

But $A \neq O$ and $B \neq O$.

40. $(AB)^T = \left(\begin{bmatrix} 1 & 2 \\ 0 & -2 \end{bmatrix}\begin{bmatrix} -3 & -1 \\ 2 & 1 \end{bmatrix} \right)^T = \begin{bmatrix} 1 & 1 \\ -4 & -2 \end{bmatrix}^T = \begin{bmatrix} 1 & -4 \\ 1 & -2 \end{bmatrix}$

$B^T A^T = \begin{bmatrix} -3 & -1 \\ 2 & 1 \end{bmatrix}^T \begin{bmatrix} 1 & 2 \\ 0 & -2 \end{bmatrix}^T = \begin{bmatrix} -3 & 2 \\ -1 & 1 \end{bmatrix}\begin{bmatrix} 1 & 0 \\ 2 & -2 \end{bmatrix} = \begin{bmatrix} 1 & -4 \\ 1 & -2 \end{bmatrix}$

42. $(AB)^T = \left(\begin{bmatrix} 2 & 1 & -1 \\ 0 & 1 & 3 \\ 4 & 0 & 2 \end{bmatrix}\begin{bmatrix} 1 & 0 & -1 \\ 2 & 1 & -2 \\ 0 & 1 & 3 \end{bmatrix} \right)^T = \begin{bmatrix} 4 & 0 & -7 \\ 2 & 4 & 7 \\ 4 & 2 & 2 \end{bmatrix}^T = \begin{bmatrix} 4 & 2 & 4 \\ 0 & 4 & 2 \\ -7 & 7 & 2 \end{bmatrix}$

$B^T A^T = \begin{bmatrix} 1 & 0 & -1 \\ 2 & 1 & -2 \\ 0 & 1 & 3 \end{bmatrix}^T \begin{bmatrix} 2 & 1 & -1 \\ 0 & 1 & 3 \\ 4 & 0 & 2 \end{bmatrix}^T = \begin{bmatrix} 1 & 2 & 0 \\ 0 & 1 & 1 \\ -1 & -2 & 3 \end{bmatrix}\begin{bmatrix} 2 & 0 & 4 \\ 1 & 1 & 0 \\ -1 & 3 & 2 \end{bmatrix} = \begin{bmatrix} 4 & 2 & 4 \\ 0 & 4 & 2 \\ -7 & 7 & 2 \end{bmatrix}$

44. (a) $A^T A = \begin{bmatrix} 1 & 3 & 0 \\ -1 & 4 & -2 \end{bmatrix}\begin{bmatrix} 1 & -1 \\ 3 & 4 \\ 0 & -2 \end{bmatrix} = \begin{bmatrix} 10 & 11 \\ 11 & 21 \end{bmatrix}$

(b) $AA^T = \begin{bmatrix} 1 & -1 \\ 3 & 4 \\ 0 & -2 \end{bmatrix}\begin{bmatrix} 1 & 3 & 0 \\ -1 & 4 & -2 \end{bmatrix} = \begin{bmatrix} 2 & -1 & 2 \\ -1 & 25 & -8 \\ 2 & -8 & 4 \end{bmatrix}$

46. (a) $A^T A = \begin{bmatrix} 4 & 2 & 14 & 6 \\ -3 & 0 & -2 & 8 \\ 2 & 11 & 12 & -5 \\ 0 & -1 & -9 & 4 \end{bmatrix}\begin{bmatrix} 4 & -3 & 2 & 0 \\ 2 & 0 & 11 & -1 \\ 14 & -2 & 12 & -9 \\ 6 & 8 & -5 & 4 \end{bmatrix} = \begin{bmatrix} 252 & 8 & 168 & -104 \\ 8 & 77 & -70 & 50 \\ 168 & -70 & 294 & -139 \\ -104 & 50 & -139 & 98 \end{bmatrix}$

(b) $AA^T = \begin{bmatrix} 4 & -3 & 2 & 0 \\ 2 & 0 & 11 & -1 \\ 14 & -2 & 12 & -9 \\ 6 & 8 & -5 & 4 \end{bmatrix}\begin{bmatrix} 4 & 2 & 14 & 6 \\ -3 & 0 & -2 & 8 \\ 2 & 11 & 12 & -5 \\ 0 & -1 & -9 & 4 \end{bmatrix} = \begin{bmatrix} 29 & 30 & 86 & -10 \\ 30 & 126 & 169 & -47 \\ 86 & 169 & 425 & -28 \\ -10 & -47 & -28 & 141 \end{bmatrix}$

30. $AT = \begin{bmatrix} 1 & 2 \\ 0 & -1 \end{bmatrix}\begin{bmatrix} 1 & 0 \\ 0 & 1 \end{bmatrix} = \begin{bmatrix} 1 & 2 \\ 0 & -1 \end{bmatrix}$

32. $A + IA = \begin{bmatrix} 1 & 2 \\ 0 & -1 \end{bmatrix} + \begin{bmatrix} 1 & 0 \\ 0 & 1 \end{bmatrix}\begin{bmatrix} 1 & 2 \\ 0 & -1 \end{bmatrix}$

$= \begin{bmatrix} 1 & 2 \\ 0 & -1 \end{bmatrix} + \begin{bmatrix} 1 & 2 \\ 0 & -1 \end{bmatrix} = \begin{bmatrix} 2 & 4 \\ 0 & -2 \end{bmatrix}$

34. $A^2 = \begin{bmatrix} 1 & 2 \\ 0 & -1 \end{bmatrix}\begin{bmatrix} 1 & 2 \\ 0 & -1 \end{bmatrix} = \begin{bmatrix} 1 & 0 \\ 0 & 1 \end{bmatrix} = I_2$

So, $A^4 = \left(A^2 \right)^2 = I_2^2 = I_2 = \begin{bmatrix} 1 & 0 \\ 0 & 1 \end{bmatrix}$.

36. In general, $AB \neq BA$ for matrices.

38. $D^T = \begin{bmatrix} 6 & -7 & 19 \\ -7 & 0 & 23 \\ 19 & 23 & -32 \end{bmatrix}^T = \begin{bmatrix} 6 & -7 & 19 \\ -7 & 0 & 23 \\ 19 & 23 & -32 \end{bmatrix}$

48.(a) False. In general, for $n \times n$ matrices A and B it is *not* true that $AB = BA$. For example, let $A = \begin{bmatrix} 1 & 1 \\ 0 & 0 \end{bmatrix}$, $B = \begin{bmatrix} 1 & 0 \\ 1 & 0 \end{bmatrix}$.

Then $AB = \begin{bmatrix} 2 & 0 \\ 0 & 0 \end{bmatrix} \neq \begin{bmatrix} 1 & 1 \\ 1 & 1 \end{bmatrix} = BA$.

(b) True. For any matrix A you have an additive inverse, namely $-A = (-1)A$. See Theorem 2.2(2) on page 621.

(c) False. Let $A = \begin{bmatrix} 1 & 1 \\ 0 & 0 \end{bmatrix}$, $B = \begin{bmatrix} 1 & 0 \\ 1 & 0 \end{bmatrix}$, $C = \begin{bmatrix} 2 & 0 \\ 0 & 0 \end{bmatrix}$. Then $AB = \begin{bmatrix} 2 & 0 \\ 0 & 0 \end{bmatrix} = AC$, but $B \neq C$.

(d) True. See Theorem 2.6(2) on page 68.

50.

$aX + A(bB) = b(AB + IB)$	Original equation
$aX + (Ab)B = b(AB + B)$	Associative property; property of the identity matrix
$aX + bAB = bAB + bB$	Property of scalar multiplication; distributive property
$aX + bAB + (-bAB) = bAB + bB + (-bAB)$	Add $-bAB$ to both sides.
$aX = bAB + bB + (-bAB)$	Additive inverse
$aX = bAB + (-bAB) + bB$	Commutative property
$aX = bB$	Additive inverse
$X = \dfrac{b}{a}B$	Divide by a.

52. $A^{20} = \begin{bmatrix} (1)^{20} & 0 & 0 \\ 0 & (-1)^{20} & 0 \\ 0 & 0 & (1)^{20} \end{bmatrix} = \begin{bmatrix} 1 & 0 & 0 \\ 0 & 1 & 0 \\ 0 & 0 & 1 \end{bmatrix}$

54. Because $A^3 = \begin{bmatrix} 8 & 0 & 0 \\ 0 & -1 & 0 \\ 0 & 0 & 27 \end{bmatrix} = \begin{bmatrix} 2^3 & 0 & 0 \\ 0 & (-1)^3 & 0 \\ 0 & 0 & (3)^3 \end{bmatrix}$, you have $A = \begin{bmatrix} 2 & 0 & 0 \\ 0 & -1 & 0 \\ 0 & 0 & 3 \end{bmatrix}$.

56. $f(A) = \begin{bmatrix} 2 & 1 & -1 \\ 1 & 0 & 2 \\ -1 & 1 & 3 \end{bmatrix}^3 - 2\begin{bmatrix} 2 & 1 & -1 \\ 1 & 0 & 2 \\ -1 & 1 & 3 \end{bmatrix}^2 + 5\begin{bmatrix} 2 & 1 & -1 \\ 1 & 0 & 2 \\ -1 & 1 & 3 \end{bmatrix} - 10\begin{bmatrix} 1 & 0 & 0 \\ 0 & 1 & 0 \\ 0 & 0 & 1 \end{bmatrix}$

$= \begin{bmatrix} 2 & 1 & -1 \\ 1 & 0 & 2 \\ -1 & 1 & 3 \end{bmatrix}\begin{bmatrix} 2 & 1 & -1 \\ 1 & 0 & 2 \\ -1 & 1 & 3 \end{bmatrix}^2 - 2\begin{bmatrix} 2 & 1 & -1 \\ 1 & 0 & 2 \\ -1 & 1 & 3 \end{bmatrix}\begin{bmatrix} 2 & 1 & -1 \\ 1 & 0 & 2 \\ -1 & 1 & 3 \end{bmatrix} + \begin{bmatrix} 10 & 5 & -5 \\ 5 & 0 & 10 \\ -5 & 5 & 15 \end{bmatrix} - \begin{bmatrix} 10 & 0 & 0 \\ 0 & 10 & 0 \\ 0 & 0 & 10 \end{bmatrix}$

$= \begin{bmatrix} 2 & 1 & -1 \\ 1 & 0 & 2 \\ -1 & 1 & 3 \end{bmatrix}\begin{bmatrix} 6 & 1 & -3 \\ 0 & 3 & 5 \\ -4 & 2 & 12 \end{bmatrix} - 2\begin{bmatrix} 6 & 1 & -3 \\ 0 & 3 & 5 \\ -4 & 2 & 12 \end{bmatrix} + \begin{bmatrix} 0 & 5 & -5 \\ 5 & -10 & 10 \\ -5 & 5 & 5 \end{bmatrix}$

$= \begin{bmatrix} 16 & 3 & -13 \\ -2 & 5 & 21 \\ -18 & 8 & 44 \end{bmatrix} - \begin{bmatrix} 12 & 2 & -6 \\ 0 & 6 & 10 \\ -8 & 4 & 24 \end{bmatrix} + \begin{bmatrix} 0 & 5 & -5 \\ 5 & -10 & 10 \\ -5 & 5 & 5 \end{bmatrix}$

$= \begin{bmatrix} 4 & 6 & -12 \\ 3 & -11 & 21 \\ -15 & 9 & 25 \end{bmatrix}$

58. $(cd)A = (cd)[a_{ij}] = [(cd)a_{ij}] = [c(da_{ij})] = c[da_{ij}] = c(dA)$

60. $(c + d)A = (c + d)[a_{ij}] = [(c + d)a_{ij}] = [ca_{ij} + da_{ij}] = [ca_{ij}] + [da_{ij}] = c[a_{ij}] + d[a_{ij}] = cA + dA$

62. (a) To show that $A(BC) = (AB)C$, compare the ijth entries in the matrices on both sides of this equality. Assume that A has size $n \times p$, B has size $p \times r$, and C has size $r \times m$. Then the entry in the kth row and the jth column of BC is

$\sum_{l=1}^{r} b_{kl}c_{lj}$. Therefore, the entry in ith row and jth column of $A(BC)$ is

$$\sum_{k=1}^{p} a_{ik} \sum_{l=1}^{r} b_{kl}c_{lj} = \sum_{k,l} a_{ik}b_{kl}c_{lj}.$$

The entry in the ith row and jth column of $(AB)C$ is $\sum_{l=1}^{r} d_{il}c_{lj}$, where d_{il} is the entry of AB in the ith row and the lth column.

So, $d_{il} = \sum_{k=1}^{p} a_{ik}b_{kl}$ for each $l = 1, \ldots, r$. So, the ijth entry of $(AB)C$ is

$$\sum_{l=1}^{r} \sum_{k=1}^{p} a_{ik}b_{kl}c_{lj} = \sum_{k,l} a_{ik}b_{kl}c_{lj}.$$

Because all corresponding entries of $A(BC)$ and $(AB)C$ are equal and both matrices are of the same size $(n \times m)$, you conclude that $A(BC) = (AB)C$.

(b) The entry in the ith row and jth column of $(A + B)C$ is $(a_{i1} + b_{i1})c_{1j} + (a_{i2} + b_{i2})c_{2j} + \cdots + (a_{in} + b_{in})c_{nj}$, whereas the entry in the ith row and jth column of $AC + BC$ is $(a_{i1}c_{1j} + \cdots + a_{in}c_{nj}) + (b_{i1}c_{1j} + \cdots + b_{in}c_{nj})$, which are equal by the distributive law for real numbers.

(c) The entry in the ith row and jth column of $c(AB)$ is $c[a_{i1}b_{1j} + a_{i2}b_{2j} + \cdots + a_{in}b_{nj}]$. The corresponding entry for $(cA)B$ is $(ca_{i1})b_{1j} + (ca_{i2})b_{2j} + \cdots + (ca_{in})b_{nj}$ and the corresponding entry for $A(cB)$ is $a_{i1}(cb_{1j}) + a_{i2}(cb_{2j}) + \cdots + a_{in}(cb_{nj})$. Because these three expressions are equal, you have shown that $c(AB) = (cA)B = A(cB)$.

64. (2) $(A + B)^T = ([a_{ij}] + [b_{ij}])^T = [a_{ij} + b_{ij}]^T = [a_{ji} + b_{ji}] = [a_{ji}] + [b_{ji}] = A^T + B^T$

(3) $(cA)^T = (c[a_{ij}])^T = [ca_{ij}]^T = [ca_{ji}] = c[a_{ji}] = c(A^T)$

(4) The entry in the ith row and jth column of $(AB)^T$ is $a_{j1}b_{1i} + a_{j2}b_{2i} + \cdots a_{jn}b_{ni}$. On the other hand, the entry in the ith row and jth column of $B^T A^T$ is $b_{1i}a_{j1} + b_{2i}a_{j2} + \cdots + b_{ni}a_{jn}$, which is the same.

66. (a) Answers will vary. *Sample answer*: $\begin{bmatrix} 0 & 1 \\ 1 & 0 \end{bmatrix}\begin{bmatrix} -1 & 1 \\ 1 & 0 \end{bmatrix} = \begin{bmatrix} 1 & 0 \\ -1 & 1 \end{bmatrix}$.

(b) Let A and B be symmetric.

If $AB = BA$, then $(AB)^T = B^T A^T = BA = AB$ and AB is symmetric.

If $(AB)^T = AB$, then $AB = (AB)^T = B^T A^T = BA$ and $AB = BA$.

68. Because $A = A^T$, this matrix is symmetric.

70. Because $-A = A^T$, this matrix is skew-symmetric.

72. If $A^T = -A$ and $B^T = -B$, then $(A + B)^T = A^T + B^T = -A - B = -(A + B)$, which implies that $A + B$ is skew-symmetric.

74. $(A - A^T)^T = A^T - (A^T)^T = A^T - A = -(A - A^T)$, which implies that $A - A^T$ is skew-symmetric.

Section 2.3 The Inverse of a Matrix

2. $AB = \begin{bmatrix} 1 & -1 \\ -1 & 2 \end{bmatrix}\begin{bmatrix} 2 & 1 \\ 1 & 1 \end{bmatrix} = \begin{bmatrix} 2-1 & 1-1 \\ -2+2 & -1+2 \end{bmatrix} = \begin{bmatrix} 1 & 0 \\ 0 & 1 \end{bmatrix}$

$BA = \begin{bmatrix} 2 & 1 \\ 1 & 1 \end{bmatrix}\begin{bmatrix} 1 & -1 \\ -1 & 2 \end{bmatrix} = \begin{bmatrix} 2-1 & -2+2 \\ 1-1 & -1+2 \end{bmatrix} = \begin{bmatrix} 1 & 0 \\ 0 & 1 \end{bmatrix}$

4. $AB = \begin{bmatrix} 1 & -1 \\ 2 & 3 \end{bmatrix}\begin{bmatrix} \frac{3}{5} & \frac{1}{5} \\ -\frac{2}{5} & \frac{1}{5} \end{bmatrix} = \begin{bmatrix} 1 & 0 \\ 0 & 1 \end{bmatrix}$

$BA = \begin{bmatrix} \frac{3}{5} & \frac{1}{5} \\ -\frac{2}{5} & \frac{1}{5} \end{bmatrix}\begin{bmatrix} 1 & -1 \\ 2 & 3 \end{bmatrix} = \begin{bmatrix} 1 & 0 \\ 0 & 1 \end{bmatrix}$

6. $AB = \begin{bmatrix} 2 & -17 & 11 \\ -1 & 11 & -7 \\ 0 & 3 & -2 \end{bmatrix}\begin{bmatrix} 1 & 1 & 2 \\ 2 & 4 & -3 \\ 3 & 6 & -5 \end{bmatrix} = \begin{bmatrix} 1 & 0 & 0 \\ 0 & 1 & 0 \\ 0 & 0 & 1 \end{bmatrix}$

$BA = \begin{bmatrix} 1 & 1 & 2 \\ 2 & 4 & -3 \\ 3 & 6 & -5 \end{bmatrix}\begin{bmatrix} 2 & -17 & 11 \\ -1 & 11 & -7 \\ 3 & 6 & -2 \end{bmatrix} = \begin{bmatrix} 1 & 0 & 0 \\ 0 & 1 & 0 \\ 0 & 0 & 1 \end{bmatrix}$

8. Use the formula

$$A^{-1} = \frac{1}{ad-bc}\begin{bmatrix} d & -b \\ -c & a \end{bmatrix},$$

where

$$A = \begin{bmatrix} a & b \\ c & d \end{bmatrix} = \begin{bmatrix} 2 & -2 \\ 2 & 2 \end{bmatrix}.$$

So, the inverse is

$$A^{-1} = \frac{1}{2(2)-(-2)(2)}\begin{bmatrix} 2 & 2 \\ -2 & 2 \end{bmatrix} = \begin{bmatrix} \frac{1}{4} & \frac{1}{4} \\ -\frac{1}{4} & \frac{1}{4} \end{bmatrix}.$$

10. Use the formula

$$A^{-1} = \frac{1}{ad-bc}\begin{bmatrix} d & -b \\ -c & a \end{bmatrix},$$

where

$$A = \begin{bmatrix} a & b \\ c & d \end{bmatrix} = \begin{bmatrix} 1 & -2 \\ 2 & -3 \end{bmatrix}.$$

So, the inverse is

$$A^{-1} = \frac{1}{(1)(-3)-(-2)(2)}\begin{bmatrix} -3 & 2 \\ -2 & 1 \end{bmatrix} = \begin{bmatrix} -3 & 2 \\ -2 & 1 \end{bmatrix}.$$

12. Using the formula

$$A^{-1} = \frac{1}{ad-bc}\begin{bmatrix} d & -b \\ -c & a \end{bmatrix},$$

where

$$A = \begin{bmatrix} a & b \\ c & d \end{bmatrix} = \begin{bmatrix} -1 & 1 \\ 3 & -3 \end{bmatrix},$$

you see that $ad-bc = (-1)(-3)-(1)(3) = 0$. So, the matrix has no inverse.

14. Adjoin the identity matrix to form

$$[A \ I] = \begin{bmatrix} 1 & 2 & 2 & 1 & 0 & 0 \\ 3 & 7 & 9 & 0 & 1 & 0 \\ -1 & -4 & -7 & 0 & 0 & 1 \end{bmatrix}.$$

Using elementary row operations, reduce the matrix as follows.

$$[I \ A^{-1}] = \begin{bmatrix} 1 & 0 & 0 & -13 & 6 & 4 \\ 0 & 1 & 0 & 12 & -5 & -3 \\ 0 & 0 & 1 & -5 & 2 & 1 \end{bmatrix}$$

16. Adjoin the identity matrix to form

$$[A \ I] = \begin{bmatrix} 10 & 5 & -7 & 1 & 0 & 0 \\ -5 & 1 & 4 & 0 & 1 & 0 \\ 3 & 2 & -2 & 0 & 0 & 1 \end{bmatrix}.$$

Using elementary row operations, reduce the matrix as follows.

$$[I \ A^{-1}] = \begin{bmatrix} 1 & 0 & 0 & -10 & -4 & 27 \\ 0 & 1 & 0 & 2 & 1 & -5 \\ 0 & 0 & 1 & -13 & -5 & 35 \end{bmatrix}$$

Therefore, the inverse is

$$A^{-1} = \begin{bmatrix} -10 & -4 & 27 \\ 2 & 1 & -5 \\ -13 & -5 & 35 \end{bmatrix}.$$

18. Adjoin the identity matrix to form

$$[A \ I] = \begin{bmatrix} 3 & 2 & 5 & 1 & 0 & 0 \\ 2 & 2 & 4 & 0 & 1 & 0 \\ -4 & 4 & 0 & 0 & 0 & 1 \end{bmatrix}.$$

Using elementary row operations, you cannot form the identity matrix on the left side. Therefore, the matrix has no inverse.

20. Adjoin the identity matrix to form

$$[A\ I] = \begin{bmatrix} -\frac{5}{6} & \frac{1}{3} & \frac{11}{6} & 1 & 0 & 0 \\ 0 & \frac{2}{3} & 2 & 0 & 1 & 0 \\ 1 & -\frac{1}{2} & -\frac{5}{2} & 0 & 0 & 1 \end{bmatrix}.$$

Using elementary row operations, you cannot form the identity matrix on the left side. Therefore, the matrix has no inverse.

22. Adjoin the identity matrix to form

$$[A\ I] = \begin{bmatrix} 0.1 & 0.2 & 0.3 & 1 & 0 & 0 \\ -0.3 & 0.2 & 0.2 & 0 & 1 & 0 \\ 0.5 & 0.5 & 0.5 & 0 & 0 & 1 \end{bmatrix}.$$

Using elementary row operations, reduce the matrix as follows.

$$[I\ A^{-1}] = \begin{bmatrix} 1 & 0 & 0 & 0 & -2 & 0.8 \\ 0 & 1 & 0 & -10 & 4 & 4.4 \\ 0 & 0 & 1 & 10 & -2 & -3.2 \end{bmatrix}$$

Therefore, the inverse is

$$A^{-1} = \begin{bmatrix} 0 & -2 & 0.8 \\ -10 & 4 & 4.4 \\ 10 & -2 & -3.2 \end{bmatrix}.$$

24. Adjoin the identity matrix to form

$$[A\ I] = \begin{bmatrix} 1 & 0 & 0 & 1 & 0 & 0 \\ 3 & 0 & 0 & 0 & 1 & 0 \\ 2 & 5 & 5 & 0 & 0 & 1 \end{bmatrix}$$

Using elementary row operations, you cannot form the identity matrix on the left side. Therefore, the matrix has no inverse.

26. Adjoin the identity matrix to form

$$[A\ I] = \begin{bmatrix} 1 & 0 & 0 & 0 & 1 & 0 & 0 & 0 \\ 0 & 2 & 0 & 0 & 0 & 1 & 0 & 0 \\ 0 & 0 & -2 & 0 & 0 & 0 & 1 & 0 \\ 0 & 0 & 0 & 3 & 0 & 0 & 0 & 1 \end{bmatrix}$$

Using elementary row operations, reduce the matrix as follows.

$$[I\ A^{-1}] = \begin{bmatrix} 1 & 0 & 0 & 0 & 1 & 0 & 0 & 0 \\ 0 & 1 & 0 & 0 & 0 & \frac{1}{2} & 0 & 0 \\ 0 & 0 & 1 & 0 & 0 & 0 & -\frac{1}{2} & 0 \\ 0 & 0 & 0 & 1 & 0 & 0 & 0 & \frac{1}{3} \end{bmatrix}$$

Therefore, the inverse is

$$A^{-1} = \begin{bmatrix} 1 & 0 & 0 & 0 \\ 0 & \frac{1}{2} & 0 & 0 \\ 0 & 0 & -\frac{1}{2} & 0 \\ 0 & 0 & 0 & \frac{1}{3} \end{bmatrix}.$$

28. Adjoin the identity matrix to form

$$[A\ I] = \begin{bmatrix} 4 & 8 & -7 & 14 & 1 & 0 & 0 & 0 \\ 2 & 5 & -4 & 6 & 0 & 1 & 0 & 0 \\ 0 & 2 & 1 & -7 & 0 & 0 & 1 & 0 \\ 3 & 6 & -5 & 10 & 0 & 0 & 0 & 1 \end{bmatrix}.$$

Using elementary row operations, reduce the matrix as follows.

$$[A\ I] = \begin{bmatrix} 1 & 0 & 0 & 0 & 27 & -10 & 4 & -29 \\ 0 & 1 & 0 & 0 & -16 & 5 & -2 & 18 \\ 0 & 0 & 1 & 0 & -17 & 4 & -2 & 20 \\ 0 & 0 & 0 & 1 & -7 & 2 & -1 & 8 \end{bmatrix}$$

Therefore the inverse is

$$A^{-1} = \begin{bmatrix} 27 & -10 & 4 & -29 \\ 16 & 5 & -2 & 18 \\ -17 & 4 & -2 & 20 \\ -7 & 2 & -1 & 8 \end{bmatrix}.$$

30. Adjoin the identity matrix to form

$$[A\ I] = \begin{bmatrix} 1 & 3 & -2 & 0 & 1 & 0 & 0 & 0 \\ 0 & 2 & 4 & 6 & 0 & 1 & 0 & 0 \\ 0 & 0 & -2 & 1 & 0 & 0 & 1 & 0 \\ 0 & 0 & 0 & 5 & 0 & 0 & 0 & 1 \end{bmatrix}.$$

Using elementary row operations, reduce the matrix as follows.

$$[I\ A^{-1}] = \begin{bmatrix} 1 & 0 & 0 & 0 & 1 & -1.5 & -4 & 2.6 \\ 0 & 1 & 0 & 0 & 0 & 0.5 & 1 & -0.8 \\ 0 & 0 & 1 & 0 & 0 & 0 & -0.5 & 0.1 \\ 0 & 0 & 0 & 1 & 0 & 0 & 0 & 0.2 \end{bmatrix}.$$

Therefore, the inverse is

$$A^{-1} = \begin{bmatrix} 1 & -1.5 & -4 & 2.6 \\ 0 & 0.5 & 1 & -0.8 \\ 0 & 0 & -0.5 & 0.1 \\ 0 & 0 & 0 & 0.2 \end{bmatrix}.$$

32. $A = \begin{bmatrix} 1 & -2 \\ -3 & 2 \end{bmatrix}$

$$ad - bc = (1)(2) - (-2)(-3) = -4$$

$$A^{-1} = -\frac{1}{4}\begin{bmatrix} 2 & 2 \\ 3 & 1 \end{bmatrix} = \begin{bmatrix} -\frac{1}{2} & -\frac{1}{2} \\ -\frac{3}{4} & -\frac{1}{4} \end{bmatrix}$$

34. $A = \begin{bmatrix} -12 & 3 \\ 5 & -2 \end{bmatrix}$

$$ad - bc = (-12)(-2) - 3(5) = 24 - 15 = 9$$

$$A^{-1} = \frac{1}{9}\begin{bmatrix} -2 & -3 \\ -5 & -12 \end{bmatrix} = \begin{bmatrix} -\frac{2}{9} & -\frac{1}{3} \\ -\frac{5}{9} & -\frac{4}{3} \end{bmatrix}$$

36. $A = \begin{bmatrix} -\frac{1}{4} & \frac{9}{4} \\ \frac{5}{3} & \frac{8}{9} \end{bmatrix}$

$ad - bc = \left(-\frac{1}{4}\right)\left(\frac{8}{9}\right) - \left(\frac{9}{4}\right)\left(\frac{5}{3}\right) = -\frac{143}{36}$

$A^{-1} = -\frac{36}{143}\begin{bmatrix} \frac{8}{9} & -\frac{9}{4} \\ -\frac{5}{3} & -\frac{1}{4} \end{bmatrix} = \begin{bmatrix} -\frac{32}{143} & \frac{81}{143} \\ \frac{60}{143} & \frac{9}{143} \end{bmatrix}$

38. $A^{-2} = \left(A^{-1}\right)^2 = \left(\frac{1}{47}\begin{bmatrix} 6 & -7 \\ 5 & 2 \end{bmatrix}\right)^2 = \frac{1}{2209}\begin{bmatrix} 1 & -56 \\ 40 & -31 \end{bmatrix}$

$A^{-2} = \left(A^2\right)^{-1} = \begin{bmatrix} -31 & 56 \\ -40 & 1 \end{bmatrix}^{-1} = \frac{1}{2209}\begin{bmatrix} 1 & -56 \\ 40 & -31 \end{bmatrix}$

The results are equal.

40. $A^{-2} = \left(A^{-1}\right)^2 = \left(\frac{1}{2}\begin{bmatrix} -15 & -4 & 28 \\ -1 & 0 & 2 \\ 23 & 6 & -42 \end{bmatrix}\right)^2 = \frac{1}{4}\begin{bmatrix} 873 & 228 & -1604 \\ 61 & 16 & -112 \\ -1317 & -344 & 2420 \end{bmatrix}$

$A^{-2} = \left(A^2\right)^{-1} = \begin{bmatrix} 48 & 4 & 32 \\ -29 & 48 & -17 \\ 22 & 9 & 15 \end{bmatrix}^{-1} = \frac{1}{4}\begin{bmatrix} 873 & 228 & -1604 \\ 61 & 16 & -112 \\ -1317 & -344 & 2420 \end{bmatrix}$

The results are equal.

42. (a) $\left(AB\right)^{-1} = B^{-1}A^{-1}$

$= \begin{bmatrix} \frac{5}{11} & \frac{2}{11} \\ \frac{3}{11} & -\frac{1}{11} \end{bmatrix}\begin{bmatrix} -\frac{2}{7} & \frac{1}{7} \\ \frac{3}{7} & \frac{2}{7} \end{bmatrix}$

$= \frac{1}{77}\begin{bmatrix} -4 & 9 \\ -9 & 1 \end{bmatrix}$

(b) $\left(A^T\right)^{-1} = \left(A^{-1}\right)^T = \begin{bmatrix} -\frac{2}{7} & \frac{1}{7} \\ \frac{3}{7} & \frac{2}{7} \end{bmatrix}^T = \begin{bmatrix} -\frac{2}{7} & \frac{3}{7} \\ \frac{1}{7} & \frac{2}{7} \end{bmatrix}$

(c) $\left(2A\right)^{-1} = \frac{1}{2}A^{-1} = \frac{1}{2}\begin{bmatrix} -\frac{2}{7} & \frac{1}{7} \\ \frac{3}{7} & \frac{2}{7} \end{bmatrix} = \begin{bmatrix} -\frac{1}{7} & \frac{1}{14} \\ \frac{3}{14} & \frac{1}{7} \end{bmatrix}$

44. (a) $\left(AB\right)^{-1} = B^{-1}A^{-1}$

$= \begin{bmatrix} 6 & 5 & -3 \\ -2 & 4 & -1 \\ 1 & 3 & 4 \end{bmatrix}\begin{bmatrix} 1 & -4 & 2 \\ 0 & 1 & 3 \\ 4 & 2 & 1 \end{bmatrix}$

$= \begin{bmatrix} -6 & -25 & 24 \\ -6 & 10 & 7 \\ 17 & 7 & 15 \end{bmatrix}$

(b) $\left(A^T\right)^{-1} = \left(A^{-1}\right)^T = \begin{bmatrix} 1 & -4 & 2 \\ 0 & 1 & 3 \\ 4 & 2 & 1 \end{bmatrix}^T = \begin{bmatrix} 1 & 0 & 4 \\ -4 & 1 & 2 \\ 2 & 3 & 1 \end{bmatrix}$

(c) $\left(2A\right)^{-1} = \frac{1}{2}A^{-1} = \frac{1}{2}\begin{bmatrix} 1 & -4 & 2 \\ 0 & 1 & 3 \\ 4 & 2 & 1 \end{bmatrix} = \begin{bmatrix} \frac{1}{2} & -2 & 1 \\ 0 & \frac{1}{2} & \frac{3}{2} \\ 2 & 1 & \frac{1}{2} \end{bmatrix}$

46. The coefficient matrix for each system is

$A = \begin{bmatrix} 2 & -1 \\ 2 & 1 \end{bmatrix}$

and the formula for the inverse of a 2×2 matrix produces

$A^{-1} = \frac{1}{2+2}\begin{bmatrix} 1 & 1 \\ -2 & 2 \end{bmatrix} = \begin{bmatrix} \frac{1}{4} & \frac{1}{4} \\ -\frac{1}{2} & \frac{1}{2} \end{bmatrix}$.

(a) $\mathbf{x} = A^{-1}\mathbf{b} = \begin{bmatrix} \frac{1}{4} & \frac{1}{4} \\ -\frac{1}{2} & \frac{1}{2} \end{bmatrix}\begin{bmatrix} -3 \\ 7 \end{bmatrix} = \begin{bmatrix} 1 \\ 5 \end{bmatrix}$

The solution is: $x = 1$ and $y = 5$.

(b) $\mathbf{x} = A^{-1}\mathbf{b} = \begin{bmatrix} \frac{1}{4} & \frac{1}{4} \\ -\frac{1}{2} & \frac{1}{2} \end{bmatrix}\begin{bmatrix} -1 \\ -3 \end{bmatrix} = \begin{bmatrix} -1 \\ -1 \end{bmatrix}$

The solution is: $x = -1$ and $y = -1$.

48. The coefficient matrix for each system is

$A = \begin{bmatrix} 1 & 1 & -2 \\ 1 & -2 & 1 \\ 1 & -1 & -1 \end{bmatrix}$.

Using the algorithm to invert a matrix, you find that the inverse is

$A^{-1} = \begin{bmatrix} 1 & 1 & -1 \\ \frac{2}{3} & \frac{1}{3} & -1 \\ \frac{1}{3} & \frac{2}{3} & -1 \end{bmatrix}$.

(a) $\mathbf{x} = A^{-1}\mathbf{b} = \begin{bmatrix} 1 & 1 & -1 \\ \frac{2}{3} & \frac{1}{3} & -1 \\ \frac{1}{3} & \frac{2}{3} & -1 \end{bmatrix}\begin{bmatrix} 0 \\ 0 \\ -1 \end{bmatrix} = \begin{bmatrix} 1 \\ 1 \\ 1 \end{bmatrix}$

The solution is: $x_1 = 1$, $x_2 = 1$, and $x_3 = 1$.

(b) $\mathbf{x} = A^{-1}\mathbf{b} = \begin{bmatrix} 1 & 1 & -1 \\ \frac{2}{3} & \frac{1}{3} & -1 \\ \frac{1}{3} & \frac{2}{3} & -1 \end{bmatrix}\begin{bmatrix} -1 \\ 2 \\ 0 \end{bmatrix} = \begin{bmatrix} 1 \\ 0 \\ 1 \end{bmatrix}$

The solution is: $x_1 = 1$, $x_2 = 0$, and $x_3 = 1$.

50. Using a graphing utility or computer software program, you have

$$A\mathbf{x} = \mathbf{b}$$

$$\mathbf{x} = A^{-1}\mathbf{b} = \begin{bmatrix} 1 \\ 2 \\ -1 \\ 0 \\ 1 \end{bmatrix}$$

where

$$A = \begin{bmatrix} 1 & 1 & -1 & 3 & -1 \\ 2 & 1 & 1 & 1 & 1 \\ 1 & 1 & -1 & 2 & -1 \\ 2 & 1 & 4 & 1 & -1 \\ 3 & 1 & 1 & -2 & 1 \end{bmatrix}, \mathbf{x} = \begin{bmatrix} x_1 \\ x_2 \\ x_3 \\ x_4 \\ x_5 \end{bmatrix}, \text{ and } \mathbf{b} = \begin{bmatrix} 3 \\ 4 \\ 3 \\ -1 \\ 5 \end{bmatrix}.$$

The solution is: $x_1 = 1$, $x_2 = 2$, $x_3 = -1$, $x_4 = 0$, and $x_5 = 1$.

52. Using a graphing utility or computer software program, you have

$$A\mathbf{x} = \mathbf{b}$$

$$\mathbf{x} = A^{-1}\mathbf{b} = \begin{bmatrix} -1 \\ 2 \\ 1 \\ 3 \\ 0 \\ 1 \end{bmatrix}$$

where

$$A = \begin{bmatrix} 4 & -2 & 4 & 2 & -5 & -1 \\ 3 & 6 & -5 & -6 & 3 & 3 \\ 2 & -3 & 1 & 3 & -1 & -2 \\ -1 & 4 & -4 & -6 & 2 & 4 \\ 3 & -1 & 5 & 2 & -3 & -5 \\ -2 & 3 & -4 & -6 & 1 & 2 \end{bmatrix}, \mathbf{x} = \begin{bmatrix} x_1 \\ x_2 \\ x_3 \\ x_4 \\ x_5 \\ x_6 \end{bmatrix}, \text{ and }$$

$$\mathbf{b} = \begin{bmatrix} 1 \\ -11 \\ 0 \\ -9 \\ 1 \\ -12 \end{bmatrix}.$$

The solution is: $x_1 = -1$, $x_2 = 2$, $x_3 = 1$, $x_4 = 3$, $x_5 = 0$, and $x_6 = 1$.

54. The inverse of A is given by

$$A^{-1} = \frac{1}{x-4}\begin{bmatrix} -2 & -x \\ 1 & 2 \end{bmatrix}.$$

Letting $A^{-1} = A$, you find that $\dfrac{1}{x-4} = -1$.

So, $x = 3$.

56. The matrix $\begin{bmatrix} x & 2 \\ -3 & 4 \end{bmatrix}$ will be singular if

$ad - bc = (x)(4) - (-3)(2) = 0$, which implies that

$4x = -6$ or $x = -\frac{3}{2}$.

58. First, find $4A$.

$$4A = \left[(4A)^{-1}\right]^{-1} = \frac{1}{4+12}\begin{bmatrix} 2 & -4 \\ 3 & 2 \end{bmatrix} = \begin{bmatrix} \frac{1}{8} & -\frac{1}{4} \\ \frac{3}{16} & \frac{1}{8} \end{bmatrix}$$

Then, multiply by $\frac{1}{4}$ to obtain

$$A = \frac{1}{4}(4A) = \frac{1}{4}\begin{bmatrix} \frac{1}{8} & -\frac{1}{4} \\ \frac{3}{16} & \frac{1}{8} \end{bmatrix} = \begin{bmatrix} \frac{1}{32} & -\frac{1}{16} \\ \frac{3}{64} & \frac{1}{32} \end{bmatrix}.$$

60. Using the formula for the inverse of a 2×2 matrix, you have

$$A^{-1} = \frac{1}{ad-bc}\begin{bmatrix} d & -b \\ -c & a \end{bmatrix}$$

$$= \frac{1}{\sec^2\theta - \tan^2\theta}\begin{bmatrix} \sec\theta & -\tan\theta \\ -\tan\theta & \sec\theta \end{bmatrix}$$

$$= \begin{bmatrix} \sec\theta & -\tan\theta \\ -\tan\theta & \sec\theta \end{bmatrix}.$$

62. Adjoin the identity matrix to form

$$[F \quad I] = \begin{bmatrix} 0.017 & 0.010 & 0.008 & 1 & 0 & 0 \\ 0.010 & 0.012 & 0.010 & 0 & 1 & 0 \\ 0.008 & 0.010 & 0.017 & 0 & 0 & 1 \end{bmatrix}.$$

Using elementary row operations, reduce the matrix as follows.

$$[I \quad F^{-1}] = \begin{bmatrix} 1 & 0 & 0 & 115.56 & -100 & 4.44 \\ 0 & 1 & 0 & -100 & 250 & -100 \\ 0 & 0 & 1 & 4.44 & -100 & 115.56 \end{bmatrix}$$

So, $F^{-1} = \begin{bmatrix} 115.56 & -100 & 4.44 \\ -100 & 250 & -100 \\ 4.44 & -100 & 115.56 \end{bmatrix}$ and

$$\mathbf{w} = F^{-1}\mathbf{d} = \begin{bmatrix} 115.56 & -100 & 4.44 \\ -100 & 250 & -100 \\ 4.44 & -100 & 115.56 \end{bmatrix}\begin{bmatrix} 0 \\ 0.15 \\ 0 \end{bmatrix} = \begin{bmatrix} -15 \\ 37.5 \\ -15 \end{bmatrix}.$$

64. (a) True. See Theorem 2.8, part 1 on page 67.

   (b) False. For example, consider the matrix
   $\begin{bmatrix} 1 & 1 \\ 0 & 0 \end{bmatrix}$, which is not invertible, but

   $1 \cdot 1 - 0 \cdot 0 = 1 \neq 0.$

   (c) False. If A is a square matrix then the system
   $A\mathbf{x} = \mathbf{b}$ has a unique solution if and only if A is a
   nonsingular matrix.

66. $A^T\left(A^{-1}\right)^T = \left(A^{-1}A\right)^T = I_n^T = I_n$ and

   $\left(A^{-1}\right)^T A^T = \left(AA^{-1}\right)^T = I_n^T = I_n$

   So, $\left(A^{-1}\right)^T = \left(A^T\right)^{-1}.$

68. Because C is invertible, you can multiply both sides of
   the equation $CA = CB$ by C^{-1} on the left to obtain the
   following.

   $C^{-1}(CA) = C^{-1}(CB)$

   $\left(C^{-1}C\right)A = \left(C^{-1}C\right)B$

   $\qquad IA = IB$

   $\qquad A = B$

76. $A = \begin{bmatrix} 1 & 2 \\ -2 & 1 \end{bmatrix}$

   (a) $A^2 - 2A + 5I = \begin{bmatrix} -3 & 4 \\ -4 & -3 \end{bmatrix} - \begin{bmatrix} 2 & 4 \\ -4 & 2 \end{bmatrix} + \begin{bmatrix} 5 & 0 \\ 0 & 5 \end{bmatrix} = \begin{bmatrix} 0 & 0 \\ 0 & 0 \end{bmatrix}$

   (b) $A\left(\frac{1}{5}(2I - A)\right) = \frac{1}{5}\left(2A - A^2\right) = \frac{1}{5}(5I) = I$

   Similarly, $\left(\frac{1}{5}(2I - A)\right)A = I.$ Or, $\frac{1}{5}(2I - A) = \frac{1}{5}\begin{bmatrix} 1 & -2 \\ 2 & 1 \end{bmatrix} = A^{-1}$ directly.

   (c) The calculation in part (b) did not depend on the entries of A.

78. Let C be the inverse of $(I - AB)$, that is $C = (I - AB)^{-1}$. Then $C(I - AB) = (I - AB)C = I$. Consider the matrix
   $I + BCA$. Claim that this matrix is the inverse of $I - BA$. To check this claim, show that
   $(I + BCA)(I - BA) = (I - BA)(I + BCA) = I.$
   First, show

   $(I - BA)(I + BCA) = I - BA + BCA - BABCA$

   $\qquad\qquad\qquad\qquad = I - BA + B(C - ABC)A$

   $\qquad\qquad\qquad\qquad = I - BA + B\underbrace{((I - AB)C)}_{I}A$

   $\qquad\qquad\qquad\qquad = I - BA + BA = I$

   Similarly, show $(I + BCA)(I - BA) = I.$

80. Answers will vary. *Sample answer*:

   $A = \begin{bmatrix} 1 & 0 \\ -1 & 0 \end{bmatrix}$ or $A = \begin{bmatrix} 1 & 0 \\ 1 & 0 \end{bmatrix}$

70. Because $ABC = I$, A is invertible and $A^{-1} = BC$.
   So, $ABC\ A = A$ and $BC\ A = I.$

   So, $B^{-1} = CA.$

72. Let $A^2 = A$ and suppose A is nonsingular. Then,
   A^{-1} exists, and you have the following.

   $A^{-1}\left(A^2\right) = A^{-1}A$

   $\left(A^{-1}A\right)A = I$

   $\qquad A = I$

74. A has an inverse if $a_{ii} \neq 0$ for all $i = 1 \dots n$ and

   $A^{-1} = \begin{bmatrix} \dfrac{1}{a_{11}} & 0 & 0 & \cdots & 0 \\ 0 & \dfrac{1}{a_{22}} & 0 & \cdots & 0 \\ \vdots & \vdots & \vdots & & \vdots \\ 0 & 0 & 0 & \cdots & \dfrac{1}{a_{nn}} \end{bmatrix}.$

82. $AA^{-1} = \begin{bmatrix} a & b \\ c & d \end{bmatrix} \left(\dfrac{1}{ad-bc} \right) \begin{bmatrix} d & -b \\ -c & a \end{bmatrix} = \dfrac{1}{ad-bc} \begin{bmatrix} a & b \\ c & d \end{bmatrix} \begin{bmatrix} d & -b \\ -c & a \end{bmatrix}$

$\qquad\quad = \dfrac{1}{ad-bc} \begin{bmatrix} ad-bc & 0 \\ 0 & ad-bc \end{bmatrix} = \begin{bmatrix} 1 & 0 \\ 0 & 1 \end{bmatrix}$

$\quad A^{-1}A = \dfrac{1}{ad-bc} \begin{bmatrix} d & -b \\ -c & a \end{bmatrix} \begin{bmatrix} a & b \\ c & d \end{bmatrix}$

$\qquad\quad = \dfrac{1}{ad-bc} \begin{bmatrix} ad-bc & 0 \\ 0 & ad-bc \end{bmatrix} = \begin{bmatrix} 1 & 0 \\ 0 & 1 \end{bmatrix}$

Section 2.4 Elementary Matrices

2. This matrix *is* not elementary, because it is not square.

4. This matrix *is* elementary. It can be obtained by interchanging the two rows of I_2.

6. This matrix *is* elementary. It can be obtained by multiplying the first row of I_3 by 2, and adding the result to the third row.

8. This matrix is *not* elementary, because two elementary row operations are required to obtain it from I_4.

10. C is obtained by adding the third row of A to the first row. So,

$$E = \begin{bmatrix} 1 & 0 & 1 \\ 0 & 1 & 0 \\ 0 & 0 & 1 \end{bmatrix}.$$

12. A is obtained by adding -1 times the third row of C to the first row. So,

$$E = \begin{bmatrix} 1 & 0 & -1 \\ 0 & 1 & 0 \\ 0 & 0 & 1 \end{bmatrix}.$$

14.

Matrix	Elementary Row Operation	Elementary Matrix
$\begin{bmatrix} 1 & -1 & 2 & -2 \\ 0 & 3 & -3 & 6 \\ 0 & 0 & 2 & 2 \end{bmatrix}$	$R_1 \leftrightarrow R_2$	$\begin{bmatrix} 0 & 1 & 0 \\ 1 & 0 & 0 \\ 0 & 0 & 1 \end{bmatrix}$
$\begin{bmatrix} 1 & -1 & 2 & -2 \\ 0 & 1 & -1 & 2 \\ 0 & 0 & 2 & 2 \end{bmatrix}$	$\left(\frac{1}{3}\right)R_2 \rightarrow R_2$	$\begin{bmatrix} 1 & 0 & 0 \\ 0 & \frac{1}{3} & 0 \\ 0 & 0 & 1 \end{bmatrix}$
$\begin{bmatrix} 1 & -1 & 2 & -2 \\ 0 & 1 & -1 & 2 \\ 0 & 0 & 1 & 1 \end{bmatrix}$	$\left(\frac{1}{2}\right)R_3 \rightarrow R_3$	$\begin{bmatrix} 1 & 0 & 0 \\ 0 & 1 & 0 \\ 0 & 0 & \frac{1}{2} \end{bmatrix}$

So, $\begin{bmatrix} 1 & 0 & 0 \\ 0 & 1 & 0 \\ 0 & 0 & \frac{1}{2} \end{bmatrix} \begin{bmatrix} 1 & 0 & 0 \\ 0 & \frac{1}{3} & 0 \\ 0 & 0 & 1 \end{bmatrix} \begin{bmatrix} 0 & 1 & 0 \\ 1 & 0 & 0 \\ 0 & 0 & 1 \end{bmatrix} \begin{bmatrix} 0 & 3 & -3 & 6 \\ 1 & -1 & 2 & -2 \\ 0 & 0 & 2 & 2 \end{bmatrix} = \begin{bmatrix} 1 & -1 & 2 & -2 \\ 0 & 1 & -1 & 2 \\ 0 & 0 & 1 & 1 \end{bmatrix}.$

16. <u>Matrix</u>   <u>Elementary Row Operation</u>   <u>Elementary Matrix</u>

$$\begin{bmatrix} 1 & 3 & 0 \\ 0 & -1 & -1 \\ 3 & -2 & -4 \end{bmatrix} \qquad (-2)R_1 + R_2 \rightarrow R_2 \qquad \begin{bmatrix} 1 & 0 & 0 \\ -2 & 1 & 0 \\ 0 & 0 & 1 \end{bmatrix}$$

$$\begin{bmatrix} 1 & 3 & 0 \\ 0 & -1 & -1 \\ 0 & -11 & -4 \end{bmatrix} \qquad (-3)R_1 + R_3 \rightarrow R_3 \qquad \begin{bmatrix} 1 & 0 & 0 \\ 0 & 1 & 0 \\ -3 & 0 & 1 \end{bmatrix}$$

$$\begin{bmatrix} 1 & 3 & 0 \\ 0 & 1 & 1 \\ 0 & -11 & -4 \end{bmatrix} \qquad (-1)R_2 \rightarrow R_2 \qquad \begin{bmatrix} 1 & 0 & 0 \\ 0 & -1 & 0 \\ 0 & 0 & 1 \end{bmatrix}$$

$$\begin{bmatrix} 1 & 3 & 0 \\ 0 & 1 & 1 \\ 0 & 0 & 7 \end{bmatrix} \qquad (11)R_2 + R_3 \rightarrow R_3 \qquad \begin{bmatrix} 1 & 0 & 0 \\ 0 & 1 & 0 \\ 0 & 11 & 1 \end{bmatrix}$$

$$\begin{bmatrix} 1 & 3 & 0 \\ 0 & 1 & 1 \\ 0 & 0 & 1 \end{bmatrix} \qquad \left(\tfrac{1}{7}\right)R_3 \rightarrow R_3 \qquad \begin{bmatrix} 1 & 0 & 0 \\ 0 & 1 & 0 \\ 0 & 0 & \tfrac{1}{7} \end{bmatrix}$$

So, $\begin{bmatrix} 1 & 0 & 0 \\ 0 & 1 & 0 \\ 0 & 0 & \tfrac{1}{7} \end{bmatrix}\begin{bmatrix} 1 & 0 & 0 \\ 0 & 1 & 0 \\ 0 & 11 & 1 \end{bmatrix}\begin{bmatrix} 1 & 0 & 0 \\ 0 & -1 & 0 \\ 0 & 0 & 1 \end{bmatrix}\begin{bmatrix} 1 & 0 & 0 \\ 0 & 1 & 0 \\ -3 & 0 & 1 \end{bmatrix}\begin{bmatrix} 1 & 0 & 0 \\ -2 & 1 & 0 \\ 0 & 0 & 1 \end{bmatrix}\begin{bmatrix} 1 & 3 & 0 \\ 2 & 5 & -1 \\ 3 & -2 & -4 \end{bmatrix} = \begin{bmatrix} 1 & 3 & 0 \\ 0 & 1 & 1 \\ 0 & 0 & 1 \end{bmatrix}.$

18. To obtain the inverse matrix, reverse the elementary row operation that produced it. So, multiply the first row by $\frac{1}{25}$ to obtain

$$E^{-1} = \begin{bmatrix} \tfrac{1}{5} & 0 \\ 0 & 1 \end{bmatrix}.$$

20. To obtain the inverse matrix, reverse the elementary row operation that produced it. So, add 3 times the second row to the third row to obtain

$$E^{-1} = \begin{bmatrix} 1 & 0 & 0 \\ 0 & 1 & 0 \\ 0 & 3 & 1 \end{bmatrix}.$$

22. To obtain the inverse matrix, reverse the elementary row operation that produced it. So, add $-k$ times the third row to the second row to obtain

$$E^{-1} = \begin{bmatrix} 1 & 0 & 0 & 0 \\ 0 & 1 & -k & 0 \\ 0 & 0 & 1 & 0 \\ 0 & 0 & 0 & 1 \end{bmatrix}.$$

24. Find a sequence of elementary row operations that can be used to rewrite A in reduced row-echelon form.

$$\begin{bmatrix} 1 & 0 \\ 1 & 1 \end{bmatrix} \left(\tfrac{1}{2}\right)R_1 \rightarrow R_1 \qquad E_1 = \begin{bmatrix} \tfrac{1}{2} & 0 \\ 0 & 1 \end{bmatrix}$$

$$\begin{bmatrix} 1 & 0 \\ 0 & 1 \end{bmatrix} R_2 - R_1 \rightarrow R_2 \qquad E_2 = \begin{bmatrix} 1 & 0 \\ -1 & 1 \end{bmatrix}$$

Use the elementary matrices to find the inverse.

$$A^{-1} = E_2 E_1 = \begin{bmatrix} 1 & 0 \\ -1 & 1 \end{bmatrix}\begin{bmatrix} \tfrac{1}{2} & 0 \\ 0 & 1 \end{bmatrix} = \begin{bmatrix} \tfrac{1}{2} & 0 \\ -\tfrac{1}{2} & 1 \end{bmatrix}$$

26. Find a sequence of elementary row operations that can be used to rewrite A in reduced row-echelon form.

$$\begin{bmatrix} 1 & 0 & -2 \\ 0 & 1 & \frac{1}{2} \\ 0 & 0 & 1 \end{bmatrix} \left(\tfrac{1}{2}\right)R_2 \rightarrow R_2 \qquad E_1 = \begin{bmatrix} 1 & 0 & 0 \\ 0 & \frac{1}{2} & 0 \\ 0 & 0 & 1 \end{bmatrix}$$

$$\begin{bmatrix} 1 & 0 & 0 \\ 0 & 1 & \frac{1}{2} \\ 0 & 0 & 1 \end{bmatrix} \begin{array}{l} R_1 + 2R_3 \rightarrow R_1 \\[2pt] \end{array} \qquad E_2 = \begin{bmatrix} 1 & 0 & 2 \\ 0 & 1 & 0 \\ 0 & 0 & 1 \end{bmatrix}$$

$$\begin{bmatrix} 1 & 0 & 0 \\ 0 & 1 & \frac{1}{2} \\ 0 & 0 & 1 \end{bmatrix} \begin{array}{l} R_2 - \left(\tfrac{1}{2}\right)R_3 \rightarrow R_2 \end{array} \ E_3 = \begin{bmatrix} 1 & 0 & 0 \\ 0 & 1 & -\frac{1}{2} \\ 0 & 0 & 1 \end{bmatrix}$$

Use the elementary matrices to find the inverse.

$$A^{-1} = E_3 E_2 E_1 = \begin{bmatrix} 1 & 0 & 0 \\ 0 & 1 & -\frac{1}{2} \\ 0 & 0 & 1 \end{bmatrix}\begin{bmatrix} 1 & 0 & 2 \\ 0 & 1 & 0 \\ 0 & 0 & 1 \end{bmatrix}\begin{bmatrix} 1 & 0 & 0 \\ 0 & \frac{1}{2} & 0 \\ 0 & 0 & 1 \end{bmatrix}$$

$$= \begin{bmatrix} 1 & 0 & 2 \\ 0 & 1 & -\frac{1}{2} \\ 0 & 0 & 1 \end{bmatrix}\begin{bmatrix} 1 & 0 & 0 \\ 0 & \frac{1}{2} & 0 \\ 0 & 0 & 1 \end{bmatrix} = \begin{bmatrix} 1 & 0 & 2 \\ 0 & \frac{1}{2} & -\frac{1}{2} \\ 0 & 0 & 1 \end{bmatrix}$$

28. The matrix $A = \begin{bmatrix} 0 & 1 \\ 1 & 0 \end{bmatrix}$ is itself an elementary matrix, so the factorization is

$$A = \begin{bmatrix} 0 & 1 \\ 1 & 0 \end{bmatrix}.$$

30. Reduce the matrix $A = \begin{bmatrix} 1 & 1 \\ 2 & 1 \end{bmatrix}$ as follows.

Matrix	Elementary Row Operation	Elementary Matrix
$\begin{bmatrix} 1 & 1 \\ 0 & -1 \end{bmatrix}$	Add -2 times row one to row two.	$E_1 = \begin{bmatrix} 1 & 0 \\ -2 & 1 \end{bmatrix}$
$\begin{bmatrix} 1 & 1 \\ 0 & 1 \end{bmatrix}$	Multiply row two by -1.	$E_2 = \begin{bmatrix} 1 & 0 \\ 0 & -1 \end{bmatrix}$
$\begin{bmatrix} 1 & 0 \\ 0 & 1 \end{bmatrix}$	Add -1 times row two to row one.	$E_3 = \begin{bmatrix} 1 & -1 \\ 0 & 1 \end{bmatrix}$

So, one way to factor A is

$$A = E_1^{-1} E_2^{-1} E_3^{-1} = \begin{bmatrix} 1 & 0 \\ 2 & 1 \end{bmatrix}\begin{bmatrix} 1 & 0 \\ 0 & -1 \end{bmatrix}\begin{bmatrix} 1 & 1 \\ 0 & 1 \end{bmatrix}.$$

32. Reduce the matrix $A = \begin{bmatrix} 1 & 2 & 3 \\ 2 & 5 & 6 \\ 1 & 3 & 4 \end{bmatrix}$ as follows.

Matrix	Elementary Row Operation	Elementary Matrix
$\begin{bmatrix} 1 & 2 & 3 \\ 0 & 1 & 0 \\ 1 & 3 & 4 \end{bmatrix}$	Add -2 times row one to row two.	$E_1 = \begin{bmatrix} 1 & 0 & 0 \\ -2 & 1 & 0 \\ 0 & 0 & 1 \end{bmatrix}$
$\begin{bmatrix} 1 & 2 & 3 \\ 0 & 1 & 0 \\ 0 & 1 & 1 \end{bmatrix}$	Add -1 times row one to row three.	$E_2 = \begin{bmatrix} 1 & 0 & 0 \\ 0 & 1 & 0 \\ -1 & 0 & 1 \end{bmatrix}$
$\begin{bmatrix} 1 & 2 & 3 \\ 0 & 1 & 0 \\ 0 & 0 & 1 \end{bmatrix}$	Add -1 times row two to row three.	$E_3 = \begin{bmatrix} 1 & 0 & 0 \\ 0 & 1 & 0 \\ 0 & -1 & 1 \end{bmatrix}$
$\begin{bmatrix} 1 & 2 & 0 \\ 0 & 1 & 0 \\ 0 & 0 & 1 \end{bmatrix}$	Add -3 times row three to row one.	$E_4 = \begin{bmatrix} 1 & 0 & -3 \\ 0 & 1 & 0 \\ 0 & 0 & 1 \end{bmatrix}$
$\begin{bmatrix} 1 & 0 & 0 \\ 0 & 1 & 0 \\ 0 & 0 & 1 \end{bmatrix}$	Add -2 times row two to row one.	$E_5 = \begin{bmatrix} 1 & -2 & 0 \\ 0 & 1 & 0 \\ 0 & 0 & 1 \end{bmatrix}$

So, one way to factor A is

$$A = E_1^{-1}E_2^{-1}E_3^{-1}E_4^{-1}E_5^{-1} = \begin{bmatrix} 1 & 0 & 0 \\ 2 & 1 & 0 \\ 0 & 0 & 1 \end{bmatrix}\begin{bmatrix} 1 & 0 & 0 \\ 0 & 1 & 0 \\ 1 & 0 & 1 \end{bmatrix}\begin{bmatrix} 1 & 0 & 0 \\ 0 & 1 & 0 \\ 0 & 1 & 1 \end{bmatrix}\begin{bmatrix} 1 & 0 & 3 \\ 0 & 1 & 0 \\ 0 & 0 & 1 \end{bmatrix}\begin{bmatrix} 1 & 2 & 0 \\ 0 & 1 & 0 \\ 0 & 0 & 1 \end{bmatrix}.$$

34. Find a sequence of elementary row operations that can be used to rewrite A in reduced row-echelon form.

$$\begin{bmatrix} 1 & 0 & 0 & \frac{1}{2} \\ 0 & 1 & 0 & 1 \\ 0 & 0 & -1 & 2 \\ 1 & 0 & 0 & -2 \end{bmatrix} \left(\tfrac{1}{4}\right)R_1 \rightarrow R_1 \qquad\qquad E_1 = \begin{bmatrix} \frac{1}{4} & 0 & 0 & 0 \\ 0 & 1 & 0 & 0 \\ 0 & 0 & 1 & 0 \\ 0 & 0 & 0 & 1 \end{bmatrix}$$

$$\begin{bmatrix} 1 & 0 & 0 & \frac{1}{2} \\ 0 & 1 & 0 & 1 \\ 0 & 0 & -1 & 2 \\ 0 & 0 & 0 & -\frac{5}{2} \end{bmatrix} R_4 - R_1 \rightarrow R_4 \qquad\qquad E_2 = \begin{bmatrix} 1 & 0 & 0 & 0 \\ 0 & 1 & 0 & 0 \\ 0 & 0 & 1 & 0 \\ -1 & 0 & 0 & 1 \end{bmatrix}$$

$$\begin{bmatrix} 1 & 0 & 0 & \frac{1}{2} \\ 0 & 1 & 0 & 1 \\ 0 & 0 & -1 & 2 \\ 0 & 0 & 0 & 1 \end{bmatrix} \left(-\tfrac{2}{5}\right)R_4 \rightarrow R_4 \qquad\qquad E_3 = \begin{bmatrix} 1 & 0 & 0 & 0 \\ 0 & 1 & 0 & 0 \\ 0 & 0 & 1 & 0 \\ 0 & 0 & 0 & -\frac{2}{5} \end{bmatrix}$$

$$\begin{bmatrix} 1 & 0 & 0 & \frac{1}{2} \\ 0 & 1 & 0 & 1 \\ 0 & 0 & 1 & -2 \\ 0 & 0 & 0 & 1 \end{bmatrix} -R_3 \rightarrow R_3 \qquad\qquad E_4 = \begin{bmatrix} 1 & 0 & 0 & 0 \\ 0 & 1 & 0 & 0 \\ 0 & 0 & -1 & 0 \\ 0 & 0 & 0 & 1 \end{bmatrix}$$

$$\begin{bmatrix} 1 & 0 & 0 & 0 \\ 0 & 1 & 0 & 1 \\ 0 & 0 & 1 & -2 \\ 0 & 0 & 0 & 1 \end{bmatrix} R_1 - \left(\tfrac{1}{2}\right)R_4 \rightarrow R_1 \qquad\qquad E_5 = \begin{bmatrix} 1 & 0 & 0 & -\frac{1}{2} \\ 0 & 1 & 0 & 0 \\ 0 & 0 & 1 & 0 \\ 0 & 0 & 0 & 1 \end{bmatrix}$$

$$\begin{bmatrix} 1 & 0 & 0 & 0 \\ 0 & 1 & 0 & 0 \\ 0 & 0 & 1 & -2 \\ 0 & 0 & 0 & 1 \end{bmatrix} R_2 - R_4 \rightarrow R_2 \qquad\qquad E_6 = \begin{bmatrix} 1 & 0 & 0 & 0 \\ 0 & 1 & 0 & -1 \\ 0 & 0 & 1 & 0 \\ 0 & 0 & 0 & 1 \end{bmatrix}$$

$$\begin{bmatrix} 1 & 0 & 0 & 0 \\ 0 & 1 & 0 & 0 \\ 0 & 0 & 1 & 0 \\ 0 & 0 & 0 & 1 \end{bmatrix} R_3 + 2R_4 \rightarrow R_3 \qquad\qquad E_7 = \begin{bmatrix} 1 & 0 & 0 & 0 \\ 0 & 1 & 0 & 0 \\ 0 & 0 & 1 & 2 \\ 0 & 0 & 0 & 1 \end{bmatrix}$$

So, one way to factor A is

$$A = E_1^{-1} E_2^{-1} E_3^{-1} E_4^{-1} E_5^{-1} E_6^{-1} E_7^{-1}$$

$$= \begin{bmatrix} 4 & 0 & 0 & 0 \\ 0 & 1 & 0 & 0 \\ 0 & 0 & 1 & 0 \\ 0 & 0 & 0 & 1 \end{bmatrix} \begin{bmatrix} 1 & 0 & 0 & 0 \\ 0 & 1 & 0 & 0 \\ 0 & 0 & 1 & 0 \\ 1 & 0 & 0 & 1 \end{bmatrix} \begin{bmatrix} 1 & 0 & 0 & 0 \\ 0 & 1 & 0 & 0 \\ 0 & 0 & 1 & 0 \\ 0 & 0 & 0 & -\frac{5}{2} \end{bmatrix} \begin{bmatrix} 1 & 0 & 0 & 0 \\ 0 & 1 & 0 & 0 \\ 0 & 0 & -1 & 0 \\ 0 & 0 & 0 & 1 \end{bmatrix} \begin{bmatrix} 1 & 0 & 0 & \frac{1}{2} \\ 0 & 1 & 0 & 0 \\ 0 & 0 & 1 & 0 \\ 0 & 0 & 0 & 1 \end{bmatrix} \begin{bmatrix} 1 & 0 & 0 & 0 \\ 0 & 1 & 0 & 1 \\ 0 & 0 & 1 & 0 \\ 0 & 0 & 0 & 1 \end{bmatrix} \begin{bmatrix} 1 & 0 & 0 & 0 \\ 0 & 1 & 0 & 0 \\ 0 & 0 & 1 & -2 \\ 0 & 0 & 0 & 1 \end{bmatrix}.$$

36. (a) False. It is impossible to obtain the zero matrix by applying any elementary row operation to the identity matrix.

(b) True. If $A = E_1 E_2 \ldots E_k$, where each E_i is an elementary matrix, then A is invertible (because every elementary matrix is) and $A^{-1} = E_k^{-1} \ldots E_2^{-1} E_1^{-1}$.

(c) True. See equivalent conditions (2) and (3) of Theorem 2.15 on page 78.

38. (a) EA has the same rows as A except the two rows that are interchanged in E will be interchanged in EA.

(b) Multiplying a matrix on the left by E interchanges the same two rows that are interchanged from I_n in E. So, multiplying E by itself interchanges the rows twice and so $E^2 = I_n$.

40. First, factor A as a product of elementary matrices.

$$A = E_1^{-1}E_2^{-1}E_3^{-1} = \begin{bmatrix} 1 & 0 & 0 \\ 0 & 1 & 0 \\ a & 0 & 1 \end{bmatrix}\begin{bmatrix} 1 & 0 & 0 \\ 0 & 1 & 0 \\ 0 & b & 1 \end{bmatrix}\begin{bmatrix} 1 & 0 & 0 \\ 0 & 1 & 0 \\ 0 & 0 & c \end{bmatrix}$$

So, $A^{-1} = \left(E_1^{-1}E_2^{-1}E_3^{-1}\right)^{-1} = E_3E_2E_1$.

$$\begin{bmatrix} 1 & 0 & 0 \\ 0 & 1 & 0 \\ 0 & 0 & \dfrac{1}{c} \end{bmatrix}\begin{bmatrix} 1 & 0 & 0 \\ 0 & 1 & 0 \\ 0 & -b & 1 \end{bmatrix}\begin{bmatrix} 1 & 0 & 0 \\ 0 & 1 & 0 \\ -a & 0 & 1 \end{bmatrix} = \begin{bmatrix} 1 & 0 & 0 \\ 0 & 1 & 0 \\ -\dfrac{a}{c} & -\dfrac{b}{c} & \dfrac{1}{c} \end{bmatrix}$$

42. Matrix   Elementary Matrix

$$\begin{bmatrix} -2 & 1 \\ -6 & 4 \end{bmatrix} = A$$

$$\begin{bmatrix} -2 & 1 \\ 0 & 1 \end{bmatrix} = U \qquad E_1 = \begin{bmatrix} 1 & 0 \\ -3 & 1 \end{bmatrix}$$

$$E_1A = U \Rightarrow A = E_1^{-1}U = \begin{bmatrix} 1 & 0 \\ 3 & 1 \end{bmatrix}\begin{bmatrix} -2 & 1 \\ 0 & 1 \end{bmatrix} = LU$$

44. Matrix   Elementary Matrix

$$\begin{bmatrix} 2 & 0 & 0 \\ 0 & -3 & 1 \\ 10 & 12 & 3 \end{bmatrix} = A$$

$$\begin{bmatrix} 2 & 0 & 0 \\ 0 & -3 & 1 \\ 0 & 12 & 3 \end{bmatrix} \qquad E_1 = \begin{bmatrix} 1 & 0 & 0 \\ 0 & 1 & 0 \\ -5 & 0 & 1 \end{bmatrix}$$

$$\begin{bmatrix} 2 & 0 & 0 \\ 0 & -3 & 1 \\ 0 & 0 & 7 \end{bmatrix} = U \qquad E_2 = \begin{bmatrix} 1 & 0 & 0 \\ 0 & 1 & 0 \\ 0 & 4 & 1 \end{bmatrix}$$

$$E_2E_1A = U \Rightarrow A = E_1^{-1}E_2^{-1}U$$

$$= \begin{bmatrix} 1 & 0 & 0 \\ 0 & 1 & 0 \\ 5 & -4 & 1 \end{bmatrix}\begin{bmatrix} 2 & 0 & 0 \\ 0 & -3 & 1 \\ 0 & 0 & 7 \end{bmatrix}$$

$$= LU$$

46. (a) Matrix   Elementary Matrix

$$\begin{bmatrix} 2 & 0 & 0 & 0 \\ -2 & 1 & -1 & 0 \\ 6 & 2 & 1 & 0 \\ 0 & 0 & 0 & -1 \end{bmatrix} = A$$

$$\begin{bmatrix} 2 & 0 & 0 & 0 \\ 0 & 1 & -1 & 0 \\ 6 & 2 & 1 & 0 \\ 0 & 0 & 0 & -1 \end{bmatrix} \qquad E_1 = \begin{bmatrix} 1 & 0 & 0 & 0 \\ 1 & 1 & 0 & 0 \\ 0 & 0 & 1 & 0 \\ 0 & 0 & 0 & 1 \end{bmatrix}$$

$$\begin{bmatrix} 2 & 0 & 0 & 0 \\ 0 & 1 & -1 & 0 \\ 0 & 2 & 1 & 0 \\ 0 & 0 & 0 & -1 \end{bmatrix} \qquad E_2 = \begin{bmatrix} 1 & 0 & 0 & 0 \\ 0 & 1 & 0 & 0 \\ -3 & 0 & 1 & 0 \\ 0 & 0 & 0 & 1 \end{bmatrix}$$

$$\begin{bmatrix} 2 & 0 & 0 & 0 \\ 0 & 1 & -1 & 0 \\ 0 & 0 & 3 & 0 \\ 0 & 0 & 0 & -1 \end{bmatrix} = U \qquad E_3 = \begin{bmatrix} 1 & 0 & 0 & 0 \\ 0 & 1 & 0 & 0 \\ 0 & -2 & 1 & 0 \\ 0 & 0 & 0 & 1 \end{bmatrix}$$

$$E_3E_2E_1A = U \Rightarrow A = E_1^{-1}E_2^{-1}E_3^{-1}U$$

$$= \begin{bmatrix} 1 & 0 & 0 & 0 \\ -1 & 1 & 0 & 0 \\ 3 & 2 & 1 & 0 \\ 0 & 0 & 0 & 1 \end{bmatrix}\begin{bmatrix} 2 & 0 & 0 & 0 \\ 0 & 1 & -1 & 0 \\ 0 & 0 & 3 & 0 \\ 0 & 0 & 0 & -1 \end{bmatrix}$$

$$= LU$$

(b) $Ly = b$:

$$\begin{bmatrix} 1 & 0 & 0 & 0 \\ -1 & 1 & 0 & 0 \\ 3 & 2 & 1 & 0 \\ 0 & 0 & 0 & 1 \end{bmatrix}\begin{bmatrix} y_1 \\ y_2 \\ y_3 \\ y_4 \end{bmatrix} = \begin{bmatrix} 4 \\ -4 \\ 15 \\ -1 \end{bmatrix}$$

$y_1 = 4,\ -y_1 + y_2 = -4 \Rightarrow y_2 = 0,$

$3y_1 + 2y_2 + y_3 = 15 \Rightarrow y_3 = 3,$ and $y_4 = -1$

(c) $Ux = y$:

$$\begin{bmatrix} 2 & 0 & 0 & 0 \\ 0 & 1 & -1 & 0 \\ 0 & 0 & 3 & 0 \\ 0 & 0 & 0 & -1 \end{bmatrix}\begin{bmatrix} x_1 \\ x_2 \\ x_3 \\ x_4 \end{bmatrix} = \begin{bmatrix} 4 \\ 0 \\ 3 \\ -1 \end{bmatrix}$$

$x_4 = 1,\ x_3 = 1,\ x_2 - x_3 = 0 \Rightarrow x_2 = 1,$ and

$x_1 = 2$

So, the solution to the system $Ax = b$ is:

$x_1 = 2,\ x_2 = x_3 = x_4 = 1.$

48. (a) When an elementary row operation is performed on a matrix A, perform the same operation on I to obtain the matrix E.

    (b) Keep track of the row operations used to reduce A to an upper triangular matrix U. If A row reduces to U using only the row operation of adding a multiple of one row to another row below it, then the inverse of the product of the elementary matrices is the matrix L, and $A = LU$.

    (c) For the system $Ax = b$, find an LU factorization of A. Then solve the system $Ly = b$ for y and $Ux = y$ for x.

50. $A^2 = \begin{bmatrix} 0 & 1 \\ 1 & 0 \end{bmatrix}\begin{bmatrix} 0 & 1 \\ 1 & 0 \end{bmatrix} = \begin{bmatrix} 1 & 0 \\ 0 & 1 \end{bmatrix} \neq A.$

Because $A^2 \neq A$, A is *not* idempotent.

52. $A^2 = \begin{bmatrix} 0 & 1 & 0 \\ 1 & 0 & 0 \\ 0 & 0 & 1 \end{bmatrix}\begin{bmatrix} 0 & 1 & 0 \\ 1 & 0 & 0 \\ 0 & 0 & 1 \end{bmatrix} = \begin{bmatrix} 1 & 0 & 0 \\ 0 & 1 & 0 \\ 0 & 0 & 1 \end{bmatrix}.$

Because $A^2 \neq A$, A is *not* idempotent.

54. Assume A is idempotent. Then

$$A^2 = A$$
$$\left(A^2\right)^T = A^T$$
$$\left(A^T A^T\right) = A^T$$

which means that A^T is idempotent.

Now assume A^T is idempotent. Then

$$A^T A^T = A^T$$
$$\left(A^T A^T\right)^T = \left(A^T\right)^T$$
$$AA = A$$

which means that A is idempotent.

56. $(AB)^2 = (AB)(AB)$

$$= A(BA)B$$
$$= A(AB)B$$
$$= (AA)(BB)$$
$$= AB$$

So, $(AB)^2 = AB$, and AB is idempotent.

58. If A is row-equivalent to B, then

$$A = E_k \cdots E_2 E_1 B,$$

where $E_1, \ldots, E_k$ are elementary matrices.

So,

$$B = E_1^{-1} E_2^{-1} \cdots E_k^{-1} A,$$

which shows that B is row equivalent to A.

60. Suppose

$$A = \begin{bmatrix} 0 & 1 \\ 1 & 0 \end{bmatrix} = \begin{bmatrix} a & 0 \\ b & c \end{bmatrix}\begin{bmatrix} d & e \\ 0 & f \end{bmatrix} = \begin{bmatrix} ad & ae \\ bd & be + cf \end{bmatrix}.$$

Because $0 = ad$, either $a = 0$ or $d = 0$.

If $a = 0$, then $ae = 0 = 1$, which is impossible.

If $d = 0$, then $bd = 0 = 1$, which is impossible.

Section 2.5   Applications of Matrix Operations

2. This matrix *is* stochastic because each entry is between 0 and 1, and each column adds up to 1.

4. The matrix *is* stochastic because $0 \leq a_{ij} \leq 1$ and each column adds up to 1.

6. Form the matrix representing the given transition probabilities. A represents infected mice and B noninfected.

$$P = \begin{matrix} \overset{\text{From}}{\overline{A \quad\; B}} \\ \begin{bmatrix} 0.2 & 0.1 \\ 0.8 & 0.9 \end{bmatrix}\begin{matrix} A \\ B \end{matrix} \end{matrix}\Big\}\text{To}$$

The state matrix representing the current population is

$$X = \begin{bmatrix} 100 \\ 900 \end{bmatrix}\begin{matrix} A \\ B \end{matrix}.$$

(a) The state matrix for next week is

$$PX = \begin{bmatrix} 0.2 & 0.1 \\ 0.8 & 0.9 \end{bmatrix}\begin{bmatrix} 100 \\ 900 \end{bmatrix} = \begin{bmatrix} 110 \\ 890 \end{bmatrix}.$$

So, next week 110 will be infected.

(b) The state matrix for the week after next is

$$P(PX) = \begin{bmatrix} 0.2 & 0.1 \\ 0.8 & 0.9 \end{bmatrix}\begin{bmatrix} 110 \\ 890 \end{bmatrix} = \begin{bmatrix} 111 \\ 889 \end{bmatrix}.$$

In 2 weeks, 111 will be infected.

8. Form the matrix representing the given transition probabilities. Let A represent an hour or more of TV and B less than 1 hour.

$$P = \begin{matrix} \overset{\text{From}}{\overline{A \quad\; B}} \\ \begin{bmatrix} 0 & 0.25 \\ 1 & 0.75 \end{bmatrix}\begin{matrix} A \\ B \end{matrix} \end{matrix}\text{To}$$

The state matrix representing the current distribution is

$$X = \begin{bmatrix} 100 \\ 100 \end{bmatrix}.$$

(a) The state matrix for 1 day later is

$$PX = \begin{bmatrix} 0 & 0.25 \\ 1 & 0.75 \end{bmatrix}\begin{bmatrix} 100 \\ 100 \end{bmatrix} = \begin{bmatrix} 25 \\ 175 \end{bmatrix}.$$

So, 25 students will watch TV for an hour or more tomorrow.

(a) In 2 days, the state matrix is

$$P(PX) = \begin{bmatrix} 0 & 0.25 \\ 1 & 0.75 \end{bmatrix}\begin{bmatrix} 25 \\ 175 \end{bmatrix} \approx \begin{bmatrix} 44 \\ 156 \end{bmatrix}.$$

So, 44 students will watch TV for an hour or more in 2 days.

(c) In 30 days, the state matrix will be $P^{30}X = \begin{bmatrix} 40 \\ 160 \end{bmatrix}.$

So, 40 students will watch TV for an hour or more in 30 days.

10. First, find

$$PX = \begin{bmatrix} 0.6 & 0.1 & 0.1 \\ 0.2 & 0.7 & 0.1 \\ 0.2 & 0.2 & 0.8 \end{bmatrix}\begin{bmatrix} 100 \\ 100 \\ 800 \end{bmatrix} = \begin{bmatrix} 150 \\ 170 \\ 680 \end{bmatrix} \text{ and } P^2 X = P(PX) = \begin{bmatrix} 175 \\ 217 \\ 608 \end{bmatrix}.$$

Continuing, you have $P^3 X = \begin{bmatrix} 187.5 \\ 247.7 \\ 564.8 \end{bmatrix}$.

Finally, the steady state matrix for P is $\begin{bmatrix} 200 \\ 300 \\ 500 \end{bmatrix}$ because

$$\begin{bmatrix} 0.6 & 0.1 & 0.1 \\ 0.2 & 0.7 & 0.1 \\ 0.2 & 0.2 & 0.8 \end{bmatrix}\begin{bmatrix} 200 \\ 300 \\ 500 \end{bmatrix} = \begin{bmatrix} 200 \\ 300 \\ 500 \end{bmatrix}.$$

12. Divide the message into groups of three and form the uncoded matrices.

P L E A S E _ S E N D _ M O N E Y _

$\begin{bmatrix} 16 & 12 & 5 \end{bmatrix}$ $\begin{bmatrix} 1 & 19 & 5 \end{bmatrix}$ $\begin{bmatrix} 0 & 19 & 5 \end{bmatrix}$ $\begin{bmatrix} 14 & 4 & 0 \end{bmatrix}$ $\begin{bmatrix} 13 & 15 & 14 \end{bmatrix}$ $\begin{bmatrix} 5 & 25 & 0 \end{bmatrix}$

Multiplying each uncoded row matrix on the right by A yields the following coded row matrices.

$$\begin{bmatrix} 16 & 12 & 5 \end{bmatrix} A = \begin{bmatrix} 16 & 12 & 5 \end{bmatrix}\begin{bmatrix} 4 & 2 & 1 \\ -3 & -3 & -1 \\ 3 & 2 & 1 \end{bmatrix} = \begin{bmatrix} 43 & 6 & 9 \end{bmatrix}$$

$$\begin{bmatrix} 1 & 19 & 5 \end{bmatrix} A = \begin{bmatrix} -38 & -45 & -13 \end{bmatrix}$$
$$\begin{bmatrix} 0 & 19 & 5 \end{bmatrix} A = \begin{bmatrix} -42 & -47 & -14 \end{bmatrix}$$
$$\begin{bmatrix} 14 & 4 & 0 \end{bmatrix} A = \begin{bmatrix} 44 & 16 & 10 \end{bmatrix}$$
$$\begin{bmatrix} 13 & 15 & 14 \end{bmatrix} A = \begin{bmatrix} 49 & 9 & 12 \end{bmatrix}$$
$$\begin{bmatrix} 5 & 25 & 0 \end{bmatrix} A = \begin{bmatrix} -55 & -65 & -20 \end{bmatrix}$$

So, the coded message is

43, 6, 9, −38, −45, −13, −42, 47, −14, 44, 16, 10, 49, 9, 12, −55, −65, −20.

14. Divide the message into groups of four and form the uncoded matrices.

H E L P _ I S _ C O M I N G _ _

$\begin{bmatrix} 8 & 5 & 12 & 16 \end{bmatrix}$ $\begin{bmatrix} 0 & 9 & 19 & 0 \end{bmatrix}$ $\begin{bmatrix} 3 & 15 & 13 & 9 \end{bmatrix}$ $\begin{bmatrix} 14 & 7 & 0 & 0 \end{bmatrix}$

Multiplying each uncoded row matrix on the right by A yields the coded row matrices

$$\begin{bmatrix} 8 & 5 & 12 & 16 \end{bmatrix} A = \begin{bmatrix} 8 & 5 & 12 & 16 \end{bmatrix}\begin{bmatrix} -2 & 3 & -1 & -1 \\ -1 & 1 & 1 & 1 \\ -1 & -1 & 1 & 2 \\ 3 & 1 & -2 & -4 \end{bmatrix}$$

$$= \begin{bmatrix} 15 & 33 & -23 & -43 \end{bmatrix}$$

$$\begin{bmatrix} 0 & 9 & 19 & 0 \end{bmatrix} A = \begin{bmatrix} -28 & -10 & 28 & 47 \end{bmatrix}$$
$$\begin{bmatrix} 3 & 15 & 13 & 9 \end{bmatrix} A = \begin{bmatrix} -7 & 20 & 7 & 2 \end{bmatrix}$$
$$\begin{bmatrix} 14 & 7 & 0 & 0 \end{bmatrix} A = \begin{bmatrix} -35 & 49 & -7 & -7 \end{bmatrix}.$$

So, the coded message is

15, 33, −23, −43, −28, −10, 28, 47, −7, 20, 7, 2, −35, 49, −7, −7.

16. Find $A^{-1} = \begin{bmatrix} -4 & 3 \\ 3 & -2 \end{bmatrix}$, and multiply each coded row matrix on the right by A^{-1} to find the associated uncoded row matrix.

$$\begin{bmatrix} 85 & 120 \end{bmatrix} \begin{bmatrix} -4 & 3 \\ 3 & -2 \end{bmatrix} = \begin{bmatrix} 20 & 15 \end{bmatrix} \Rightarrow \text{T, O}$$

$$\begin{bmatrix} 6 & 8 \end{bmatrix} A^{-1} = \begin{bmatrix} 0 & 2 \end{bmatrix} \Rightarrow \_, \text{B}$$

$$\begin{bmatrix} 10 & 15 \end{bmatrix} A^{-1} = \begin{bmatrix} 5 & 0 \end{bmatrix} \Rightarrow \text{E}, \_$$

$$\begin{bmatrix} 84 & 117 \end{bmatrix} A^{-1} = \begin{bmatrix} 15 & 18 \end{bmatrix} \Rightarrow \text{O, R}$$

$$\begin{bmatrix} 42 & 56 \end{bmatrix} A^{-1} = \begin{bmatrix} 0 & 14 \end{bmatrix} \Rightarrow \_, \text{N}$$

$$\begin{bmatrix} 90 & 125 \end{bmatrix} A^{-1} = \begin{bmatrix} 15 & 20 \end{bmatrix} \Rightarrow \text{O, T}$$

$$\begin{bmatrix} 60 & 80 \end{bmatrix} A^{-1} = \begin{bmatrix} 0 & 20 \end{bmatrix} \Rightarrow \_, \text{T}$$

$$\begin{bmatrix} 30 & 45 \end{bmatrix} A^{-1} = \begin{bmatrix} 15 & 0 \end{bmatrix} \Rightarrow \text{O}, \_$$

$$\begin{bmatrix} 19 & 26 \end{bmatrix} A^{-1} = \begin{bmatrix} 2 & 5 \end{bmatrix} \Rightarrow \text{B, E}$$

So, the message is TO_BE_OR_NOT_TO_BE.

18. Find $A^{-1} = \begin{bmatrix} 11 & 2 & -8 \\ 4 & 1 & -3 \\ -8 & -1 & 6 \end{bmatrix}$, and multiply each coded row matrix on the right by A^{-1} to find the associated uncoded row matrix.

$$\begin{bmatrix} 112 & -140 & 83 \end{bmatrix} A^{-1} = \begin{bmatrix} 112 & -140 & 83 \end{bmatrix} \begin{bmatrix} 11 & 2 & -8 \\ 4 & 1 & -3 \\ -8 & -1 & 6 \end{bmatrix} = \begin{bmatrix} 8 & 1 & 22 \end{bmatrix} \Rightarrow \text{H, A, V}$$

$$\begin{bmatrix} 19 & -25 & 13 \end{bmatrix} A^{-1} = \begin{bmatrix} 5 & 0 & 1 \end{bmatrix} \Rightarrow \text{E}, \_, \text{A}$$

$$\begin{bmatrix} 72 & -76 & 61 \end{bmatrix} A^{-1} = \begin{bmatrix} 0 & 7 & 18 \end{bmatrix} \Rightarrow \_, \text{G, R}$$

$$\begin{bmatrix} 95 & -118 & 71 \end{bmatrix} A^{-1} = \begin{bmatrix} 5 & 1 & 20 \end{bmatrix} \Rightarrow \text{E, A, T}$$

$$\begin{bmatrix} 20 & 21 & 38 \end{bmatrix} A^{-1} = \begin{bmatrix} 0 & 23 & 5 \end{bmatrix} \Rightarrow \_, \text{W, E}$$

$$\begin{bmatrix} 35 & -23 & 36 \end{bmatrix} A^{-1} = \begin{bmatrix} 5 & 11 & 5 \end{bmatrix} \Rightarrow \text{E, K, E}$$

$$\begin{bmatrix} 42 & -48 & 32 \end{bmatrix} A^{-1} = \begin{bmatrix} 14 & 4 & 0 \end{bmatrix} \Rightarrow \text{N, D}, \_$$

The message is HAVE_A_GREAT_WEEKEND_.

20. Let $A^{-1} = \begin{bmatrix} a & b \\ c & d \end{bmatrix}$ and find that

$$\begin{array}{cc} & \_\quad\text{S} \\ \begin{bmatrix} -19 & -19 \end{bmatrix} \begin{bmatrix} a & b \\ c & d \end{bmatrix} = \begin{bmatrix} 0 & 19 \end{bmatrix} \end{array}$$

$$\begin{array}{cc} & \text{U}\quad\text{E} \\ \begin{bmatrix} 37 & 16 \end{bmatrix} \begin{bmatrix} a & b \\ c & d \end{bmatrix} = \begin{bmatrix} 21 & 5 \end{bmatrix}. \end{array}$$

This produces a system of 4 equations.

$$\begin{aligned}
-19a \quad\quad\quad - 19c \quad\quad\quad &= 0 \\
- 19b \quad\quad\quad - 19d &= 19 \\
37a \quad\quad + 16c \quad\quad\quad &= 21 \\
37b \quad\quad + 16d &= 5.
\end{aligned}$$

Solving this system, you find $a = 1$, $b = 1$, $c = -1$, and $d = -2$. So,

$$A^{-1} = \begin{bmatrix} 1 & 1 \\ -1 & -2 \end{bmatrix}.$$

Multiply each coded row matrix on the right by A^{-1} to yield the uncoded row matrices.

$$\begin{bmatrix} 3 & 1 \end{bmatrix}, \begin{bmatrix} 14 & 3 \end{bmatrix}, \begin{bmatrix} 5 & 12 \end{bmatrix}, \begin{bmatrix} 0 & 15 \end{bmatrix}, \begin{bmatrix} 18 & 4 \end{bmatrix},$$

$$\begin{bmatrix} 5 & 18 \end{bmatrix}, \begin{bmatrix} 19 & 0 \end{bmatrix}, \begin{bmatrix} 0 & 19 \end{bmatrix}, \begin{bmatrix} 21 & 5 \end{bmatrix}.$$

This corresponds to the message CANCEL_ORDERS_SUE.

22. You have

$$\begin{bmatrix} 45 & -35 \end{bmatrix}\begin{bmatrix} w & x \\ y & z \end{bmatrix} = \begin{bmatrix} 10 & 15 \end{bmatrix} \text{ and}$$

$$\begin{bmatrix} 38 & -30 \end{bmatrix}\begin{bmatrix} w & x \\ y & z \end{bmatrix} = \begin{bmatrix} 8 & 14 \end{bmatrix}.$$

So, $45w - 35y = 10$ and $45x - 35z = 15$
$38w - 30y = 8$ $\qquad 38x - 30z = 14$.

Solving these two systems gives $w = y = 1$, $x = -2$, and $z = -3$. So,

$$A^{-1} = \begin{bmatrix} 1 & -2 \\ 1 & -3 \end{bmatrix}.$$

(b) Decoding, you have:

$\begin{bmatrix} 45 & -35 \end{bmatrix}A^{-1} = \begin{bmatrix} 10 & 15 \end{bmatrix} \Rightarrow$ J, O
$\begin{bmatrix} 38 & -30 \end{bmatrix}A^{-1} = \begin{bmatrix} 8 & 14 \end{bmatrix} \Rightarrow$ H, N
$\begin{bmatrix} 18 & -18 \end{bmatrix}A^{-1} = \begin{bmatrix} 0 & 18 \end{bmatrix} \Rightarrow$ _, R
$\begin{bmatrix} 35 & -30 \end{bmatrix}A^{-1} = \begin{bmatrix} 5 & 20 \end{bmatrix} \Rightarrow$ E, T
$\begin{bmatrix} 81 & -60 \end{bmatrix}A^{-1} = \begin{bmatrix} 21 & 18 \end{bmatrix} \Rightarrow$ U, R
$\begin{bmatrix} 42 & -28 \end{bmatrix}A^{-1} = \begin{bmatrix} 14 & 0 \end{bmatrix} \Rightarrow$ N, _
$\begin{bmatrix} 75 & -55 \end{bmatrix}A^{-1} = \begin{bmatrix} 20 & 15 \end{bmatrix} \Rightarrow$ T, O
$\begin{bmatrix} 2 & -2 \end{bmatrix}A^{-1} = \begin{bmatrix} 0 & 2 \end{bmatrix} \Rightarrow$ _, B
$\begin{bmatrix} 22 & -21 \end{bmatrix}A^{-1} = \begin{bmatrix} 1 & 19 \end{bmatrix} \Rightarrow$ A, S
$\begin{bmatrix} 15 & -10 \end{bmatrix}A^{-1} = \begin{bmatrix} 5 & 0 \end{bmatrix} \Rightarrow$ E, _

The message is JOHN_RETURN_TO_BASE_.

24. Use the given information to find D.

$$\overset{\text{User}}{\overset{\overline{A \quad B}}{}}$$

$$D = \begin{bmatrix} 0.30 & 0.20 \\ 0.40 & 0.40 \end{bmatrix}\begin{matrix} A \\ B \end{matrix}\Big\} \text{Supplier}$$

The equation $X = DX + E$ may be rewritten in the form $(I - D)X = E$, that is

$$\begin{bmatrix} 0.7 & -0.2 \\ -0.4 & 0.6 \end{bmatrix}X = \begin{bmatrix} 10,000 \\ 20,000 \end{bmatrix}.$$

Solve this system by using Gauss-Jordan elimination to obtain

$$x \approx \begin{bmatrix} 29,412 \\ 52,941 \end{bmatrix}.$$

26 From the given matrix D, form the linear system $X = DX + E$, which can be written as $(I - D)X = E$, that is

$$\begin{bmatrix} 0.8 & -0.4 & -0.4 \\ -0.4 & 0.8 & -0.2 \\ 0 & -0.2 & 0.8 \end{bmatrix}X = \begin{bmatrix} 5000 \\ 2000 \\ 8000 \end{bmatrix}.$$

Solving this system, $X = \begin{bmatrix} 21,875 \\ 17,000 \\ 14,250 \end{bmatrix}$.

28. (a) The line that best fits the given points is shown in the graph.

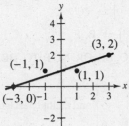

(b) Using the matrices

$$X = \begin{bmatrix} 1 & -3 \\ 1 & -1 \\ 1 & 1 \\ 1 & 3 \end{bmatrix} \text{ and } Y = \begin{bmatrix} 0 \\ 1 \\ 1 \\ 2 \end{bmatrix},$$

you have $X^T X = \begin{bmatrix} 4 & 0 \\ 0 & 20 \end{bmatrix}$, $X^T Y = \begin{bmatrix} 4 \\ 6 \end{bmatrix}$, and

$$A = \left(X^T X\right)^{-1} X^T Y = \begin{bmatrix} \frac{1}{4} & 0 \\ 0 & \frac{1}{20} \end{bmatrix}\begin{bmatrix} 4 \\ 6 \end{bmatrix} = \begin{bmatrix} 1 \\ \frac{3}{10} \end{bmatrix}.$$

So, the least squares regression line is $y = \frac{3}{10}x + 1$.

(c) Solving $Y = XA + E$ for E, you have

$$E = Y - XA = \begin{bmatrix} -0.1 \\ 0.3 \\ -0.3 \\ 0.1 \end{bmatrix}.$$

So, the sum of the squares error is $E^T E = 0.2$.

30. (a) The line that best fits the given points is shown in the graph.

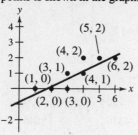

(b) Using the matrices

$$X = \begin{bmatrix} 1 & 1 \\ 1 & 2 \\ 1 & 3 \\ 1 & 3 \\ 1 & 4 \\ 1 & 4 \\ 1 & 5 \\ 1 & 6 \end{bmatrix} \text{ and } Y = \begin{bmatrix} 0 \\ 0 \\ 0 \\ 1 \\ 1 \\ 2 \\ 2 \\ 2 \end{bmatrix},$$

you have

$$X^T X = \begin{bmatrix} 8 & 28 \\ 28 & 116 \end{bmatrix}, X^T Y = \begin{bmatrix} 8 \\ 37 \end{bmatrix}, \text{ and } A = \left(X^T X \right)^{-1} \left(X^T Y \right) = \begin{bmatrix} -\frac{3}{4} \\ \frac{1}{2} \end{bmatrix}.$$

So, the least squares regression line is $y = \frac{1}{2}x - \frac{3}{4}$.

(c) Solving $Y = XA + E$ for E, you have

$$E = Y - XA = \begin{bmatrix} \frac{1}{4} & -\frac{1}{4} & -\frac{3}{4} & \frac{1}{4} & -\frac{1}{4} & \frac{3}{4} & \frac{1}{4} & -\frac{1}{4} \end{bmatrix}^T$$

and the sum of the squares error is $E^T E = 1.5$.

32. Using the matrices

$$X = \begin{bmatrix} 1 & 1 \\ 1 & 3 \\ 1 & 5 \end{bmatrix} \text{ and } Y = \begin{bmatrix} 0 \\ 3 \\ 6 \end{bmatrix},$$

you have

$$X^T X = \begin{bmatrix} 1 & 1 & 1 \\ 1 & 3 & 5 \end{bmatrix} \begin{bmatrix} 1 & 1 \\ 1 & 3 \\ 1 & 5 \end{bmatrix} = \begin{bmatrix} 3 & 9 \\ 9 & 35 \end{bmatrix},$$

$$X^T Y = \begin{bmatrix} 1 & 1 & 1 \\ 1 & 3 & 5 \end{bmatrix} \begin{bmatrix} 0 \\ 3 \\ 6 \end{bmatrix} = \begin{bmatrix} 9 \\ 39 \end{bmatrix}, \text{ and }$$

$$A = \left(X^T X \right)^{-1} \left(X^T Y \right) = \begin{bmatrix} -\frac{3}{2} \\ \frac{3}{2} \end{bmatrix}.$$

So, the least squares regression line is $y = \frac{3}{2}x - \frac{3}{2}$.

34. Using matrices

$$X = \begin{bmatrix} 1 & -4 \\ 1 & -2 \\ 1 & 2 \\ 1 & 4 \end{bmatrix} \text{ and } Y = \begin{bmatrix} -1 \\ 0 \\ 4 \\ 5 \end{bmatrix},$$

you have

$$X^T X = \begin{bmatrix} 4 & 0 \\ 0 & 40 \end{bmatrix}, \quad X^T Y = \begin{bmatrix} 8 \\ 32 \end{bmatrix}, \text{ and }$$

$$A = \left(X^T X \right)^{-1} \left(X^T Y \right) = \begin{bmatrix} \frac{1}{4} & 0 \\ 0 & \frac{1}{40} \end{bmatrix} \begin{bmatrix} 8 \\ 32 \end{bmatrix} = \begin{bmatrix} 2 \\ 0.8 \end{bmatrix}.$$

So, the least squares regression line is $y = 0.8x + 2$.

36. Using matrices

$$X = \begin{bmatrix} 1 & -3 \\ 1 & -1 \\ 1 & 1 \\ 1 & 3 \end{bmatrix} \text{ and } Y = \begin{bmatrix} 4 \\ 2 \\ 1 \\ 0 \end{bmatrix},$$

you have

$$X^T X = \begin{bmatrix} 4 & 0 \\ 0 & 20 \end{bmatrix}, \quad X^T Y = \begin{bmatrix} 7 \\ -13 \end{bmatrix}, \text{ and }$$

$$A = \left(X^T X \right)^{-1} \left(X^T Y \right) = \begin{bmatrix} \frac{1}{4} & 0 \\ 0 & \frac{1}{20} \end{bmatrix} \begin{bmatrix} 7 \\ -13 \end{bmatrix} = \begin{bmatrix} \frac{7}{4} \\ -\frac{13}{20} \end{bmatrix}$$

So, the least squares regression line is $y = -0.65x + 1.75$.

38. Using matrices

$$X = \begin{bmatrix} 1 & 0 \\ 1 & 4 \\ 1 & 5 \\ 1 & 8 \\ 1 & 10 \end{bmatrix} \text{ and } Y = \begin{bmatrix} 6 \\ 3 \\ 0 \\ -4 \\ -5 \end{bmatrix},$$

you have

$$X^T X = \begin{bmatrix} 1 & 1 & 1 & 1 & 1 \\ 0 & 4 & 5 & 8 & 10 \end{bmatrix} \begin{bmatrix} 1 & 0 \\ 1 & 4 \\ 1 & 5 \\ 1 & 8 \\ 1 & 10 \end{bmatrix} = \begin{bmatrix} 5 & 27 \\ 27 & 205 \end{bmatrix},$$

$$X^T Y = \begin{bmatrix} 1 & 1 & 1 & 1 & 1 \\ 0 & 4 & 5 & 8 & 10 \end{bmatrix} \begin{bmatrix} 6 \\ 3 \\ 0 \\ -4 \\ -5 \end{bmatrix} = \begin{bmatrix} 0 \\ -70 \end{bmatrix}, \text{ and}$$

$$A = \left(X^T X\right)^{-1}\left(X^T Y\right) = \tfrac{1}{296} \begin{bmatrix} 205 & -27 \\ -27 & 5 \end{bmatrix} \begin{bmatrix} 0 \\ -70 \end{bmatrix}$$

$$= \tfrac{1}{296} \begin{bmatrix} 1890 \\ -350 \end{bmatrix}.$$

So, the least squares regression line is
$$y = -\tfrac{175}{148}x + \tfrac{945}{148}.$$

42. (a) Using matrices

$$X = \begin{bmatrix} 1 & 100 \\ 1 & 120 \\ 1 & 140 \end{bmatrix} \text{ and } Y = \begin{bmatrix} 75 \\ 68 \\ 55 \end{bmatrix},$$

you have

$$X^T X = \begin{bmatrix} 1 & 1 & 1 \\ 100 & 120 & 140 \end{bmatrix} \begin{bmatrix} 1 & 100 \\ 1 & 120 \\ 1 & 140 \end{bmatrix} = \begin{bmatrix} 3 & 360 \\ 360 & 44{,}000 \end{bmatrix},$$

$$X^T Y = \begin{bmatrix} 198 \\ 23{,}360 \end{bmatrix}, \text{ and}$$

$$A = \left(X^T X\right)^{-1}\left(X^T Y\right) = \tfrac{1}{2400} \begin{bmatrix} 44{,}000 & -360 \\ -360 & 3 \end{bmatrix} \begin{bmatrix} 198 \\ 23{,}360 \end{bmatrix} = \tfrac{1}{2400} \begin{bmatrix} 302{,}400 \\ -1200 \end{bmatrix} = \begin{bmatrix} 126 \\ -0.5 \end{bmatrix}.$$

So, the least squares regression line is $y = -0.5x + 126$.

(b)

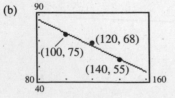

(120, 68)
(100, 75)
(140, 55)

(d) When $x = 170$, $y = -0.5(170) + 126 = 41\%$.

40. (a) Using matrices

$$X = \begin{bmatrix} 1 & 25 \\ 1 & 30 \\ 1 & 35 \\ 1 & 40 \end{bmatrix} \text{ and } Y = \begin{bmatrix} 82 \\ 75 \\ 67 \\ 55 \end{bmatrix},$$

you have

$$X^T X = \begin{bmatrix} 4 & 130 \\ 130 & 4350 \end{bmatrix}, \quad X^T Y = \begin{bmatrix} 279 \\ 8845 \end{bmatrix},$$

and

$$A = \left(X^T X\right)^{-1} X^T Y = \begin{bmatrix} 127.6 \\ -1.78 \end{bmatrix}.$$

So, the least squares regression line is
$y = -1.78x + 127.6$

(b) When $x = 32.95$,

$y = -1.78(32.95) + 127.6 = 68.95 \approx 69.$

(c)

Number (x)	100	120	140
Percent (y)	75	68	55
Model percent (y)	76	66	56

(e) When $y = 40\%$, you have $40 = -0.5x + 126$ and, therefore, $x = 172$.

44. (a) For a stochastic matrix P, every entry P_{ij} must be between 0 and 1, and the sum of the entries in each column must be 1. A stochastic matrix is used to find state matrices by repeated multiplication.

(b) To encode a message, convert the message to numbers and partition it into uncoded row matrices of size $1 \times n$. Then multiply on the right by an invertible $n \times n$ matrix A to obtain coded row matrices. To decode a message, multiply the coded row matrices on the right by A^{-1} and convert the numbers back to letters.

(c) A Leontief input-output model uses an $n \times n$ matrix to represent the input needs of an economic system, and an $n \times 1$ matrix to represent any external demands on the system.

(d) The coefficients of the least squares regression line are given by $A = \left(X^T X\right)^{-1} X^T Y$.

46. Let

$$P = \begin{bmatrix} a & b \\ 1-a & 1-b \end{bmatrix}$$

be a 2×2 stochastic matrix, and consider the system of equations $PX = X$.

$$\begin{bmatrix} a & b \\ 1-a & 1-b \end{bmatrix}\begin{bmatrix} x_1 \\ x_2 \end{bmatrix} = \begin{bmatrix} x_1 \\ x_2 \end{bmatrix}$$

You have

$$\begin{aligned} ax_1 + \qquad bx_2 &= x_1 \\ (1-a)x_1 + (1-b)x_2 &= x_2 \end{aligned}$$

or

$$\begin{aligned} (a-1)x_1 + bx_2 &= 0 \\ (1-a)x_1 - bx_2 &= 0. \end{aligned}$$

Letting $x_1 = b$ and $x_2 = 1 - a$, you have the 2×1 state matrix X satisfying $PX = X$

$$X = \begin{bmatrix} b \\ 1-a \end{bmatrix}.$$

Review Exercises for Chapter 2

2. $-2\begin{bmatrix} 1 & 2 \\ 5 & -4 \\ 6 & 0 \end{bmatrix} + 8\begin{bmatrix} 7 & 1 \\ 1 & 2 \\ 1 & 4 \end{bmatrix} = \begin{bmatrix} -2 & -4 \\ -10 & 8 \\ -12 & 0 \end{bmatrix} + \begin{bmatrix} 56 & 8 \\ 8 & 16 \\ 8 & 32 \end{bmatrix} = \begin{bmatrix} 54 & 4 \\ -2 & 24 \\ -4 & 32 \end{bmatrix}$

4. $\begin{bmatrix} 1 & 5 \\ 2 & -4 \end{bmatrix}\begin{bmatrix} 6 & -2 & 8 \\ 4 & 0 & 0 \end{bmatrix} = \begin{bmatrix} 1(6)+5(4) & 1(-2)+5(0) & 1(8)+5(0) \\ 2(6)-4(4) & 2(-2)-4(0) & 2(8)-4(0) \end{bmatrix} = \begin{bmatrix} 26 & -2 & 8 \\ -4 & -4 & 16 \end{bmatrix}$

6. $\begin{bmatrix} 2 & 1 \\ 6 & 0 \end{bmatrix}\begin{bmatrix} 4 & 2 \\ -3 & 1 \end{bmatrix} + \begin{bmatrix} -2 & 4 \\ 0 & 4 \end{bmatrix} = \begin{bmatrix} 5 & 5 \\ 24 & 12 \end{bmatrix} + \begin{bmatrix} -2 & 4 \\ 0 & 4 \end{bmatrix} = \begin{bmatrix} 3 & 9 \\ 24 & 16 \end{bmatrix}$

8. Letting $A = \begin{bmatrix} 2 & -1 \\ 3 & 2 \end{bmatrix}$, $\mathbf{x} = \begin{bmatrix} x_1 \\ x_2 \end{bmatrix}$, and $\mathbf{b} = \begin{bmatrix} 5 \\ -4 \end{bmatrix}$, the system can be written as

$$A\mathbf{x} = \mathbf{b}$$

$$\begin{bmatrix} 2 & -1 \\ 3 & 2 \end{bmatrix}\begin{bmatrix} x_1 \\ x_2 \end{bmatrix} = \begin{bmatrix} 5 \\ -4 \end{bmatrix}.$$

Using Gaussian elimination, the solution of the system is

$$\mathbf{x} = \begin{bmatrix} \frac{6}{7} \\ -\frac{23}{7} \end{bmatrix}.$$

10. Letting

$$A = \begin{bmatrix} 2 & 3 & 1 \\ 2 & -3 & -3 \\ 4 & -2 & 3 \end{bmatrix}, \mathbf{x} = \begin{bmatrix} x_1 \\ x_2 \\ x_3 \end{bmatrix}, \text{ and } \mathbf{b} = \begin{bmatrix} 10 \\ 22 \\ -2 \end{bmatrix}, \text{ the}$$

system can be written as

$$A\mathbf{x} = \mathbf{b}$$

$$\begin{bmatrix} 2 & 3 & 1 \\ 2 & -3 & -3 \\ 4 & -2 & 3 \end{bmatrix}\begin{bmatrix} x_1 \\ x_2 \\ x_3 \end{bmatrix} = \begin{bmatrix} 10 \\ 22 \\ -2 \end{bmatrix}.$$

Using Gaussian elimination, the solution of the system is

$$\mathbf{x} = \begin{bmatrix} 5 \\ 2 \\ -6 \end{bmatrix}.$$

12. $A^T = \begin{bmatrix} 3 & 2 \\ -1 & 0 \end{bmatrix}$

$A^T A = \begin{bmatrix} 3 & 2 \\ -1 & 0 \end{bmatrix}\begin{bmatrix} 3 & -1 \\ 2 & 0 \end{bmatrix} = \begin{bmatrix} 13 & -3 \\ -3 & 1 \end{bmatrix}$

$AA^T = \begin{bmatrix} 3 & -1 \\ 2 & 0 \end{bmatrix}\begin{bmatrix} 3 & 2 \\ -1 & 0 \end{bmatrix} = \begin{bmatrix} 10 & 6 \\ 6 & 4 \end{bmatrix}$

14. $A^T = \begin{bmatrix} 1 \\ -2 \\ -3 \end{bmatrix}$

$A^T A = \begin{bmatrix} 1 \\ -2 \\ -3 \end{bmatrix}\begin{bmatrix} 1 & -2 & -3 \end{bmatrix} = \begin{bmatrix} 1 & -2 & -3 \\ -2 & 4 & 6 \\ -3 & 6 & 9 \end{bmatrix}$

$AA^T = \begin{bmatrix} 1 & -2 & -3 \end{bmatrix}\begin{bmatrix} 1 \\ -2 \\ -3 \end{bmatrix} = \begin{bmatrix} 14 \end{bmatrix}$

16. From the formula

$A^{-1} = \dfrac{1}{ad - bc}\begin{bmatrix} d & -b \\ -c & a \end{bmatrix},$

you see that $ad - bc = 4(2) - (-1)(-8) = 0$, and so the matrix has no inverse.

18. Begin by adjoining the identity matrix to the given matrix.

$[A \quad I] = \begin{bmatrix} 1 & 1 & 1 & 1 & 0 & 0 \\ 0 & 1 & 1 & 0 & 1 & 0 \\ 0 & 0 & 1 & 0 & 0 & 1 \end{bmatrix}$

This matrix reduces to

$[I \quad A^{-1}] = \begin{bmatrix} 1 & 0 & 0 & 1 & -1 & 0 \\ 0 & 1 & 0 & 0 & 1 & -1 \\ 0 & 0 & 1 & 0 & 0 & 1 \end{bmatrix}.$

So, the inverse matrix is

$A^{-1} = \begin{bmatrix} 1 & -1 & 0 \\ 0 & 1 & -1 \\ 0 & 0 & 1 \end{bmatrix}.$

20.
$$\begin{array}{ccc} A & x & b \end{array}$$
$$\begin{bmatrix} 2 & -1 \\ 3 & 4 \end{bmatrix}\begin{bmatrix} x \\ y \end{bmatrix} = \begin{bmatrix} 5 \\ -2 \end{bmatrix}$$

Because $A^{-1} = \dfrac{1}{11}\begin{bmatrix} 4 & 1 \\ -3 & 2 \end{bmatrix} = \begin{bmatrix} \frac{4}{11} & \frac{1}{11} \\ -\frac{3}{11} & \frac{2}{11} \end{bmatrix}$, solve the equation

$A\mathbf{x} = \mathbf{b}$ as follows.

$\mathbf{x} = A^{-1}\mathbf{b} = \begin{bmatrix} \frac{4}{11} & \frac{1}{11} \\ -\frac{3}{11} & \frac{2}{11} \end{bmatrix}\begin{bmatrix} 5 \\ -2 \end{bmatrix} = \begin{bmatrix} \frac{18}{11} \\ -\frac{19}{11} \end{bmatrix}$

22.
$$\begin{array}{ccc} A & x & b \end{array}$$
$$\begin{bmatrix} 0 & 1 & 2 \\ 3 & 2 & 1 \\ 4 & -3 & -4 \end{bmatrix}\begin{bmatrix} x \\ y \\ z \end{bmatrix} = \begin{bmatrix} 0 \\ -1 \\ -7 \end{bmatrix}$$

Using Gauss-Jordan elimination, you find that

$A^{-1} = \begin{bmatrix} \frac{5}{18} & \frac{1}{9} & \frac{1}{6} \\ -\frac{8}{9} & \frac{4}{9} & -\frac{1}{3} \\ \frac{17}{18} & -\frac{2}{9} & \frac{1}{6} \end{bmatrix}$

Solve the equation $A\mathbf{x} = \mathbf{b}$ as follows.

$\mathbf{x} = A^{-1}\mathbf{b} = \begin{bmatrix} \frac{5}{18} & \frac{1}{9} & \frac{1}{6} \\ -\frac{8}{9} & \frac{4}{9} & -\frac{1}{3} \\ \frac{17}{18} & -\frac{2}{9} & \frac{1}{6} \end{bmatrix}\begin{bmatrix} 0 \\ -1 \\ -7 \end{bmatrix} = \begin{bmatrix} -\frac{23}{18} \\ \frac{17}{9} \\ -\frac{17}{18} \end{bmatrix}$

24.
$$\begin{array}{ccc} A & x & b \end{array}$$
$$\begin{bmatrix} 3 & 2 \\ 1 & 4 \end{bmatrix}\begin{bmatrix} x_1 \\ x_2 \end{bmatrix} = \begin{bmatrix} 1 \\ -3 \end{bmatrix}$$

Because $A^{-1} = \dfrac{1}{10}\begin{bmatrix} 4 & -2 \\ -1 & 3 \end{bmatrix} = \begin{bmatrix} \frac{2}{5} & -\frac{1}{5} \\ -\frac{1}{10} & \frac{3}{10} \end{bmatrix}$, solve the

equation $A\mathbf{x} = \mathbf{b}$ as follows.

$\mathbf{x} = A^{-1}\mathbf{b} = \begin{bmatrix} \frac{2}{5} & -\frac{1}{5} \\ -\frac{1}{10} & \frac{3}{10} \end{bmatrix}\begin{bmatrix} 1 \\ -3 \end{bmatrix} = \begin{bmatrix} 1 \\ -1 \end{bmatrix}$

26.
$$\begin{array}{ccc} A & x & b \end{array}$$
$$\begin{bmatrix} 1 & 1 & 2 \\ 1 & -1 & 1 \\ 2 & 1 & 1 \end{bmatrix}\begin{bmatrix} x_1 \\ x_2 \\ x_3 \end{bmatrix} = \begin{bmatrix} 0 \\ -1 \\ 2 \end{bmatrix}$$

Using Gauss-Jordan elimination, you find that

$A^{-1} = \begin{bmatrix} -\frac{2}{5} & \frac{1}{5} & \frac{3}{5} \\ \frac{1}{5} & -\frac{3}{5} & \frac{1}{5} \\ \frac{3}{5} & \frac{1}{5} & -\frac{2}{5} \end{bmatrix}.$

Solve the equation $A\mathbf{x} = \mathbf{b}$ as follows.

$\mathbf{x} = A^{-1}\mathbf{b} = \begin{bmatrix} -\frac{2}{5} & \frac{1}{5} & \frac{3}{5} \\ \frac{1}{5} & -\frac{3}{5} & \frac{1}{5} \\ \frac{3}{5} & \frac{1}{5} & -\frac{2}{5} \end{bmatrix}\begin{bmatrix} 0 \\ -1 \\ 2 \end{bmatrix} = \begin{bmatrix} 1 \\ 1 \\ -1 \end{bmatrix}$

28. Because $(2A)^{-1} = \begin{bmatrix} 2 & 4 \\ 0 & 1 \end{bmatrix}$, you can use the formula for

the inverse of a 2×2 matrix to obtain

$2A = \begin{bmatrix} 2 & 4 \\ 0 & 1 \end{bmatrix}^{-1} = \dfrac{1}{2 - 0}\begin{bmatrix} 1 & -4 \\ 0 & 2 \end{bmatrix} = \dfrac{1}{2}\begin{bmatrix} 1 & -4 \\ 0 & 2 \end{bmatrix}.$

So, $A = \dfrac{1}{4}\begin{bmatrix} 1 & -4 \\ 0 & 2 \end{bmatrix} = \begin{bmatrix} \frac{1}{4} & -1 \\ 0 & \frac{1}{2} \end{bmatrix}.$

30. The matrix $\begin{bmatrix} 2 & x \\ 1 & 4 \end{bmatrix}$ will be nonsingular if

$ad - bc = (2)(4) - (1)(x) \neq 0$, which implies that

$x \neq 8$.

32. Because the given matrix represents 6 times the second row, the inverse will be $\frac{1}{6}$ times the second row.

$$\begin{bmatrix} 1 & 0 & 0 \\ 0 & \frac{1}{6} & 0 \\ 0 & 0 & 1 \end{bmatrix}$$

For Exercises 34 and 36, answers will vary. Sample answers are shown below.

34. Begin by finding a sequence of elementary row operations to write A in reduced row-echelon form.

Matrix	Elementary Row Operation	Elementary Matrix
$\begin{bmatrix} 1 & -4 \\ -3 & 13 \end{bmatrix}$	Interchange the rows.	$E_1 = \begin{bmatrix} 0 & 1 \\ 1 & 0 \end{bmatrix}$
$\begin{bmatrix} 1 & -4 \\ 0 & 1 \end{bmatrix}$	Add 3 times row 1 to row 2.	$E_2 = \begin{bmatrix} 1 & 0 \\ 3 & 1 \end{bmatrix}$
$\begin{bmatrix} 1 & 0 \\ 0 & 1 \end{bmatrix}$	Add 4 times row 2 to row 1.	$E_3 = \begin{bmatrix} 1 & 4 \\ 0 & 1 \end{bmatrix}$

Then, you can factor A as follows.

$$A = E_1^{-1}E_2^{-1}E_3^{-1} = \begin{bmatrix} 0 & 1 \\ 1 & 0 \end{bmatrix}\begin{bmatrix} 1 & 0 \\ -3 & 1 \end{bmatrix}\begin{bmatrix} 1 & -4 \\ 0 & 1 \end{bmatrix}$$

36. Begin by finding a sequence of elementary row operations to write A in reduced row-echelon form.

Matrix	Elementary Row Operation	Elementary Matrix
$\begin{bmatrix} 1 & 0 & 2 \\ 0 & 2 & 0 \\ 1 & 0 & 3 \end{bmatrix}$	Multiply row one by $\frac{1}{3}$.	$E_1 = \begin{bmatrix} \frac{1}{3} & 0 & 0 \\ 0 & 1 & 0 \\ 0 & 0 & 1 \end{bmatrix}$
$\begin{bmatrix} 1 & 0 & 2 \\ 0 & 2 & 0 \\ 0 & 0 & 1 \end{bmatrix}$	Add -1 times row one to row three.	$E_2 = \begin{bmatrix} 1 & 0 & 0 \\ 0 & 1 & 0 \\ -1 & 0 & 1 \end{bmatrix}$
$\begin{bmatrix} 1 & 0 & 0 \\ 0 & 2 & 0 \\ 0 & 0 & 1 \end{bmatrix}$	Add -2 times row three to row one.	$E_3 = \begin{bmatrix} 1 & 0 & -2 \\ 0 & 1 & 0 \\ 0 & 0 & 1 \end{bmatrix}$
$\begin{bmatrix} 1 & 0 & 0 \\ 0 & 1 & 0 \\ 0 & 0 & 1 \end{bmatrix}$	Multiply row two by $\frac{1}{2}$.	$E_4 = \begin{bmatrix} 1 & 0 & 0 \\ 0 & \frac{1}{2} & 0 \\ 0 & 0 & 1 \end{bmatrix}$

So, you can factor A as follows.

$$A = E_1^{-1}E_2^{-1}E_3^{-1}E_4^{-1} = \begin{bmatrix} 3 & 0 & 0 \\ 0 & 1 & 0 \\ 0 & 0 & 1 \end{bmatrix}\begin{bmatrix} 1 & 0 & 0 \\ 0 & 1 & 0 \\ 1 & 0 & 1 \end{bmatrix}\begin{bmatrix} 1 & 0 & 2 \\ 0 & 1 & 0 \\ 0 & 0 & 1 \end{bmatrix}\begin{bmatrix} 1 & 0 & 0 \\ 0 & 2 & 0 \\ 0 & 0 & 1 \end{bmatrix}$$

38. Letting $A = \begin{bmatrix} a & b \\ c & d \end{bmatrix}$, you have

$$A^2 = \begin{bmatrix} a & b \\ c & d \end{bmatrix}\begin{bmatrix} a & b \\ c & d \end{bmatrix} = \begin{bmatrix} a^2 + bc & ab + bd \\ ac + dc & cb + d^2 \end{bmatrix} = \begin{bmatrix} 0 & 0 \\ 0 & 0 \end{bmatrix}.$$

So, many answers are possible.

$\begin{bmatrix} 0 & 0 \\ 0 & 0 \end{bmatrix}, \begin{bmatrix} 0 & 1 \\ 0 & 0 \end{bmatrix}$, etc.

40. There are many possible answers.

$$A = \begin{bmatrix} 0 & 1 \\ 0 & 0 \end{bmatrix}, \; B = \begin{bmatrix} 1 & 0 \\ 0 & 0 \end{bmatrix} \Rightarrow AB = \begin{bmatrix} 0 & 1 \\ 0 & 0 \end{bmatrix}\begin{bmatrix} 1 & 0 \\ 0 & 0 \end{bmatrix} = \begin{bmatrix} 0 & 0 \\ 0 & 0 \end{bmatrix} = O$$

But, $BA = \begin{bmatrix} 1 & 0 \\ 0 & 0 \end{bmatrix}\begin{bmatrix} 0 & 1 \\ 0 & 0 \end{bmatrix} = \begin{bmatrix} 0 & 1 \\ 0 & 0 \end{bmatrix} \neq O.$

42. Because $\left(A^{-1} + B^{-1} \right)\left(A^{-1} + B^{-1} \right) = I$, if $\left(A^{-1} + B^{-1} \right)^{-1}$ exists, it is sufficient to show that $\left(A^{-1} + B^{-1} \right)\left(A(A + B)^{-1}B \right) = I$ for equality of the second factors in each equation.

$$
\begin{aligned}
\left(A^{-1} + B^{-1} \right)\left(A(A + B)^{-1}B \right) &= A^{-1}\left(A(A + B)^{-1}B \right) + B^{-1}\left(A(A + B)^{-1}B \right) \\
&= A^{-1}A(A + B)^{-1}B + B^{-1}A(A + B)^{-1}B \\
&= I(A + B)^{-1}B + B^{-1}A(A + B)^{-1}B \\
&= \left(I + B^{-1}A \right)\left((A + B)^{-1}B \right) \\
&= \left(B^{-1}B + B^{-1}A \right)\left((A + B)^{-1}B \right) \\
&= B^{-1}(B + A)(A + B)^{-1}B \\
&= B^{-1}(A + B)(A + B)^{-1}B \\
&= B^{-1}IB \\
&= B^{-1}B \\
&= I
\end{aligned}
$$

Therefore, $\left(A^{-1} + B^{-1} \right)^{-1} = A(A + B)^{-1}B.$

44.

Matrix	Elementary Matrix
$\begin{bmatrix} 1 & 1 & 1 \\ 1 & 2 & 2 \\ 1 & 2 & 3 \end{bmatrix} = A$	
$\begin{bmatrix} 1 & 1 & 1 \\ 0 & 1 & 1 \\ 1 & 2 & 3 \end{bmatrix}$	$E_1 = \begin{bmatrix} 1 & 0 & 0 \\ -1 & 1 & 0 \\ 0 & 0 & 1 \end{bmatrix}$
$\begin{bmatrix} 1 & 1 & 1 \\ 0 & 1 & 1 \\ 0 & 1 & 2 \end{bmatrix}$	$E_2 = \begin{bmatrix} 1 & 0 & 0 \\ 0 & 1 & 0 \\ -1 & 0 & 1 \end{bmatrix}$
$\begin{bmatrix} 1 & 1 & 1 \\ 0 & 1 & 1 \\ 0 & 0 & 1 \end{bmatrix} = U$	$E_3 = \begin{bmatrix} 1 & 0 & 0 \\ 0 & 1 & 0 \\ 0 & -1 & 1 \end{bmatrix}$

$$E_3E_2E_1A = U \Rightarrow A = E_1^{-1}E_2^{-1}E_3^{-1}U = \begin{bmatrix} 1 & 0 & 0 \\ 1 & 1 & 0 \\ 1 & 1 & 1 \end{bmatrix}\begin{bmatrix} 1 & 1 & 1 \\ 0 & 1 & 1 \\ 0 & 0 & 1 \end{bmatrix} = LU$$

46.   Matrix   Elementary Matrix

$$\begin{bmatrix} 2 & 1 & 1 & -1 \\ 0 & 3 & 1 & -1 \\ 0 & 0 & -2 & 0 \\ 2 & 1 & 1 & -2 \end{bmatrix} = A$$

$$\begin{bmatrix} 2 & 1 & 1 & -1 \\ 0 & 3 & 1 & -1 \\ 0 & 0 & -2 & 0 \\ 0 & 0 & 0 & -1 \end{bmatrix} = U \qquad E = \begin{bmatrix} 1 & 0 & 0 & 0 \\ 0 & 1 & 0 & 0 \\ 0 & 0 & 1 & 0 \\ -1 & 0 & 0 & 0 \end{bmatrix}$$

$$EA = U \Rightarrow A = \begin{bmatrix} 1 & 0 & 0 & 0 \\ 0 & 1 & 0 & 0 \\ 0 & 0 & 1 & 0 \\ 1 & 0 & 0 & 1 \end{bmatrix} \begin{bmatrix} 2 & 1 & 1 & -1 \\ 0 & 3 & 1 & -1 \\ 0 & 0 & -2 & 0 \\ 0 & 0 & 0 & -1 \end{bmatrix} = LU$$

$$L\mathbf{y} = \mathbf{b}: \begin{bmatrix} 1 & 0 & 0 & 0 \\ 0 & 1 & 0 & 0 \\ 0 & 0 & 1 & 0 \\ 1 & 0 & 0 & 1 \end{bmatrix} \begin{bmatrix} y_1 \\ y_2 \\ y_3 \\ y_4 \end{bmatrix} = \begin{bmatrix} 7 \\ -3 \\ 2 \\ 8 \end{bmatrix} \Rightarrow \mathbf{y} = \begin{bmatrix} 7 \\ -3 \\ 2 \\ 1 \end{bmatrix}$$

$$U\mathbf{x} = \mathbf{y}: \begin{bmatrix} 2 & 1 & 1 & -1 \\ 0 & 3 & 1 & -1 \\ 0 & 0 & -2 & 0 \\ 0 & 0 & 0 & -1 \end{bmatrix} \begin{bmatrix} x_1 \\ x_2 \\ x_3 \\ x_4 \end{bmatrix} = \begin{bmatrix} 7 \\ -3 \\ 2 \\ 1 \end{bmatrix} \Rightarrow \mathbf{x} = \begin{bmatrix} 4 \\ -1 \\ -1 \\ -1 \end{bmatrix}$$

48. (a) False. The product of a 2×3 matrix and a 3×5 matrix is a 2×5 matrix.

   (b) True. See Theorem 2.6, (part 4) on page 57.

50. (a) True. $\left(ABA^{-1}\right)^2 = \left(ABA^{-1}\right)\left(ABA^{-1}\right) = AB\left(A^{-1}A\right)BA^{-1} = ABIBA^{-1} = AB^2A^{-1}$

   (b) False. Let $A = \begin{bmatrix} 1 & 0 \\ 0 & 1 \end{bmatrix}$ and $B = \begin{bmatrix} -1 & 0 \\ 0 & -1 \end{bmatrix}$.

   Then $A + B = \begin{bmatrix} 0 & 0 \\ 0 & 0 \end{bmatrix}$.

   $A + B$ is a *singular* matrix, while both A and B are *nonsingular* matrices.

52. (a) Use *scalar multiplication* to find L.

$$L = \tfrac{2}{3}C = \tfrac{2}{3}\begin{bmatrix} 627 & 681 \\ 135 & 150 \end{bmatrix} = \begin{bmatrix} \tfrac{2}{3}(627) & \tfrac{2}{3}(681) \\ \tfrac{2}{3}(135) & \tfrac{2}{3}(150) \end{bmatrix} = \begin{bmatrix} 418 & 454 \\ 90 & 100 \end{bmatrix}$$

   (b) Use *matrix addition* to find M.

$$M = C - L = \begin{bmatrix} 627 & 681 \\ 135 & 150 \end{bmatrix} - \begin{bmatrix} 418 & 454 \\ 90 & 100 \end{bmatrix} = \begin{bmatrix} 627 - 418 & 681 - 454 \\ 135 - 90 & 150 - 100 \end{bmatrix} = \begin{bmatrix} 209 & 227 \\ 45 & 50 \end{bmatrix}$$

54. (a) In matrix B, grading system 1 counts each midterm as 25% of the grade and the final exam as 50% of the grade. Grading system 2 counts each midterm as 20% of the grade and the final exam as 60% of the grade.

(b) $AB = \begin{bmatrix} 78 & 82 & 80 \\ 84 & 88 & 85 \\ 92 & 93 & 90 \\ 88 & 86 & 90 \\ 74 & 78 & 80 \\ 96 & 95 & 98 \end{bmatrix} \begin{bmatrix} 0.25 & 0.20 \\ 0.25 & 0.20 \\ 0.50 & 0.60 \end{bmatrix} = \begin{bmatrix} 80 & 80 \\ 85.5 & 85.4 \\ 91.25 & 91 \\ 88.5 & 88.8 \\ 78 & 78.4 \\ 96.75 & 97 \end{bmatrix}$

(c) $\begin{bmatrix} B & B \\ B & B \\ A & A \\ B & B \\ C & C \\ A & A \end{bmatrix}$

56. $f(A) = \begin{bmatrix} 2 & 1 \\ -1 & 0 \end{bmatrix}^3 - 3\begin{bmatrix} 2 & 1 \\ -1 & 0 \end{bmatrix} + 2\begin{bmatrix} 1 & 0 \\ 0 & 1 \end{bmatrix}$

$= \begin{bmatrix} 4 & 3 \\ -3 & -2 \end{bmatrix} - \begin{bmatrix} 6 & 3 \\ -3 & 0 \end{bmatrix} + \begin{bmatrix} 2 & 0 \\ 0 & 2 \end{bmatrix}$

$= \begin{bmatrix} 0 & 0 \\ 0 & 0 \end{bmatrix}$

58. This matrix *is* stochastic because $0 \leq a_{ij} \leq 1$ and each column adds up to 1.

60. $PX = \begin{bmatrix} 0.6 & 0.2 & 0.0 \\ 0.2 & 0.7 & 0.1 \\ 0.2 & 0.1 & 0.9 \end{bmatrix}\begin{bmatrix} 1000 \\ 1000 \\ 1000 \end{bmatrix} = \begin{bmatrix} 800 \\ 1000 \\ 1200 \end{bmatrix};$

$P^2X = P\begin{bmatrix} 800 \\ 1000 \\ 1200 \end{bmatrix} = \begin{bmatrix} 680 \\ 980 \\ 1340 \end{bmatrix};$

$P^3X = P\begin{bmatrix} 680 \\ 980 \\ 1340 \end{bmatrix} = \begin{bmatrix} 604 \\ 956 \\ 1440 \end{bmatrix}.$

62. If you continue the computation in Exercise 61, you find that the steady state is

$X = \begin{bmatrix} 140,000 \\ 100,000 \\ 60,000 \end{bmatrix},$

which can be verified by calculating

$PX = X.$

64. The uncoded row matrices are

B E A M _ M E _ U P _ S C O T T Y _

$\begin{bmatrix} 2 & 5 & 1 \end{bmatrix}$ $\begin{bmatrix} 13 & 0 & 13 \end{bmatrix}$ $\begin{bmatrix} 5 & 0 & 21 \end{bmatrix}$ $\begin{bmatrix} 16 & 0 & 19 \end{bmatrix}$ $\begin{bmatrix} 3 & 15 & 20 \end{bmatrix}$ $\begin{bmatrix} 20 & 25 & 0 \end{bmatrix}$

Multiplying each 1×3 matrix on the right by A yields the coded row matrices.

$\begin{bmatrix} 17 & 6 & 20 \end{bmatrix}$ $\begin{bmatrix} 0 & 0 & 13 \end{bmatrix}$ $\begin{bmatrix} -32 & -16 & -43 \end{bmatrix}$ $\begin{bmatrix} -6 & -3 & 7 \end{bmatrix}$ $\begin{bmatrix} 11 & -2 & -3 \end{bmatrix}$ $\begin{bmatrix} 115 & 45 & 155 \end{bmatrix}$

So, the coded message is

17, 6, 20, 0, 0, 13, −32, −16, −43, −6, −3, 7, 11, −2, −3, 115, 45, 155.

66. Find A^{-1} to be

$$A^{-1} = \begin{bmatrix} -3 & -4 \\ 1 & 1 \end{bmatrix}$$

and the coded row matrices are

$$[11 \quad 52], [-8 \quad -9], [-13 \quad -39], [5 \quad 20], [12 \quad 56], [5 \quad 20], [-2 \quad 7], [9 \quad 41], [25 \quad 100].$$

Multiplying each coded row matrix on the right by A^{-1} yields the uncoded row matrices.

$$\begin{array}{ccccccccc} \text{S} \quad \text{H} & \text{O} \quad \text{W} & \_ \quad \text{M} & \text{E} \quad \_ & \text{T} \quad \text{H} & \text{E} \quad \_ & \text{M} \quad \text{O} & \text{N} \quad \text{E} & \text{Y} \quad \_ \\ [19 \quad 8] & [15 \quad 23] & [0 \quad 13] & [5 \quad 0] & [20 \quad 8] & [5 \quad 0] & [13 \quad 15] & [14 \quad 5] & [25 \quad 0] \end{array}$$

So, the message is SHOW_ME_THE_MONEY_.

68. Find A^{-1} to be

$$A^{-1} = \begin{bmatrix} -40 & 16 & 9 \\ 13 & -5 & -3 \\ 5 & -2 & 1 \end{bmatrix}$$

and the coded row matrices are

$$[23 \quad 20 \quad 132], [54 \quad 128 \quad 102], [32 \quad 21 \quad 203], [6 \quad 10 \quad 23], [21 \quad 15 \quad 129], [36 \quad 46 \quad 173], [29 \quad 72 \quad 45].$$

Multiplying each coded row matrix on the right by A^{-1} yields the uncoded row matrices.

$$\begin{array}{ccccccc} \_ \quad \text{D} \quad \text{O} & \text{N} \quad \text{T} \quad \_ & \text{H} \quad \text{A} \quad \text{V} & \text{E} \quad \_ \quad \text{A} & \_ \quad \text{C} \quad \text{O} & \text{W} \quad \_ \quad \text{M} & \text{A} \quad \text{N} \quad \_ \\ [0 \quad 4 \quad 15] & [14 \quad 20 \quad 0] & [8 \quad 1 \quad 22] & [5 \quad 0 \quad 1] & [0 \quad 3 \quad 15] & [23 \quad 0 \quad 15] & [1 \quad 14 \quad 0] \end{array}$$

So, the message is _DONT_HAVE_A_COW_MAN_.

70. Find A^{-1} to be

$$A^{-1} = \begin{bmatrix} \frac{4}{13} & \frac{2}{13} & \frac{1}{13} \\ \frac{8}{13} & -\frac{9}{13} & \frac{2}{13} \\ \frac{5}{13} & -\frac{4}{13} & -\frac{2}{13} \end{bmatrix},$$

and multiply each coded row matrix on the right by A^{-1} to find the associated uncoded row matrix.

$$[66 \quad 27 \quad -31]A^{-1} = [66 \quad 27 \quad -31]\begin{bmatrix} \frac{4}{13} & \frac{2}{13} & \frac{1}{13} \\ \frac{8}{13} & -\frac{9}{13} & \frac{2}{13} \\ \frac{5}{13} & -\frac{4}{13} & -\frac{2}{13} \end{bmatrix} = [25 \quad 1 \quad 14] \Rightarrow \text{Y, A, N}$$

$$[37 \quad 5 \quad -9]A^{-1} = [11 \quad 5 \quad 5] \Rightarrow \text{K, E, E}$$
$$[61 \quad 46 \quad -73]A^{-1} = [19 \quad 0 \quad 23] \Rightarrow \text{S, \_, W}$$
$$[46 \quad -14 \quad 9]A^{-1} = [9 \quad 14 \quad 0] \Rightarrow \text{I, N, \_}$$
$$[94 \quad 21 \quad -49]A^{-1} = [23 \quad 15 \quad 18] \Rightarrow \text{W, O, R}$$
$$[32 \quad -4 \quad 12]A^{-1} = [12 \quad 4 \quad 0] \Rightarrow \text{L, D, \_}$$
$$[66 \quad 31 \quad -53]A^{-1} = [19 \quad 5 \quad 18] \Rightarrow \text{S, E, R}$$
$$[47 \quad 33 \quad -67]A^{-1} = [9 \quad 5 \quad 19] \Rightarrow \text{I, E, S}$$

The message is YANKEES_WIN_WORLD_SERIES.

72. Solve the equation $X = DX + E$ for X to obtain $(I - D)X = E$, which corresponds to solving the augmented matrix.

$$\begin{bmatrix} 0.9 & -0.3 & -0.2 & 3000 \\ 0 & 0.8 & -0.3 & 3500 \\ -0.4 & -0.1 & 0.9 & 8500 \end{bmatrix}$$

The solution to this system is

$$X = \begin{bmatrix} 10000 \\ 10000 \\ 15000 \end{bmatrix}.$$

74. Using the matrices

$$X = \begin{bmatrix} 1 & 2 \\ 1 & 3 \\ 1 & 4 \\ 1 & 5 \\ 1 & 6 \end{bmatrix} \text{ and } Y = \begin{bmatrix} 1 \\ 3 \\ 2 \\ 4 \\ 4 \end{bmatrix},$$

you have

$$X^T X = \begin{bmatrix} 5 & 20 \\ 20 & 90 \end{bmatrix}, \ X^T Y = \begin{bmatrix} 14 \\ 63 \end{bmatrix}, \text{ and}$$

$$A = \left(X^T X \right)^{-1} X^T Y = \begin{bmatrix} 1.8 & -0.4 \\ -0.4 & 0.1 \end{bmatrix} \begin{bmatrix} 14 \\ 63 \end{bmatrix} = \begin{bmatrix} 0 \\ 0.7 \end{bmatrix}.$$

So, the least squares regression line is $y = 0.7x$.

76. Using the matrices

$$X = \begin{bmatrix} 1 & -2 \\ 1 & -1 \\ 1 & 0 \\ 1 & 1 \\ 1 & 2 \end{bmatrix} \text{ and } Y = \begin{bmatrix} 4 \\ 2 \\ 1 \\ -2 \\ -3 \end{bmatrix}, \text{ you have}$$

$$X^T X = \begin{bmatrix} 5 & 0 \\ 0 & 10 \end{bmatrix}, \ X^T Y = \begin{bmatrix} 2 \\ -18 \end{bmatrix}, \text{ and}$$

$$A = \left(X^T X \right)^{-1} X^T Y = \begin{bmatrix} \frac{1}{5} & 0 \\ 0 & \frac{1}{10} \end{bmatrix} \begin{bmatrix} 2 \\ -18 \end{bmatrix} \begin{bmatrix} 0.4 \\ -1.8 \end{bmatrix}.$$

So, the least squares regression line is

$y = -1.8x + 0.4$, or $y = -\frac{9}{5}x + \frac{2}{5}$.

78. (a) Using the matrices $X = \begin{bmatrix} 1 & 4 \\ 1 & 5 \\ 1 & 6 \\ 1 & 7 \\ 1 & 8 \\ 1 & 9 \end{bmatrix}$ and $Y = \begin{bmatrix} 182.1 \\ 207.9 \\ 233.0 \\ 255.4 \\ 270.3 \\ 285.6 \end{bmatrix}$, you have

$$X^T X = \begin{bmatrix} 1 & 1 & 1 & 1 & 1 & 1 \\ 4 & 5 & 6 & 7 & 8 & 9 \end{bmatrix} \begin{bmatrix} 1 & 4 \\ 1 & 5 \\ 1 & 6 \\ 1 & 7 \\ 1 & 8 \\ 1 & 9 \end{bmatrix} = \begin{bmatrix} 6 & 39 \\ 39 & 271 \end{bmatrix},$$

and $X^T Y = \begin{bmatrix} 1 & 1 & 1 & 1 & 1 & 1 \\ 4 & 5 & 6 & 7 & 8 & 9 \end{bmatrix} \begin{bmatrix} 182.1 \\ 207.9 \\ 233.0 \\ 255.4 \\ 270.3 \\ 285.6 \end{bmatrix} = \begin{bmatrix} 1434.3 \\ 9686.5 \end{bmatrix}.$

Now, using $\left(X^T X \right)^{-1}$ to find the coefficient matrix A, you have

$$A = \left(X^T X \right)^{-1} X^T Y = \frac{1}{105} \begin{bmatrix} 271 & -39 \\ -39 & 6 \end{bmatrix} \begin{bmatrix} 1434.3 \\ 9686.5 \end{bmatrix} \approx \begin{bmatrix} 104.02 \\ 20.77 \end{bmatrix}.$$

So, the least squares regression line is $y = 20.77x + 104.02$.

(b) Using a graphing utility, the regression line is $y = 20.77x + 104.02$.

(c)

Year	2004	2005	2006	2007	2008	2009
Actual	182.1	207.9	233.0	255.4	270.3	285.6
Estimated	187.1	207.9	228.6	249.4	270.2	291.0

The estimated values are close to the actual values.

Project Solutions for Chapter 2

1 Exploring Matrix Multiplication

1. Test 1 seems to be the more difficult test. The averages were:

   Test 1 average $= 75$

   Test 2 average $= 85.5$

2. Anna, David, Chris, Bruce

3. $M \begin{bmatrix} 1 \\ 0 \end{bmatrix}$ represents scores on the first test.

   $M \begin{bmatrix} 0 \\ 1 \end{bmatrix}$ represents scores on the second test.

4. $\begin{bmatrix} 1 & 0 & 0 & 0 \end{bmatrix} M$ represents Anna's scores.

   $\begin{bmatrix} 0 & 0 & 1 & 0 \end{bmatrix} M$ represents Chris's scores.

5. $M \begin{bmatrix} 1 \\ 1 \end{bmatrix}$ represents the sum of the test scores for each

   student, and $\frac{1}{2} M \begin{bmatrix} 1 \\ 1 \end{bmatrix}$ represents each students' average.

6. $\begin{bmatrix} 1 & 1 & 1 & 1 \end{bmatrix} M$ represents the sum of scores on each test;
   $\frac{1}{4} \begin{bmatrix} 1 & 1 & 1 & 1 \end{bmatrix} M$ represents the average on each test.

7. $\begin{bmatrix} 1 & 1 & 1 & 1 \end{bmatrix} M \begin{bmatrix} 1 \\ 1 \end{bmatrix}$ represents the overall points total for

   all students on all tests.

8. $\frac{1}{8} \begin{bmatrix} 1 & 1 & 1 & 1 \end{bmatrix} M \begin{bmatrix} 1 \\ 1 \end{bmatrix} = 80.25$

9. $M \begin{bmatrix} 1.1 \\ 1.0 \end{bmatrix}$

2 Nilpotent Matrices

1. $A^2 \neq 0$ and $A^3 = 0$, so the index is 3.

2. (a) Nilpotent of index 2
   (b) Not nilpotent
   (c) Nilpotent of index 2
   (d) Not nilpotent
   (e) Nilpotent of index 2
   (f) Nilpotent of index 3

3. $\begin{bmatrix} 0 & 0 & 1 \\ 0 & 0 & 0 \\ 0 & 0 & 0 \end{bmatrix}$ index 2; $\begin{bmatrix} 0 & 1 & 1 \\ 0 & 0 & 1 \\ 0 & 0 & 0 \end{bmatrix}$ index 3

4. $\begin{bmatrix} 0 & 0 & 0 & 1 \\ 0 & 0 & 0 & 0 \\ 0 & 0 & 0 & 0 \\ 0 & 0 & 0 & 0 \end{bmatrix}$ index 2; $\begin{bmatrix} 0 & 0 & 1 & 1 \\ 0 & 0 & 0 & 1 \\ 0 & 0 & 0 & 0 \\ 0 & 0 & 0 & 0 \end{bmatrix}$ index 3;

   $\begin{bmatrix} 0 & 1 & 1 & 1 \\ 0 & 0 & 1 & 1 \\ 0 & 0 & 0 & 1 \\ 0 & 0 & 0 & 0 \end{bmatrix}$ index 4

5. $\begin{bmatrix} 0 & 1 & 1 & 1 & 1 \\ 0 & 0 & 1 & 1 & 1 \\ 0 & 0 & 0 & 1 & 1 \\ 0 & 0 & 0 & 0 & 1 \\ 0 & 0 & 0 & 0 & 0 \end{bmatrix}$

6. No. If A is nilpotent and invertible, then $A^k = O$ for some k and $A^{k-1} \neq O$. So,

   $$A^{-1}A = I \Rightarrow O = A^{-1}A^k = \left(A^{-1}A\right)A^{k-1} = IA^{k-1} \neq O,$$

   which is impossible.

7. If A is nilpotent, then $\left(A^k\right)^T = \left(A^T\right)^k = O.$ But $\left(A^T\right)^{k-1} = \left(A^{k-1}\right)^T \neq O$, which shows that A^T is nilpotent with the same index.

8. Let A be nilpotent of index k. Then

   $$(I - A)\left(A^{k-1} + A^{k-2} + \cdots + A^2 + A + I\right) = I - A^k = I,$$

   which shows that

   $$\left(A^{k-1} + A^{k-2} + \cdots + A^2 + A + I\right)$$

   is the inverse of $I - A$.

C H A P T E R 3
Determinants

CHAPTER 3
Determinants

Section 3.1   The Determinant of a Matrix

2. The determinant of a matrix of order 1 is the entry in the matrix. So, $\det[-3] = -3$.

4. $\begin{vmatrix} -3 & 1 \\ 5 & 2 \end{vmatrix} = -3(2) - 5(1) = -11$

6. $\begin{vmatrix} 2 & -2 \\ 4 & 3 \end{vmatrix} = 2(3) - 4(-2) = 14$

8. $\begin{vmatrix} \frac{1}{3} & 5 \\ 4 & -9 \end{vmatrix} = \frac{1}{3} \cdot (-9) - 5 \cdot 4 = -23$

10. $\begin{vmatrix} 2 & -3 \\ -6 & 9 \end{vmatrix} = 2(9) - (-6)(-3) = 0$

12. $\begin{vmatrix} \lambda - 2 & 0 \\ 4 & \lambda - 4 \end{vmatrix} = (\lambda - 2)(\lambda - 4) - 4(0) = \lambda^2 - 6\lambda + 8$

14. (a) The minors of the matrix are as follows.

$M_{11} = |1| = 1 \qquad M_{12} = |2| = 2$

$M_{21} = |0| = 0 \qquad M_{22} = |-1| = -1$

   (b) The cofactors of the matrix are as follows.

$C_{11} = (-1)^2 M_{11} = 1 \qquad C_{12} = (-1)^3 M_{12} = -2$

$C_{21} = (-1)^3 M_{21} = 0 \qquad C_{22} = (-1)^4 M_{22} = -1$

16. (a) The minors of the matrix are shown below.

$M_{11} = \begin{vmatrix} 3 & 1 \\ -7 & -8 \end{vmatrix} = -17 \quad M_{12} = \begin{vmatrix} 6 & 1 \\ 4 & -8 \end{vmatrix} = -52 \quad M_{13} = \begin{vmatrix} 6 & 3 \\ 4 & -7 \end{vmatrix} = -54$

$M_{21} = \begin{vmatrix} 4 & 2 \\ -7 & -8 \end{vmatrix} = -18 \quad M_{22} = \begin{vmatrix} -3 & 2 \\ 4 & -8 \end{vmatrix} = 16 \quad M_{23} = \begin{vmatrix} -3 & 4 \\ 4 & -7 \end{vmatrix} = 5$

$M_{31} = \begin{vmatrix} 4 & 2 \\ 3 & 1 \end{vmatrix} = -2 \quad M_{32} = \begin{vmatrix} -3 & 2 \\ 6 & 1 \end{vmatrix} = -15 \quad M_{33} = \begin{vmatrix} -3 & 4 \\ 6 & 3 \end{vmatrix} = -33$

   (b) The cofactors of the matrix are as follows.

$C_{11} = (-1)^2 M_{11} = -17 \qquad C_{12} = (-1)^3 M_{12} = 52 \qquad C_{13} = (-1)^4 M_{13} = -54$

$C_{21} = (-1)^3 M_{21} = 18 \qquad C_{22} = (-1)^4 M_{22} = 16 \qquad C_{23} = (-1)^5 M_{23} = -5$

$C_{31} = (-1)^4 M_{31} = -2 \qquad C_{32} = (-1)^5 M_{32} = 15 \qquad C_{33} = (-1)^6 M_{33} = -33$

18. (a) You found the cofactors of the matrix in Exercise 16. Now find the determinant by expanding along the third row.

$\begin{vmatrix} -3 & 4 & 2 \\ 6 & 3 & 1 \\ 4 & -7 & -8 \end{vmatrix} = 4C_{31} - 7C_{32} - 8C_{33} = 4(-2) - 7(15) - 8(-33) = 151$

   (b) Expand along the first column.

$\begin{vmatrix} -3 & 4 & 2 \\ 6 & 3 & 1 \\ 4 & -7 & -8 \end{vmatrix} = -3C_{11} + 6C_{21} + 4C_{31} = -3(-17) + 6(18) + 4(-2) = 151$

20. Expand along the third row because it has a zero.

$\begin{vmatrix} 2 & -1 & 3 \\ 1 & 4 & 4 \\ 1 & 0 & 2 \end{vmatrix} = 1\begin{vmatrix} -1 & 3 \\ 4 & 4 \end{vmatrix} - 0\begin{vmatrix} 2 & 3 \\ 1 & 4 \end{vmatrix} + 2\begin{vmatrix} 2 & -1 \\ 1 & 4 \end{vmatrix} = 1(-16) + 2(9) = 2$

22. Expand along the first row because it has two zeros.

$$\begin{vmatrix} -3 & 0 & 0 \\ 7 & 11 & 0 \\ 1 & 2 & 2 \end{vmatrix} = -3\begin{vmatrix} 11 & 0 \\ 2 & 2 \end{vmatrix} - 0\begin{vmatrix} 7 & 0 \\ 1 & 2 \end{vmatrix} + 0\begin{vmatrix} 7 & 11 \\ 1 & 2 \end{vmatrix} = -3(22) = -66$$

24. Expand along the first row.

$$\begin{vmatrix} 0.1 & 0.2 & 0.3 \\ -0.3 & 0.2 & 0.2 \\ 0.5 & 0.4 & 0.4 \end{vmatrix} = 0.1\begin{vmatrix} 0.2 & 0.2 \\ 0.4 & 0.4 \end{vmatrix} - 0.2\begin{vmatrix} -0.3 & 0.2 \\ 0.5 & 0.4 \end{vmatrix} + 0.3\begin{vmatrix} -0.3 & 0.2 \\ 0.5 & 0.4 \end{vmatrix}$$

$$= 0.1(0) - 0.2(-0.22) + 0.3(-0.22)$$

$$= -0.022$$

26. Expand along the first row.

$$\begin{vmatrix} x & y & 1 \\ -2 & -2 & 1 \\ 1 & 5 & 1 \end{vmatrix} = x\begin{vmatrix} -2 & 1 \\ 5 & 1 \end{vmatrix} - y\begin{vmatrix} -2 & 1 \\ 1 & 1 \end{vmatrix} + 1\begin{vmatrix} -2 & -2 \\ 1 & 5 \end{vmatrix}$$

$$= x(-7) - y(-3) + (-8)$$

$$= -7x + 3y - 8$$

28. Expand along the first row, because it has two zeros.

$$\begin{vmatrix} 3 & 0 & 7 & 0 \\ 2 & 6 & 11 & 12 \\ 4 & 1 & -1 & 2 \\ 1 & 5 & 2 & 10 \end{vmatrix} = 3\begin{vmatrix} 6 & 11 & 12 \\ 1 & -1 & 2 \\ 5 & 2 & 10 \end{vmatrix} + 7\begin{vmatrix} 2 & 6 & 12 \\ 4 & 1 & 2 \\ 1 & 5 & 10 \end{vmatrix}$$

The determinants of the 3×3 matrices are:

$$\begin{vmatrix} 6 & 11 & 12 \\ 1 & -1 & 2 \\ 5 & 2 & 10 \end{vmatrix} = 6\begin{vmatrix} -1 & 2 \\ 2 & 10 \end{vmatrix} - 11\begin{vmatrix} 1 & 2 \\ 5 & 10 \end{vmatrix} + 12\begin{vmatrix} 1 & -1 \\ 5 & 2 \end{vmatrix}$$

$$= 6(-10 - 4) - 11(10 - 10) + 12(2 + 5) = -84 + 84 = 0$$

$$\begin{vmatrix} 2 & 6 & 12 \\ 4 & 1 & 2 \\ 1 & 5 & 10 \end{vmatrix} = 2\begin{vmatrix} 1 & 2 \\ 5 & 10 \end{vmatrix} - 6\begin{vmatrix} 4 & 2 \\ 1 & 10 \end{vmatrix} + 12\begin{vmatrix} 4 & 1 \\ 1 & 5 \end{vmatrix}$$

$$= 2(10 - 10) - 6(40 - 2) + 12(20 - 1) = 0$$

So, the determinant of the original matrix is $3(0) + 7(0) = 0$.

30. Expand along the first row.

$$\begin{vmatrix} w & x & y & z \\ 10 & 15 & -25 & 30 \\ -30 & 20 & -15 & -10 \\ 30 & 35 & -25 & -40 \end{vmatrix} = w\begin{vmatrix} 15 & -25 & 30 \\ 20 & -15 & -10 \\ 35 & -25 & -40 \end{vmatrix} - x\begin{vmatrix} 10 & -25 & 30 \\ -30 & -15 & -10 \\ 30 & -25 & -40 \end{vmatrix} + y\begin{vmatrix} 10 & 15 & 30 \\ -30 & 20 & -10 \\ 30 & 35 & -40 \end{vmatrix} - z\begin{vmatrix} 10 & 15 & -25 \\ -30 & 20 & -15 \\ 30 & 35 & -25 \end{vmatrix}$$

The determinants of the 3×3 matrices are:

$$\begin{vmatrix} 15 & -25 & 30 \\ 20 & -15 & -10 \\ 35 & -25 & -40 \end{vmatrix} = 15\begin{vmatrix} -15 & -10 \\ -25 & -40 \end{vmatrix} + 25\begin{vmatrix} 20 & -10 \\ 35 & -40 \end{vmatrix} + 30\begin{vmatrix} 20 & -15 \\ 30 & -25 \end{vmatrix}$$

$$= 15(600 - 250) + 25(-800 + 350) + 30(-500 + 525)$$

$$= 5250 - 11{,}250 + 750$$

$$= -5250$$

$$\begin{vmatrix} 10 & -25 & 30 \\ -30 & -15 & -10 \\ 30 & -25 & -40 \end{vmatrix} = 10\begin{vmatrix} -15 & -10 \\ -25 & -40 \end{vmatrix} + 25\begin{vmatrix} -30 & -10 \\ 30 & -40 \end{vmatrix} + 30\begin{vmatrix} -30 & -15 \\ 30 & 25 \end{vmatrix}$$

$$= 10(600 - 250) + 25(1200 + 300) + 30(750 + 450)$$

$$= 3500 + 37{,}500 + 36{,}000$$

$$= 77{,}000$$

$$\begin{vmatrix} 10 & 15 & 30 \\ -30 & 20 & -10 \\ 30 & 35 & -40 \end{vmatrix} = 10\begin{vmatrix} 20 & -10 \\ 35 & -40 \end{vmatrix} - 15\begin{vmatrix} -30 & -10 \\ 30 & -40 \end{vmatrix} + 30\begin{vmatrix} -30 & 20 \\ 30 & 35 \end{vmatrix}$$

$$= 10(-800 + 350) - 15(1200 + 300) + 30(-1050 - 600)$$

$$= -4500 - 22{,}500 + 49{,}500$$

$$= -76{,}500$$

$$\begin{vmatrix} 10 & 15 & -25 \\ -30 & 20 & -15 \\ 30 & 35 & -25 \end{vmatrix} = 10\begin{vmatrix} 20 & -15 \\ 35 & -25 \end{vmatrix} - 15\begin{vmatrix} -30 & -15 \\ 30 & -25 \end{vmatrix} - 25\begin{vmatrix} -30 & 20 \\ 30 & 35 \end{vmatrix}$$

$$= 10(-500 + 525) - 15(750 + 450) - 25(-1050 - 600)$$

$$\doteq 250 - 18{,}000 + 41{,}250$$

$$= 23{,}500$$

So, the determinant is $-5250w - 77{,}000x - 76{,}500y - 23{,}500z$.

32. Expand along the second row because it has all zeros.
So, the determinant of the matrix is zero.

34. Copy the first two columns and complete the diagonal products as follows.

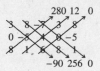

Add the lower three products and subtract the upper
three products to find the determinant.

$$\begin{vmatrix} 3 & 8 & -7 \\ 0 & -5 & 4 \\ 8 & 1 & 6 \end{vmatrix} = -90 + 256 + 0 - 280 - 12 - 0 = -126$$

36. $$\begin{vmatrix} 4 & 3 & 2 & 5 \\ 1 & 6 & -1 & 2 \\ -3 & 2 & 4 & 5 \\ 6 & 1 & 3 & -2 \end{vmatrix} = -1098$$

38. $$\begin{vmatrix} 8 & 5 & 1 & -2 & 0 \\ -1 & 0 & 7 & 1 & 6 \\ 0 & 8 & 6 & 5 & -3 \\ 1 & 2 & 5 & -8 & 4 \\ 2 & 6 & -2 & 0 & 6 \end{vmatrix} = 48{,}834$$

40. The determinant of a triangular matrix is the product of the elements on the main diagonal.

$$\begin{vmatrix} 5 & 0 & 0 \\ 0 & 6 & 0 \\ 0 & 0 & -3 \end{vmatrix} = 5(6)(-3) = -90$$

42. The determinant of a triangular matrix is the product of the elements on the main diagonal.

$$\begin{vmatrix} 4 & 0 & 0 & 0 \\ -1 & \frac{1}{2} & 0 & 0 \\ 3 & 5 & 3 & 0 \\ -8 & 7 & 0 & -2 \end{vmatrix} = 4\left(\frac{1}{2}\right)(3)(-2) = -12$$

44. (a) False. The determinant of a triangular matrix is equal to the *product* of the entries on the main diagonal. For example, if

$$A = \begin{bmatrix} 1 & 0 \\ 0 & 2 \end{bmatrix},$$

then $\det(A) = 2 \neq 3 = 1 + 2$.

(b) True. See Theorem 3.1 on page 107.

(c) True. This is because in a cofactor expansion each cofactor gets multiplied by the corresponding entry. If this entry is zero, the product would be zero independent of the value of the cofactor.

46. $(x + 1)(x - 2) - 1(-2) = 0$

$$x^2 - x - 2 + 2 = 0$$
$$x^2 - x = 0$$
$$x(x - 1) = 0$$
$$x = 0, 1$$

48. $(x + 3)(x - 1) - (-4)(1) = 0$

$$x^2 + 2x - 3 + 4 = 0$$
$$x^2 + 2x + 1 = 0$$
$$(x + 1)^2 = 0$$
$$x = -1$$

50. $\begin{vmatrix} \lambda - 1 & 1 \\ 4 & \lambda - 3 \end{vmatrix} = (\lambda - 1)(\lambda - 3) - 4(1)$

$$= \lambda^2 - 4\lambda + 3 - 4$$
$$= \lambda^2 - 4\lambda - 1$$

The determinant is zero when $\lambda^2 - 4\lambda - 1 = 0$. Use the Quadratic Formula to find λ.

$$\lambda = \frac{-(-4) \pm \sqrt{(-4)^2 - 4(1)(-1)}}{2(1)}$$

$$= \frac{4 \pm \sqrt{20}}{2} = \frac{4 \pm 2\sqrt{5}}{2} = 2 \pm \sqrt{5}$$

52. $\begin{vmatrix} \lambda & 0 & 1 \\ 0 & \lambda & 3 \\ 2 & 2 & \lambda - 2 \end{vmatrix} = \lambda \begin{vmatrix} \lambda & 3 \\ 2 & \lambda - 2 \end{vmatrix} + 1\begin{vmatrix} 0 & \lambda \\ 2 & 2 \end{vmatrix}$

$$= \lambda(\lambda^2 - 2\lambda - 6) + 1(0 - 2\lambda)$$
$$= \lambda^3 - 2\lambda^2 - 8\lambda$$
$$= \lambda(\lambda^2 - 2\lambda - 8)$$
$$= \lambda(\lambda - 4)(\lambda + 2)$$

The determinant is zero when $\lambda(\lambda - 4)(\lambda + 2) = 0$. So, $\lambda = 0, 4, -2$.

54. $\begin{vmatrix} 3x^2 & -3y^2 \\ 1 & 1 \end{vmatrix} = (3x^2)(1) - 1(-3y^2) = 3x^2 + 3y^2$

56. $\begin{vmatrix} e^{-x} & xe^{-x} \\ -e^{-x} & (1 - x)e^{-x} \end{vmatrix} = (e^{-x})(1 - x)e^{-x} - (-e^{-x})(xe^{-x})$

$$= (1 - x)e^{-2x} + xe^{-2x}$$
$$= (1 - x + x)(e^{-2x}) = e^{-2x}$$

58. $\begin{vmatrix} x & x \ln x \\ 1 & 1 + \ln x \end{vmatrix} = x(1 + \ln x) - 1(x \ln x)$

$$= x + x \ln x - x \ln x = x$$

60. The system of linear equations will have a unique solution if and only if the coefficient matrix is invertible. Using the formula for the inverse of a 2×2 matrix, this is equivalent to $ad - bc \neq 0$. So,

$$ad - bc = \begin{vmatrix} a & b \\ c & d \end{vmatrix} \neq 0$$

is the required condition for the system to have a unique solution.

62. Evaluating the left side yields

$$\begin{vmatrix} w & cx \\ y & cz \end{vmatrix} = cwz - cxy.$$

Evaluating the right side yields

$$c\begin{vmatrix} w & x \\ y & z \end{vmatrix} = c(wz - xy) = cwz - cxy.$$

64. Evaluating the left side yields

$$\begin{vmatrix} w & x \\ cw & cx \end{vmatrix} = cwx - cwx = 0.$$

66. Expand the left side of the equation along the first row.

$$\begin{vmatrix} 1 & 1 & 1 \\ a & b & c \\ a^3 & b^3 & c^3 \end{vmatrix} = 1\begin{vmatrix} b & c \\ b^3 & c^3 \end{vmatrix} - 1\begin{vmatrix} a & c \\ a^3 & c^3 \end{vmatrix} + 1\begin{vmatrix} a & b \\ a^3 & b^3 \end{vmatrix}$$

$$= bc^3 - b^3c - ac^3 + a^3c + ab^3 - a^3b$$

$$= b(c^3 - a^3) + b^3(a - c) + ac(a^2 - c^2)$$

$$= (c - a)[bc^2 + abc + ba^2 - b^3 - a^2c - ac^2]$$

$$= (c - a)[c^2(b - a) + ac(b - a) + b(a - b)(a + b)]$$

$$= (c - a)(b - a)[c^2 + ac - ab - b^2]$$

$$= (c - a)(b - a)[(c - b)(c + b) + a(c - b)]$$

$$= (c - a)(b - a)(c - b)(c + b + a)$$

$$= (a - b)(b - c)(c - a)(a + b + c)$$

68. (a) Take the determinant of the $(n - 1) \times (n - 1)$ matrix that is left after deleting the ith row and jth column.

(b) If $i + j$ is odd, then $C_{ij} = -M_{ij}$. If $i + j$ is even, then $C_{ij} = M_{ij}$.

(c) $|A| = a_{11}C_{11} + a_{12}C_{12} + \ldots + a_{1n}C_{1n}$

Section 3.2   Determinants and Elementary Operations

2. Because the second row is a multiple of the first row, the determinant is zero.

4. Because the first and third rows are the same, the determinant is zero.

6. Because the first and third rows are interchanged, the sign of the determinant is changed.

8. Because 2 has been factored out of the first column, the first determinant is 2 times the second one.

10. Because 2 has been factored out of the second column and 3 factored out of the third column, the first determinant is 6 times the second one.

12. Because 6 has been factored out of each row, the first determinant is 6^4 times the second one.

14. Because a multiple of the first row of the matrix on the left was added to the second row to produce the matrix on the right, the determinants are equal.

16. Because a multiple of the second column of the matrix on the left was added to the third column to produce the matrix on the right, the determinants are equal.

18. Because the second and third rows are interchanged, the sign of the determinant is changed.

20. Because the sixth column is a multiple of the second column, the determinant is zero.

22. Expand by cofactors along the second row.

$$\begin{vmatrix} -1 & 3 & 2 \\ 0 & 2 & 0 \\ 1 & 1 & -1 \end{vmatrix} = 2\begin{vmatrix} -1 & 2 \\ 1 & -1 \end{vmatrix} = 2(1 - 2) = -2$$

A graphing utility or a software program gives the same determinant, -2.

24. $$\begin{vmatrix} 3 & 2 & 1 & 1 \\ -1 & 0 & 2 & 0 \\ 4 & 1 & -1 & 0 \\ 3 & 1 & 1 & 0 \end{vmatrix} = \begin{vmatrix} 3 & 2 & 1 & 1 \\ -1 & 0 & 2 & 0 \\ 4 & 1 & -1 & 0 \\ -1 & 0 & 2 & 0 \end{vmatrix}$$

$$= \begin{vmatrix} 3 & 2 & 1 & 1 \\ -1 & 0 & 2 & 0 \\ 4 & 1 & -1 & 0 \\ 0 & 0 & 0 & 0 \end{vmatrix}$$

Because there is an entire row of zeros, the determinant is 0. A graphing utility or a software program gives the same determinant, 0.

26. $$\begin{vmatrix} 1 & 1 & 1 \\ 2 & -1 & -2 \\ 1 & -2 & -1 \end{vmatrix} = \begin{vmatrix} 1 & 1 & 1 \\ 0 & -3 & -4 \\ 0 & -3 & -2 \end{vmatrix}$$

$$= \begin{vmatrix} 1 & 1 & 1 \\ 0 & -3 & -4 \\ 0 & 0 & 2 \end{vmatrix} = 1(-3)(2) = -6$$

28. $\begin{vmatrix} 3 & 0 & 6 \\ 2 & -3 & 4 \\ 1 & -2 & 2 \end{vmatrix} = \begin{vmatrix} 3 & 0 & 0 \\ 2 & -3 & 0 \\ 1 & -2 & 0 \end{vmatrix} = 0$

30. $\begin{vmatrix} 3 & 8 & -7 \\ 0 & -5 & 4 \\ 6 & 1 & 6 \end{vmatrix} = \begin{vmatrix} 3 & 8 & -7 \\ 0 & -5 & 4 \\ 0 & -15 & 20 \end{vmatrix}$

$\qquad = \begin{vmatrix} 3 & 8 & -7 \\ 0 & -5 & 4 \\ 0 & 0 & 8 \end{vmatrix}$

$\qquad = 3(-5)(8)$

$\qquad = -120$

32. $\begin{vmatrix} 9 & -4 & 2 & 5 \\ 2 & 7 & 6 & -5 \\ 4 & 1 & -2 & 0 \\ 7 & 3 & 4 & 10 \end{vmatrix} = \begin{vmatrix} 9 & -4 & 2 & 5 \\ 11 & 3 & 8 & 0 \\ 4 & 1 & -2 & 0 \\ -11 & 11 & 0 & 0 \end{vmatrix}$

$\qquad = \begin{vmatrix} 9 & -4 & 2 & 5 \\ 27 & 7 & 0 & 0 \\ 4 & 1 & -2 & 0 \\ -11 & 11 & 0 & 0 \end{vmatrix}$

$\qquad = (-5)\begin{vmatrix} 27 & 7 & 0 \\ 4 & 1 & -2 \\ -11 & 11 & 0 \end{vmatrix}$

$\qquad = (-5)(2)\begin{vmatrix} 27 & 7 \\ -11 & 11 \end{vmatrix}$

$\qquad = (-10)(11)\begin{vmatrix} 27 & 7 \\ -1 & 1 \end{vmatrix}$

$\qquad = (-110)(27 + 7)$

$\qquad = -3740$

34. $\begin{vmatrix} 0 & -3 & 8 & 2 \\ 8 & 1 & -1 & 6 \\ -4 & 6 & 0 & 9 \\ -7 & 0 & 0 & 14 \end{vmatrix} = \begin{vmatrix} 0 & -3 & 8 & 2 \\ 8 & 1 & -1 & 22 \\ -4 & 6 & 0 & 1 \\ -7 & 0 & 0 & 0 \end{vmatrix}$

$\qquad = 7\begin{vmatrix} -3 & 8 & 2 \\ 1 & -1 & 22 \\ 6 & 0 & 1 \end{vmatrix}$

$\qquad = 7\begin{vmatrix} -15 & 8 & 2 \\ -131 & -1 & 22 \\ 0 & 0 & 1 \end{vmatrix}$

$\qquad = 7(15 + 1048)$

$\qquad = 7441$

36. $\begin{vmatrix} 3 & -2 & 4 & 3 & 1 \\ -1 & 0 & 2 & 1 & 0 \\ 5 & -1 & 0 & 3 & 2 \\ 4 & 7 & -8 & 0 & 0 \\ 1 & 2 & 3 & 0 & 2 \end{vmatrix} = \begin{vmatrix} 3 & -2 & 4 & 3 & 1 \\ -1 & 0 & 2 & 1 & 0 \\ -1 & 3 & -8 & -3 & 0 \\ 4 & 7 & -8 & 0 & 0 \\ -5 & 6 & -5 & -6 & 0 \end{vmatrix}$

$\qquad = \begin{vmatrix} -1 & 0 & 2 & 1 \\ -1 & 3 & -8 & -3 \\ 4 & 7 & -8 & 0 \\ -5 & 6 & -5 & -6 \end{vmatrix}$

$\qquad = \begin{vmatrix} -1 & 0 & 2 & 1 \\ -4 & 3 & -2 & 0 \\ 4 & 7 & -8 & 0 \\ -11 & 6 & 7 & 0 \end{vmatrix}$

$\qquad = -\begin{vmatrix} -4 & 3 & -2 \\ 4 & 7 & -8 \\ -11 & 6 & 7 \end{vmatrix}$

$\qquad = -\begin{vmatrix} 0 & 10 & -10 \\ 4 & 7 & -8 \\ -11 & 6 & 7 \end{vmatrix}$

$\qquad = -10\begin{vmatrix} 0 & 1 & -1 \\ 4 & 7 & -8 \\ -11 & 6 & 7 \end{vmatrix}$

$\qquad = -10\big[(-1)(28 - 88) - 1(24 + 77)\big]$

$\qquad = 410$

38. (a) False. Adding a multiple of one row to another does not change the value of the determinant.

   (b) True. See page 114.

   (c) True. In this case you can transform a matrix into a matrix with a row of zeros, which has zero determinant as can be seen by expanding by cofactors along that row. You achieve this transformation by adding a multiple of one row to another (which does not change the determinant of a matrix).

40. $\begin{vmatrix} 0 & 0 & 1 \\ 0 & 1 & 0 \\ 1 & 0 & 0 \end{vmatrix} = -\begin{vmatrix} 1 & 0 & 0 \\ 0 & 1 & 0 \\ 0 & 0 & 1 \end{vmatrix} = -1$

42. $\begin{vmatrix} 1 & 0 & 0 \\ 0 & 1 & 0 \\ 0 & k & 1 \end{vmatrix} = \begin{vmatrix} 1 & 0 & 0 \\ 0 & 1 & 0 \\ 0 & 0 & 1 \end{vmatrix} = 1$

44. $\begin{vmatrix} 1+a & 1 & 1 \\ 1 & 1+b & 1 \\ 1 & 1 & 1+c \end{vmatrix} = \begin{vmatrix} 0 & -a & -a-c-ac \\ 0 & b & -c \\ 1 & 1 & 1+c \end{vmatrix}$

$= ac - b(-a - c - ac)$

$= ac + ab + bc + abc$

$= \dfrac{abc(ac + ab + bc + abc)}{abc}$

$= abc\left(1 + \dfrac{1}{b} + \dfrac{1}{c} + \dfrac{1}{a}\right)$

46. (a) $\begin{vmatrix} 0 & b & 0 \\ a & 0 & 0 \\ 0 & 0 & c \end{vmatrix} = \begin{vmatrix} 0 & 4 & 0 \\ 1 & 0 & 0 \\ 0 & 0 & -3 \end{vmatrix}$

$= -\begin{vmatrix} 1 & 0 & 0 \\ 0 & 4 & 0 \\ 0 & 0 & -3 \end{vmatrix}$

$= -(1)(4)(-3)$

$= 12$

(b) $\begin{vmatrix} a & 0 & 1 \\ 0 & c & 0 \\ b & 0 & -16 \end{vmatrix} = \begin{vmatrix} 1 & 0 & 1 \\ 0 & -3 & 0 \\ 4 & 0 & -16 \end{vmatrix}$

Expand by cofactors in the second row.

$\begin{vmatrix} 1 & 0 & 1 \\ 0 & -3 & 0 \\ 4 & 0 & -16 \end{vmatrix} = -3\begin{vmatrix} 1 & 1 \\ 4 & -16 \end{vmatrix} = -3(-16 - 4) = 60$

48. If B is obtained from A by multiplying a row of A by a nonzero constant c, then

$$\det(B) = \det\begin{bmatrix} a_{11} & \cdots & a_{1n} \\ \vdots & & \\ ca_{i1} & \cdots & ca_{in} \\ \vdots & & \\ a_{n1} & \cdots & a_{nn} \end{bmatrix} = ca_{i1}C_{i1} + \ldots + ca_{in}C_{in} = c(a_{i1}C_{i1} + \ldots + a_{in}C_{in}) = c\det(A).$$

Section 3.3 Properties of Determinants

2. (a) $|A| = \begin{vmatrix} 1 & 2 \\ 2 & 4 \end{vmatrix} = 0$

(b) $|B| = \begin{vmatrix} -1 & 2 \\ 3 & 0 \end{vmatrix} = -6$

(c) $AB = \begin{bmatrix} 1 & 2 \\ 2 & 4 \end{bmatrix}\begin{bmatrix} -1 & 2 \\ 3 & 0 \end{bmatrix} = \begin{bmatrix} 5 & 2 \\ 10 & 4 \end{bmatrix}$

(d) $|AB| = \begin{vmatrix} 5 & 2 \\ 10 & 4 \end{vmatrix} = 0$

Notice that $|A||B| = 0(-6) = 0 = |AB|$.

4. (a) $|A| = \begin{vmatrix} 2 & 0 & 1 \\ 1 & -1 & 2 \\ 3 & 1 & 0 \end{vmatrix} = 0$

(b) $|B| = \begin{vmatrix} 2 & -1 & 4 \\ 0 & 1 & 3 \\ 3 & -2 & 1 \end{vmatrix} = -7$

(c) $AB = \begin{bmatrix} 2 & 0 & 1 \\ 1 & -1 & 2 \\ 3 & 1 & 0 \end{bmatrix}\begin{bmatrix} 2 & -1 & 4 \\ 0 & 1 & 3 \\ 3 & -2 & 1 \end{bmatrix} = \begin{bmatrix} 7 & -4 & 9 \\ 8 & -6 & 3 \\ 6 & -2 & 15 \end{bmatrix}$

(d) $|AB| = \begin{vmatrix} 7 & -4 & 9 \\ 8 & -6 & 3 \\ 6 & -2 & 15 \end{vmatrix} = 0$

Notice that $|A||B| = 0(-7) = 0 = |AB|$.

6. (a) $|A| = \begin{vmatrix} 3 & 2 & 4 & 0 \\ 1 & -1 & 2 & 1 \\ 0 & 0 & 3 & 1 \\ -1 & 1 & 1 & 0 \end{vmatrix} = \begin{vmatrix} 3 & 2 & 4 & 0 \\ 1 & -1 & -1 & 0 \\ 0 & 0 & 3 & 1 \\ -1 & 1 & 1 & 0 \end{vmatrix} = \begin{vmatrix} 3 & 2 & 4 & 0 \\ 1 & -1 & -1 & 0 \\ 0 & 0 & 3 & 1 \\ 0 & 0 & 0 & 0 \end{vmatrix} = 0$

(b) $|B| = \begin{vmatrix} 4 & 2 & -1 & 0 \\ 1 & 1 & 2 & -1 \\ 0 & 0 & 2 & 1 \\ -1 & 0 & 0 & 0 \end{vmatrix} = \begin{vmatrix} 2 & -1 & 0 \\ 1 & 2 & -1 \\ 0 & 2 & 1 \end{vmatrix} = \begin{vmatrix} 2 & -1 & 0 \\ 1 & 4 & 0 \\ 0 & 2 & 1 \end{vmatrix} = 9$

(c) $AB = \begin{bmatrix} 3 & 2 & 4 & 0 \\ 1 & -1 & 2 & 1 \\ 0 & 0 & 3 & 1 \\ -1 & 1 & 1 & 0 \end{bmatrix}\begin{bmatrix} 4 & 2 & -1 & 0 \\ 1 & 1 & 2 & -1 \\ 0 & 0 & 2 & 1 \\ -1 & 0 & 0 & 0 \end{bmatrix} = \begin{bmatrix} 14 & 8 & 9 & 2 \\ 2 & 1 & 1 & 3 \\ -1 & 0 & 6 & 3 \\ -3 & -1 & 5 & 0 \end{bmatrix}$

(d) $|AB| = \begin{vmatrix} 14 & 8 & 9 & 2 \\ 2 & 1 & 1 & 3 \\ -1 & 0 & 6 & 3 \\ -3 & -1 & 5 & 0 \end{vmatrix} = \begin{vmatrix} 14 & 8 & 9 & 2 \\ -1 & 0 & 6 & 3 \\ -1 & 0 & 6 & 3 \\ -3 & -1 & 5 & 0 \end{vmatrix} = \begin{vmatrix} 14 & 8 & 9 & 2 \\ -1 & 0 & 6 & 3 \\ 0 & 0 & 0 & 0 \\ -3 & -1 & 5 & 0 \end{vmatrix} = 0$

Notice that $|A||B| = 0 \cdot 9 = 0 = |AB|$.

8. $|A| = \begin{vmatrix} 5 & 15 \\ 10 & -20 \end{vmatrix} = 5^2\begin{vmatrix} 1 & 3 \\ 2 & -4 \end{vmatrix} = 5^2(-10) = -250$

10. $|A| = \begin{vmatrix} 4 & 16 & 0 \\ 12 & -8 & 8 \\ 16 & 20 & -4 \end{vmatrix} = 4^3\begin{vmatrix} 1 & 4 & 0 \\ 3 & -2 & 2 \\ 4 & 5 & -1 \end{vmatrix}$

$= 4^3\begin{vmatrix} 1 & 4 & 0 \\ 11 & 8 & 0 \\ 4 & 5 & -1 \end{vmatrix}$

$= (-64)(-36) = 2304$

12. $|A| = \begin{vmatrix} 40 & 25 & 10 \\ 30 & 5 & 20 \\ 15 & 35 & 45 \end{vmatrix} = 5^3\begin{vmatrix} 8 & 5 & 2 \\ 6 & 1 & 4 \\ 3 & 7 & 9 \end{vmatrix}$

$= 5^3\begin{vmatrix} -22 & 0 & -18 \\ 6 & 1 & 4 \\ -39 & 0 & -19 \end{vmatrix}$

$= 125(-284) = -35,500$

14. (a) $|A| = \begin{vmatrix} 1 & -2 \\ 1 & 0 \end{vmatrix} = 2$

(b) $|B| = \begin{vmatrix} 3 & -2 \\ 0 & 0 \end{vmatrix} = 0$

(c) $|A + B| = \begin{vmatrix} \begin{bmatrix} 1 & -2 \\ 1 & 0 \end{bmatrix} + \begin{bmatrix} 3 & -2 \\ 0 & 0 \end{bmatrix} \end{vmatrix} = \begin{vmatrix} 4 & -4 \\ 1 & 0 \end{vmatrix} = 4$

Notice that $|A| + |B| = 2 + 0 = 2 \neq |A + B|$.

16. (a) $|A| = \begin{vmatrix} 0 & 1 & 2 \\ 1 & -1 & 0 \\ 2 & 1 & 1 \end{vmatrix} = \begin{vmatrix} 0 & 1 & 2 \\ 1 & -1 & 0 \\ 0 & 3 & 1 \end{vmatrix} = 5$

(b) $|B| = \begin{vmatrix} 0 & 1 & -1 \\ 2 & 1 & 1 \\ 0 & 1 & 1 \end{vmatrix} = -2(2) = -4$

(c) $|A + B| = \begin{vmatrix} \begin{bmatrix} 0 & 1 & 2 \\ 1 & -1 & 0 \\ 2 & 1 & 1 \end{bmatrix} + \begin{bmatrix} 0 & 1 & -1 \\ 2 & 1 & 1 \\ 0 & 1 & 1 \end{bmatrix} \end{vmatrix}$

$= \begin{vmatrix} 0 & 2 & 1 \\ 3 & 0 & 1 \\ 2 & 2 & 2 \end{vmatrix} = \begin{vmatrix} 0 & 2 & 1 \\ 3 & 0 & 1 \\ 2 & 0 & 1 \end{vmatrix} = -2$

Notice that $|A| + |B| = 5 + (-4) = 1 \neq |A + B|$.

18. Because

$\begin{vmatrix} 3 & -6 \\ 4 & 2 \end{vmatrix} = 30 \neq 0,$

the matrix is nonsingular.

20. Because

$\begin{vmatrix} 1 & 0 & 4 \\ 0 & 6 & 3 \\ 2 & -1 & 4 \end{vmatrix} = -21 \neq 0,$

the matrix is nonsingular.

22. Because

$$\begin{vmatrix} 2 & -\frac{1}{2} & 8 \\ 1 & -\frac{1}{4} & 4 \\ -\frac{5}{2} & \frac{3}{2} & 8 \end{vmatrix} = 0,$$

the matrix is singular.

24. Because

$$\begin{vmatrix} 0.8 & 0.2 & -0.6 & 0.1 \\ -1.2 & 0.6 & 0.6 & 0 \\ 0.7 & -0.3 & 0.1 & 0 \\ 0.2 & -0.3 & 0.6 & 0 \end{vmatrix} = 0.015 \neq 0,$$

the matrix is nonsingular.

26. $A^{-1} = \frac{1}{6}\begin{bmatrix} 2 & 2 \\ -2 & 1 \end{bmatrix} = \begin{bmatrix} \frac{1}{3} & \frac{1}{3} \\ -\frac{1}{3} & \frac{1}{6} \end{bmatrix}$

$|A^{-1}| = \frac{1}{3}\left(\frac{1}{6}\right) - \left(-\frac{1}{3}\right)\left(\frac{1}{3}\right) = \frac{1}{18} + \frac{1}{9} = \frac{1}{6}$

Notice that $|A| = 6$.

So, $|A^{-1}| = \frac{1}{|A|} = \frac{1}{6}$.

30. $A^{-1} = \begin{vmatrix} 2 & -3 & \frac{7}{2} & 4 \\ 1 & -3 & \frac{3}{2} & 3 \\ 0 & 1 & 0 & -1 \\ 0 & 1 & -\frac{1}{2} & -1 \end{vmatrix}$

$|A^{-1}| = \begin{vmatrix} 2 & -3 & \frac{7}{2} & 4 \\ 1 & -3 & \frac{3}{2} & 3 \\ 0 & 1 & 0 & -1 \\ 0 & 1 & -\frac{1}{2} & -1 \end{vmatrix} = \begin{vmatrix} 2 & -3 & \frac{7}{2} & 4 \\ 1 & -3 & \frac{3}{2} & 3 \\ 0 & 1 & 0 & -1 \\ 0 & 0 & -\frac{1}{2} & 0 \end{vmatrix} = \frac{1}{2}\begin{vmatrix} 2 & -3 & 4 \\ 1 & -3 & 3 \\ 0 & 1 & -1 \end{vmatrix} = \frac{1}{2}\begin{vmatrix} 0 & 3 & -2 \\ 1 & -3 & 3 \\ 0 & 1 & -1 \end{vmatrix} = \frac{1}{2}$

Notice that $|A| = \begin{vmatrix} 0 & 1 & 0 & 3 \\ 1 & -2 & -3 & 1 \\ 0 & 0 & 2 & -2 \\ 1 & -2 & -4 & 1 \end{vmatrix} = \begin{vmatrix} 0 & 1 & 0 & 3 \\ 0 & 0 & 1 & 0 \\ 0 & 0 & 2 & -2 \\ 1 & -2 & -4 & 1 \end{vmatrix} = -\begin{vmatrix} 1 & 0 & 3 \\ 0 & 1 & 0 \\ 0 & 2 & -2 \end{vmatrix} = 2.$

So, $|A^{-1}| = \frac{1}{|A|} = \frac{1}{2}$.

28. $A^{-1} = \begin{bmatrix} -\frac{1}{2} & 1 & -\frac{1}{2} \\ 2 & -1 & 0 \\ \frac{3}{2} & -1 & \frac{1}{2} \end{bmatrix}$

$|A^{-1}| = \begin{vmatrix} -\frac{1}{2} & 1 & -\frac{1}{2} \\ 2 & -1 & 0 \\ \frac{3}{2} & -1 & \frac{1}{2} \end{vmatrix} = \begin{vmatrix} 1 & 0 & 0 \\ 2 & -1 & 0 \\ \frac{3}{2} & -1 & \frac{1}{2} \end{vmatrix} = -\frac{1}{2}$

Notice that $|A| = \begin{vmatrix} 1 & 0 & 1 \\ 2 & -1 & 2 \\ 1 & -2 & 3 \end{vmatrix} = \begin{vmatrix} 1 & 0 & 1 \\ 2 & -1 & 2 \\ -3 & 0 & -1 \end{vmatrix} = -2.$

So, $|A^{-1}| - \frac{1}{|A|} = -\frac{1}{2}.$

32. The coefficient matrix of the system is

$\begin{bmatrix} 3 & -4 \\ \frac{2}{3} & -\frac{8}{9} \end{bmatrix}.$

Because the determinant of this matrix is zero, the system does not have a unique solution.

34. The coefficient matrix of the system is

$$\begin{bmatrix} 1 & 1 & -1 \\ 2 & -1 & 1 \\ 3 & -2 & 2 \end{bmatrix}.$$

Because the determinant of this matrix is zero, the system does not have a unique solution.

36. The coefficient matrix of the system is

$$\begin{bmatrix} 1 & -1 & -1 & -1 \\ 1 & 1 & -1 & -1 \\ 1 & 1 & 1 & -1 \\ 1 & 1 & 1 & 1 \end{bmatrix}.$$

Because the determinant of this matrix is 8, and not zero, the system has a unique solution.

38. First obtain $|A| = \begin{vmatrix} -4 & 10 \\ 5 & 6 \end{vmatrix} = -74.$

(a) $|A^T| = |A| = -74$

(b) $|A^2| = |A||A| = (-74)^2 = 5476$

(c) $|AA^T| = |A||A^T| = (-74)(-74) = 5476$

(d) $|2A| = 2^2|A| = 4(-74) = -296$

(e) $|A^{-1}| = \dfrac{1}{|A|} = \dfrac{1}{(-74)} = -\dfrac{1}{74}$

40. First obtain $|A| = \begin{vmatrix} 1 & 5 & 4 \\ 0 & -6 & 2 \\ 0 & 0 & -3 \end{vmatrix} = 18.$

(a) $|A^T| = |A| = 18$

(b) $|A^2| = |A||A| = 18^2 = 324$

(c) $|AA^T| = |A||A^T| = (18)(18) = 324$

(d) $|2A| = 2^3|A| = 8(18) = 144$

(e) $|A^{-1}| = \dfrac{1}{|A|} = \dfrac{1}{18}$

42. First observe $|A| = \begin{vmatrix} 4 & 1 & 9 \\ -1 & 0 & -2 \\ -3 & 3 & 0 \end{vmatrix} = 3.$

(a) $|A^T| = |A| = 3$

(b) $|A^2| = |A||A| = 9$

(c) $|AA^T| = |A||A^T| = 9$

(d) $|2A| = 2^3|A| = 24$

(e) $|A^{-1}| = \dfrac{1}{|A|} = \dfrac{1}{3}$

44. First observe that $|A| = \begin{vmatrix} 2 & 0 & 0 & 1 \\ 0 & -3 & 0 & 0 \\ 0 & 0 & 4 & 0 \\ 1 & 0 & 0 & 1 \end{vmatrix} = -12.$

(a) $|A^T| = |A| = -12$

(b) $|A^2| = |A||A| = 144$

(c) $|AA^T| = |A||A^T| = 144$

(d) $|2A| = 2^4|A| = -192$

(e) $|A^{-1}| = \dfrac{1}{|A|} = -\dfrac{1}{12}$

46. (a) $|A| = \begin{vmatrix} -2 & 4 \\ 6 & 8 \end{vmatrix} = -16 - 24 = -40$

(b) $|A^T| = |A| = -40$

(c) $|A^2| = |A||A| = |A|^2 = 1600$

(d) $|2A| = 2^2|A| = -160$

(e) $|A^{-1}| = \dfrac{1}{|A|} = -\dfrac{1}{40}$

48. $|A| = \begin{vmatrix} \frac{3}{4} & \frac{2}{3} & -\frac{1}{4} \\ \frac{2}{3} & 1 & \frac{1}{3} \\ -\frac{1}{4} & \frac{1}{3} & \frac{3}{4} \end{vmatrix} = -\frac{1}{36}.$

(a) $|A^T| = |A| = -\frac{1}{36}$

(b) $|A^2| = |A||A| = \frac{1}{1296}$

(c) $|2A| = 2^3|A| = -\frac{2}{9}$

(d) $|A^{-1}| = \dfrac{1}{|A|} = -36$

50. (a) $|A| = \begin{vmatrix} 6 & 5 & 1 & -1 \\ -2 & 4 & 3 & 5 \\ 6 & 1 & -4 & -2 \\ 2 & 2 & 1 & 3 \end{vmatrix} = -312$

(b) $|A^T| = |A| = -312$

(c) $|A^2| = |A||A| = |A|^2 = 97,344$

(d) $|2A| = 2^4|A| = -4992$

(e) $|A^{-1}| = \dfrac{1}{|A|} = -\dfrac{1}{312}$

52. (a) $|AB| = |A||B| = 4(5) = 20$

(b) $|2A| = 2^3|A| = 8(4) = 32$

(c) Because $|A| \neq 0$ and $|B| \neq 0$, A and B are nonsingular.

(d) $|A^{-1}| = \dfrac{1}{|A|} = \dfrac{1}{4}$, $|B^{-1}| = \dfrac{1}{|B|} = \dfrac{1}{5}$

(e) $\left|(AB)^T\right| = |AB| = 20$

54. Find the values of k that make A singular by setting $|A| = 0$.

$$|A| = \begin{vmatrix} k - 1 & 2 \\ 2 & k + 2 \end{vmatrix}$$

$$= (k - 1)(k + 2) - 4$$

$$= k^2 + k - 6$$

$$= (k + 3)(k - 2) = 0$$

which implies that $k = -3$ or $k = 2$.

60. Expand the determinant on the left

$$\begin{vmatrix} a + b & a & a \\ a & a + b & a \\ a & a & a + b \end{vmatrix} = (a + b)\left((a + b)^2 - a^2\right) - a\left((a + b)a - a^2\right) + a\left(a^2 - a(a + b)\right)$$

$$= (a + b)\left(2ab + b^2\right) - a(ab) + a(-ab)$$

$$= 2a^2b + ab^2 + 2ab^2 + b^3 - 2a^2b$$

$$= b^2(3a + b).$$

62. Because the rows of A all add up to zero, you have

$$|A| = \begin{vmatrix} 2 & -1 & -1 \\ -3 & 1 & 2 \\ 0 & -2 & 2 \end{vmatrix} = \begin{vmatrix} 2 & -1 & 0 \\ -3 & 1 & 0 \\ 0 & -2 & 0 \end{vmatrix} = 0.$$

64. Calculating the determinant of A by expanding along the first row is equivalent to calculating the determinant of A^T by expanding along the first column. Because the determinant of a matrix can be found by expanding along any row or column, you see that $|A| = |A^T|$.

66. (a) False. Let

$$A = \begin{bmatrix} 1 & 0 \\ 0 & 1 \end{bmatrix} \quad \text{and} \quad B = \begin{bmatrix} -1 & 0 \\ 0 & -1 \end{bmatrix}.$$

Then $\det(A) = \det(B) = 1 \neq 0 = \det(A + B)$

(b) True. Because

$$\det(A) = \det(B), \det(AB) = \det(A)\det(B)$$

$$= \det(A)\det(A)$$

$$= \det(AA)$$

$$= \det(A^2).$$

(c) True. See page 123 for equivalent conditions for nonsingular matrices and Theorem 3.7 on page 122.

56. Find the values of k that make A singular by setting $|A| = 0$. Using the second column in the cofactor expansion, you have

$$|A| = \begin{vmatrix} 1 & k & 2 \\ -2 & 0 & -k \\ 3 & 1 & -4 \end{vmatrix} = -k\begin{vmatrix} -2 & -k \\ 3 & -4 \end{vmatrix} - 1\begin{vmatrix} 1 & 2 \\ -2 & -k \end{vmatrix}$$

$$= -k(8 + 3k) - (-k + 4)$$

$$= -3k^2 - 7k - 4$$

$$= -(3k + 4)(k + 1).$$

So, $|A| = 0$ implies that $k = -\frac{4}{3}$ or $k = -1$.

58. Given that AB is singular, then $|AB| = |A||B| = 0$. So, either $|A|$ or $|B|$ must be zero, which implies that either A or B is singular.

68. $|A^{10}| = |A|^{10} = 0 \Rightarrow |A| = 0 \Rightarrow A$ is singular.

70. If the order of A is odd, then $(-1)^n = -1$, and the result of Exercise 61 implies that $|A| = -|A|$ or $|A| = 0$.

72. Because

$$A^{-1} = \begin{bmatrix} 1 & 0 \\ -1 & 1 \end{bmatrix} \quad \text{and} \quad A^T = \begin{bmatrix} 1 & 1 \\ 0 & 1 \end{bmatrix},$$

$A^{-1} \neq A^T$ and the matrix is *not* orthogonal.

74. Because

$$A^{-1} = \begin{bmatrix} \dfrac{1}{\sqrt{2}} & -\dfrac{1}{\sqrt{2}} \\ -\dfrac{1}{\sqrt{2}} & -\dfrac{1}{\sqrt{2}} \end{bmatrix} = A^T,$$

this matrix *is* orthogonal.

76. Because

$$A^{-1} = \begin{bmatrix} \frac{1}{\sqrt{2}} & 0 & -\frac{1}{\sqrt{2}} \\ 0 & 1 & 0 \\ -\frac{1}{\sqrt{2}} & 0 & \frac{1}{\sqrt{2}} \end{bmatrix} = A^T,$$

this matrix *is* orthogonal.

78. $A = \begin{bmatrix} \frac{3}{5} & 0 & -\frac{4}{5} \\ 0 & 1 & 0 \\ \frac{4}{5} & 0 & \frac{3}{5} \end{bmatrix}$

Using a graphing calculator or a software program you have

(a), (b) $A^{-1} = \begin{bmatrix} \frac{3}{5} & 0 & \frac{4}{5} \\ 0 & 1 & 0 \\ -\frac{4}{5} & 0 & \frac{3}{5} \end{bmatrix} = A^T.$

(c)   As shown in Exercise 76, if A is an orthogonal matrix, then $|A| = \pm 1$. For this given A, you have $|A| = 1$.

Because $A^{-1} = A^T$, A is an orthogonal matrix.

80. Let A be an idempotent matrix, and let $x = \det(A)$. Then $A^2 = A$ so $\det(A^2) = \det(A)$. You also have

$\det(A^2) = \det(A \cdot A) = \det(A) \cdot \det(A) = \det(A)^2$. So, $x = \det(A)$ is a real number such that $x^2 = x$. Solving the last equation for x you obtain $x = 0$ or $x = 1$.

Section 3.4   Applications of Determinants

2. The matrix of cofactors is

$$\begin{bmatrix} |4| & -|0| \\ -|0| & |-1| \end{bmatrix} = \begin{bmatrix} 4 & 0 \\ 0 & -1 \end{bmatrix}.$$

So, the adjoint of A is

$$\text{adj}(A) = \begin{bmatrix} 4 & 0 \\ 0 & -1 \end{bmatrix}^T = \begin{bmatrix} 4 & 0 \\ 0 & -1 \end{bmatrix}.$$

Because $|A| = -4$, the inverse of A is

$$A^{-1} = \frac{1}{|A|}\text{adj}(A) = -\frac{1}{4}\begin{bmatrix} 4 & 0 \\ 0 & -1 \end{bmatrix} = \begin{bmatrix} -1 & 0 \\ 0 & \frac{1}{4} \end{bmatrix}.$$

4. The matrix of cofactors is

$$\begin{bmatrix} \begin{vmatrix} 1 & -1 \\ 2 & 2 \end{vmatrix} & -\begin{vmatrix} 0 & -1 \\ 2 & 2 \end{vmatrix} & \begin{vmatrix} 0 & 1 \\ 2 & 2 \end{vmatrix} \\ -\begin{vmatrix} 2 & 3 \\ 2 & 2 \end{vmatrix} & \begin{vmatrix} 1 & 3 \\ 2 & 2 \end{vmatrix} & -\begin{vmatrix} 1 & 2 \\ 2 & 2 \end{vmatrix} \\ \begin{vmatrix} 2 & 3 \\ 1 & -1 \end{vmatrix} & -\begin{vmatrix} 1 & 3 \\ 0 & -1 \end{vmatrix} & \begin{vmatrix} 1 & 2 \\ 0 & 1 \end{vmatrix} \end{bmatrix} = \begin{bmatrix} 4 & -2 & -2 \\ 2 & -4 & 2 \\ -5 & 1 & 1 \end{bmatrix}.$$

So, the adjoint of A is

$$\text{adj}(A) = \begin{bmatrix} 4 & 2 & -5 \\ -2 & -4 & 1 \\ -2 & 2 & 1 \end{bmatrix}.$$

Because $|A| = -6$, the inverse of A is

$$A^{-1} = \frac{1}{|A|}\text{adj}(A) = \begin{bmatrix} -\frac{2}{3} & -\frac{1}{3} & \frac{5}{6} \\ \frac{1}{3} & \frac{2}{3} & -\frac{1}{6} \\ \frac{1}{3} & -\frac{1}{3} & -\frac{1}{6} \end{bmatrix}.$$

6. The matrix of cofactors is

$$\begin{bmatrix} \begin{vmatrix} 2 & 3 \\ -1 & -2 \end{vmatrix} & -\begin{vmatrix} 1 & 3 \\ -1 & -2 \end{vmatrix} & \begin{vmatrix} 1 & 2 \\ -1 & -1 \end{vmatrix} \\ -\begin{vmatrix} 1 & 1 \\ 1 & -2 \end{vmatrix} & \begin{vmatrix} 0 & 1 \\ -1 & -2 \end{vmatrix} & -\begin{vmatrix} 0 & 1 \\ -1 & -1 \end{vmatrix} \\ \begin{vmatrix} 1 & 1 \\ 2 & 3 \end{vmatrix} & -\begin{vmatrix} 0 & 1 \\ 1 & 3 \end{vmatrix} & \begin{vmatrix} 0 & 1 \\ 0 & 2 \end{vmatrix} \end{bmatrix} = \begin{bmatrix} -1 & -1 & 1 \\ 1 & 1 & -1 \\ 1 & 1 & -1 \end{bmatrix}.$$

So, the adjoint of A is

$$\text{adj}(A) = \begin{bmatrix} -1 & 1 & 1 \\ -1 & 1 & 1 \\ 1 & -1 & -1 \end{bmatrix}.$$

Because $\det(A) = 0$, the matrix A has no inverse.

8. The matrix of cofactors is

$$\begin{bmatrix} \begin{vmatrix} 1 & 0 & 1 \\ 0 & 1 & 1 \\ 1 & 1 & 1 \end{vmatrix} & \begin{vmatrix} 1 & 0 & 1 \\ 1 & 1 & 1 \\ 0 & 1 & 1 \end{vmatrix} & \begin{vmatrix} 1 & 1 & 1 \\ 1 & 0 & 1 \\ 0 & 1 & 1 \end{vmatrix} & -\begin{vmatrix} 1 & 1 & 0 \\ 1 & 0 & 1 \\ 0 & 1 & 1 \end{vmatrix} \\ -\begin{vmatrix} 1 & 1 & 0 \\ 0 & 1 & 1 \\ 1 & 1 & 1 \end{vmatrix} & \begin{vmatrix} 1 & 1 & 0 \\ 1 & 1 & 1 \\ 0 & 1 & 1 \end{vmatrix} & -\begin{vmatrix} 1 & 1 & 0 \\ 1 & 0 & 1 \\ 0 & 1 & 1 \end{vmatrix} & \begin{vmatrix} 1 & 1 & 1 \\ 1 & 0 & 1 \\ 0 & 1 & 1 \end{vmatrix} \\ \begin{vmatrix} 1 & 1 & 0 \\ 1 & 0 & 1 \\ 1 & 1 & 1 \end{vmatrix} & -\begin{vmatrix} 1 & 1 & 0 \\ 1 & 0 & 1 \\ 0 & 1 & 1 \end{vmatrix} & \begin{vmatrix} 1 & 1 & 0 \\ 1 & 1 & 1 \\ 0 & 1 & 1 \end{vmatrix} & -\begin{vmatrix} 1 & 1 & 1 \\ 1 & 1 & 0 \\ 0 & 1 & 1 \end{vmatrix} \\ -\begin{vmatrix} 1 & 1 & 0 \\ 1 & 0 & 1 \\ 0 & 1 & 1 \end{vmatrix} & \begin{vmatrix} 1 & 1 & 0 \\ 1 & 0 & 1 \\ 1 & 1 & 1 \end{vmatrix} & -\begin{vmatrix} 1 & 1 & 0 \\ 1 & 1 & 1 \\ 1 & 0 & 1 \end{vmatrix} & \begin{vmatrix} 1 & 1 & 1 \\ 1 & 1 & 0 \\ 1 & 0 & 1 \end{vmatrix} \end{bmatrix} = \begin{bmatrix} -1 & -1 & -1 & 2 \\ -1 & -1 & 2 & -1 \\ -1 & 2 & -1 & -1 \\ 2 & -1 & -1 & -1 \end{bmatrix}.$$

So, the adjoint of A is $\text{adj}(A) = \begin{bmatrix} -1 & -1 & -1 & 2 \\ -1 & -1 & 2 & -1 \\ -1 & 2 & -1 & -1 \\ 2 & -1 & -1 & -1 \end{bmatrix}$. Because $\det(A) = -3$, the inverse of A is

$$A^{-1} = \frac{1}{|A|}\text{adj}(A) = \begin{bmatrix} \frac{1}{3} & \frac{1}{3} & \frac{1}{3} & -\frac{2}{3} \\ \frac{1}{3} & \frac{1}{3} & -\frac{2}{3} & \frac{1}{3} \\ \frac{1}{3} & -\frac{2}{3} & \frac{1}{3} & \frac{1}{3} \\ -\frac{2}{3} & \frac{1}{3} & \frac{1}{3} & \frac{1}{3} \end{bmatrix}.$$

10. Following the proof of Theorem 3.10, you have

$A \, \text{adj}(A) = |A| I.$

Now, if A is not invertible, then $|A| = 0$, and

$A \, \text{adj}(A)$ is the zero matrix.

12. $\text{adj}(\text{adj}(A)) = \text{adj}(|A|A^{-1})$

$= \det(|A|A^{-1})(|A|A^{-1})^{-1}$

$= |A|^n |A^{-1}| \frac{1}{|A|} A = |A|^{n-2} A$

14. $A = \begin{bmatrix} -1 & 3 \\ 1 & 2 \end{bmatrix} \Rightarrow \text{adj}(A) = \begin{bmatrix} 2 & -1 \\ -3 & -1 \end{bmatrix} \Rightarrow$

$$\text{adj}(\text{adj}(A)) = \begin{bmatrix} -1 & 3 \\ 1 & 2 \end{bmatrix} = |A|^0 \begin{bmatrix} -1 & 3 \\ 1 & 2 \end{bmatrix}$$

So, $\text{adj}(\text{adj}(A)) = |A|^{n-2} A$.

16. Illustrate the formula $\text{adj}(A^{-1}) = [\text{adj}(A)]^{-1}$ in the case

$A = \begin{bmatrix} 1 & 3 \\ 1 & 2 \end{bmatrix}$.

$A = \begin{bmatrix} 1 & 3 \\ 1 & 2 \end{bmatrix} \Rightarrow A^{-1} = \begin{bmatrix} -2 & 3 \\ 1 & -1 \end{bmatrix}$ and

$\text{adj}(A^{-1}) = \begin{bmatrix} -1 & -1 \\ -3 & -2 \end{bmatrix}$.

On the other hand, $\text{adj}(A) = \begin{bmatrix} 2 & -1 \\ -3 & 1 \end{bmatrix}$ and

$(\text{adj}(A))^{-1} = \begin{bmatrix} -1 & -1 \\ -3 & -2 \end{bmatrix}$.

18. The coefficient matrix is

$A = \begin{bmatrix} 2 & -1 \\ 3 & 2 \end{bmatrix}$, where $|A| = 7$.

Because $|A| \neq 0$, you can use Cramer's Rule.

$A_1 = \begin{bmatrix} -10 & -1 \\ -1 & 2 \end{bmatrix}$, $|A_1| = -21$

$A_2 = \begin{bmatrix} 2 & -10 \\ 3 & -1 \end{bmatrix}$, $|A_2| = 28$.

The solution is

$x_1 = \dfrac{|A_1|}{|A|} = -\dfrac{21}{7} = -3$

$x_2 = \dfrac{|A_2|}{|A|} = \dfrac{28}{7} = 4$.

20. The coefficient matrix is

$A = \begin{bmatrix} 18 & 12 \\ 30 & 24 \end{bmatrix}$, where $|A| = 72$.

Because $|A| \neq 0$, you can use Cramer's Rule.

$A_1 = \begin{bmatrix} 13 & 12 \\ 23 & 24 \end{bmatrix}$, $|A_1| = 36$

$A_2 = \begin{bmatrix} 18 & 13 \\ 30 & 23 \end{bmatrix}$, $|A_2| = 24$

The solution is

$x_1 = \dfrac{|A_1|}{|A|} = \dfrac{36}{72} = \dfrac{1}{2}$

$x_2 = \dfrac{|A_2|}{|A|} = \dfrac{24}{72} = \dfrac{1}{3}$.

22. The coefficient matrix is

$A = \begin{bmatrix} 13 & -6 \\ 26 & -12 \end{bmatrix}$, where $|A| = 0$.

Because $|A| = 0$, Cramer's Rule cannot be applied. (The system does not have a solution.)

24. The coefficient matrix is

$A = \begin{bmatrix} -0.4 & 0.8 \\ 0.2 & 0.3 \end{bmatrix}$, where $|A| = -0.28$.

Because $|A| \neq 0$, you can use Cramer's Rule.

$A_1 = \begin{bmatrix} 1.6 & 0.8 \\ 0.6 & 0.3 \end{bmatrix}$, $|A_1| = 0$

$A_2 = \begin{bmatrix} -0.4 & 1.6 \\ 0.2 & 0.6 \end{bmatrix}$, $|A_2| = -0.56$

The solution is

$x_1 = \dfrac{|A_1|}{|A|} = \dfrac{0}{-0.28} = 0$

$x_2 = \dfrac{|A_2|}{|A|} = \dfrac{-0.56}{-0.28} = 2$.

26. The coefficient matrix is

$A = \begin{bmatrix} 4 & -2 & 3 \\ 2 & 2 & 5 \\ 8 & -5 & -2 \end{bmatrix}$, where $|A| = -82$.

Because $|A| \neq 0$, you can use Cramer's Rule.

$A_1 = \begin{bmatrix} -2 & -2 & 3 \\ 16 & 2 & 5 \\ 4 & -5 & -2 \end{bmatrix}$, $|A_1| = -410$

$A_2 = \begin{bmatrix} 4 & -2 & 3 \\ 2 & 16 & 5 \\ 8 & 4 & -2 \end{bmatrix}$, $|A_2| = -656$

$A_3 = \begin{bmatrix} 4 & -2 & -2 \\ 2 & 2 & 16 \\ 8 & -5 & 4 \end{bmatrix}$, $|A_3| = 164$

The solution is

$x_1 = \dfrac{|A_1|}{|A|} = \dfrac{-410}{-82} = 5$

$x_2 = \dfrac{|A_2|}{|A|} = \dfrac{-656}{-82} = 8$

$x_3 = \dfrac{|A_3|}{|A|} = \dfrac{164}{-82} = -2$.

28. The coefficient matrix is

$$A = \begin{bmatrix} 14 & -21 & -7 \\ -4 & 2 & -2 \\ 56 & -21 & 7 \end{bmatrix}, \quad \text{where } |A| = 1568.$$

Because $|A| \neq 0$, you can use Cramer's Rule.

$$A_1 = \begin{bmatrix} -21 & -21 & -7 \\ 2 & 2 & -2 \\ 7 & -21 & 7 \end{bmatrix}, \quad |A_1| = 1568$$

$$A_2 = \begin{bmatrix} 14 & -21 & -7 \\ -4 & 2 & -2 \\ 56 & 7 & 7 \end{bmatrix}, \quad |A_2| = 3136$$

$$A_3 = \begin{bmatrix} 14 & -21 & -21 \\ -4 & 2 & 2 \\ 56 & -21 & 7 \end{bmatrix}, \quad |A_3| = -1568$$

The solution is

$$x_1 = \frac{|A_1|}{|A|} = \frac{1568}{1568} = 1$$

$$x_2 = \frac{|A_2|}{|A|} = \frac{3136}{1568} = 2$$

$$x_3 = \frac{|A_3|}{|A|} = -\frac{1568}{1568} = -1.$$

30. The coefficient matrix is

$$A = \begin{bmatrix} 2 & 3 & 5 \\ 3 & 5 & 9 \\ 5 & 9 & 17 \end{bmatrix}, \quad \text{where } |A| = 0.$$

Because $|A| = 0$, Cramer's Rule cannot be applied.

(The system does not have a solution.)

32. The coefficient matrix is

$$A = \begin{bmatrix} -8 & 7 & -10 \\ 12 & 3 & -5 \\ 15 & -9 & 2 \end{bmatrix}.$$

$$A_1 = \begin{bmatrix} -151 & 7 & -10 \\ 86 & 3 & -5 \\ 187 & -9 & 2 \end{bmatrix}, \quad A_2 = \begin{bmatrix} -8 & -151 & -10 \\ 12 & 86 & -5 \\ 15 & 187 & 2 \end{bmatrix},$$

$$A_3 = \begin{bmatrix} -8 & 7 & -151 \\ 12 & 3 & 86 \\ 15 & -9 & 187 \end{bmatrix}$$

Using a graphing utility, $|A| = 1149$, $|A_1| = 11{,}490$, $|A_2| = -3447$, and $|A_3| = 5745$.

So, $x_1 = \dfrac{|A_1|}{|A|} = \dfrac{11{,}490}{1149} = 10$,

$x_2 = \dfrac{|A_2|}{|A|} = \dfrac{-3447}{1149} = -3$, and $x_3 = \dfrac{|A_3|}{|A|} = \dfrac{5745}{1149} = 5.$

34. The coefficient matrix is

$$A = \begin{bmatrix} -1 & -1 & 0 & 1 \\ 3 & 5 & 5 & 0 \\ 0 & 0 & 2 & 1 \\ -2 & -3 & -3 & 0 \end{bmatrix}.$$

$$A_1 = \begin{bmatrix} -8 & -1 & 0 & 1 \\ 24 & 5 & 5 & 0 \\ -6 & 0 & 2 & 1 \\ -15 & -3 & -3 & 0 \end{bmatrix}, \quad A_2 = \begin{bmatrix} -1 & -8 & 0 & 1 \\ 3 & 24 & 5 & 0 \\ 0 & -6 & 2 & 1 \\ -2 & -15 & -3 & 0 \end{bmatrix},$$

$$A_3 = \begin{bmatrix} -1 & -1 & -8 & 1 \\ 3 & 5 & 24 & 0 \\ 0 & 0 & -6 & 1 \\ -2 & -3 & -15 & 0 \end{bmatrix}, \quad A_4 = \begin{bmatrix} -1 & -1 & 0 & -8 \\ 3 & 5 & 5 & 24 \\ 0 & 0 & 2 & -6 \\ -2 & -3 & -3 & -15 \end{bmatrix}$$

Using a graphing utility, $|A| = 1$, $|A_1| = 3$, $|A_2| = 7$, $|A_3| = -4$, and $|A_4| = 2.$

So, $x_1 = \dfrac{|A_1|}{A} = \dfrac{3}{1} = 3$,

$x_2 = \dfrac{|A_2|}{A} = \dfrac{7}{1} = 7$, $x_3 = \dfrac{|A_3|}{|A|} = \dfrac{-4}{1} = -4$ and

$x_4 = \dfrac{|A_4|}{|A|} = \dfrac{2}{1} = 2.$

36. Draw the altitude from vertex C to side c, then from trigonometry

$$c = a \cos B + b \cos A.$$

Similarly, the other two equations follow by using the other altitudes. Now use Cramer's Rule to solve for $\cos C$ in this system of three equations.

$$\cos C = \frac{\begin{vmatrix} 0 & c & a \\ c & 0 & b \\ b & a & c \end{vmatrix}}{\begin{vmatrix} 0 & c & b \\ c & 0 & a \\ b & a & 0 \end{vmatrix}}$$

$$= \frac{-c(c^2 - b^2) + a(ac)}{-c(-ba) + b(ac)} = \frac{a^2 + b^2 - c^2}{2ab}.$$

Solving for c^2 you obtain

$$2ab \cos C = a^2 + b^2 - c^2$$

$$c^2 = a^2 + b^2 - 2ab \cos C.$$

38. Use the formula for area as follows.

$$\text{Area} = \pm \frac{1}{2} \begin{vmatrix} x_1 & y_1 & 1 \\ x_2 & y_2 & 1 \\ x_3 & y_3 & 1 \end{vmatrix} = \pm \frac{1}{2} \begin{vmatrix} 1 & 1 & 1 \\ 2 & 4 & 1 \\ 4 & 2 & 1 \end{vmatrix} = \pm \frac{1}{2}(-8) = 4.$$

40. Use the formula for area as follows.

$$\text{Area} = \pm\frac{1}{2}\begin{vmatrix} x_1 & y_1 & 1 \\ x_2 & y_2 & 1 \\ x_3 & y_3 & 1 \end{vmatrix} = \pm\frac{1}{2}\begin{vmatrix} 1 & 1 & 1 \\ -1 & 1 & 1 \\ 0 & -2 & 1 \end{vmatrix} = \pm\frac{1}{2}(6) = 3$$

42. Use the fact that

$$\begin{vmatrix} x_1 & y_1 & 1 \\ x_2 & y_2 & 1 \\ x_3 & y_3 & 1 \end{vmatrix} = \begin{vmatrix} -1 & 0 & 1 \\ 1 & 1 & 1 \\ 3 & 3 & 1 \end{vmatrix} = 2$$

to determine that the three points are not collinear.

44. Use the fact that

$$\begin{vmatrix} x_1 & y_1 & 1 \\ x_2 & y_2 & 1 \\ x_3 & y_3 & 1 \end{vmatrix} = \begin{vmatrix} -1 & -3 & 1 \\ -4 & 7 & 1 \\ 2 & -13 & 1 \end{vmatrix} = 0$$

to determine that the three points are collinear.

46. Find the equation as follows.

$$0 = \begin{vmatrix} x & y & 1 \\ x_1 & y_1 & 1 \\ x_2 & y_2 & 1 \end{vmatrix} = \begin{vmatrix} x & y & 1 \\ -4 & 7 & 1 \\ 2 & 4 & 1 \end{vmatrix} = 3x + 6y - 30$$

So, an equation of the line is $2y + x = 10$.

48. Find the equation as follows.

$$0 = \begin{vmatrix} x & y & 1 \\ x_1 & y_1 & 1 \\ x_2 & y_2 & 1 \end{vmatrix} = \begin{vmatrix} x & y & 1 \\ 1 & 4 & 1 \\ 3 & 4 & 1 \end{vmatrix} = 2y - 8$$

So, an equation of the line is $y = 4$.

50. Use the formula for volume as follows.

$$\text{Volume} = \pm\frac{1}{6}\begin{vmatrix} x_1 & y_1 & z_1 & 1 \\ x_2 & y_2 & z_2 & 1 \\ x_3 & y_3 & z_3 & 1 \\ x_4 & y_4 & z_4 & 1 \end{vmatrix}$$

$$= \pm\frac{1}{6}\begin{vmatrix} 1 & 1 & 1 & 1 \\ 0 & 0 & 0 & 1 \\ 2 & 1 & -1 & 1 \\ -1 & 1 & 2 & 1 \end{vmatrix} = \frac{1}{6}(3) = \frac{1}{2}$$

52. Use the formula for volume as follows.

$$\text{Volume} = \pm\frac{1}{6}\begin{vmatrix} x_1 & y_1 & z_1 & 1 \\ x_2 & y_2 & z_2 & 1 \\ x_3 & y_3 & z_3 & 1 \\ x_4 & y_4 & z_4 & 1 \end{vmatrix}$$

$$= \pm\frac{1}{6}\begin{vmatrix} 0 & 0 & 0 & 1 \\ 0 & 2 & 0 & 1 \\ 3 & 0 & 0 & 1 \\ 1 & 1 & 4 & 1 \end{vmatrix} = \pm\frac{1}{6}(24) = 4$$

54. Use the fact that

$$\begin{vmatrix} x_1 & y_1 & z_1 & 1 \\ x_2 & y_2 & z_2 & 1 \\ x_3 & y_3 & z_3 & 1 \\ x_4 & y_4 & z_4 & 1 \end{vmatrix} = \begin{vmatrix} 1 & 2 & 3 & 1 \\ -1 & 0 & 1 & 1 \\ 0 & -2 & -5 & 1 \\ 2 & 6 & 11 & 1 \end{vmatrix} = 0$$

to determine that the four points are coplanar.

56. Use the fact that

$$\begin{vmatrix} x_1 & y_1 & z_1 & 1 \\ x_2 & y_2 & z_2 & 1 \\ x_3 & y_3 & z_3 & 1 \\ x_4 & y_4 & z_4 & 1 \end{vmatrix} = \begin{vmatrix} 1 & 2 & 7 & 1 \\ -3 & 6 & 6 & 1 \\ 4 & 4 & 2 & 1 \\ 3 & 3 & 4 & 1 \end{vmatrix} = -1$$

to determine that the four points are not coplanar.

58. Find the equation as follows.

$$0 = \begin{vmatrix} x & y & z & 1 \\ x_1 & y_1 & z_1 & 1 \\ x_2 & y_2 & z_2 & 1 \\ x_3 & y_3 & z_3 & 1 \end{vmatrix} = \begin{vmatrix} x & y & z & 1 \\ 0 & -1 & 0 & 1 \\ 1 & 1 & 0 & 1 \\ 2 & 1 & 2 & 1 \end{vmatrix}$$

$$= x\begin{vmatrix} -1 & 0 & 1 \\ 1 & 0 & 1 \\ 1 & 2 & 1 \end{vmatrix} - y\begin{vmatrix} 0 & 0 & 1 \\ 1 & 0 & 1 \\ 2 & 2 & 1 \end{vmatrix} + z\begin{vmatrix} 0 & -1 & 1 \\ 1 & 1 & 1 \\ 2 & 1 & 1 \end{vmatrix} - \begin{vmatrix} 0 & -1 & 0 \\ 1 & 1 & 0 \\ 2 & 1 & 2 \end{vmatrix}$$

$$= 4x - 2y - 2z - 2, \quad \text{or} \quad 2x - y - z = 1$$

60. Find the equation as follows.

$$0 = \begin{vmatrix} x & y & z & 1 \\ x_1 & y_1 & z_1 & 1 \\ x_2 & y_2 & z_2 & 1 \\ x_3 & y_3 & z_3 & 1 \end{vmatrix} = \begin{vmatrix} x & y & z & 1 \\ 1 & 2 & 7 & 1 \\ 4 & 4 & 2 & 1 \\ 3 & 3 & 4 & 1 \end{vmatrix}$$

$$= x\begin{vmatrix} 2 & 7 & 1 \\ 4 & 2 & 1 \\ 3 & 4 & 1 \end{vmatrix} - y\begin{vmatrix} 1 & 7 & 1 \\ 4 & 2 & 1 \\ 3 & 4 & 1 \end{vmatrix} + z\begin{vmatrix} 1 & 2 & 1 \\ 4 & 4 & 1 \\ 3 & 3 & 1 \end{vmatrix} - \begin{vmatrix} 1 & 2 & 7 \\ 4 & 4 & 2 \\ 3 & 3 & 4 \end{vmatrix}$$

$$= -x - y - z + 10, \quad \text{or} \quad x + y + z = 10$$

Review Exercises for Chapter 3

2. Using the formula for the determinant of a 2×2 matrix, you have

$$\begin{vmatrix} 0 & -3 \\ 1 & 2 \end{vmatrix} = 0(2) - (1)(-3) = 3.$$

4. Using the formula for the determinant of a 2×2 matrix, you have

$$\begin{vmatrix} -2 & 0 \\ 0 & 3 \end{vmatrix} = (-2)(3) - (0)(0) = -6.$$

10.
$$\begin{vmatrix} -15 & 0 & 3 \\ 3 & 9 & -6 \\ 12 & -3 & 6 \end{vmatrix} = 3^3 \begin{vmatrix} -5 & 0 & 1 \\ 1 & 3 & -2 \\ 4 & -1 & 2 \end{vmatrix} = 27 \begin{vmatrix} -5 & 0 & 1 \\ -9 & 3 & 0 \\ 14 & -1 & 0 \end{vmatrix} = 27 \begin{vmatrix} -9 & 3 \\ 14 & -1 \end{vmatrix}$$

$$= 27(9 - 42)$$

$$= -891$$

12. The determinant of a triangular matrix is the product of its diagonal entries. So, the determinant equals $2(1)(3)(-1) = -6$.

14.
$$\begin{vmatrix} 3 & -1 & 2 & 1 \\ -2 & 0 & 1 & -3 \\ -1 & 2 & -3 & 4 \\ -2 & 1 & -2 & 1 \end{vmatrix} = \begin{vmatrix} 3 & -1 & 2 & 1 \\ -2 & 0 & 1 & -3 \\ 5 & 0 & 1 & 6 \\ 1 & 0 & 0 & 2 \end{vmatrix}$$

$$= -(-1)\begin{vmatrix} -2 & 1 & -3 \\ 5 & 1 & 6 \\ 1 & 0 & 2 \end{vmatrix}$$

$$= 1\begin{vmatrix} 1 & -3 \\ 1 & 6 \end{vmatrix} + 2\begin{vmatrix} -2 & 1 \\ 5 & 1 \end{vmatrix}$$

$$= 9 + 2(-7) = -5$$

6. The determinant of a triangular matrix is the product of the entries along the main diagonal.

$$\begin{vmatrix} 5 & 0 & 2 \\ 0 & -1 & 3 \\ 0 & 0 & 1 \end{vmatrix} = 5(-1)(1) = -5$$

8. The determinant is 0, because the matrix has a column of zeros.

16.
$$\begin{vmatrix} 1 & 2 & -1 & 3 & 4 \\ 2 & 3 & -1 & 2 & -2 \\ 1 & 2 & 0 & 1 & -1 \\ 1 & 0 & 2 & -1 & 0 \\ 0 & -1 & 1 & 0 & 2 \end{vmatrix} = \begin{vmatrix} 1 & 2 & -1 & 3 & 4 \\ 0 & -1 & 1 & -4 & -10 \\ 0 & 0 & 1 & -2 & -5 \\ 0 & -2 & 3 & -4 & -4 \\ 0 & -1 & 1 & 0 & 2 \end{vmatrix}$$

$$= -\begin{vmatrix} 1 & -1 & 4 & 10 \\ 0 & 1 & -2 & -5 \\ 0 & 1 & 4 & 16 \\ 0 & 0 & 4 & 12 \end{vmatrix}$$

$$= -\begin{vmatrix} 1 & -2 & -5 \\ 0 & 6 & 21 \\ 0 & 4 & 12 \end{vmatrix}$$

$$= -(72 - 84) = 12$$

62. Cramer's Rule was used correctly.

64. Given the system of linear equations,

$$\begin{cases} a_1 x + b_1 y = c_1 \\ a_2 x + b_2 y = c_2 \end{cases}$$

if $\begin{vmatrix} a_1 & b_1 \\ a_2 & b_2 \end{vmatrix} = 0$, then the lines must be parallel or coinciding.

82   *Chapter 3   Determinants*

18. $\begin{vmatrix} 0 & 0 & 0 & 0 & 2 \\ 0 & 0 & 0 & 2 & 0 \\ 0 & 0 & 2 & 0 & 0 \\ 0 & 2 & 0 & 0 & 0 \\ 2 & 0 & 0 & 0 & 0 \end{vmatrix} = 2\begin{vmatrix} 0 & 0 & 0 & 2 \\ 0 & 0 & 2 & 0 \\ 0 & 2 & 0 & 0 \\ 2 & 0 & 0 & 0 \end{vmatrix}$

$= 2(-2)\begin{vmatrix} 0 & 0 & 2 \\ 0 & 2 & 0 \\ 2 & 0 & 0 \end{vmatrix}$

$= -4(2)\begin{vmatrix} 0 & 2 \\ 2 & 0 \end{vmatrix} = (-8)(-4) = 32$

20. Because the second and third columns are interchanged, the sign of the determinant is changed.

22. Because a multiple of the first row of the matrix on the left was added to the second row to produce the matrix on the right, the determinants are equal.

24. (a) $|A| = \begin{vmatrix} 1 & 2 & 3 \\ 4 & 5 & 6 \\ 7 & 8 & 0 \end{vmatrix} = 27$

(b) $|B| = \begin{vmatrix} 1 & 2 & 1 \\ 0 & -1 & 1 \\ 0 & 2 & 3 \end{vmatrix} = -5$

(c) $AB = \begin{bmatrix} 1 & 6 & 12 \\ 4 & 15 & 27 \\ 7 & 6 & 15 \end{bmatrix}$

(d) $|AB| = -135$

Notice that $|A||B| = |AB| = -135$.

26. First find

$|A| = \begin{vmatrix} 3 & 0 & 1 \\ -1 & 0 & 0 \\ 2 & 1 & 2 \end{vmatrix} = -1.$

(a) $|A^T| = |A| = -1$

(b) $|A^3| = |A|^3 = (-1)^3 = -1$

(c) $|A^T A| = |A^T||A| = (-1)(-1) = 1$

(d) $|5A| = 5^3|A| = 125(-1) = -125$

28. (a) $|A| = \begin{vmatrix} 2 & -1 & 4 \\ 5 & 0 & 3 \\ 1 & -2 & 0 \end{vmatrix} = \begin{vmatrix} 2 & -1 & 4 \\ 5 & 0 & 3 \\ -3 & 0 & -8 \end{vmatrix} = 1\begin{vmatrix} 5 & 3 \\ -3 & -8 \end{vmatrix} = -31$

(b) $|A^{-1}| = \dfrac{1}{|A|} = -\dfrac{1}{31}.$

30. $A^{-1} = \dfrac{1}{74}\begin{bmatrix} 7 & -2 \\ 2 & 10 \end{bmatrix} = \begin{bmatrix} \frac{7}{74} & -\frac{1}{37} \\ \frac{1}{37} & \frac{5}{37} \end{bmatrix}$

$|A^{-1}| = \dfrac{7}{74}\left(\dfrac{5}{37}\right) - \left(\dfrac{1}{37}\right)\left(-\dfrac{1}{37}\right)$

$= \dfrac{35}{2738} + \dfrac{1}{1369} = \dfrac{1}{74}$

Notice that $|A| = 74$.

So, $|A^{-1}| = \dfrac{1}{|A|} = \dfrac{1}{74}.$

32. $A^{-1} = \begin{bmatrix} -\frac{2}{3} & \frac{1}{6} & 0 \\ -\frac{2}{3} & \frac{1}{6} & -1 \\ \frac{1}{2} & 0 & \frac{1}{2} \end{bmatrix}$

$|A^{-1}| = \begin{vmatrix} -\frac{2}{3} & \frac{1}{6} & 0 \\ -\frac{2}{3} & \frac{1}{6} & -1 \\ \frac{1}{2} & 0 & \frac{1}{2} \end{vmatrix} = \begin{vmatrix} 0 & 0 & 1 \\ -\frac{2}{3} & \frac{1}{6} & -1 \\ \frac{1}{2} & 0 & \frac{1}{2} \end{vmatrix} = -\dfrac{1}{12}$

Notice that

$|A| = \begin{vmatrix} -1 & 1 & 2 \\ 2 & 4 & 8 \\ 1 & -1 & 0 \end{vmatrix} = 1(8-8) - (-1)(-8-4) = -12.$

So, $|A^{-1}| = \dfrac{1}{|A|} = -\dfrac{1}{12}.$

34. (a) $\begin{bmatrix} 2 & 1 & 2 & 6 \\ -1 & 2 & -3 & 0 \\ 3 & 2 & -1 & 6 \end{bmatrix} \Rightarrow \begin{bmatrix} 1 & -2 & 3 & 0 \\ 2 & 1 & 2 & 6 \\ 3 & 2 & -1 & 6 \end{bmatrix}$

$\Rightarrow \begin{bmatrix} 1 & -2 & 3 & 0 \\ 0 & 5 & -4 & 6 \\ 0 & 8 & -10 & 6 \end{bmatrix}$

$\Rightarrow \begin{bmatrix} 1 & -2 & 3 & 0 \\ 0 & 1 & -\frac{4}{5} & \frac{6}{5} \\ 0 & 0 & 1 & 1 \end{bmatrix}$

So, $x_3 = 1$, $x_2 = \frac{6}{5} + \frac{4}{5}(1) = 2$, and

$x_1 = 0 - 3(1) + 2(2) = 1$.

(b) $\begin{bmatrix} 1 & -2 & 3 & 0 \\ 0 & 1 & -\frac{4}{5} & \frac{6}{5} \\ 0 & 0 & 1 & 1 \end{bmatrix} \Rightarrow \begin{bmatrix} 1 & 0 & \frac{7}{5} & \frac{12}{5} \\ 0 & 1 & -\frac{4}{5} & \frac{6}{5} \\ 0 & 0 & 1 & 1 \end{bmatrix}$

$\Rightarrow \begin{bmatrix} 1 & 0 & 0 & 1 \\ 0 & 1 & 0 & 2 \\ 0 & 0 & 1 & 1 \end{bmatrix}$

So, $x_1 = 1$, $x_2 = 2$, and $x_3 = 1$.

(c) The coefficient matrix is

$A = \begin{bmatrix} 2 & 1 & 2 \\ -1 & 2 & -3 \\ 3 & 2 & -1 \end{bmatrix}$ and $|A| = -18$.

Also, $A_1 = \begin{bmatrix} 6 & 1 & 2 \\ 0 & 2 & -3 \\ 6 & 2 & -1 \end{bmatrix}$ and $|A_1| = -18$,

$A_2 = \begin{bmatrix} 2 & 6 & 2 \\ -1 & 0 & -3 \\ 3 & 6 & -1 \end{bmatrix}$ and $|A_2| = -36$,

$A_3 = \begin{bmatrix} 2 & 1 & 6 \\ -1 & 2 & 0 \\ 3 & 2 & 6 \end{bmatrix}$ and $|A_3| = -18$.

So, $x_1 = \frac{-18}{-18} = 1$, $x_2 = \frac{-36}{-18} = 2$, and

$x_3 = \frac{-18}{-18} = 1$.

36. (a) $\begin{bmatrix} 2 & 3 & 5 & 4 \\ 3 & 5 & 9 & 7 \\ 5 & 9 & 13 & 17 \end{bmatrix} \Rightarrow \begin{bmatrix} 1 & \frac{3}{2} & \frac{5}{2} & 2 \\ 3 & 5 & 9 & 7 \\ 5 & 9 & 13 & 17 \end{bmatrix}$

$\Rightarrow \begin{bmatrix} 1 & \frac{3}{2} & \frac{5}{2} & 2 \\ 0 & \frac{1}{2} & \frac{3}{2} & 1 \\ 0 & \frac{3}{2} & \frac{1}{2} & 7 \end{bmatrix}$

$\Rightarrow \begin{bmatrix} 1 & \frac{3}{2} & \frac{5}{2} & 2 \\ 0 & 1 & 3 & 2 \\ 0 & 0 & 1 & -1 \end{bmatrix}$

So, $x_3 = -1$, $x_2 = 2 - 3(-1) = 5$, and

$x_1 = 2 - \frac{5}{2}(-1) - \frac{3}{2}(5) = -3$.

(b) $\begin{bmatrix} 1 & \frac{3}{2} & \frac{5}{2} & 2 \\ 0 & 1 & 3 & 2 \\ 0 & 0 & 1 & -1 \end{bmatrix} \Rightarrow \begin{bmatrix} 1 & 0 & -2 & -1 \\ 0 & 1 & 3 & 2 \\ 0 & 0 & 1 & -1 \end{bmatrix}$

$\Rightarrow \begin{bmatrix} 1 & 0 & 0 & -3 \\ 0 & 1 & 0 & 5 \\ 0 & 0 & 1 & -1 \end{bmatrix}$

So, $x_1 = -3$, $x_2 = 5$, and $x_3 = -1$.

(c) The coefficient matrix is

$A = \begin{bmatrix} 2 & 3 & 5 \\ 3 & 5 & 9 \\ 5 & 9 & 13 \end{bmatrix}$ and $|A| = -4$.

Also, $A_1 = \begin{bmatrix} 4 & 3 & 5 \\ 7 & 5 & 9 \\ 17 & 9 & 13 \end{bmatrix}$ and $|A_1| = 12$,

$A_2 = \begin{bmatrix} 2 & 4 & 5 \\ 3 & 7 & 9 \\ 5 & 17 & 13 \end{bmatrix}$ and $|A_2| = -20$,

$A_3 = \begin{bmatrix} 2 & 3 & 4 \\ 3 & 5 & 7 \\ 5 & 9 & 17 \end{bmatrix}$ and $|A_3| = 4$.

So, $x_1 = \frac{12}{-4} = -3$, $x_2 = \frac{-20}{-4} = 5$, and

$x_3 = \frac{4}{-4} = -1$.

38. Because the determinant of the coefficient matrix is

$\begin{vmatrix} 2 & -5 \\ 3 & -7 \end{vmatrix} = 1 \neq 0$,

the system has a unique solution.

40. Because the determinant of the coefficient matrix is

$$\begin{vmatrix} 2 & 3 & 1 \\ 2 & -3 & -3 \\ 8 & 6 & 0 \end{vmatrix} = 0,$$

the system does not have a unique solution.

42. Because the determinant of the coefficient matrix is

$$\begin{vmatrix} 1 & 5 & 3 & 0 & 0 \\ 4 & 2 & 5 & 0 & 0 \\ 0 & 0 & 3 & 8 & 6 \\ 2 & 4 & 0 & 0 & -2 \\ 2 & 0 & -1 & 0 & 0 \end{vmatrix} = -896 \neq 0,$$

the system has a unique solution.

48.
$$\begin{vmatrix} a & 1 & 1 & 1 \\ 1 & a & 1 & 1 \\ 1 & 1 & a & 1 \\ 1 & 1 & 1 & a \end{vmatrix} = \begin{vmatrix} 0 & 1-a^2 & 1-a & 1-a \\ 1 & a & 1 & 1 \\ 0 & 1-a & a-1 & 0 \\ 0 & 1-a & 0 & a-1 \end{vmatrix}$$

$$= -\begin{vmatrix} 1-a^2 & 1-a & 1-a \\ 1-a & a-1 & 0 \\ 1-a & 0 & a-1 \end{vmatrix}$$

$$= (1-a)^3 \begin{vmatrix} 1+a & 1 & 1 \\ 1 & -1 & 0 \\ 1 & 0 & -1 \end{vmatrix} \quad \text{(factoring out } (1-a) \text{ from each row)}$$

$$= (1-a)^3 \big(1(1) - 1(-1 - a - 1)\big) \quad \text{(expanding along the third row)}$$

$$= (1-a)^3 (a+3)$$

50. $J(u, v) = \begin{vmatrix} \dfrac{\partial x}{\partial u} & \dfrac{\partial x}{\partial v} \\ \dfrac{\partial y}{\partial u} & \dfrac{\partial y}{\partial v} \end{vmatrix} = \begin{vmatrix} a & b \\ c & d \end{vmatrix} = ad - bc$

52. $J(u, v, w) = \begin{vmatrix} 1 & -1 & 1 \\ 2v & 2u & 0 \\ 1 & 1 & 1 \end{vmatrix}$

$$= 1(2u) + 1(2v) + 1(2v - 2u) = 4v$$

54. Use the information given in the table on page 138.
Cofactor expansion would cost:

$$(3,628,799)(0.001) + (6,235,300)(0.003) = \$22,334.70.$$

Row reduction would cost much less:

$$(285)(0.001) + 339(0.003) = \$1.30.$$

44. (a) $|BA| = |B||A| = 5(-2) = -10$

(b) $|B^4| = |B|^4 = 5^4 = 625$

(c) $|2A| = 2^3|A| = 2^3(-2) = -16$

(d) $\left|(AB)^T\right| = |AB| = |A||B| = -10$

(e) $|B^{-1}| = \dfrac{1}{|A|} = \dfrac{1}{5}$

46. $\begin{vmatrix} 1 & 0 & 2 \\ 1 & -1 & 2 \\ 5 & 1 & 0 \end{vmatrix} = \begin{vmatrix} 1 & 0 & 2 \\ 1 & -1 & 2 \\ 2 & 1 & -1 \end{vmatrix} + \begin{vmatrix} 1 & 0 & 2 \\ 1 & -1 & 2 \\ 3 & 0 & 1 \end{vmatrix}$

$$10 = 5 + 5$$

56. Because $|B| \neq 0$, B^{-1} exists, and you can let

$$C = AB^{-1}, \text{ then}$$

$$A = CB \quad \text{and} \quad |C| = |AB^{-1}| = |A||B^{-1}| = |A|\frac{1}{|B|} = 1.$$

58. The matrix of cofactors is given by

$$\begin{bmatrix} \begin{vmatrix} 1 & 2 \\ 0 & -1 \end{vmatrix} & -\begin{vmatrix} 0 & 2 \\ 0 & -1 \end{vmatrix} & \begin{vmatrix} 0 & 1 \\ 0 & 0 \end{vmatrix} \\[2mm] -\begin{vmatrix} -1 & 1 \\ 0 & -1 \end{vmatrix} & \begin{vmatrix} 1 & 1 \\ 0 & -1 \end{vmatrix} & -\begin{vmatrix} 1 & -1 \\ 0 & 0 \end{vmatrix} \\[2mm] \begin{vmatrix} -1 & 1 \\ 1 & 2 \end{vmatrix} & -\begin{vmatrix} 1 & 1 \\ 0 & 2 \end{vmatrix} & \begin{vmatrix} 1 & -1 \\ 0 & 1 \end{vmatrix} \end{bmatrix} = \begin{bmatrix} -1 & 0 & 0 \\ -1 & -1 & 0 \\ -3 & -2 & 1 \end{bmatrix}.$$

So, the adjoint is

$$\text{adj} \begin{bmatrix} 1 & -1 & 1 \\ 0 & 1 & 2 \\ 0 & 0 & -1 \end{bmatrix} = \begin{bmatrix} -1 & -1 & -3 \\ 0 & -1 & -2 \\ 0 & 0 & 1 \end{bmatrix}.$$

60. The determinant of the coefficient matrix is

$$\begin{vmatrix} 2 & 1 \\ 3 & -1 \end{vmatrix} = -5 \neq 0.$$

So, the system has a unique solution. Using Cramer's Rule,

$$A_1 = \begin{bmatrix} 0.3 & 1 \\ -1.3 & -1 \end{bmatrix}, \; |A_1| = 1.0$$

$$A_2 = \begin{bmatrix} 2 & 0.3 \\ 3 & -1.3 \end{bmatrix}, \; |A_2| = -3.5.$$

So,

$$x = \frac{|A_1|}{|A|} = \frac{1}{-5} = -0.2$$

$$y = \frac{|A_2|}{|A|} = \frac{-3.5}{-5} = 0.7.$$

62. The determinant of the coefficient matrix is

$$\begin{vmatrix} 4 & 4 & 4 \\ 4 & -2 & -8 \\ 8 & 2 & -4 \end{vmatrix} = 0.$$

So, Cramer's Rule does not apply. (The system does not have a solution.)

64. The coefficient matrix is $A = \begin{bmatrix} 4 & -1 & 1 \\ 2 & 2 & 3 \\ 5 & -2 & 6 \end{bmatrix}$.

$$A_1 = \begin{bmatrix} -5 & -1 & 1 \\ 10 & 2 & 3 \\ 1 & -2 & 6 \end{bmatrix}, A_2 = \begin{bmatrix} 4 & -5 & 1 \\ 2 & 10 & 3 \\ 5 & 1 & 6 \end{bmatrix},$$

$$A_3 = \begin{bmatrix} 4 & -1 & -5 \\ 2 & 2 & 10 \\ 5 & -2 & 1 \end{bmatrix}$$

Using a graphing utility, $|A| = 55$, $|A_1| = -55$, $|A_2| = 165$, and $|A_3| = 110$.

So, $x_1 = |A_1|/|A| = -1$, $x_2 = |A_2|/|A| = 3$, and $x_3 = |A_3|/|A| = 2$.

66. Use the formula for area as follows.

$$\text{Area} = \pm\frac{1}{2}\begin{vmatrix} x_1 & y_1 & 1 \\ x_2 & y_2 & 1 \\ x_3 & y_3 & 1 \end{vmatrix} = \pm\frac{1}{2}\begin{vmatrix} -4 & 0 & 1 \\ 4 & 0 & 1 \\ 0 & 6 & 1 \end{vmatrix}$$

$$= \pm\frac{1}{2}(-6)(-4 - 4) = 24$$

68. Find the equation as follows.

$$0 = \begin{vmatrix} x & y & 1 \\ x_1 & y_1 & 1 \\ x_2 & y_2 & 1 \end{vmatrix} = \begin{vmatrix} x & y & 1 \\ 2 & 5 & 1 \\ 6 & -1 & 1 \end{vmatrix} = x(6) - y(-4) - 32$$

So, an equation of the line is $2y + 3x = 16$.

70. Find the equation as follows.

$$0 = \begin{vmatrix} x & y & z & 1 \\ x_1 & y_1 & z_1 & 1 \\ x_2 & y_2 & z_2 & 1 \\ x_3 & y_3 & z_3 & 1 \end{vmatrix}$$

$$= \begin{vmatrix} x & y & z & 1 \\ 0 & 0 & 0 & 1 \\ 2 & -1 & 1 & 1 \\ -3 & 2 & 5 & 1 \end{vmatrix}$$

$$= 1\begin{vmatrix} x & y & z \\ 2 & -1 & 1 \\ -3 & 2 & 5 \end{vmatrix}$$

$$= x(-7) - y(13) + z(1) = 0.$$

So, the equation of the plane is $7x + 13y - z = 0$.

72. (a) $49a + 7b + c = 1465$

$64a + 8b + c = 1547$

$81a + 9b + c = 1623$

(b) The coefficient matrix is

$$A = \begin{bmatrix} 49 & 7 & 1 \\ 64 & 8 & 1 \\ 81 & 9 & 1 \end{bmatrix} \quad \text{and} \quad |A| = -2.$$

Also, $A_1 = \begin{bmatrix} 1465 & 7 & 1 \\ 1547 & 8 & 1 \\ 1623 & 9 & 1 \end{bmatrix}$ and $|A_1| = 6$,

$$A_2 = \begin{bmatrix} 49 & 1465 & 1 \\ 64 & 1547 & 1 \\ 81 & 1623 & 1 \end{bmatrix} \quad \text{and} \quad |A_2| = -254,$$

$$A_3 = \begin{bmatrix} 49 & 7 & 1465 \\ 64 & 8 & 1547 \\ 81 & 9 & 1623 \end{bmatrix} \quad \text{and} \quad |A_3| = -1446.$$

So, $a = \dfrac{6}{-2} = -3$, $b = \dfrac{-254}{-2} = 127$, and

$c = \dfrac{-1446}{-2} = 723.$

(c)

(d) The function fits the data exactly.

74. (a) True. If either A or B is singular, then $\det(A)$ or $\det(B)$ is zero (Theorem 3.7), but then

$\det(AB) = \det(A)\det(B) = 0 \neq -1$, which leads to a contradiction.

(b) False. $\det(2A) = 2^3 \det(A) = 8 \cdot 5 = 40 \neq 10$.

(c) False. Let A and B be the 3×3 identity matrix I_3. Then $\det(A) = \det(B) = \det(I_3) = 1$, but

$\det(A + B) = \det(2I_3) = 2^3 \cdot 1 = 8$ while $\det(A) + \det(B) = 1 + 1 = 2$.

76. (a) False. The *transpose* of the matrix of cofactors of A is called the adjoint matrix of A.

(b) False. Cramer's Rule requires the determinant of this matrix to be in the *numerator*. The denominator is always $\det(A)$, where A is the coefficient matrix of the system (assuming, of course, that it is nonsingular).

Project Solutions for Chapter 3

1 Stochastic Matrices

1. $P\mathbf{x}_1 = P\begin{bmatrix} 7 \\ 10 \\ 4 \end{bmatrix} = \begin{bmatrix} 7 \\ 10 \\ 4 \end{bmatrix}$

$P\mathbf{x}_2 = P\begin{bmatrix} 0 \\ -1 \\ 1 \end{bmatrix} = \begin{bmatrix} 0 \\ -.65 \\ .65 \end{bmatrix}$

$P\mathbf{x}_3 = P\begin{bmatrix} -2 \\ 1 \\ 1 \end{bmatrix} = \begin{bmatrix} -1.1 \\ .55 \\ .55 \end{bmatrix}$

2. $S = \begin{bmatrix} 7 & 0 & -2 \\ 10 & -1 & 1 \\ 4 & 1 & 1 \end{bmatrix} \qquad S^{-1}PS = \begin{bmatrix} 1 & 0 & 0 \\ 0 & .65 & 0 \\ 0 & 0 & .55 \end{bmatrix} = D$

The entries along D are the corresponding eigenvalues of P.

3. $S^{-1}PS = D \Rightarrow PS = SD \Rightarrow P = SDS^{-1}$. Then

$P^n = (SDS^{-1})^n = (SDS^{-1})(SDS^{-1}) \cdots (SDS^{-1}) = SD^n S^{-1}$.

For $n = 10$, $D^n = \begin{bmatrix} 1 & 0 & 0 \\ 0 & (0.65)^{10} & 0 \\ 0 & 0 & (0.55)^{10} \end{bmatrix} \Rightarrow P^{10} = SD^{10}S^{-1} \approx \begin{bmatrix} 0.335 & 0.332 & 0.332 \\ 0.473 & 0.481 & 0.468 \\ 0.192 & 0.186 & 0.200 \end{bmatrix} \Rightarrow P^{10}X \approx \begin{bmatrix} 33{,}287 \\ 47{,}147 \\ 19{,}566 \end{bmatrix}$.

2 The Cayley-Hamilton Theorem

1. $|\lambda I - A| = \begin{vmatrix} \lambda - 2 & 2 \\ 2 & \lambda + 1 \end{vmatrix} = \lambda^2 - \lambda - 6$

$A^2 - A - 6I = \begin{bmatrix} 2 & -2 \\ -2 & -1 \end{bmatrix}\begin{bmatrix} 2 & -2 \\ -2 & -1 \end{bmatrix} - \begin{bmatrix} 2 & -2 \\ -2 & -1 \end{bmatrix} - 6\begin{bmatrix} 1 & 0 \\ 0 & 1 \end{bmatrix} = \begin{bmatrix} 8 & -2 \\ -2 & 5 \end{bmatrix} - \begin{bmatrix} 8 & -2 \\ -2 & 5 \end{bmatrix} = \begin{bmatrix} 0 & 0 \\ 0 & 0 \end{bmatrix}$

2. $|\lambda I - A| = \begin{vmatrix} \lambda - 6 & 0 & -4 \\ 2 & \lambda - 1 & -3 \\ -2 & 0 & \lambda - 4 \end{vmatrix} = \lambda^3 - 11\lambda^2 + 26\lambda - 16$

$A^3 - 11A^2 + 26A - 16I = \begin{bmatrix} 344 & 0 & 336 \\ -36 & 1 & -1 \\ 168 & 0 & 176 \end{bmatrix} - 11\begin{bmatrix} 44 & 0 & 40 \\ -8 & 1 & 7 \\ 20 & 0 & 24 \end{bmatrix} + 26\begin{bmatrix} 6 & 0 & 4 \\ -2 & 1 & 3 \\ 2 & 0 & 4 \end{bmatrix} - 16\begin{bmatrix} 1 & 0 & 0 \\ 0 & 1 & 0 \\ 0 & 0 & 1 \end{bmatrix} = \begin{bmatrix} 0 & 0 & 0 \\ 0 & 0 & 0 \\ 0 & 0 & 0 \end{bmatrix}$

3. $|\lambda I - A| = \begin{vmatrix} \lambda - a & -b \\ -c & \lambda - d \end{vmatrix} = \lambda^2 - (a + d)\lambda + (ad - bc)$

$A^2 - (a + d)A + (ad - bc)I = \begin{bmatrix} a^2 + bc & ab + bd \\ ac + dc & bc + d^2 \end{bmatrix} - (a + d)\begin{bmatrix} a & b \\ c & d \end{bmatrix} + (ad - bc)\begin{bmatrix} 1 & 0 \\ 0 & 1 \end{bmatrix} = \begin{bmatrix} 0 & 0 \\ 0 & 0 \end{bmatrix}$

4. $\left(\dfrac{1}{c_0}\right)\left(-A^{n-1} - c_{n-1}A^{n-2} - \cdots - c_2 A - c_1 I\right)A = \dfrac{1}{c_0}\left(-A^n - c_{n-1}A^{n-1} - \cdots - c_2 A^2 - c_1 A\right) = \dfrac{1}{c_0}(c_0 I) = I$

Because $c_0 I = -A^n - c_{n-1}A^{n-1} - \cdots - c_2 A^2 - c_1 A$ from the equation, $p(A) = 0$.

$|\lambda I - A| = \begin{vmatrix} \lambda - 1 & -2 \\ -3 & \lambda - 5 \end{vmatrix} = \lambda^2 - 6\lambda - 1$

$A^{-1} = \dfrac{1}{(-1)}(-A + 6I) = A - 6I = \begin{bmatrix} -5 & 2 \\ 3 & -1 \end{bmatrix}$

5. (a) Because $A^2 = 2A + I$ you have $A^3 = 2A^2 + A = 2(2A + I) + A = 5A + 2I$.

$A^3 = 5\begin{bmatrix} 3 & -1 \\ 2 & -1 \end{bmatrix} + 2\begin{bmatrix} 1 & 0 \\ 0 & 1 \end{bmatrix} = \begin{bmatrix} 17 & -5 \\ 10 & -3 \end{bmatrix}$

Similarly, $A^4 = 2A^3 + A^2 = 2(5A + 2I) + (2A + I) = 12A + 5I$. Therefore,

$A^4 = 12\begin{bmatrix} 3 & -1 \\ 2 & -1 \end{bmatrix} + 5\begin{bmatrix} 1 & 0 \\ 0 & 1 \end{bmatrix} = \begin{bmatrix} 41 & -12 \\ 24 & -7 \end{bmatrix}$.

Note: This approach is a lot more efficient because you can calculate A^n without calculating all the previous powers of A.

(b) First, calculate the characteristic polynomial of A.

$|\lambda I - A| = \begin{vmatrix} \lambda & 0 & -1 \\ -2 & \lambda - 2 & 1 \\ -1 & 0 & \lambda - 2 \end{vmatrix} = \lambda^3 - 4\lambda^2 + 3\lambda + 2$.

By the Cayley-Hamilton Theorem, $A^3 - 4A^2 + 3A + 2I = O$ or $A^3 = 4A^2 - 3A - 2I$. Now you can write any positive power A^n as a linear combination of A^2, A and I. For example,

$A^4 = 4A^3 - 3A^2 - 2A = 4(4A^2 - 3A - 2I) - 3A^2 - 2A = 13A^2 - 14A - 8I$,

$A^5 = 4A^4 - 3A^3 - 2A^2 = 4(13A^2 - 14A - 8I) - 3(4A^2 - 3A - 2I) - 2A^2 = 38A^2 - 47A - 26I$.

Here

$A = \begin{bmatrix} 0 & 0 & 1 \\ 2 & 2 & -1 \\ 1 & 0 & 2 \end{bmatrix}$, $A^2 = AA = \begin{bmatrix} 0 & 0 & 1 \\ 2 & 2 & -1 \\ 1 & 0 & 2 \end{bmatrix}\begin{bmatrix} 0 & 0 & 1 \\ 2 & 2 & -1 \\ 1 & 0 & 2 \end{bmatrix} = \begin{bmatrix} 1 & 0 & 2 \\ 3 & 4 & -2 \\ 2 & 0 & 5 \end{bmatrix}$.

With this method, you can calculate A^5 directly without calculating A^3 and A^4 first.

$A^5 = 38A^2 - 47A - 26I = 38\begin{bmatrix} 1 & 0 & 2 \\ 3 & 4 & -2 \\ 2 & 0 & 5 \end{bmatrix} - 47\begin{bmatrix} 0 & 0 & 1 \\ 2 & 2 & -1 \\ 1 & 0 & 2 \end{bmatrix} - 26\begin{bmatrix} 1 & 0 & 0 \\ 0 & 1 & 0 \\ 0 & 0 & 1 \end{bmatrix} = \begin{bmatrix} 12 & 0 & 29 \\ 20 & 32 & -29 \\ 29 & 0 & 70 \end{bmatrix}$

Similarly,

$A^4 = 13A^2 - 14A - 8I = 13\begin{bmatrix} 1 & 0 & 2 \\ 3 & 4 & -2 \\ 2 & 0 & 5 \end{bmatrix} - 14\begin{bmatrix} 0 & 0 & 1 \\ 2 & 2 & -1 \\ 1 & 0 & 2 \end{bmatrix} - 8\begin{bmatrix} 1 & 0 & 0 \\ 0 & 1 & 0 \\ 0 & 0 & 1 \end{bmatrix} = \begin{bmatrix} 5 & 0 & 12 \\ 11 & 16 & -12 \\ 12 & 0 & 29 \end{bmatrix}$

$A^3 = 4A^2 - 3A - 2I = \begin{bmatrix} 2 & 0 & 5 \\ 6 & 8 & -5 \\ 5 & 0 & 12 \end{bmatrix}$.

CHAPTER 4
Vector Spaces

CHAPTER 4
Vector Spaces

Section 4.1   Vectors in R^n

2. $\mathbf{v} = (-6, 3)$

4.

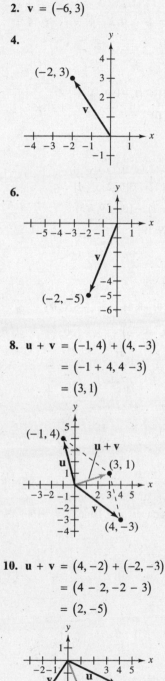

6.

8. $\mathbf{u} + \mathbf{v} = (-1, 4) + (4, -3)$
$= (-1 + 4, 4 - 3)$
$= (3, 1)$

10. $\mathbf{u} + \mathbf{v} = (4, -2) + (-2, -3)$
$= (4 - 2, -2 - 3)$
$= (2, -5)$

12. $\mathbf{v} = \mathbf{u} + \mathbf{w} = (-2, 3) + (-3, -2) = (-5, 1)$

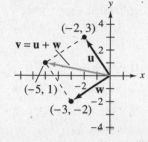

14. $\mathbf{v} = -\mathbf{u} + \mathbf{w} = -(-2, 3) + (-3, -2) = (-1, -5)$

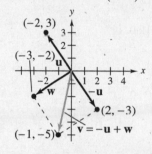

16. $\mathbf{v} = \mathbf{u} - 2\mathbf{w} = (-2, 3) - 2(-3, -2) = (4, 7)$

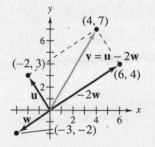

18. (a) $4\mathbf{v} = 4(3, -2) = (12, -8)$

   (b) $-\frac{1}{2}\mathbf{v} = -\frac{1}{2}(3, -2) = \left(-\frac{3}{2}, 1\right)$

   (c) $0\mathbf{v} = 0(3, -2) = (0, 0)$

20. $\mathbf{u} - \mathbf{v} + 2\mathbf{w} = (1, 2, 3) - (2, 2, -1) + 2(4, 0, -4)$

$\qquad = (-1, 0, 4) + (8, 0, -8) = (7, 0, -4).$

22. $5\mathbf{u} - 3\mathbf{v} - \frac{1}{2}\mathbf{w} = 5(1, 2, 3) - 3(2, 2, -1) - \frac{1}{2}(4, 0, -4)$

$\qquad = (5, 10, 15) - (6, 6, -3) - (2, 0, -2)$

$\qquad = (-3, 4, 20)$

24. $2\mathbf{u} + \mathbf{v} - \mathbf{w} + 3\mathbf{z} = \mathbf{0}$ implies that

$3\mathbf{z} = -2\mathbf{u} - \mathbf{v} + \mathbf{w}.$

So,

$3\mathbf{z} = -2(1, 2, 3) - (2, 2, -1) + (4, 0, -4)$

$\qquad = (-2, -4, -6) - (2, 2, -1) + (4, 0, -4) = (0, -6, -9).$

$\mathbf{z} = \frac{1}{3}(0, -6, -9) = (0, -2, -3).$

26. (a) $-\mathbf{v} = -(2, 0, 1) = (-2, 0, -1)$

(b) $2\mathbf{v} = 2(2, 0, 1) = (4, 0, 2)$

(c) $\frac{1}{2}\mathbf{v} = \frac{1}{2}(2, 0, 1) = \left(1, 0, \frac{1}{2}\right)$

28. (a) Because $(6, -4, 9) \neq c\left(\frac{1}{2}, -\frac{2}{3}, \frac{3}{4}\right)$ for any c, $\mathbf{u}$ is *not* a scalar multiple of $\mathbf{z}$.

(b) Because $\left(-1, \frac{4}{3}, -\frac{3}{2}\right) = -2\left(\frac{1}{2}, -\frac{2}{3}, \frac{3}{4}\right)$, $\mathbf{v}$ is a scalar multiple of $\mathbf{z}$.

30. (a) $\mathbf{u} - \mathbf{v} = (0, 4, 3, 4, 4) - (6, 8, -3, 3, -5)$

$\qquad = (-6, -4, 6, 1, 9)$

(b) $2(\mathbf{u} + 3\mathbf{v}) = 2\big[(0, 4, 3, 4, 4) + 3(6, 8, -3, 3, -5)\big]$

$\qquad = 2\big[(0, 4, 3, 4, 4) + (18, 24, -9, 9, -15)\big]$

$\qquad = 2(18, 28, -6, 13, -11)$

$\qquad = (36, 56, -12, 26, -22)$

(c) $2\mathbf{v} - \mathbf{u} = 2(6, 8, -3, 3, -5) - (0, 4, 3, 4, 4)$

$\qquad = (12, 16, -6, 6, -10) - (0, 4, 3, 4, 4)$

$\qquad = (12, 12, -9, 2, -14)$

32. Using a graphing utility with

$\mathbf{u} = (1, 2, -3, 1)$, $\mathbf{v} = (0, 2, -1, -2)$, and

$\mathbf{w} = (2, -2, 1, 3)$ you have:

(a) $\mathbf{v} + 3\mathbf{w} = (6, -4, 2, 7)$

(b) $2\mathbf{w} - \frac{1}{2}\mathbf{u} = \left(\frac{7}{2}, -5, \frac{7}{2}, \frac{11}{2}\right)$

(c) $\frac{1}{2}(4\mathbf{v} - 3\mathbf{u} + \mathbf{w}) = \left(-\frac{1}{2}, 0, 3, -4\right)$

34. $\mathbf{w} + \mathbf{u} = -\mathbf{v}$

$\mathbf{w} = -\mathbf{v} - \mathbf{u}$

$\qquad = -(0, 2, 3, -1) - (1, -1, 0, 1)$

$\qquad = (-1, -1, -3, 0)$

36. $\mathbf{w} + 3\mathbf{v} = -2\mathbf{u}$

$\mathbf{w} = -2\mathbf{u} - 3\mathbf{v}$

$\qquad = -2(1, -1, 0, 1) - 3(0, 2, 3, -1)$

$\qquad = (-2, 2, 0, -2) - (0, 6, 9, -3)$

$\qquad = (-2, -4, -9, 1)$

38. $2\mathbf{u} + \mathbf{v} - 3\mathbf{w} = \mathbf{0}$

$\mathbf{w} = \frac{2}{3}\mathbf{u} + \frac{1}{3}\mathbf{v}$

$\qquad = \frac{2}{3}(0, 0, -8, 1) + \frac{1}{3}(1, -8, 0, 7)$

$\qquad = \left(0, 0, -\frac{16}{3}, \frac{2}{3}\right) + \left(\frac{1}{3}, -\frac{8}{3}, 0, \frac{7}{3}\right)$

$\qquad = \left(\frac{1}{3}, -\frac{8}{3}, -\frac{16}{3}, 3\right)$

40. The equation

$a\mathbf{u} + b\mathbf{w} = \mathbf{v}$

$a(1, 2) + b(1, -1) = (0, 3)$

yields the system

$a + b = 0$

$2a - b = 3.$

Solving this system produces $a = 1$ and $b = -1$. So, $\mathbf{v} = \mathbf{u} - \mathbf{w}$.

42. The equation

$a\mathbf{u} + b\mathbf{w} = \mathbf{v}$

$a(1, 2) + b(1, -1) = (1, -1)$

yields the system

$a + b = 1$

$2a - b = -1.$

Solving this system produces $a = 0$ and $b = 1$. So, $\mathbf{v} = \mathbf{w} = 0\mathbf{u} + 1\mathbf{w}$.

44. The equation

$$a\mathbf{u} + b\mathbf{w} = \mathbf{v}$$

$$a(1, 2) + b(1, -1) = (1, -4)$$

yields the system

$$a + b = 1$$
$$2a - b = -4.$$

Solving this system produces $a = -1$ and $b = 2$.
So, $\mathbf{v} = -\mathbf{u} + 2\mathbf{w}$.

46. The equation

$$a\mathbf{u}_1 + b\mathbf{u}_2 + c\mathbf{u}_3 = \mathbf{v}$$

$$a(1, 3, 5) + b(2, -1, 3) + c(-3, 2, -4) = (-1, 7, 2)$$

yields the system

$$a + 2b - 3c = -1$$
$$3a - b + 2c = 7$$
$$5a + 3b - 4c = 2.$$

Solving this system you discover that there is no solution. So, $\mathbf{v}$ cannot be written as a linear combination of $\mathbf{u}_1, \mathbf{u}_2,$ and $\mathbf{u}_3$.

48. The equation

$$a\mathbf{u}_1 + b\mathbf{u}_2 + c\mathbf{u}_3 = \mathbf{v}$$

$$a(1, 3, 2, 1) + b(2, -2, -5, 4) + c(2, -1, 3, 6) = (2, 5, -4, 0)$$

yields the system

$$a + 2b + 2c = 2$$
$$3a - 2b - c = 5$$
$$2a - 5b + 3c = -4$$
$$a + 4b + 6c = 0.$$

Solving this system produces $a = 2$, $b = 1$, and $c = -1$. So, $\mathbf{v} = 2\mathbf{u}_1 + \mathbf{u}_2 - \mathbf{u}_3$.

50. Write a matrix using the given $\mathbf{u}_1, \mathbf{u}_2, \ldots, \mathbf{u}_5$ as columns and augment this matrix with $\mathbf{v}$ as a column.

$$A = \begin{bmatrix} 1 & 2 & 1 & 0 & 1 & 5 \\ 1 & 1 & 2 & 2 & 1 & 8 \\ -1 & 2 & 0 & 0 & 2 & 7 \\ 2 & -1 & 1 & 1 & -1 & -2 \\ 1 & 1 & 2 & -4 & 2 & 4 \end{bmatrix}$$

The reduced row-echelon form for A is

$$A = \begin{bmatrix} 1 & 0 & 0 & 0 & 0 & -1 \\ 0 & 1 & 0 & 0 & 0 & 1 \\ 0 & 0 & 1 & 0 & 0 & 2 \\ 0 & 0 & 0 & 1 & 0 & 1 \\ 0 & 0 & 0 & 0 & 1 & 2 \end{bmatrix}.$$

So, $\mathbf{v} = -\mathbf{u}_1 + \mathbf{u}_2 + 2\mathbf{u}_3 + \mathbf{u}_4 + 2\mathbf{u}_5$.

Verify the solution by showing that

$$-(1, 1, -1, 2, 1) + (2, 1, 2, -1, 1) + 2(1, 2, 0, 1, 2) + (0, 2, 0, 1, -4) + 2(1, 1, 2, -1, 2) = (5, 8, 7, -2, 4).$$

52. (a) True. See page 149.

(b) False. The zero vector is defined as an additive identity.

54. The equation

$$a\mathbf{v}_1 + b\mathbf{v}_2 + c\mathbf{v}_3 = \mathbf{0}$$

$$a(1, 0, 1) + b(-1, 1, 2) + c(0, 1, 3) = (0, 0, 0)$$

yields the homogeneous system

$$
\begin{aligned}
a - b \quad\quad &= 0 \\
b + c &= 0 \\
a + 2b + 3c &= 0.
\end{aligned}
$$

Solving this system produces $a = -t$, $b = -t$, and $c = t$, where t is any real number.

Letting $t = -1$, you obtain $a = 1$, $b = 1$, $c = -1$, and so, $\mathbf{v}_1 + \mathbf{v}_2 - \mathbf{v}_3 = \mathbf{0}$.

56. (1) $\mathbf{u} + \mathbf{v} = (2, -1, 3) + (3, 4, 0) = (5, 3, 3)$ is a vector in R^3.

(2) $\mathbf{u} + \mathbf{v} = (2, -1, 3) + (3, 4, 0) = (5, 3, 3) = (3, 4, 0) + (2, -1, 3) = \mathbf{v} + \mathbf{u}$

(3) $(\mathbf{u} + \mathbf{v}) + \mathbf{w} = \left[(2, -1, 3) + (3, 4, 0)\right] + (7, 8, -4)$

$$= (5, 3, 3) + (7, 8, -4) = (12, 11, -1)$$

$\mathbf{u} + (\mathbf{v} + \mathbf{w}) = (2, -1, 3) + \left[(3, 4, 0) + (7, 8, -4)\right]$

$$= (2, -1, 3) + (10, 12, -4) = (12, 11, -1)$$

So, $(\mathbf{u} + \mathbf{v}) + \mathbf{w} = \mathbf{u} + (\mathbf{v} + \mathbf{w})$.

(4) $\mathbf{u} + \mathbf{0} = (2, -1, 3) + (0, 0, 0) = (2, -1, 3) = \mathbf{u}$

(5) $\mathbf{u} + (-\mathbf{u}) = (2, -1, 3) + (-2, 1, -3) = (0, 0, 0) = \mathbf{0}$

(6) $c\mathbf{u} = 2(2, -1, 3) = (4, -2, 6)$ is a vector in R^3.

(7) $c(\mathbf{u} + \mathbf{v}) = 2\left[(2, -1, 3) + (3, 4, 0)\right] = 2(5, 3, 3) = (10, 6, 6)$

$c\mathbf{u} + c\mathbf{v} = 2(2, -1, 3) + 2(3, 4, 0) = (4, -2, 6) + (6, 8, 0) = (10, 6, 6)$

So, $c(\mathbf{u} + \mathbf{v}) = c\mathbf{u} + c\mathbf{v}$.

(8) $(c + d)\mathbf{u} = (2 + (-1))(2, -1, 3) = 1(2, -1, 3) = (2, -1, 3)$

$c\mathbf{u} + d\mathbf{u} = 2(2, -1, 3) + (-1)(2, -1, 3)$

$$= (4, -2, 6) + (-2, 1, -3) = (2, -1, 3)$$

So, $(c + d)\mathbf{u} = c\mathbf{u} + d\mathbf{u}$.

(9) $c(d\mathbf{u}) = 2((-1)(2, -1, 3)) = 2(-2, 1, -3) = (-4, 2, -6)$

$(cd)\mathbf{u} = (2(-1))(2, -1, 3) = (-2)(2, -1, 3) = (-4, 2, -6)$

So, $c(d\mathbf{u}) = (cd)\mathbf{u}$.

(10) $1\mathbf{u} = 1(2, -1, 3) = (2, -1, 3) = \mathbf{u}$

58. Prove each of the ten properties.

(1) $\mathbf{u} + \mathbf{v} = (u_1, \ldots, u_n) + (v_1, \ldots, v_n) = (u_1 + v_1, \ldots, u_n + v_n)$ is a vector in R^n.

(2) $\mathbf{u} + \mathbf{v} = (u_1, \ldots, u_n) + (v_1, \ldots, v_n) = (u_1 + v_1, \ldots, u_n + v_n)$

$$= (v_1 + u_1, \ldots, v_n + u_n)$$

$$= (v_1, \ldots, v_n) + (u_1, \ldots, u_n) = \mathbf{v} + \mathbf{u}$$

(3) $(\mathbf{u} + \mathbf{v}) + \mathbf{w} = \left[(u_1, \ldots, u_n) + (v_1, \ldots, v_n)\right] + (w_1, \ldots, w_n)$

$\qquad\qquad\quad = (u_1 + v_1, \ldots, u_n + v_n) + (w_1, \ldots, w_n)$

$\qquad\qquad\quad = \left((u_1 + v_1) + w_1, \ldots, (u_n + v_n) + w_n\right)$

$\qquad\qquad\quad = (u_1 + (v_1 + w_1), \ldots, u_n + (v_n + w_n))$

$\qquad\qquad\quad = (u_1, \ldots, u_n) + (v_1 + w_1, \ldots, v_n + w_n)$

$\qquad\qquad\quad = (u_1, \ldots, u_n) + \left[(v_1, \ldots, v_n) + (w_1, \ldots, w_n)\right]$

$\qquad\qquad\quad = \mathbf{u} + (\mathbf{v} + \mathbf{w})$

(4) $\mathbf{u} + \mathbf{0} = (u_1, \ldots, u_n) + (0, \ldots, 0) = (u_1 + 0, \ldots, u_n + 0) = (u_1, \ldots, u_n) = \mathbf{u}$

(5) $\mathbf{u} + (-\mathbf{u}) = (u_1, \ldots, u_n) + (-u_1, \ldots, -u_n)$

$\qquad\qquad\;\; = (u_1 - u_1, \ldots, u_n - u_n) = (0, \ldots, 0) = \mathbf{0}$

(6) $c\mathbf{u} = c(u_1, \ldots, u_n) = (cu_1, \ldots, cu_n)$ is a vector in R^n.

(7) $c(\mathbf{u} + \mathbf{v}) = c\left[(u_1, \ldots, u_n) + (v_1, \ldots, v_n)\right] = c(u_1 + v_1, \ldots, u_n + v_n)$

$\qquad\qquad\;\; = (c(u_1 + v_1), \ldots, c(u_n + v_n)) = (cu_1 + cv_1, \ldots, cu_n + cv_n)$

$\qquad\qquad\;\; = (cu_1, \ldots, cu_n) + (cv_1, \ldots, cv_n)$

$\qquad\qquad\;\; = c(u_1, \ldots, u_n) + c(v_1, \ldots, cv_n) = c\mathbf{u} + c\mathbf{v}$

(8) $(c + d)\mathbf{u} = (c + d)(u_1, \ldots, u_n) = \left((c + d)u_1, \ldots, (c + d)u_n\right)$

$\qquad\qquad\;\; = (cu_1 + du_1, \ldots, cu_n + du_n)$

$\qquad\qquad\;\; = (cu_1, \ldots, cu_n) + (du_1, \ldots, du_n)$

$\qquad\qquad\;\; = c\mathbf{u} + d\mathbf{u}$

(9) $c(d\mathbf{u}) = c(d(u_1, \ldots, u_n)) = c(du_1, \ldots, du_n) = (c(du_1), \ldots, c(du_n))$

$\qquad\quad = ((cd)u_1, \ldots, (cd)u_n) = (cd)(u_1, \ldots, u_n) = (cd)\mathbf{u}$

(10) $1\mathbf{u} = 1(u_1, \ldots, u_n) = (1u_1, \ldots, 1u_1) = (u_1, \ldots, u_n) = \mathbf{u}$

60. (a)

(b) $\mathbf{u} + \mathbf{v} = (3, -4) + (9, 1) = (12, -3)$

(c) $2\mathbf{v} - \mathbf{u} = 2(9, 1) - (3, -4) = (18, 2) - (3, -4) = (15, 6)$

(d) The equation

$\qquad a\mathbf{u} + b\mathbf{v} = \mathbf{w}$

$\quad a(3, -4) + b(9, 1) = (39, 0)$

yields the system

$\quad 3a + 9b = 39$

$\quad -4a + b = 0.$

Solving this system produces $a = 1$ and $b = 4$. So, $\mathbf{w} = \mathbf{u} + 4\mathbf{v}$.

62. (a) Additive identity

    (b) Distributive property

    (c) Add $-c\mathbf{0}$ to both sides.

    (d) Additive inverse and associative property

    (e) Additive inverse

    (f) Additive identity

64. (a) Additive inverse

    (b) Transitive property

    (c) Add $\mathbf{v}$ to both sides.

    (d) Associative property

    (e) Additive inverse

    (f) Additive identity

Section 4.2 Vector Spaces

2. The additive identity of $C(-\infty, \infty)$ is the zero function,
   $$f(x) = 0.$$

4. The additive identity of $M_{1,4}$ is the 1×4 zero matrix
   $$[0 \quad 0 \quad 0 \quad 0].$$

6. The additive identity of $M_{2,2}$ is the 2×2 zero matrix
   $$\begin{bmatrix} 0 & 0 \\ 0 & 0 \end{bmatrix}.$$

8. In $C(-\infty, \infty)$, the additive inverse of $f(x)$ is $-f(x)$.

10. In $M_{1,4}$, the additive inverse of $[v_1 \quad v_2 \quad v_3 \quad v_4]$ is
    $$[-v_1 \quad -v_2 \quad -v_3 \quad -v_4].$$

12. In $M_{2,2}$, the additive inverse of
    $$\begin{bmatrix} a & b \\ c & d \end{bmatrix} \quad \text{is} \quad \begin{bmatrix} -a & -b \\ -c & -d \end{bmatrix}.$$

14. $M_{1,1}$ with the standard operations is a vector space. All ten vector space axioms hold.

16. This set is *not* a vector space. The set is not closed under addition or scalar multiplication. For example,
    $(-x^5 + x^4) + (x^5 - x^3) = x^4 - x^3$ is not a fifth-degree polynomial.

18. This set is *not* a vector space. Axiom 1 fails. For example, given $f(x) = x + 1$ and $g(x) = -x - 1$,
    $f(x) + g(x) = 0$ is not of the form $ax + b$, where $a, b \neq 0$.

20. This set is *not* a vector space. Axiom 1 fails. For example, given $f(x) = x^2$ and $g(x) = -x^2 + x$,
    $f(x) + g(x) = x$ is not a quadratic function.

22. This set is *not* a vector space. Axiom 6 fails. A counterexample is $-2(4, 1) = (-8, -2)$ is not in the set because $x < 0$, $y < 0$.

24. This set is a vector space. All ten vector space axioms hold.

26. This set is *not* a vector space. The set is not closed under addition nor scalar multiplication. A counterexample is
    $$\begin{bmatrix} 1 & 1 \\ 1 & 1 \end{bmatrix} + \begin{bmatrix} 1 & 1 \\ 1 & 1 \end{bmatrix} = \begin{bmatrix} 2 & 2 \\ 2 & 2 \end{bmatrix}.$$
    Each matrix on the left is in the set, but the sum is not in the set.

28. This set is *not* a vector space. Axiom 1 fails. For example,
    $$\begin{bmatrix} 1 & 0 & 0 \\ 0 & 1 & 0 \\ 0 & 0 & 1 \end{bmatrix} + \begin{bmatrix} 1 & 1 & 1 \\ 1 & 1 & 1 \\ 1 & 1 & 1 \end{bmatrix} = \begin{bmatrix} 2 & 1 & 1 \\ 1 & 2 & 1 \\ 1 & 1 & 2 \end{bmatrix}.$$
    Each matrix on the left is in the set, but the matrix on the right is not.

30. This set is *not* a vector space. The set is not closed under addition nor scalar multiplication. A counterexample is
    $$\begin{bmatrix} 1 & 0 \\ 0 & 1 \end{bmatrix} + \begin{bmatrix} 1 & 0 \\ 0 & -1 \end{bmatrix} = \begin{bmatrix} 2 & 0 \\ 0 & 0 \end{bmatrix}.$$
    Each matrix on the left is nonsingular, and the sum is not.

32. This set is a vector space. All ten vector space axioms hold.

34. This set is a vector space. All ten vector space axioms hold.

36. (a) Axiom 10 fails. For example,
    $$1(2, 3, 4) = (2, 3, 0) \neq (2, 3, 4).$$

    (b) Axiom 4 fails because there is no zero vector. For instance,
    $$(2, 3, 4) + (x, y, z) = (0, 0, 0) \neq (2, 3, 4) \text{ for all choices of } (x, y, z).$$

(c) Axiom 7 fails. For example,

$$2\big[(1,1,1) + (1,1,1)\big] = 2(3,3,3) = (6,6,6)$$
$$2(1,1,1) + 2(1,1,1) = (2,2,2) + (2,2,2) = (5,5,5).$$

So, $c(\mathbf{u} + \mathbf{v}) \neq c\mathbf{u} + c\mathbf{v}.$

(d) $(x_1, y_1, z_1) + (x_2, y_2, z_2) = (x_1 + x_2 + 1, y_1 + y_2 + 1, z_1 + z_2 + 1)$

$$c(x, y, z) = (cx + c - 1, cy + c - 1, cz + c - 1)$$

This is a vector space. Verify the 10 axioms.

(1) $(x_1, y_1, z_1) + (x_2, y_2, z_2) \in R^3$

(2) $(x_1, y_1, z_1) + (x_2, y_2, z_2) = (x_1 + x_2 + 1, y_1 + y_2 + 1, z_1 + z_2 + 1)$

$$= (x_2 + x_1 + 1, y_2 + y_1 + 1, z_2 + z_1 + 1)$$
$$= (x_2, y_2, z_2) + (x_1, y_1, z_1)$$

(3) $(x_1, y_1, z_1) + \big[(x_2, y_2, z_2) + (x_3, y_3, z_3)\big]$

$$= (x_1, y_1, z_1) + (x_2 + x_3 + 1, y_2 + y_3 + 1, z_2 + z_3 + 1)$$
$$= (x_1 + (x_2 + x_3 + 1) + 1, y_1 + (y_2 + y_3 + 1) + 1, z_1 + (z_2 + z_3 + 1) + 1)$$
$$= ((x_1 + x_2 + 1) + x_3 + 1, (y_1 + y_2 + 1) + y_3 + 1, (z_1 + z_2 + 1) + z_3 + 1)$$
$$= (x_1 + x_2 + 1, y_1 + y_2 + 1, z_1 + z_2 + 1) + (x_3, y_3, z_3)$$
$$= \big[(x_1, y_1, z_1) + (x_2, y_2, z_2)\big] + (x_3, y_3, z_3)$$

(4) $\mathbf{0} = (-1, -1, -1)$: $(x, y, z) + (-1, -1, -1) = (x - 1 + 1, y - 1 + 1, z - 1 + 1)$

$$= (x, y, z)$$

(5) $-(x, y, z) = (-x - 2, -y - 2, -z - 2)$:

$$(x, y, z) + (-(x, y, z)) = (x, y, z) + (-x - 2, -y - 2, -z - 2)$$
$$= (x - x - 2 + 1, y - y - 2 + 1, z - z - 2 + 1)$$
$$= (-1, -1, -1)$$
$$= \mathbf{0}$$

(6) $c(x, y, z) \in R^3$

(7) $c\big((x_1, y_1, z_1) + (x_2, y_2, z_2)\big)$

$$= c(x_1 + x_2 + 1, y_1 + y_2 + 1, z_1 + z_2 + 1)$$
$$= \big(c(x_1 + x_2 + 1) + c - 1, c(y_1 + y_2 + 1) + c - 1, c(z_1 + z_2 + 1) + c - 1\big)$$
$$= (cx_1 + c - 1 + cx_2 + c - 1 + 1, cy_1 + c - 1 + cy_2 + c - 1 + 1, cz_1 + c - 1 + cz_2 + c - 1 + 1)$$
$$= (cx_1 + c - 1, cy_1 + c - 1, cz_1 + c - 1) + (cx_2 + c - 1, cy_2 + c - 1, cz_2 + c - 1)$$
$$= c(x_1, y_1, z_1) + c(x_2, y_2, z_2)$$

(8) $(c + d)(x, y, z) = \big((c + d)x + c + d - 1, (c + d)y + c + d - 1, (c + d)z + c + d - 1\big)$

$$= (cx + c - 1 + dx + d - 1 + 1, cy + c - 1 + dy + d - 1 + 1, cz + c - 1 + dz + d - 1 + 1)$$
$$= (cx + c - 1, cy + c - 1, cz + c - 1) + (dx + d - 1, dy + d - 1, dz + d - 1)$$
$$= c(x, y, z) + d(x, y, z)$$

(9) $c\big(d(x, y, z)\big) = c\big(dx + d - 1, dy + d - 1, dz + d - 1\big)$

$\qquad = \big(c(dx + d - 1) + c - 1, c(dy + d - 1) + c - 1, c(dz + d - 1) + c - 1\big)$

$\qquad = \big((cd)x + cd - 1, (cd)y + cd - 1, (cd)z + cd - 1\big)$

$\qquad = (cd)(x, y, z)$

(10) $1(x, y, z) = \big(1x + 1 - 1, 1y + 1 - 1, 1z + 1 - 1\big)$

$\qquad = (x, y, z)$

Note: In general, if V is a vector space and a is a constant vector, then the set V together with the operations

$\qquad u \oplus v = (u + a) + (v + a) - a$

$\qquad c * u = c(u + a) - a$

is also a vector space. Letting $a = (1, 1, 1) \in R^3$ gives the above example.

38. Verify the ten axioms in the definition of vector space.

(1) $\mathbf{u} + \mathbf{v} = (u, 2u) + (v, 2v) = (u + v, 2u + 2v)$

$\qquad = \big(u + v, 2(u + v)\big)$ is in the set.

(2) $\mathbf{u} + \mathbf{v} = (u, 2u) + (v, 2v) = (u + v, 2u + 2v)$

$\qquad = (v + u, 2v + 2u) = (v, 2v) + (u, 2u) = \mathbf{v} + \mathbf{u}$

(3) $\mathbf{u} + (\mathbf{v} + \mathbf{w}) = (u, 2u) + \big[(v, 2v) + (w, 2w)\big] = (u, 2u) + (v + w, 2v + 2w)$

$\qquad = \big(u + (v + w), 2u + (2v + 2w)\big) = \big((u + v) + w, (2u + 2v) + 2w\big)$

$\qquad = (u + v, 2u + 2v) + (w, 2w) = \big[(u, 2u) + (v, 2v)\big] + (w, 2w)$

$\qquad = (\mathbf{u} + \mathbf{v}) + \mathbf{w}$

(4)   The zero vector is

$\qquad \mathbf{0} = (0, 0)$

$\qquad \mathbf{u} + \mathbf{0} = (u, 2u) + (0, 0) = (u, 2u) = \mathbf{u}.$

(5)   The additive inverse of $(u, 2u)$ is

$\qquad (-u, -2u) = \big(-u, 2(-u)\big).$

$\qquad \mathbf{u} + (-\mathbf{u}) = (u, 2u) + \big(-u, 2(-u)\big) = (0, 0) = \mathbf{0}$

(6) $c\mathbf{u} = c(u, 2u) = \big(cu, 2(cu)\big)$ is in the set.

(7) $c(\mathbf{u} + \mathbf{v}) = c\big[(u, 2u) + (v, 2v)\big] = c(u + v, 2u + 2v)$

$\qquad = \big(c(u + v), c(2u + 2v)\big) = \big(cu + cv, c(2u) + c(2v)\big)$

$\qquad = \big(cu, c(2u)\big) + \big(cv, c(2v)\big) = c(u, 2u) + c(v, 2v)$

$\qquad = c\mathbf{u} + c\mathbf{v}$

(8) $(c + d)\mathbf{u} = (c + d)(u, 2u) = \big((c + d)u, (c + d)2u\big) = \big(cu + du, c(2u) + d(2u)\big)$

$\qquad = \big(cu, c(2u)\big) + \big(du, d(2u)\big) = c(u, 2u) + d(u, 2u)$

$\qquad = c\mathbf{u} + d\mathbf{u}$

(9) $c(d\mathbf{u}) = c\big(d(u, 2u)\big) = c\big(du, d(2u)\big) = \big(c(du), c(d(2u))\big)$

$\qquad = \big((cd)u, (cd)(2u)\big) = (cd)(u, 2u) = (cd)\mathbf{u}$

(10) $1(\mathbf{u}) = 1(u, 2u) = (u, 2u) = \mathbf{u}$

40. (a) A set on which vector addition and scalar multiplication are defined is a vector space when the following properties hold.

    1. $\mathbf{u}, \mathbf{v} \in V \Rightarrow \mathbf{u} + \mathbf{v} \in V$

    2. $\mathbf{u} + \mathbf{v} = \mathbf{v} + \mathbf{u}$

    3. $\mathbf{u} + (\mathbf{v} + \mathbf{w}) = (\mathbf{u} + \mathbf{v}) + \mathbf{w}$

    4. $\mathbf{0} \in V$ such that $\mathbf{u} + \mathbf{0} = \mathbf{u}$ for all $\mathbf{u} \in V$.

    5. If $\mathbf{u} \in V$, then $-\mathbf{u} \in V$ and $\mathbf{u} + (-\mathbf{u}) = \mathbf{0}$.

    6. If $\mathbf{u} \in V, c \in R, c\mathbf{u} \in V$.

    7. $c(\mathbf{u} + \mathbf{v}) = c\mathbf{u} + c\mathbf{v}$

    8. $(c + d)\mathbf{u} = c\mathbf{u} + d\mathbf{u}$

    9. $c(d\mathbf{u}) = (cd)\mathbf{u}$

    10. $1(\mathbf{u}) = \mathbf{u}$

  (b) The set of all polynomials of degree 6 or less is a vector space.

    The set of all sixth-degree polynomials is not a vector space.

42. R^{∞} is a vector space. Verify the ten vector space axioms.

(1) $\mathbf{u} + \mathbf{v} = (u_1 + v_1, u_2 + v_2, u_3 + v_3, \ldots)$ is in R^{∞}.

(2) $\mathbf{u} + \mathbf{v} = (u_1, u_2, u_3, \ldots) + (v_1, v_2, v_3, \ldots) = (u_1 + v_1, u_2 + v_2, u_3 + v_3, \ldots) = (v_1 + u_1, v_2 + u_2, v_3 + u_3, \ldots) = \mathbf{v} + \mathbf{u}$

(3) $\mathbf{u} + (\mathbf{v} + \mathbf{w}) = (u_1, u_2, u_3, \ldots) + (v_1 + w_1, v_2 + w_2, v_3 + w_3, \ldots)$

$$= (u_1 + (v_1 + w_1), u_2 + (v_2 + w_2), u_3 + (v_3 + w_3), \ldots)$$

$$= ((u_1 + v_1) + w_1, (u_2 + v_2) + w_2, (u_3 + v_3) + w_3, \ldots)$$

$$= (u_1 + v_1, u_2 + v_2, u_3 + v_3, \ldots) + (w_1, w_2, w_3, \ldots)$$

$$= (\mathbf{u} + \mathbf{v}) + \mathbf{w}$$

(4) The zero vector is

$$\mathbf{0} = (0, 0, 0, \ldots)$$

$$\mathbf{u} + \mathbf{0} = (u_1, u_2, u_3, \ldots) + (0, 0, 0, \ldots) = (u_1, u_2, u_3, \ldots).$$

(5) The additive inverse of $\mathbf{u}$ is

$$-\mathbf{u} = (-u_1, -u_2, -u_3, \ldots)$$

$$\mathbf{u} + (-\mathbf{u}) = (u_1 + (-u_1), u_2 + (-u_2), u_3 + (-u_3), \ldots) = (0, 0, 0, \ldots) = \mathbf{0}.$$

(6) $c\mathbf{u} = (cu_1, cu_2, cu_3, \ldots)$ is in the set.

(7) $c(\mathbf{u} + \mathbf{v}) = c(u_1 + v_1, u_2 + v_2, u_3 + v_3, \ldots)$

$$= (c(u_1 + v_1), c(u_2 + v_2), c(u_3 + v_3), \ldots)$$

$$= (cu_1 + cv_1, cu_2 + cv_2, cu_3 + cv_3, \ldots)$$

$$= (cu_1, cu_2, cu_3, \ldots) + (cv_1, cv_2, cv_3, \ldots)$$

$$= c\mathbf{u} + c\mathbf{v}$$

(8) $(c + d)\mathbf{u} = ((c + d)u_1, (c + d)u_2, (c + d)u_3, \ldots) = (cu_1 + du_1, cu_2 + du_2, cu_3 + du_3, \ldots) = c\mathbf{u} + d\mathbf{u}$

(9) $c(d\mathbf{u}) = c(du_1, du_2, du_3, \ldots) = (c(du_1), c(du_2), c(du_3), \ldots) = ((cd)u_1, (cd)u_2, (cd)u_3, \ldots) = (cd)\mathbf{u}$

(10) $1\mathbf{u} = (1u_1, 1u_2, 1u_3, \ldots) = (u_1, u_2, u_3, \ldots) = \mathbf{u}$

44. (a) Add $-\mathbf{w}$ to both sides.

   (b) Associative property

   (c) Additive inverse

   (d) Additive identity

46. (a) True. For a set with two operations to be a vector space, *all* ten axioms must be satisfied. Therefore, if one of the axioms fails, then this set cannot be a vector space.

   (b) False. The first axiom is not satisfied, because $x + (1 - x) = 1$ is not a polynomial of degree 1, but is a sum of polynomials of degree 1.

   (c) True. This set is a vector space because all ten vector space axioms hold.

48. $(-1)\mathbf{v} + 1(\mathbf{v}) = (-1 + 1)\mathbf{v} = 0\mathbf{v} = \mathbf{0}$. Also, $-\mathbf{v} + \mathbf{v} = \mathbf{0}$. So, $(-1)\mathbf{v}$ and $-\mathbf{v}$ are both additive inverses of $\mathbf{v}$. Because the additive inverse of a vector is unique, $(-1)\mathbf{v} = -\mathbf{v}$.

Section 4.3   Subspaces of Vector Spaces

2. Because W is nonempty and $W \subset R^3$, you need only check that W is closed under addition and scalar multiplication. Given

$$(x_1, y_1, 2x_1 - 3y_1) \quad \text{and} \quad (x_2, y_2, 2x_2 - 3y_2),$$

it follows that

$$(x_1, y_1, 2x_1 - 3y_1) + (x_2, y_2, 2x_2 - 3y_2) = (x_1 + x_2, y_1 + y_2, 2(x_1 + x_2) - 3(y_1 + y_2)) \in W.$$

Furthermore, for any real number c and $(x, y, 2x - 3y) \in W$, it follows that

$$c(x, y, 2x - 3y) = (cx, cy, 2(cx) - 3(cy)) \in W.$$

4. Because W is nonempty and $W \subset M_{3,2}$, you need only check that W is closed under addition and scalar multiplication. Given

$$\begin{bmatrix} a_1 & b_1 \\ a_1 + b_1 & 0 \\ 0 & c_1 \end{bmatrix} \in W \quad \text{and} \quad \begin{bmatrix} a_2 & b_2 \\ a_2 + b_2 & 0 \\ 0 & c_2 \end{bmatrix} \in W$$

it follows that

$$\begin{bmatrix} a_1 & b_1 \\ a_1 + b_1 & 0 \\ 0 & c_1 \end{bmatrix} + \begin{bmatrix} a_2 & b_2 \\ a_2 + b_2 & 0 \\ 0 & c_2 \end{bmatrix} = \begin{bmatrix} a_1 + a_2 & b_1 + b_2 \\ (a_1 + a_2) + (b_1 + b_2) & 0 \\ 0 & c_1 + c_2 \end{bmatrix} \in W.$$

Furthermore, for any real number d,

$$d\begin{bmatrix} a & b \\ a + b & 0 \\ 0 & c \end{bmatrix} = \begin{bmatrix} da & db \\ da + db & 0 \\ 0 & dc \end{bmatrix} \in W.$$

6. Recall from calculus that differentiability implies continuity. So, $W \subset V$. Furthermore, because W is nonempty, you need only check that W is closed under addition and scalar multiplication. Given differentiable functions f and g on $[-1, 1]$, it follows that $f + g$ is differentiable on $[-1, 1]$ and so $f + g \in W$. Also, for any real number c and for any differentiable function $f \in W$, cf is differentiable, and therefore $cf \in W$.

8. The vectors in W are of the form $(a, 1)$. This set is not closed under addition or scalar multiplication. For example,

$$(2, 1) + (2, 1) = (4, 2) \notin W$$

and

$$2(2, 1) = (4, 2) \notin W.$$

10. This set is not closed under scalar multiplication. For example,

$$\tfrac{1}{2}(4, 3) = \left(2, \tfrac{3}{2}\right) \notin W.$$

12. This set is not closed under addition. For example, consider $f(x) = -x + 1$ and $g(x) = x + 2$, and $f(x) + g(x) = 3 \notin W$.

14. This set is not closed under addition. For example, $(3, 4, 5) + (5, 12, 13) = (8, 16, 18) \notin W$.

16. This set is not closed under addition. For instance,

$$\begin{bmatrix} 4 \\ 0 \\ 2 \end{bmatrix} + \begin{bmatrix} 1 \\ 0 \\ 1 \end{bmatrix} = \begin{bmatrix} 5 \\ 0 \\ 3 \end{bmatrix} \notin W.$$

18. This set is not closed under addition or scalar multiplication. For example,

$$\begin{bmatrix} 1 & 0 \\ 0 & 1 \end{bmatrix} + \begin{bmatrix} 1 & 0 \\ 0 & 1 \end{bmatrix} = \begin{bmatrix} 2 & 0 \\ 0 & 2 \end{bmatrix} \notin W$$

$$2\begin{bmatrix} 1 & 0 \\ 0 & 1 \end{bmatrix} = \begin{bmatrix} 2 & 0 \\ 0 & 2 \end{bmatrix} \notin W.$$

20. The vectors in W are of the form (a, a^2). This set is not closed under addition or scalar multiplication. For example,

$$(3, 9) + (2, 4) = (5, 13) \notin W$$

and

$$2(3, 9) = (6, 18) \notin W.$$

22. This set is *not* a subspace because it is not closed under scalar multiplication.

24. This set is a subspace of $C(-\infty, \infty)$ because it is closed under addition and scalar multiplication..

26. This set is *not* a subspace because it is not closed under addition or scalar multiplication.

28. This set is *not* a subspace of $C(-\infty, \infty)$ because it is not closed under addition or scalar multiplication.

30. This set *is* a subspace because it is closed under addition and scalar multiplication.

32. This set *is* a subspace of $M_{m,n}$ because it is closed under addition and scalar multiplication.

34. This set is *not* a subspace because it is not closed under addition or scalar multiplication.

36. This set *is not* a subspace because it is not closed under addition

38. W is *not* a subspace of R^3. For example, $(0, 0, 4) \in W$ and $(1, 1, 4) \in W$, but $(0, 0, 4) + (1, 1, 4) = (1, 1, 8) \notin W$, so W is not closed under addition.

40. W *is* a subspace of R^3. Note first that $W \subset R^3$ and W is nonempty. If $(s_1, s_1 - t_1, t_1)$ and $(s_2, s_2 - t_2, t_2)$ are in W, then their sum is also in W.

$$(s_1, s_1 - t_1, t_1) + (s_2, s_2 - t_2, t_2) = (s_1 + s_2, (s_1 + s_2) - (t_1 + t_2), t_1 + t_2) \in W$$

Furthermore, if c is any real number,

$$c(s_1, s_1 - t_1, t_1) = (cs_1, cs_1 - ct_1, ct_1) \in W.$$

42. W is *not* a subspace of R^3. For example, $(1, 1, 1) \in W$ and $(1, 1, 1) \in W$, but their sum, $(2, 2, 2) \notin W$. So, W is not closed under addition.

44. (a) False. Zero subspace and the whole vector space are not *proper* subspaces, even though they are subspaces.

   (b) True. Because W must itself be a vector space under inherited operations, it must contain an additive identity.

   (c) True. See Theorem 4.5, part 1 on page 162.

46. Example 5 showed that $W_i \subset W_j$ for $i \leq j$. To show W_i is a subspace, show that it is closed under addition and scalar multiplication.

   W_4: If f and g are integrable, $f + g$ and cf are integrable. So, W_4 *is* a subspace.

   W_3: The sum of two continuous functions is continuous, and a continuous function multiplied by a constant is continuous. So, W_3 *is* a subspace.

   W_2: If y_1 and y_2 are differentiable, $y_1 + y_2$ and cy_1 are differentiable. So, W_2 *is* a subspace.

   W_1: The sum of two polynomials is a polynomial, and a polynomial multiplied by a constant is a polynomial. So, W_1 *is* a subspace.

   So, W_i *is* a subspace of W_j for $i \leq j$.

48. S is a subspace of $C[0, 1]$. S is nonempty because the zero function is in S. If $f_1, f_2 \in S$, then

$$\int_0^1 (f_1 + f_2)(x)dx = \int_0^1 \left[f_1(x) + f_2(x) \right] dx$$

$$= \int_0^1 f_1(x)dx + \int_0^1 f_2(x)dx$$

$$= 0 + 0 = 0 \implies f_1 + f_2 \in S.$$

If $f \in S$ and $c \in R$, then

$$\int_0^1 (cf)(x)dx = \int_0^1 cf(x)dx = c\int_0^1 f(x)dx = c0 = 0 \implies cf \in S.$$

So, S is closed under addition and scalar multiplication.

50. The commutative, associative, and distributive properties in the larger vector space still hold for a subset of the larger space. If the set is closed under addition and scalar multiplication, the remaining axioms for a vector space are satisfied, and the subset is a subspace.

52. Because W is not empty (for example, $\mathbf{x} \in W$) you need only check that W is closed under addition and scalar multiplication. Let

$$a_1\mathbf{x} + b_1\mathbf{y} + c_1\mathbf{z} \in W,$$
$$a_2\mathbf{x} + b_2\mathbf{y} + c_2\mathbf{z} \in W.$$

Then

$$(a_1\mathbf{x} + b_1\mathbf{y} + c_1\mathbf{z}) + (a_2\mathbf{x} + b_2\mathbf{y} + c_2\mathbf{z}) =$$

$$(a_1\mathbf{x} + a_2\mathbf{x}) + (b_1\mathbf{y} + b_2\mathbf{y}) + (c_1\mathbf{z} + c_2\mathbf{z}) =$$

$$(a_1 + a_2)\mathbf{x} + (b_1 + b_2)\mathbf{y} + (c_1 + c_2)\mathbf{z} \in W.$$

Similarly, if $a\mathbf{x} + b\mathbf{y} + c\mathbf{z} \in W$ and $d \in R$, then

$$d(a\mathbf{x} + b\mathbf{y} + c\mathbf{z}) = da\mathbf{x} + db\mathbf{y} + dc\mathbf{z} \in W.$$

54. Because W is not empty you need only check that W is closed under addition and scalar multiplication. Let $c \in R$ and $\mathbf{x}, \mathbf{y}, \in W$. Then $A\mathbf{x} = \mathbf{0}$ and $A\mathbf{y} = \mathbf{0}$. So,

$$A(\mathbf{x} + \mathbf{y}) = A\mathbf{x} + A\mathbf{y} = \mathbf{0} + \mathbf{0} = \mathbf{0},$$

$$A(c\mathbf{x}) = cA\mathbf{x} = c\mathbf{0} = \mathbf{0}.$$

Therefore, $\mathbf{x} + \mathbf{y} \in W$ and $c\mathbf{x} \in W$.

56. Let $V = R^2$. Consider

$$W = \{(x, 0) : x \in R\}, \quad U = \{(0, y) : y \in R\}.$$

Then $W \cup U$ is *not* a subspace of V, because it is not closed under addition. Indeed, $(1, 0), (0, 1) \in W \cup U$, but $(1, 1)$ (which is the sum of these two vectors) is not.

58. (a) $V + W$ is nonempty because $\mathbf{0} = \mathbf{0} + \mathbf{0} \in V + W$.

Let $\mathbf{u}_1, \mathbf{u}_2 \in V + W$. Then $\mathbf{u}_1 = \mathbf{v}_1 + \mathbf{w}_1, \mathbf{u}_2 = \mathbf{v}_2 + \mathbf{w}_2$, where $\mathbf{v}_i \in V$ and $\mathbf{w}_i \in W$. So,

$$\mathbf{u}_1 + \mathbf{u}_2 = (\mathbf{v}_1 + \mathbf{w}_1) + (\mathbf{v}_2 + \mathbf{w}_2) = (\mathbf{v}_1 + \mathbf{v}_2) + (\mathbf{w}_1 + \mathbf{w}_2) \in V + W.$$

For scalar c,

$$c\mathbf{u}_1 = c(\mathbf{v}_1 + \mathbf{w}_1) = c\mathbf{v}_1 + c\mathbf{w}_1 \in V + W.$$

(b) If $V = \{(x, 0): x$ is a real number$\}$ and $W = \{(0, y): y$ is a real number$\}$, then $V + W = R^2$.

Section 4.4 Spanning Sets and Linear Independence

2. (a) Solving the equation

$$c_1(1, 2, -2) + c_2(2, -1, 1) = (-4, -3, 3)$$

for c_1 and c_2 yields the system

$$c_1 + 2c_2 = -4$$
$$2c_1 - c_2 = -3$$
$$-2c_1 + c_2 = 3.$$

The solution of this system is $c_1 = -2$ and $c_1 = -1$. So, $\mathbf{z}$ can be written as a linear combination of the vectors in S.

(b) Proceed as in (a), substituting $(-2, -6, 6)$ for $(1, -5, -5)$. So, the system to be solved is

$$c_1 + 2c_2 = -2$$
$$2c_1 - c_2 = -6$$
$$-2c_1 + c_2 = 6.$$

The solution of this system is $c_1 = -\frac{14}{5}$ and $c_2 = \frac{2}{5}$. So, $\mathbf{v}$ can be written as a linear combination of the vectors in S.

(c) Proceed as in (a), substituting $(-1, -22, 22)$ for $(1, -5, -5)$. So, the system to be solved is

$$c_1 + 2c_2 = -1$$
$$2c_1 - c_2 = -22$$
$$-2c_1 + c_2 = 22.$$

The solution of this system is $c_1 = -9$ and $c_2 = 4$. So, $\mathbf{w}$ can be written as a linear combination of the vectors in S.

(d) Proceed as in (a), substituting $(1, -5, -5)$ for $(-4, -3, 3)$, which yields the system

$$c_1 + 2c_2 = 1$$
$$2c_1 - c_2 = -5$$
$$-2c_1 + c_2 = -5.$$

This system has no solution. So, $\mathbf{u}$ cannot be written as a linear combination of the vectors in S.

4. (a) Solving the equation

$$c_1(6, -7, 8, 6) + c_2(4, 6, -4, 1) = (-42, 113, -112, -60)$$

for c_1 and c_2 yields the system

$$6c_1 + 4c_2 = -42$$
$$-7c_1 + 6c_2 = 113$$
$$8c_1 - 4c_2 = -112$$
$$6c_1 + c_2 = -60.$$

The solution of this system is $c_1 = -11$ and $c_2 = 6$. So, $\mathbf{u}$ can be written as a linear combination of the vectors in S.

(b) Proceed as in (a), substituting $\left(\frac{49}{2}, \frac{99}{4}, -14, \frac{19}{2}\right)$ for $(-42, 113, -112, -60)$, which yields the system

$$6c_1 + 4c_2 = \frac{49}{2}$$
$$-7c_1 + 6c_2 = \frac{99}{4}$$
$$8c_1 - 4c_2 = -14$$
$$6c_1 + c_2 = \frac{19}{2}.$$

The solution of this system is $c_1 = \frac{3}{4}$ and $c_2 = 5$. So, $\mathbf{v}$ can be written as a linear combination of the vectors in S.

(c) Proceed as in (a), substituting $\left(-4, -14, \frac{27}{2}, \frac{53}{8}\right)$ for $(-42, 113, -112, -60)$, which yields the system

$$6c_1 + 4c_2 = -4$$
$$-7c_1 + 6c_2 = -14$$
$$8c_1 - 4c_2 = \frac{27}{2}$$
$$6c_1 + c_2 = \frac{53}{8}.$$

This system has no solution. So, $\mathbf{w}$ cannot be written as a linear combination of the vectors in S.

(d) Proceed as in (a), substituting $\left(8, 4, -1, \frac{17}{4}\right)$ for $(-42, 113, -112, -60)$, which yields the system

$$6c_1 + 4c_2 = 8$$
$$-7c_1 + 6c_2 = 4$$
$$8c_1 - 4c_2 = -1$$
$$6c_1 + c_2 = \frac{17}{4}.$$

The solution of this system is $c_1 = \frac{1}{2}$ and $c_2 = \frac{5}{4}$. So, $\mathbf{z}$ can be written as a linear combination of vectors in S.

6. From the vector equation

$$c_1 \begin{bmatrix} 2 & -3 \\ 4 & 1 \end{bmatrix} + c_2 \begin{bmatrix} 0 & 5 \\ 1 & -2 \end{bmatrix} = \begin{bmatrix} 6 & 2 \\ 9 & 11 \end{bmatrix}$$

you obtain the linear system

$$
\begin{aligned}
2c_1 \quad\quad &= 6 \\
-3c_1 + 5c_2 &= 2 \\
4c_1 + \ c_2 &= 9 \\
c_1 - 2c_2 &= 11.
\end{aligned}
$$

This system is inconsistent, and so the matrix is not a linear combination of A and B.

8. From the vector equation

$$c_1 \begin{bmatrix} 2 & -3 \\ 4 & 1 \end{bmatrix} + c_2 \begin{bmatrix} 0 & 5 \\ 1 & -2 \end{bmatrix} = \begin{bmatrix} 0 & 0 \\ 0 & 0 \end{bmatrix}$$

you obtain the trivial combination

$$0 \begin{bmatrix} 2 & -3 \\ 4 & 1 \end{bmatrix} + 0 \begin{bmatrix} 0 & 5 \\ 1 & -2 \end{bmatrix} = \begin{bmatrix} 0 & 0 \\ 0 & 0 \end{bmatrix} = 0A + 0B.$$

10. Let $\mathbf{u} = (u_1, u_2)$ be any vector in R^2. Solving the equation

$$c_1(1, -1) + c_2(2, 1) = (u_1, u_2)$$

for c_1 and c_2 yields the system

$$
\begin{aligned}
c_1 + 2c_2 &= u_1 \\
-c_1 + \ c_2 &= u_2.
\end{aligned}
$$

The system has a unique solution because the determinant of the coefficient matrix is nonzero. So, S spans R^2.

12. Let $\mathbf{u} = (u_1, u_2)$ be any vector in R^2. Solving the equation

$$c_1(2, 0) + c_2(0, 1) = (u_1, u_2)$$

for c_1 and c_2 yields the system

$$
\begin{aligned}
2c_1 \quad\quad &= u_1 \\
c_2 &= u_2.
\end{aligned}
$$

The system has a unique solution because the determinant of the coefficient matrix is nonzero. So, S spans R^2.

14. S does not span R^2 because only vectors of the form $t(1, 1)$ are in span(S). For example, $(0, 1)$ is not in span(S). S spans a line in R^2.

16. S does not span R^2 because only vectors of the form $t(1, 2)$ are in span(S). For example, $(0, 1)$ is not in span(S). S spans a line in R^2.

18. Let $\mathbf{u} = (u_1, u_2)$ be any vector in R^2. Solving the equation

$$c_1(0, 2) + c_2(1, 4) = (u_1, u_2)$$

for c_1 and c_2 yields the system

$$
\begin{aligned}
c_2 &= u_1 \\
2c_1 + 4c_2 &= u_2.
\end{aligned}
$$

The system has a unique solution because the determinant of the coefficient matrix is nonzero. So, S spans R^2.

20. Let $\mathbf{u} = (u_1, u_2)$ be any vector in R^2. Solving the equation

$$c_1(-1, 2) + c_2(2, -1) + c_3(1, 1) = (u_1, u_2)$$

for $c_1, c_2,$ and c_3 yields the system

$$
\begin{aligned}
-c_1 + 2c_2 + c_3 &= u_1 \\
2c_1 - \ c_2 + c_3 &= u_2.
\end{aligned}
$$

This system is equivalent to

$$
\begin{aligned}
c_1 - 2c_2 - \ c_3 &= -u_1 \\
3c_2 + 3c_3 &= 2u_1 + u_2.
\end{aligned}
$$

So, for any $\mathbf{u} = (u_1, u_2)$ in R^2, you can take

$c_3 = 0, c_2 = (2u_1 + u_2)/3,$ and

$c_1 = 2c_2 - u_1 = (u_1 + 2u_2)/3.$ So, S spans R^2.

22. Let $\mathbf{u} = (u_1, u_2, u_3)$ be any vector in R^3. Solving the equation

$$c_1(6, 7, 6) + c_2(3, 2, -4) + c_3(1, -3, 2) = (u_1, u_2, u_3)$$

for $c_1, c_2,$ and c_3 yields the system

$$
\begin{aligned}
6c_1 + 3c_2 + \ c_3 &= u_1 \\
7c_1 + 2c_2 - 3c_3 &= u_2 \\
6c_1 - 4c_2 + 2c_3 &= u_3.
\end{aligned}
$$

This system has a unique solution because the determinant of the coefficient matrix is nonzero. So, S spans R^3.

24. Let $\mathbf{u} = (u_1, u_2, u_3)$ be any vector in R^3. Solving the equation

$$c_1(1, 0, 1) + c_2(1, 1, 0) + c_3(0, 1, 1) = (u_1, u_2, u_3)$$

for $c_1, c_2,$ and c_3 yields the system

$$
\begin{aligned}
c_1 + c_2 \quad\quad &= u_1 \\
c_2 + c_3 &= u_2 \\
c_1 \quad\quad + c_3 &= u_3.
\end{aligned}
$$

This system has a unique solution because the determinant of the coefficient matrix is nonzero. So, S spans R^3.

26. This set does not span R^3. Notice that the third and fourth vectors are spanned by the first two.

$$(4, 0, 5) = 2(1, 0, 3) + (2, 0, -1)$$
$$(2, 0, 6) = 2(1, 0, 3)$$

So, S spans a plane in R^3.

28. Let $a_0 + a_1 x + a_2 x^2 + a_3 x^3$ be any vector in P_3. Solving the equation

$$c_1(x^2 - 2x) + c_2(x^3 + 8) + c_3(x^3 - x^2) + c_4(x^2 - 4) = a_0 + a_1 x + a_2 x^2 + a_3 x^3$$

for $c_1, c_2, c_3,$ and c_4 yields the system

$$
\begin{aligned}
c_2 + c_3 \quad\quad &= a_3 \\
c_1 \quad - c_3 + c_4 &= a_2 \\
-2c_1 \quad\quad\quad &= a_1 \\
8c_2 \quad - 4c_4 &= a_0.
\end{aligned}
$$

This system has a unique solution because the determinant of the coefficient matrix is nonzero. So, S spans P_3.

30. The set is linearly dependent because

$$(3, -6) + 3(-1, 2) = 0.$$

32. This set is linearly dependent because

$$-3(1, 0) + (1, 1) + (2, -1) = (0, 0).$$

34. Because $(-1, 3, 2)$ is not a scalar multiple of $(6, 2, 1)$, the set is linearly independent.

36. From the vector equation

$$c_1\left(\tfrac{3}{4}, \tfrac{5}{2}, \tfrac{3}{2}\right) + c_2\left(3, 4, \tfrac{7}{2}\right) + c_3\left(-\tfrac{3}{2}, 6, 2\right) = (0, 0, 0)$$

you obtain the homogeneous system

$$
\begin{aligned}
\tfrac{3}{4}c_1 + 3c_2 - \tfrac{3}{2}c_3 &= 0 \\
\tfrac{5}{2}c_1 + 4c_2 + 6c_3 &= 0 \\
\tfrac{3}{2}c_1 + \tfrac{7}{2}c_2 + 2c_3 &= 0.
\end{aligned}
$$

This system has only the trivial solution $c_1 = c_2 = c_3 = 0$. So, the set is linearly independent.

38. Because the fourth vector is a linear combination of the first three, this set is linearly dependent.

$$(1, 5, -3) = (1, 0, 0) + \tfrac{5}{4}(0, 4, 0) + \tfrac{1}{2}(0, 0, -6)$$

40. From the vector equation

$$c_1(0, 0, 0, 1) + c_2(0, 0, 1, 1) + c_3(0, 1, 1, 1) + c_4(1, 1, 1, 1) = (0, 0, 0, 0)$$

you obtain the homogeneous system

$$
\begin{aligned}
c_4 &= 0 \\
c_3 + c_4 &= 0 \\
c_2 + c_3 + c_4 &= 0 \\
c_1 + c_2 + c_3 + c_4 &= 0.
\end{aligned}
$$

This system has only the trivial solution $c_1 = c_2 = c_3 = c_4 = 0$. So, the set is linearly independent.

42. From the vector equation

$$c_1(x^2 - 1) + c_2(2x + 5) = 0 + 0x + 0x^2$$

you obtain the homogenous system

$$
\begin{aligned}
-c_1 + 5c_2 &= 0 \\
2c_2 &= 0 \\
c_1 \quad\quad &= 0.
\end{aligned}
$$

This system has only the trivial solution. So, the set is linearly independent.

44. From the vector equation

$$c_1(x^2) + c_2(x^2 + 1) = 0 + 0x + 0x^2$$

you obtain the homogenous system

$$
\begin{aligned}
c_2 &= 0 \\
0 &= 0 \\
c_1 + c_2 &= 0.
\end{aligned}
$$

This system has only the trivial solution. So, the set is linearly independent.

46. From the vector equation

$$c_1\begin{bmatrix} 1 & 0 \\ 0 & 1 \end{bmatrix} + c_2\begin{bmatrix} 0 & 1 \\ 0 & 0 \end{bmatrix} + c_3\begin{bmatrix} 0 & 0 \\ 1 & 0 \end{bmatrix} = \begin{bmatrix} 0 & 0 \\ 0 & 0 \end{bmatrix}$$

you obtain the homogeneous system

$$c_1 = 0$$
$$c_2 = 0$$
$$c_3 = 0.$$

So, the set is linearly independent.

48. The set is linearly dependent because

$$2\begin{bmatrix} 2 & 0 \\ -3 & 1 \end{bmatrix} + 3\begin{bmatrix} -4 & -1 \\ 0 & 5 \end{bmatrix} = \begin{bmatrix} -8 & -3 \\ -6 & 17 \end{bmatrix}.$$

50. One example of a nontrivial linear combination of vectors in S whose sum is the zero vector is

$$(2, 4) + 2(-1, -2) + 0(0, 6) = (0, 0).$$

Solving this equation for $(2, 4)$ yields

$$(2, 4) = -2(-1, -2) + 0(0, 6).$$

52. One example of a nontrivial linear combination of vectors in S whose sum is the zero vector is

$$2(1, 2, 3, 4) - (1, 0, 1, 2) - (1, 4, 5, 6) = (0, 0, 0, 0).$$

Solving this equation for $(1, 4, 5, 6)$ yields

$$(1, 4, 5, 6) = 2(1, 2, 3, 4) - (1, 0, 1, 2).$$

54. (a) From the vector equation

$$c_1(t, 0, 0) + c_2(0, 1, 0) + c_3(0, 0, 1) = (0, 0, 0)$$

you obtain the homogeneous system

$$tc_1 \quad\quad = 0$$
$$\quad c_2 \quad = 0$$
$$\quad\quad c_3 = 0.$$

Because $c_2 = c_3 = 0$, the set will be linearly independent if $t \neq 0$.

(b) Proceeding as in (a), you obtain the homogeneous system

$$tc_1 + tc_2 + tc_3 = 0$$
$$tc_1 + c_2 \quad\quad = 0$$
$$tc_1 \quad\quad + c_3 = 0.$$

The coefficient matrix will have a nonzero determinant if $2t^2 - t \neq 0$. That is, the set will be linearly independent if $t \neq 0$ or $t \neq \frac{1}{2}$.

56. (a) Because $(-2, 4) = -2(1, -2)$, S is linearly dependent.

(b) Because $2(1, -6, 2) = (2, -12, 4)$, S is linearly dependent.

(c) Because $(0, 0) = 0(1, 0)$, S is linearly dependent.

58. The matrix $\begin{bmatrix} 0 & 0 & 2 \\ 0 & 1 & 1 \\ 1 & 1 & 1 \end{bmatrix}$ row reduces to $\begin{bmatrix} 1 & 0 & 0 \\ 0 & 1 & 0 \\ 0 & 0 & 1 \end{bmatrix}$ and

$\begin{bmatrix} 1 & 1 & 2 \\ 1 & 1 & 1 \\ 1 & 2 & 1 \end{bmatrix}$ row reduces to $\begin{bmatrix} 1 & 0 & 0 \\ 0 & 1 & 0 \\ 0 & 0 & 1 \end{bmatrix}$ as well. So, both

sets of vectors span R^3.

60. (a) False. A set is *linearly dependent* if and only if one of the vectors of this set can be written as a linear combination of the others.

(b) True. See "Definition of Spanning Set of a Vector Space," page 171.

62. The matrix $\begin{bmatrix} 1 & 3 & 0 \\ 2 & 2 & 0 \\ 3 & 1 & 1 \end{bmatrix}$ row reduces to $\begin{bmatrix} 1 & 0 & 0 \\ 0 & 1 & 0 \\ 0 & 0 & 1 \end{bmatrix}$, which

shows that the equation

$$c_1(1, 2, 3) + c_2(3, 2, 1) + c_3(0, 0, 1)$$

only has the trivial solution. So, the three vectors are linearly independent. Furthermore, the vectors span R^3 because the coefficient matrix of the linear system

$$\begin{bmatrix} 1 & 3 & 0 \\ 2 & 2 & 0 \\ 3 & 1 & 1 \end{bmatrix}\begin{bmatrix} c_1 \\ c_2 \\ c_3 \end{bmatrix} = \begin{bmatrix} u_1 \\ u_2 \\ u_3 \end{bmatrix}$$

is nonsingular.

64. If S_1 is linearly dependent, then for some $\mathbf{u}_1, \ldots, \mathbf{u}_n, \mathbf{v} \in S_1$, $\mathbf{v} = c_1\mathbf{u}_1 + \cdots + c_n\mathbf{u}_n$. So, in S_2, you have $\mathbf{v} = c_1\mathbf{u}_1 + \cdots + c_n\mathbf{u}_n$, which implies that S_2 is linearly dependent.

66. Because $\{\mathbf{u}_1, \ldots, \mathbf{u}_n, \mathbf{v}\}$ is linearly dependent, there exist scalars $c_1, \ldots, c_n, c$ not all zero, such that

$$c_1\mathbf{u}_1 + \ldots + c_n\mathbf{u}_n + c\mathbf{v} = \mathbf{0}.$$

But, $c \neq 0$ because $\{\mathbf{u}_1, \ldots, \mathbf{u}_n\}$ are linearly independent. So,

$$c\mathbf{v} = -c_1\mathbf{u}_1 - \cdots - c_n\mathbf{u}_n \Rightarrow \mathbf{v} = \frac{-c_1}{c}\mathbf{u}_1 - \cdots - \frac{c_n}{c}\mathbf{u}_n.$$

68. Suppose $\mathbf{v}_k = c_1\mathbf{v}_1 + \cdots + c_{k-1}\mathbf{v}_{k-1}$. For any vector $\mathbf{u} \in V$,

$$\begin{aligned} \mathbf{u} &= d_1\mathbf{v}_1 + \cdots + d_{k-1}\mathbf{v}_{k-1} + d_k\mathbf{v}_k \\ &= d_1\mathbf{v}_1 + \cdots + d_{k-1}\mathbf{v}_{k-1} + d_k(c_1\mathbf{v}_1 + \cdots + c_{k-1}\mathbf{v}_{k-1}) \\ &= (d_1 + c_1d_k)\mathbf{v}_1 + \cdots + (d_{k-1} + c_{k-1}d_k)\mathbf{v}_{k-1} \end{aligned}$$

which shows that $\mathbf{u} \in \text{span}(\mathbf{v}_1, \ldots, \mathbf{v}_{k-1})$.

70. The vectors are linearly dependent because

$(\mathbf{v} - \mathbf{u}) + (\mathbf{w} - \mathbf{v}) + (\mathbf{u} - \mathbf{w}) = \mathbf{0}$.

Section 4.5   Basis and Dimension

2. There are four vectors in the standard basis for R^4.

$\{(1, 0, 0, 0), (0, 1, 0, 0), (0, 0, 1, 0), (0, 0, 0, 1)\}$

4. There are four vectors in the standard basis for $M_{4,1}$.

$$\left\{ \begin{bmatrix} 1 \\ 0 \\ 0 \\ 0 \end{bmatrix}, \begin{bmatrix} 0 \\ 1 \\ 0 \\ 0 \end{bmatrix}, \begin{bmatrix} 0 \\ 0 \\ 1 \\ 0 \end{bmatrix}, \begin{bmatrix} 0 \\ 0 \\ 0 \\ 1 \end{bmatrix} \right\}$$

6. There are three vectors in the standard basis for P_2.

$\{1, x, x^2\}$

8. A basis for R^2 can only have two vectors. Because S has three vectors, it is not a basis for R^2.

10. S is linearly dependent and does not span R^2.

12. S is linearly dependent and does not span R^2.

14. S does not span R^2, although it is linearly independent.

16. A basis for R^3 contains three linearly independent vectors. Because

$-1(2, 1, -2) + (-2, -1, 2) + (4, 2, -4) = (0, 0, 0)$

S is linearly dependent and is, therefore, not a basis for R^3.

18. S does not span R^3, although it is linearly independent.

20. S is not a basis because it has too many vectors. A basis for R^3 can only have three vectors.

22. S is not a basis because it has too many vectors. A basis for P_2 can only have three vectors.

24. S is not a basis because the vectors are linearly dependent.

$1(6x - 3) + 1(3x^2) + 3(1 - 2x - x^2) = 0$

26. A basis for $M_{2,2}$ must have four vectors. Because S only has two vectors, it is not a basis for $M_{2,2}$.

28. S does not span $M_{2,2}$, although it is linearly independent.

30. Because $\mathbf{v}_1$ and $\mathbf{v}_2$ are multiplies of each other, they do not form a basis for R^2.

32. Because $\{\mathbf{v}_1, \mathbf{v}_2\}$ consists of exactly two linearly independent vectors, it is a basis for R^2.

34. Because the vectors in S are not scalar multiples of one another, they are linearly independent. Because S consists of exactly two linearly independent vectors, it is a basis for R^2.

36. S does not span R^3, although it is linearly independent. So, S is not a basis for R^3.

38. This set contains the zero vector, and is therefore linearly dependent.

$1(0, 0, 0) + 0(1, 5, 6) + 0(6, 2, 1) = (0, 0, 0)$

So, S is not a basis for R^3.

40. To determine if the vectors of S are linearly independent, find the solution of

$c_1(1, 0, 0, 1) + c_2(0, 2, 0, 2) + c_3(1, 0, 1, 0) + c_4(0, 2, 2, 0) = (0, 0, 0, 0)$.

Because the corresponding linear system has nontrivial solutions (for instance, $c_1 = 2, c_2 = -1, c_3 = -2$, and $c_4 = 1$), the vectors are linearly dependent, and S is not a basis for R^4.

42. Form the equation

$c_1(4t - t^2) + c_2(5 + t^3) + c_3(3t + 5) + c_4(2t^3 - 3t^2) = 0$

which yields the homogeneous system

$$\begin{aligned} c_2 \quad\quad\; + 2c_4 &= 0 \\ -c_1 \quad\quad\quad\;\; - 3c_4 &= 0 \\ 4c_1 \quad\;\; + 3c_3 \quad\quad &= 0 \\ 5c_2 + 5c_3 \quad\quad &= 0. \end{aligned}$$

This system has only the trivial solution. So, S consists of exactly four linearly independent vectors. Therefore, S is a basis for P_3.

72. A set consisting of just one vector is linearly independent if it is not the zero vector.

44. Form the equation

$$c_1(t^3 - 1) + c_2(2t^2) + c_3(t + 3) + c_4(5 + 2t + 2t^2 + t^3) = 0$$

which yields the homogeneous system

$$\begin{aligned} c_1 \quad\quad + \; c_4 &= 0 \\ 2c_2 \quad + \; 2c_4 &= 0. \\ c_3 + \; 2c_4 &= 0 \\ -c_1 \quad + \; 3c_3 + \; 5c_4 &= 0. \end{aligned}$$

This system has nontrivial solutions (for instance, $c_1 = 1, c_2 = 1, c_3 = 2,$ and $c_4 = -1$). Therefore, S is not a basis for P_3 because the vectors are linearly dependent.

46. Form the equation

$$c_1\begin{bmatrix} 1 & 2 \\ -5 & 4 \end{bmatrix} + c_2\begin{bmatrix} 2 & -7 \\ 6 & 2 \end{bmatrix} + c_3\begin{bmatrix} 4 & -9 \\ 11 & 12 \end{bmatrix} + c_4\begin{bmatrix} 12 & -16 \\ 17 & 42 \end{bmatrix} = \begin{bmatrix} 0 & 0 \\ 0 & 0 \end{bmatrix}$$

which yields the homogeneous system

$$\begin{aligned} c_1 + 2c_2 + \; 4c_3 + 12c_4 &= 0 \\ 2c_1 - 7c_2 - \; 9c_3 - 16c_4 &= 0 \\ -5c_1 + 6c_2 + 11c_3 + 17c_4 &= 0 \\ 4c_1 + 2c_2 + 12c_3 + 42c_4 &= 0. \end{aligned}$$

Because this system has nontrivial solutions (for instance, $c_1 = 2, c_2 = -1, c_3 = 3,$ and $c_4 = -1$), the set is linearly dependent, and is not a basis for $M_{2,2}$.

48. Form the equation

$$c_1(1, 0, 0) + c_2(1, 1, 0) + c_3(1, 1, 1) = (0, 0, 0)$$

which yields the homogeneous system

$$\begin{aligned} c_1 + c_2 + c_3 &= 0 \\ c_2 + c_3 &= 0 \\ c_3 &= 0. \end{aligned}$$

This system has only the trivial solution, so S is a basis for R^3. Solving the system

$$\begin{aligned} c_1 + c_2 + c_3 &= 8 \\ c_2 + c_3 &= 3 \\ c_3 &= 8 \end{aligned}$$

yields $c_1 = 5, c_2 = -5,$ and $c_3 = 8$. So,

$$\mathbf{u} = 5(1, 0, 0) - 5(1, 1, 0) + 8(1, 1, 1) = (8, 3, 8).$$

50. Form the equation

$$c_1\left(\tfrac{2}{3}, \tfrac{5}{2}, 1\right) + c_2\left(1, \tfrac{3}{2}, 0\right) + c_3(2, 12, 6) = (0, 0, 0)$$

which yields the homogeneous system

$$\begin{aligned} \tfrac{2}{3}c_1 + \; c_2 + \; 2c_3 &= 0 \\ \tfrac{5}{2}c_1 + \tfrac{3}{2}c_2 + 12c_3 &= 0 \\ c_1 \quad\quad + \; 6c_3 &= 0. \end{aligned}$$

Because this system has nontrivial solutions (for instance, $c_1 = 6, c_2 = -2,$ and $c_3 = -1$), the vectors are linearly dependent. So, S is not a basis for R^3.

52. Because a basis for R has one linearly independent vector, the dimension of R is 1.

54. Because a basis for P_4 has five linearly independent vectors, the dimension of P_4 is 5.

56. Because a basis for $M_{3,2}$ has six linearly independent vectors, the dimension of $M_{3,2}$ is 6.

58. One basis for the vector space of all 3×3 symmetric matrices is

$$\left\{ \begin{bmatrix} 1 & 0 & 0 \\ 0 & 0 & 0 \\ 0 & 0 & 0 \end{bmatrix}, \begin{bmatrix} 0 & 1 & 0 \\ 1 & 0 & 0 \\ 0 & 0 & 0 \end{bmatrix}, \begin{bmatrix} 0 & 0 & 1 \\ 0 & 0 & 0 \\ 1 & 0 & 0 \end{bmatrix}, \begin{bmatrix} 0 & 0 & 0 \\ 0 & 1 & 0 \\ 0 & 0 & 0 \end{bmatrix}, \begin{bmatrix} 0 & 0 & 0 \\ 0 & 0 & 1 \\ 0 & 1 & 0 \end{bmatrix}, \begin{bmatrix} 0 & 0 & 0 \\ 0 & 0 & 0 \\ 0 & 0 & 1 \end{bmatrix} \right\}.$$

Because this basis has 6 vectors, the dimension is 6.

60. Although there are four subsets of S that contain three vectors, only three of them are bases for R^3.

$\{(1, 3, -2), (-4, 1, 1), (2, 1, 1)\}, \{(1, 3, -2), (-2, 7, -3), (2, 1, 1)\}, \{(-4, 1, 1), (-2, 7, -3), (2, 1, 1)\}$

The set $\{(1, 3, -2), (-4, 1, 1), (-2, 7, -3)\}$ is linearly dependent.

62. You can add any vector that is not in the span of
$S = \{(1, 0, 2), (0, 1, 1)\}$. For instance, the set

$\{(1, 0, 2), (0, 1, 1), (1, 0, 0)\}$ is a basis for R^3.

64. (a) W is a line through the origin (the y-axis).

(b) A basis for W is $\{(0, 1)\}$.

(c) The dimension of W is 1.

66. (a) W is a plane through the origin.

(b) A basis for W is $\{(2, 1, 0), (-1, 0, 1)\}$, obtained by letting $s = 1, t = 0$, and then $s = 0, t = 1$.

(c) The dimension of W is 2.

68. (a) A basis for W $\{(5, -3, 1, 1)\}$.

(b) The dimension of W is 1.

70. (a) A basis for W is $\{(1, 0, 1, 2), (4, 1, 0, -1)\}$.

(b) The dimension of W is 2.

72. (a) True. See Theorem 4.10, page 183, and "Definition of Dimension of a Vector Space," page 185.

(b) False. A set of $n - 1$ vectors could be linearly dependent. For instance, they can all be multiples of each other.

74. (1) Let $S = \{v_1, \ldots, v_n\}$ be a linearly independent set of vectors. Suppose, by way of contradiction, that S does not span V. Then there exists $v \in V$ such that $v \notin \text{span}(v_1, \ldots, v_n)$. So, the set $\{v_1, \ldots, v_n, v\}$ is linearly independent, which is impossible by Theorem 4.10. So, S does span V, and therefore is a basis.

(2) Let $S = \{v_1, \ldots, v_n\}$ span V. Suppose, by way of contradiction, that S is linearly dependent. Then, some $v_i \in S$ is a linear combination of the other vectors in S. Without loss of generality, you can assume that v_n is a linear combination of $v_1, \ldots, v_{n-1}$, and therefore, $\{v_1, \ldots, v_{n-1}\}$ spans V. But, $n - 1$ vectors span a vector space of at most dimension $n - 1$, a contradiction. So, S is linearly independent, and therefore a basis.

76. (a) Since the dimension of R^3 is three, any basis must have exactly three vectors. S_1 cannot span R^3.

(b) Four vectors in R^3 must form a linearly dependent set.

(c) If S_3 is linearly independent, it will be a basis for R^3.

78. Let the number of vectors in S be n. If S is linearly independent, then you are done. If not, some $v \in S$ is a linear combination of other vectors in S. Let $S_1 = S - v$. Note that $\text{span}(S) = \text{span}(S_1)$ because v is a linear combination of vectors in S_1. You now consider spanning set S_1. If S_1 is linearly independent, you are done. If not, repeat the process of removing a vector, which is a linear combination of other vectors in S_1, to obtain spanning set S_2. Continue this process with S_2. Note that this process would terminate because the original set S is a finite set and each removal produces a spanning set with fewer vectors than the previous spanning set. So, in at most $n - 1$ steps, the process would terminate leaving you with minimal spanning set, which is linearly independent and is contained in S.

Section 4.6   Rank of a Matrix and Systems of Linear Equations

2. (a) $(6, 5, -1)$

(b) $[6], [5], [-1]$

4. (a) $(0, 2, -3), (3, 1, 0), (-2, -1, 2)$

(b) $\begin{bmatrix} 0 \\ 3 \\ -2 \end{bmatrix}, \begin{bmatrix} 2 \\ 1 \\ -1 \end{bmatrix}, \begin{bmatrix} -3 \\ 0 \\ 2 \end{bmatrix}$

6. (a) A basis for the row space is $\{(0, 1, -2)\}$.

(b) Because this matrix is already row-reduced, the rank is 1.

8. (a) A basis for the row space is $\left\{\left(1, 0, \frac{4}{5}\right), \left(0, 1, \frac{1}{5}\right)\right\}$.

(b) Because this matrix row reduces to

$\begin{bmatrix} 1 & 0 & \frac{4}{5} \\ 0 & 1 & \frac{1}{5} \\ 0 & 0 & 0 \end{bmatrix}$

the rank of the matrix is 2.

10. (a) A basis for the row space is $\{(1, 0, 0, 0, 0), (0, 1, 0, 0, 0), (0, 0, 1, 0, 0), (0, 0, 0, 1, 0), (0, 0, 0, 0, 1)\}$.

(b) Because this matrix row reduces to

$$\begin{bmatrix} 1 & 0 & 0 & 0 & 0 \\ 0 & 1 & 0 & 0 & 0 \\ 0 & 0 & 1 & 0 & 0 \\ 0 & 0 & 0 & 1 & 0 \\ 0 & 0 & 0 & 0 & 1 \end{bmatrix}$$

the rank of the matrix is 5.

12. Use $\mathbf{v}_1$, $\mathbf{v}_2$, and $\mathbf{v}_3$ to form the rows of matrix A. Then write A in row-echelon form.

$$A = \begin{bmatrix} 4 & 2 & -1 \\ 1 & 2 & -8 \\ 0 & 1 & 2 \end{bmatrix} \begin{matrix} \mathbf{v}_1 \\ \mathbf{v}_2 \\ \mathbf{v}_3 \end{matrix} \to B = \begin{bmatrix} 1 & 0 & 0 \\ 0 & 1 & 0 \\ 0 & 0 & 1 \end{bmatrix} \begin{matrix} \mathbf{w}_1 \\ \mathbf{w}_2 \\ \mathbf{w}_3 \end{matrix}$$

So, the nonzero row vectors of B

$\mathbf{w}_1 = (1, 0, 0)$, $\mathbf{w}_2 = (0, 1, 0)$, and $\mathbf{w}_3 = (0, 0, 1)$

form a basis for the row space of A. That is, they form a basis for the subspace spanned by S.

14. Use $\mathbf{v}_1$, $\mathbf{v}_2$, and $\mathbf{v}_3$ to form the rows of matrix A. Then write A in row-echelon form.

$$A = \begin{bmatrix} 1 & 2 & 2 \\ -1 & 0 & 0 \\ 1 & 1 & 1 \end{bmatrix} \begin{matrix} \mathbf{v}_1 \\ \mathbf{v}_2 \\ \mathbf{v}_3 \end{matrix} \to B = \begin{bmatrix} 1 & 0 & 0 \\ 0 & 1 & 1 \\ 0 & 0 & 0 \end{bmatrix} \begin{matrix} \mathbf{w}_1 \\ \mathbf{w}_2 \end{matrix}$$

So, the nonzero row vectors of B

$\mathbf{w}_1 = (1, 0, 0)$ and $\mathbf{w}_2 = (0, 1, 1)$

form a basis for the row space of A. That is, they form a basis for the subspace spanned by S.

16. Begin by forming the matrix whose rows are vectors in S.

$$\begin{bmatrix} 6 & -3 & 6 & 34 \\ 3 & -2 & 3 & 19 \\ 8 & 3 & -9 & 6 \\ -2 & 0 & 6 & -5 \end{bmatrix}$$

This matrix reduces to

$$\begin{bmatrix} 1 & 0 & 0 & 0 \\ 0 & 1 & 0 & 0 \\ 0 & 0 & 1 & 0 \\ 0 & 0 & 0 & 1 \end{bmatrix}.$$

So, a basis for span(S) is

$\{(1, 0, 0, 0), (0, 1, 0, 0), (0, 0, 1, 0), (0, 0, 0, 1)\}$.

$\big(\text{span}(S) = R^4\big)$

18. Begin by forming the matrix whose rows are the vectors in S.

$$\begin{bmatrix} 2 & 5 & -3 & -2 \\ -2 & -3 & 2 & -5 \\ 1 & 3 & -2 & 2 \\ -1 & -5 & 3 & 5 \end{bmatrix}$$

This matrix reduces to

$$\begin{bmatrix} 1 & 0 & 0 & 3 \\ 0 & 1 & 0 & -13 \\ 0 & 0 & 1 & -19 \\ 0 & 0 & 0 & 0 \end{bmatrix}.$$

So, a basis for span(S) is

$\{(1, 0, 0, 3), (0, 1, 0, -13), (0, 0, 1, -19)\}$.

20. (a) A basis for the column space is $\{[1]\}$.

(b) Because this matrix is already row-reduced, the rank is 1.

22. (a) Row-reducing the transpose of the original matrix produces

$$\begin{bmatrix} 1 & 0 & -\frac{2}{5} \\ 0 & 1 & \frac{3}{5} \\ 0 & 0 & 0 \end{bmatrix}.$$

So, a basis for the column space is $\left\{ \begin{bmatrix} 1 \\ 0 \\ -\frac{2}{5} \end{bmatrix}, \begin{bmatrix} 0 \\ 1 \\ \frac{3}{5} \end{bmatrix} \right\}$.

Equivalently, a basis for the column space consists of columns 1 and 2 of the original matrix

$$\left\{ \begin{bmatrix} 4 \\ 6 \\ 2 \end{bmatrix}, \begin{bmatrix} 20 \\ -5 \\ -11 \end{bmatrix} \right\}.$$

(b) Because this matrix row reduces to

$$\begin{bmatrix} 1 & 0 & \frac{1}{4} \\ 0 & 1 & \frac{3}{2} \\ 0 & 0 & 0 \end{bmatrix}$$

the rank of the matrix is 2.

24. (a) Row reducing the transpose of the original matrix produces

$$\begin{bmatrix} 1 & 0 & 0 & 0 & 0 \\ 0 & 1 & 0 & 0 & 0 \\ 0 & 0 & 1 & 0 & 0 \\ 0 & 0 & 0 & 1 & 0 \\ 0 & 0 & 0 & 0 & 1 \end{bmatrix}.$$

So, a basis for the column space is

$$\left\{ \begin{bmatrix} 1 \\ 0 \\ 0 \\ 0 \\ 0 \end{bmatrix}, \begin{bmatrix} 0 \\ 1 \\ 0 \\ 0 \\ 0 \end{bmatrix}, \begin{bmatrix} 0 \\ 0 \\ 1 \\ 0 \\ 0 \end{bmatrix}, \begin{bmatrix} 0 \\ 0 \\ 0 \\ 1 \\ 0 \end{bmatrix}, \begin{bmatrix} 0 \\ 0 \\ 0 \\ 0 \\ 1 \end{bmatrix} \right\}.$$

(b) Because this matrix row reduces to

$$\begin{bmatrix} 1 & 0 & 0 & 0 & 0 \\ 0 & 1 & 0 & 0 & 0 \\ 0 & 0 & 1 & 0 & 0 \\ 0 & 0 & 0 & 1 & 0 \\ 0 & 0 & 0 & 0 & 1 \end{bmatrix}$$

the rank of the matrix is 5.

26. Solving the system $A\mathbf{x} = \mathbf{0}$ yields only the trivial solution $\mathbf{x} = (0, 0)$. So, the dimension of the solution space is 0. The solution space consists of the zero vector itself.

28. Solving the system $A\mathbf{x} = \mathbf{0}$ yields solutions of the form $(-4s - 2t, s, t)$, where s and t are any real numbers. The dimension of the solution space is 2, and a basis is $\{(-4, 1, 0), (-2, 0, 1)\}$.

30. Solving the system $A\mathbf{x} = \mathbf{0}$ yields solutions of the form $(-4t, t, 0)$, where t is any real number. The dimension of the solution space is 1, and a basis is $\{(-4, 1, 0)\}$.

32. Solving the system $A\mathbf{x} = \mathbf{0}$ yields solutions of the form $(2s - t, s, t)$, where s and t are any real numbers. The dimension of the solution space is 2, and a basis is $\{(-1, 0, 1), (2, 1, 0)\}$.

34. Solving the system $A\mathbf{x} = \mathbf{0}$ yields solutions of the form $(2s - 5t, -s + t, s, t)$, where s and t are any real numbers. The dimension of the solution set is 2, and a basis is $\{(-5, 1, 0, 1), (2, -1, 1, 0)\}$.

36. The only solution of the system $A\mathbf{x} = \mathbf{0}$ is the trivial solution. So, the solution space is $\{(0, 0, 0, 0)\}$ whose dimension is 0.

38. (a) The system yields solutions of the form (t, t), where t is any real number and a basis for the solution space is $\{(1, 1)\}$.

(b) The dimension of the solution space is 1.

40. (a) The only solution of this system is the trivial solution $x = y = z = 0$. So, the basis for the solution space is $\{(0, 0, 0)\}$.

(b) The dimension of the solution space is 0.

42. (a) This system yields solutions of the form $(4t - 2s, s, t)$, where s and t are any real numbers. A basis for the solution space is $\{(-2, 1, 0), (4, 0, 1)\}$.

(b) The dimension of the solution space is 2.

44. (a) This system yields solutions of the form $\left(\frac{5}{8}t, -\frac{15}{8}t, \frac{9}{8}t, t\right)$, where t is any real number. A basis for the solution space is $\left\{\left(\frac{5}{8}, -\frac{15}{8}, \frac{9}{8}, 1\right)\right\}$ or $\{(5, -15, 9, 8)\}$.

(b) The dimension of the solution space is 1.

46. (a) This system yields solutions of the form $\left(-t + 2s - r, -4t - 8s - \frac{1}{3}r, r, s, t\right)$, where $r, s,$ and t are any real numbers. A basis for the solution space is $\left\{(-1, -4, 0, 0, 1), (2, -8, 0, 1, 0), \left(-1, -\frac{1}{3}, 1, 0, 0\right)\right\}$.

(b) The dimension of the solution space is 3.

48. (a) $\text{rank}(A) = \text{rank}(B) = 3$

$\text{nullity}(A) = n - r = 5 - 3 = 2$

(b) Choosing $x_3 = s$ and $x_5 = t$ as the free variables, you have

$x_1 = -s - t$

$x_2 = 2s - 3t$

$x_3 = s$

$x_4 = 5t$

$x_5 = t.$

A basis for nullspace is

$\{(-1, 2, 1, 0, 0), (-1, -3, 0, 5, 1)\}.$

(c) A basis for the row space of A (which is equal to the row space of B) is

$\{(1, 0, 1, 0, 1), (0, 1, -2, 0, 3), (0, 0, 0, 1, -5)\}.$

(d) A basis for the column space A (which is *not* the same as the column space of B) is

$\{(-2, 1, 3, 1), (-5, 3, 11, 7), (0, 1, 7, 5)\}.$

(e) Linearly dependent

(f) (i) and (iii) are linearly independent, while (ii) is linearly dependent.

50. (a) The system $Ax = b$ is consistent because its augmented matrix reduces to

$$\begin{bmatrix} 1 & -2 & 0 & 4 \\ 0 & 0 & 1 & 0 \\ 0 & 0 & 0 & 0 \end{bmatrix}.$$

(b) The solutions of $Ax = b$ are of the form $(4 + 2t, t, 0)$, where t is any real number. That is,

$$x = \begin{bmatrix} 4 \\ 0 \\ 0 \end{bmatrix} + t \begin{bmatrix} 2 \\ 1 \\ 0 \end{bmatrix},$$

where

$$x_p = \begin{bmatrix} 4 \\ 0 \\ 0 \end{bmatrix} \quad \text{and} \quad x_h = t \begin{bmatrix} 2 \\ 1 \\ 0 \end{bmatrix}.$$

52. This system $Ax = b$ is inconsistent because its augmented matrix reduces to

$$\begin{bmatrix} 1 & 0 & 4 & 2 & 0 \\ 0 & 1 & -2 & 4 & 0 \\ 0 & 0 & 0 & 0 & 1 \end{bmatrix}.$$

54. (a) The system $Ax = b$ is consistent because its augmented matrix reduces to

$$\begin{bmatrix} 1 & 0 & 4 & -5 & 6 & 0 \\ 0 & 1 & 2 & 2 & 4 & 1 \\ 0 & 0 & 0 & 0 & 0 & 0 \end{bmatrix}.$$

(b) The solutions of the system are of the form

$(-6t + 5s - 4r, 1 - 4t - 2s - 2r, r, s, t),$

where $r, s,$ and t are any real numbers. That is,

$$x = \begin{bmatrix} 0 \\ 1 \\ 0 \\ 0 \\ 0 \end{bmatrix} + r \begin{bmatrix} -4 \\ -2 \\ 1 \\ 0 \\ 0 \end{bmatrix} + s \begin{bmatrix} 5 \\ -2 \\ 0 \\ 1 \\ 0 \end{bmatrix} + t \begin{bmatrix} -6 \\ -4 \\ 0 \\ 0 \\ 1 \end{bmatrix},$$

where

$$x_p = \begin{bmatrix} 0 \\ 1 \\ 0 \\ 0 \\ 0 \end{bmatrix} \quad \text{and} \quad x_h = r \begin{bmatrix} -4 \\ -2 \\ 1 \\ 0 \\ 0 \end{bmatrix} + s \begin{bmatrix} 5 \\ -2 \\ 0 \\ 1 \\ 0 \end{bmatrix} + t \begin{bmatrix} -6 \\ -4 \\ 0 \\ 0 \\ 1 \end{bmatrix}.$$

56. The vector b is not in the column space of A because the linear system $Ax = b$ is inconsistent.

58. The vector b is in the column space of A if the equation $Ax = b$ is consistent. Because $Ax = b$ has the solution

$$x = \begin{bmatrix} -\frac{5}{4} \\ \frac{3}{4} \\ -\frac{1}{2} \end{bmatrix},$$

b is in the column space of A. Furthermore,

$$b = -\frac{5}{4} \begin{bmatrix} 1 \\ -1 \\ 2 \end{bmatrix} + \frac{3}{4} \begin{bmatrix} 3 \\ 1 \\ 0 \end{bmatrix} - \frac{1}{2} \begin{bmatrix} 0 \\ 0 \\ 1 \end{bmatrix} = \begin{bmatrix} 1 \\ 2 \\ -3 \end{bmatrix}.$$

60. Many examples are possible. For instance,

$$\begin{bmatrix} 1 & 0 \\ 0 & 0 \end{bmatrix} \begin{bmatrix} 0 & 0 \\ 0 & 1 \end{bmatrix} = \begin{bmatrix} 0 & 0 \\ 0 & 0 \end{bmatrix}.$$

rank 1 rank 1 rank 0

62. Let $\begin{bmatrix} a_{ij} \end{bmatrix} = A$ be an $m \times n$ matrix in row-echelon form. The nonzero row vectors $\mathbf{r}_1, \dots, \mathbf{r}_k$ of A have the form (if the first column of A is not all zero)

$$\mathbf{r}_1 = \left(e_{11}, \dots, e_{1p}, \dots, e_{1q}, \dots\right)$$

$$\mathbf{r}_2 = \left(0, \dots, 0, e_{2p}, \dots, e_{2q}, \dots\right)$$

$$\mathbf{r}_3 = \left(0, \dots, 0, 0, \dots, 0, e_{3q}, \dots\right)$$

and so forth, where e_{11}, e_{2p}, e_{3q} denote leading ones. Then the equation

$$c_1 \mathbf{r}_1 + c_2 \mathbf{r}_2 + \cdots + c_k \mathbf{r}_k = \mathbf{0}$$

implies that

$$c_1 e_{11} = 0, c_1 e_{1p} + c_2 e_{2p} = 0, c_1 e_{1q} + c_2 e_{2q} + c_3 e_{3q} = 0$$

and so forth. You can conclude in turn that $c_1 = 0$, $c_2 = 0, \dots, c_k = 0$, and so the row vectors are linearly independent.

64. Suppose that the three points are collinear. If they are on the same vertical line, then $x_1 = x_2 = x_3$. So, the matrix has two equal columns, and its rank is less than 3. Similarly, if the three points lie on the nonvertical line $y = mx + b$, you have

$$\begin{bmatrix} x_1 & y_1 & 1 \\ x_2 & y_2 & 1 \\ x_3 & y_3 & 1 \end{bmatrix} = \begin{bmatrix} x_1 & mx_1 + b & 1 \\ x_2 & mx_2 + b & 1 \\ x_3 & mx_3 + b & 1 \end{bmatrix}.$$

Because the second column is a linear combination of the first and third columns, this determinant is zero, and the rank is less than 3.

On the other hand, if the rank of the matrix

$$\begin{bmatrix} x_1 & y_1 & 1 \\ x_2 & y_2 & 1 \\ x_3 & y_3 & 1 \end{bmatrix}$$

is less than 3, then the determinant is zero, which implies that the three points are collinear.

66. For $n = 2$, $\begin{bmatrix} 1 & 2 \\ 3 & 4 \end{bmatrix}$ has rank 2.

For $n = 3$, $\begin{bmatrix} 1 & 2 & 3 \\ 4 & 5 & 6 \\ 7 & 8 & 9 \end{bmatrix}$ has rank 2.

In general, for $n \geq 2$, the rank is 2, because rows $3, \dots, n$, are linear combinations of the first two rows. For example, $R_3 = 2R_2 - R_1$.

68. Let

$$\mathbf{x} \in N(A) \Rightarrow A\mathbf{x} = \mathbf{0} \Rightarrow A^T A \mathbf{x} = \mathbf{0} \Rightarrow \mathbf{x} \in N(A^T A).$$

70. (a) True. See Theorem 4.13, page 190.

(b) False. The dimension of the solution space of $A\mathbf{x} = \mathbf{0}$ for $m \times n$ matrix of rank r is $n - r$. See Theorem 4.17, page 196.

72. (a) The row space and column space of a matrix have the same dimension, so the column space has a dimension of 2.

(b) 2

(c) $(\text{rank}) + (\text{nullity}) = (\text{number of columns})$, so the nullity is 3.

(d) 3

74. Let A be an $m \times n$ matrix.

(a) If $A\mathbf{x} = \mathbf{b}$ is consistent for all vectors $\mathbf{b}$, then the augmented matrix $\begin{bmatrix} A & \mathbf{b} \end{bmatrix}$ cannot row-reduce to $\begin{bmatrix} U & \mathbf{b}' \end{bmatrix}$, where the last row of U consists of all zeros. So, the rank of A is m. Conversely, if the rank of A is m, then $\text{rank}(A) = \text{rank}\left(\begin{bmatrix} A & \mathbf{b} \end{bmatrix}\right)$ for all vectors $\mathbf{b}$, which implies that $A\mathbf{x} = \mathbf{b}$ is consistent.

(b) $A\mathbf{x}$ is a linear combination $x_1 \mathbf{a}_1 + \cdots + x_n \mathbf{a}_n$ of the columns of A. So, $A\mathbf{x} = x_1 \mathbf{a}_1 + \cdots + x_n \mathbf{a}_n = \mathbf{0}$ has only the trivial solution $x_1 = \cdots = x_n = 0$ if and only if $\mathbf{a}_1, \cdots, \mathbf{a}_n$ are linearly independent.

76. The rank of the matrix is at most 3. So, the dimension of the row space is at most 3, and any four vectors in the row space must form a linearly dependent set.

Section 4.7 Coordinates and Change of Basis

2. $\begin{bmatrix} 1 \\ -3 \\ 0 \end{bmatrix}$

4. $\begin{bmatrix} -6 \\ 12 \\ -4 \\ 9 \\ -8 \end{bmatrix}$

6. Because $[\mathbf{x}]_B = \begin{bmatrix} -2 \\ 3 \end{bmatrix}$, you can write

$$\mathbf{x} = -2(-1, 4) + 3(4, -1) = (14, -11)$$

which implies that the coordinates of $\mathbf{x}$ relative to the standard basis S are $[\mathbf{x}]_S = \begin{bmatrix} 14 \\ -11 \end{bmatrix}$.

8. Because $[\mathbf{x}]_B = \begin{bmatrix} 2 \\ 0 \\ 4 \end{bmatrix}$, you can write

$$\mathbf{x} = 2\left(\tfrac{3}{4}, \tfrac{5}{2}, \tfrac{3}{2}\right) + 0\left(3, 4, \tfrac{7}{2}\right) + 4\left(-\tfrac{3}{2}, 6, 2\right) = \left(-\tfrac{9}{2}, 29, 11\right)$$

which implies that the coordinates of $\mathbf{x}$ relative to the standard basis S are $[\mathbf{x}_S] = \begin{bmatrix} -\tfrac{9}{2} \\ 29 \\ 11 \end{bmatrix}$.

10. Because $[\mathbf{x}]_B = \begin{bmatrix} -2 \\ 3 \\ 4 \\ 1 \end{bmatrix}$, you can write

$$\mathbf{x} = -2(4, 0, 7, 3) + 3(0, 5, -1, -1) + 4(-3, 4, 2, 1) + 1(0, 1, 5, 0) = (-20, 32, -4, -5)$$

which implies that the coordinates of $\mathbf{x}$ relative to the standard basis S are

$$[\mathbf{x}]_S = \begin{bmatrix} -20 \\ 32 \\ -4 \\ -5 \end{bmatrix}.$$

12. Begin by writing $\mathbf{x}$ as a linear combination of the vectors in B.

$$\mathbf{x} = (-26, 32) = c_1(-6, 7) + c_2(4, -3)$$

Equating corresponding components yields the following system of linear equations.

$$\begin{aligned} -6c_1 + 4c_2 &= -26 \\ 7c_1 - 3c_2 &= 32 \end{aligned}$$

The solution of this system is $c_1 = 5$ and $c_2 = 1$. So, $\mathbf{x} = 5(-6, 7) + 1(4, -3)$ and $[\mathbf{x}]_B = \begin{bmatrix} 5 \\ 1 \end{bmatrix}$.

14. Begin by writing $\mathbf{x}$ as a linear combination of the vectors in B.

$$\mathbf{x} = \left(3, -\tfrac{1}{2}, 8\right) = c_1\left(\tfrac{3}{2}, 4, 1\right) + c_2\left(\tfrac{3}{4}, \tfrac{5}{2}, 0\right) + c_3\left(1, \tfrac{1}{2}, 2\right)$$

Equating corresponding components yields the following system of linear equations.

$$\begin{aligned} \tfrac{3}{2}c_1 + \tfrac{3}{4}c_2 + c_3 &= 3 \\ 4c_1 + \tfrac{5}{2}c_2 + \tfrac{1}{2}c_3 &= -\tfrac{1}{2} \\ c_1 \qquad\quad + 2c_3 &= 8 \end{aligned}$$

The solution of this system is $c_1 = 2, c_2 = -4$, and $c_3 = 3$. So, $\mathbf{x} = 2\left(\tfrac{3}{2}, 4, 1\right) - 4\left(\tfrac{3}{4}, \tfrac{5}{2}, 0\right) + 3\left(1, \tfrac{1}{2}, 2\right)$ and $[\mathbf{x}]_B = \begin{bmatrix} 2 \\ -4 \\ 3 \end{bmatrix}$.

16. Begin by writing **x** as a linear combination of the vectors in B.

$\mathbf{x} = (0, -20, 7, 15) = c_1(9, -3, 15, 4) + c_2(3, 0, 0, 1) + c_3(0, -5, 6, 8) + c_4(3, -4, 2, -3)$

Equating corresponding components yields the following system of linear equations.

$$\begin{aligned} 9c_1 + 3c_2 \qquad\quad + 3c_4 &= 0 \\ -3c_1 \qquad\quad - 5c_3 - 4c_4 &= -20 \\ 15c_1 \qquad\quad + 6c_3 + 2c_4 &= 7 \\ 4c_1 + c_2 + 8c_3 - 3c_4 &= 15 \end{aligned}$$

The solution of this system is $c_1 = -1, c_2 = 1, c_3 = 3,$ and $c_4 = 2.$

So, $(0, -20, 7, 15) = -1(9, -3, 15, 4) + 1(3, 0, 0, 1) + 3(0, -5, 6, 8) + 2(3, -4, 2, -3)$ and $[\mathbf{x}]_B = \begin{bmatrix} -1 \\ 1 \\ 3 \\ 2 \end{bmatrix}.$

18. Begin by forming the matrix

$[B' \ B] = \begin{bmatrix} 1 & 5 & 1 & 0 \\ 1 & 6 & 0 & 1 \end{bmatrix}$

and then use Gauss-Jordan elimination to produce

$[I_2 \ P^{-1}] = \begin{bmatrix} 1 & 0 & 6 & -5 \\ 0 & 1 & -1 & 1 \end{bmatrix}.$

So, the transition matrix from B to B' is

$P^{-1} = \begin{bmatrix} 6 & -5 \\ -1 & 1 \end{bmatrix}.$

20. Begin by forming the matrix

$[B' \ B] = \begin{bmatrix} 1 & 0 & 1 & 1 \\ 0 & 1 & 1 & 0 \end{bmatrix}.$

Because this matrix is already in the form $[I_2 \ P^{-1}]$, you see that the transition matrix from B to B' is

$P^{-1} = \begin{bmatrix} 1 & 1 \\ 1 & 0 \end{bmatrix}.$

22. Begin by forming the matrix

$[B' \ B] = \begin{bmatrix} 1 & 2 & 2 & 1 & 0 & 0 \\ 3 & 7 & 9 & 0 & 1 & 0 \\ -1 & -4 & -7 & 0 & 0 & 1 \end{bmatrix}$

and then use Gauss-Jordan elimination to produce

$[I_3 \ P^{-1}] = \begin{bmatrix} 1 & 0 & 0 & -13 & 6 & 4 \\ 0 & 1 & 0 & 12 & -5 & -3 \\ 0 & 0 & 1 & -5 & 2 & 1 \end{bmatrix}.$

So, the transition matrix from B to B' is

$P^{-1} = \begin{bmatrix} -13 & 6 & 4 \\ 12 & -5 & -3 \\ -5 & 2 & 1 \end{bmatrix}.$

24. Begin by forming the matrix

$[B' \ B] = \begin{bmatrix} 1 & 0 & 0 & 1 & 2 & 5 \\ 0 & 1 & 0 & 3 & -1 & 6 \\ 0 & 0 & 1 & 2 & 2 & 1 \end{bmatrix}.$

Because this matrix is already in the form $[I_3 \ P^{-1}]$, the transition matrix from B to B' is

$P^{-1} = \begin{bmatrix} 1 & 2 & 5 \\ 3 & -1 & 6 \\ 2 & 2 & 1 \end{bmatrix}.$

26. Begin by forming the matrix

$[B' \ B] = \begin{bmatrix} 1 & -1 & -2 & 3 \\ 2 & 0 & 1 & 2 \end{bmatrix}$

and then use Gauss-Jordan elimination to produce

$[I_2 \ P^{-1}] = \begin{bmatrix} 1 & 0 & \frac{1}{2} & 1 \\ 0 & 1 & \frac{5}{2} & -2 \end{bmatrix}.$

So, the transition matrix from B to B' is

$P^{-1} = \begin{bmatrix} \frac{1}{2} & 1 \\ \frac{5}{2} & -2 \end{bmatrix}.$

28. Begin by forming the matrix

$[B' \ B] = \begin{bmatrix} 2 & 0 & -3 & 1 & 0 & 0 \\ -1 & 2 & 2 & 0 & 1 & 0 \\ 4 & 1 & 1 & 0 & 0 & 1 \end{bmatrix}$

and then use Gauss-Jordan elimination to produce

$[I_3 \ P^{-1}] = \begin{bmatrix} 1 & 0 & 0 & 0 & -\frac{1}{9} & \frac{2}{9} \\ 0 & 1 & 0 & \frac{1}{3} & \frac{14}{27} & -\frac{1}{27} \\ 0 & 0 & 1 & -\frac{1}{3} & -\frac{2}{27} & \frac{4}{27} \end{bmatrix}.$

So, the transition matrix from B to B' is

$P^{-1} = \begin{bmatrix} 0 & -\frac{1}{9} & \frac{2}{9} \\ \frac{1}{3} & \frac{14}{27} & -\frac{1}{27} \\ -\frac{1}{3} & -\frac{2}{27} & \frac{4}{27} \end{bmatrix}.$

30. Begin by forming the matrix

$$[B' \ B] = \begin{bmatrix} 1 & 0 & -1 & 3 & 1 & 1 \\ 1 & 1 & 4 & 2 & 1 & 2 \\ -1 & 2 & 0 & 1 & 2 & 0 \end{bmatrix}.$$

and then use Gauss-Jordan elimination to produce

$$[I_3 \ P^{-1}] = \begin{bmatrix} 1 & 0 & 0 & \frac{27}{11} & \frac{8}{11} & \frac{12}{11} \\ 0 & 1 & 0 & \frac{19}{11} & \frac{15}{11} & \frac{6}{11} \\ 0 & 0 & 1 & -\frac{6}{11} & -\frac{3}{11} & \frac{1}{11} \end{bmatrix}.$$

So, the transition matrix from B to B' is

$$P^{-1} = \begin{bmatrix} \frac{27}{11} & \frac{8}{11} & \frac{12}{11} \\ \frac{19}{11} & \frac{15}{11} & \frac{6}{11} \\ -\frac{6}{11} & -\frac{3}{11} & \frac{1}{11} \end{bmatrix}.$$

32. Begin by forming the matrix

$$[B' \ B] = \begin{bmatrix} 1 & 0 & 0 & 0 & 1 & 0 & 0 & 0 \\ 1 & 1 & 0 & 0 & 0 & 1 & 0 & 0 \\ 1 & 1 & 1 & 0 & 0 & 0 & 1 & 0 \\ 1 & 1 & 1 & 1 & 0 & 0 & 0 & 1 \end{bmatrix}$$

and then use Gauss-Jordan elimination to produce

$$[I_4 \ P^{-1}] = \begin{bmatrix} 1 & 0 & 0 & 0 & 1 & 0 & 0 & 0 \\ 0 & 1 & 0 & 0 & -1 & 1 & 0 & 0 \\ 0 & 0 & 1 & 0 & 0 & -1 & 1 & 0 \\ 0 & 0 & 0 & 1 & 0 & 0 & -1 & 1 \end{bmatrix}.$$

So, the transition matrix from B to B' is

$$P^{-1} = \begin{bmatrix} 1 & 0 & 0 & 0 \\ -1 & 1 & 0 & 0 \\ 0 & -1 & 1 & 0 \\ 0 & 0 & -1 & 1 \end{bmatrix}.$$

34. Begin by forming the matrix

$$[B' \ B] = \begin{bmatrix} 2 & 3 & 0 & 2 & 0 & 1 & 0 & 0 & 0 & 0 \\ 4 & -1 & 0 & -1 & 1 & 0 & 1 & 0 & 0 & 0 \\ -2 & 0 & -2 & 2 & 2 & 0 & 0 & 1 & 0 & 0 \\ 1 & 1 & 4 & 1 & -3 & 0 & 0 & 0 & 1 & 0 \\ 0 & 2 & 5 & 1 & 1 & 0 & 0 & 0 & 0 & 1 \end{bmatrix}$$

and then use Gauss-Jordan elimination to produce

$$[I_5 \ P^{-1}] = \begin{bmatrix} 1 & 0 & 0 & 0 & 0 & \frac{12}{157} & \frac{32}{157} & \frac{5}{314} & \frac{10}{157} & -\frac{7}{157} \\ 0 & 1 & 0 & 0 & 0 & \frac{45}{157} & -\frac{37}{157} & -\frac{99}{314} & -\frac{41}{157} & \frac{13}{157} \\ 0 & 0 & 1 & 0 & 0 & -\frac{17}{157} & \frac{7}{157} & \frac{3}{157} & \frac{12}{157} & \frac{23}{157} \\ 0 & 0 & 0 & 1 & 0 & -\frac{1}{157} & \frac{47}{314} & \frac{287}{628} & \frac{103}{314} & -\frac{25}{314} \\ 0 & 0 & 0 & 0 & 1 & -\frac{4}{157} & \frac{31}{314} & \frac{49}{628} & -\frac{59}{314} & \frac{57}{314} \end{bmatrix}.$$

So, the transition matrix from B to B' is

$$P^{-1} = \begin{bmatrix} \frac{12}{157} & \frac{32}{157} & \frac{5}{314} & \frac{10}{157} & -\frac{7}{157} \\ \frac{45}{157} & -\frac{37}{157} & -\frac{99}{314} & -\frac{41}{157} & \frac{13}{157} \\ -\frac{17}{157} & \frac{7}{157} & \frac{3}{157} & \frac{12}{157} & \frac{23}{157} \\ -\frac{1}{157} & \frac{47}{314} & \frac{287}{628} & \frac{103}{314} & -\frac{25}{314} \\ -\frac{4}{157} & \frac{31}{314} & \frac{49}{628} & -\frac{59}{314} & \frac{57}{314} \end{bmatrix}.$$

36. (a) $[B' \ B] = \begin{bmatrix} 1 & 32 & 2 & 6 \\ 1 & 31 & -2 & 3 \end{bmatrix} \Rightarrow \begin{bmatrix} 1 & 0 & -126 & -90 \\ 0 & 1 & 4 & 3 \end{bmatrix} = [I \ P^{-1}] \Rightarrow P^{-1} = \begin{bmatrix} -126 & -90 \\ 4 & 3 \end{bmatrix}$

(b) $[B \ B'] = \begin{bmatrix} 2 & 6 & 1 & 32 \\ -2 & 3 & 1 & 31 \end{bmatrix} \Rightarrow \begin{bmatrix} 1 & 0 & -\frac{1}{6} & -5 \\ 0 & 1 & \frac{2}{9} & 7 \end{bmatrix} = [I \ P] \Rightarrow P = \begin{bmatrix} -\frac{1}{6} & -5 \\ \frac{2}{9} & 7 \end{bmatrix}.$

(c) $PP^{-1} = \begin{bmatrix} -\frac{1}{6} & -5 \\ \frac{2}{9} & 7 \end{bmatrix} \begin{bmatrix} -126 & -90 \\ 4 & 3 \end{bmatrix} = \begin{bmatrix} 1 & 0 \\ 0 & 1 \end{bmatrix}$

(d) $[\mathbf{x}]_B = P[\mathbf{x}]_{B'} = \begin{bmatrix} -\frac{1}{6} & -5 \\ \frac{2}{9} & 7 \end{bmatrix} \begin{bmatrix} 2 \\ -1 \end{bmatrix} = \begin{bmatrix} \frac{14}{3} \\ -\frac{59}{9} \end{bmatrix}$

38. (a) $[B' \quad B] = \begin{bmatrix} 2 & 0 & 1 & 1 & 1 & 0 \\ 2 & 1 & 0 & 1 & -1 & 0 \\ 0 & 1 & 1 & 1 & 1 & 1 \end{bmatrix} \Rightarrow \begin{bmatrix} 1 & 0 & 0 & \frac{1}{4} & -\frac{1}{4} & -\frac{1}{4} \\ 0 & 1 & 0 & \frac{1}{2} & -\frac{1}{2} & \frac{1}{2} \\ 0 & 0 & 1 & \frac{1}{2} & \frac{3}{2} & \frac{1}{2} \end{bmatrix} = [I \quad P^{-1}] \Rightarrow P^{-1} = \begin{bmatrix} \frac{1}{4} & -\frac{1}{4} & -\frac{1}{4} \\ \frac{1}{2} & -\frac{1}{2} & \frac{1}{2} \\ \frac{1}{2} & \frac{3}{2} & \frac{1}{2} \end{bmatrix}$

(b) $[B \quad B'] = \begin{bmatrix} 1 & 1 & 0 & 2 & 0 & 1 \\ 1 & -1 & 0 & 2 & 1 & 0 \\ 1 & 1 & 1 & 0 & 1 & 1 \end{bmatrix} \Rightarrow \begin{bmatrix} 1 & 0 & 0 & 2 & \frac{1}{2} & \frac{1}{2} \\ 0 & 1 & 0 & 0 & -\frac{1}{2} & \frac{1}{2} \\ 0 & 0 & 1 & -2 & 1 & 0 \end{bmatrix} = [I \quad P] \Rightarrow P = \begin{bmatrix} 2 & \frac{1}{2} & \frac{1}{2} \\ 0 & -\frac{1}{2} & \frac{1}{2} \\ -2 & 1 & 0 \end{bmatrix}.$

(c) $PP^{-1} = \begin{bmatrix} 2 & \frac{1}{2} & \frac{1}{2} \\ 0 & -\frac{1}{2} & \frac{1}{2} \\ -2 & 1 & 0 \end{bmatrix} \begin{bmatrix} \frac{1}{4} & -\frac{1}{4} & -\frac{1}{4} \\ \frac{1}{2} & -\frac{1}{2} & \frac{1}{2} \\ \frac{1}{2} & \frac{3}{2} & \frac{1}{2} \end{bmatrix} = \begin{bmatrix} 1 & 0 & 0 \\ 0 & 1 & 0 \\ 0 & 0 & 1 \end{bmatrix}$

(d) $[\mathbf{x}]_B = P[\mathbf{x}]_{B'} = \begin{bmatrix} 2 & \frac{1}{2} & \frac{1}{2} \\ 0 & -\frac{1}{2} & \frac{1}{2} \\ -2 & 1 & 0 \end{bmatrix} \begin{bmatrix} 2 \\ 3 \\ 1 \end{bmatrix} = \begin{bmatrix} 6 \\ -1 \\ -1 \end{bmatrix}$

40. (a) $[B' \quad B] = \begin{bmatrix} 1 & 4 & -2 & 1 & 2 & -4 \\ 2 & 1 & 5 & 3 & -5 & 2 \\ -2 & -4 & 8 & 4 & 2 & -6 \end{bmatrix}$

$[I \quad P^{-1}] = \begin{bmatrix} 1 & 0 & 0 & -\frac{11}{16} & -\frac{55}{16} & -\frac{73}{16} \\ 0 & 1 & 0 & \frac{25}{32} & \frac{45}{32} & -\frac{83}{32} \\ 0 & 0 & 1 & \frac{23}{32} & \frac{3}{32} & -\frac{29}{32} \end{bmatrix}$

So, $P^{-1} = \begin{bmatrix} -\frac{11}{16} & -\frac{55}{16} & \frac{73}{16} \\ \frac{25}{32} & \frac{45}{32} & -\frac{83}{32} \\ \frac{23}{32} & \frac{3}{32} & -\frac{29}{32} \end{bmatrix}.$

(b) $[B \quad B'] = \begin{bmatrix} 1 & 2 & -4 & 1 & 4 & -2 \\ 3 & -5 & 2 & 2 & 1 & 5 \\ 4 & 2 & -6 & -2 & -4 & 8 \end{bmatrix}$

$[I \quad P] = \begin{bmatrix} 1 & 0 & 0 & -\frac{33}{13} & -\frac{86}{13} & \frac{80}{13} \\ 0 & 1 & 0 & -\frac{37}{13} & -\frac{85}{13} & \frac{57}{13} \\ 0 & 0 & 1 & -\frac{30}{13} & -\frac{77}{13} & \frac{55}{13} \end{bmatrix}$

So, $P = \begin{bmatrix} -\frac{33}{13} & -\frac{86}{13} & \frac{80}{13} \\ -\frac{37}{13} & -\frac{85}{13} & \frac{57}{13} \\ -\frac{30}{13} & -\frac{77}{13} & \frac{55}{13} \end{bmatrix}.$

(c) Using a graphing utility, you have $PP^{-1} = I.$

(d) $[\mathbf{x}]_B = P[\mathbf{x}]_{B'} = P \begin{bmatrix} -1 \\ 0 \\ 2 \end{bmatrix} = \begin{bmatrix} \frac{193}{13} \\ \frac{151}{13} \\ \frac{140}{13} \end{bmatrix}$

42. (a) $[B' \quad B] = [B' \quad I_n] \Rightarrow [I_n \quad (B')^{-1}] = [I_n \quad P^{-1}]$

$\Rightarrow (B')^{-1} = P^{-1}$

(b) $[B' \quad B] = [I_n \quad B] \Rightarrow B = P^{-1}$

(c) $[B \quad B'] = [I_n \quad B'] \Rightarrow B' = P$

(d) $[B \quad B'] = [B \quad I_n] \Rightarrow [I_n \quad B^{-1}] - [I_n \quad P]$

$\Rightarrow B^{-1} = P$

44. The standard basis for P_3 is $S = \{1, x, x^2, x^3\}$ and

because $p = 13(1) + 114(x) + 3(x^2) + 0(x^3)$

it follows that

$[p]_S = \begin{bmatrix} 13 \\ 114 \\ 3 \\ 0 \end{bmatrix}.$

46. The standard basis for P_3 is $S = \{1, x, x^2, x^3\}$ and

because $p = -2(1) - 3(x) + 0(x^2) + 4(x^3)$

it follows that

$[p]_S = \begin{bmatrix} -2 \\ -3 \\ 0 \\ 4 \end{bmatrix}.$

48. The standard basis in $M_{3,1}$ is

$$S = \left\{ \begin{bmatrix} 1 \\ 0 \\ 0 \end{bmatrix}, \begin{bmatrix} 0 \\ 1 \\ 0 \end{bmatrix}, \begin{bmatrix} 0 \\ 0 \\ 1 \end{bmatrix} \right\}$$

and because

$$X = 2\begin{bmatrix} 1 \\ 0 \\ 0 \end{bmatrix} - 1\begin{bmatrix} 0 \\ 1 \\ 0 \end{bmatrix} + 4\begin{bmatrix} 0 \\ 0 \\ 1 \end{bmatrix}$$

it follows that

$$[X]_S = \begin{bmatrix} 2 \\ -1 \\ 4 \end{bmatrix}.$$

50. The standard basis in $M_{3,1}$ is

$$S = \left\{ \begin{bmatrix} 1 \\ 0 \\ 0 \end{bmatrix}, \begin{bmatrix} 0 \\ 1 \\ 0 \end{bmatrix}, \begin{bmatrix} 0 \\ 0 \\ 1 \end{bmatrix} \right\}$$

and because

$$X = 1\begin{bmatrix} 1 \\ 0 \\ 0 \end{bmatrix} + 0\begin{bmatrix} 0 \\ 1 \\ 0 \end{bmatrix} - 4\begin{bmatrix} 0 \\ 0 \\ 1 \end{bmatrix}$$

it follows that

$$[X]_S = \begin{bmatrix} 1 \\ 0 \\ -4 \end{bmatrix}.$$

52. (a) True. See discussion before Example 5, page 208.

(b) False. $[p]_S = [-3 \ 1 \ 5]^T$.

54. Let P be the transition matrix from B'' to B' and let Q be the transition matrix from B' to B. Then for any vector **x**, the coordinate matrices with respect to these bases are related as follows.

$$[\mathbf{x}]_{B'} = P[\mathbf{x}]_{B''} \quad \text{and} \quad [\mathbf{x}]_B = Q[\mathbf{x}]_{B'}$$

Then the transition matrix from B'' to B is QP because

$$[\mathbf{x}]_B = Q[\mathbf{x}]_{B'} = QP[\mathbf{x}]_{B''}.$$

So, the transition matrix from B to B'', which is the inverse of the transition matrix from B'' to B, is equal to

$$(QP)^{-1} = P^{-1}Q^{-1}.$$

Section 4.8 Applications of Vector Spaces

2. (a) If $y = e^x$, then $y''' = e^x$ and $y''' + y = 2e^x \neq 0$. So, e^x *is not* a solution of the equation.

(b) If $y = e^{-x}$, then $y''' = -e^{-x}$ and $y''' + y = 0$. So, e^{-x} *is* a solution of the equation.

(c) If $y = e^{-2x}$, then $y''' = -8e^{-2x}$ and $y''' + y = -7e^{-2x} \neq 0$. So, e^{-2x} *is not* a solution of the equation.

(d) If $y = 2e^{-x}$, then $y''' = -2e^{-x}$ and $y''' + y = 0$. So, $2e^{-x}$ *is* a solution of the equation.

4. (a) If $y = e^{-2x}$, then $y' = -2e^{-2x}$ and $y'' = 4e^{-2x}$. So,

$$y'' + 4y' + 4y = 4e^{-2x} + 4(-2e^{-2x}) + 4(e^{-2x}) = 0, \text{ and } e^{-2x} \text{ is a solution.}$$

(b) If $y = xe^{-2x}$, then $y' = (1 - 2x)e^{-2x}$ and $y'' = (4x - 4)e^{-2x}$. So,

$$y'' + 4y' + 4y = (4x - 4)e^{-2x} + 4(1 - 2x)e^{-2x} + 4xe^{-2x} = 0, \text{ and } xe^{-2x} \text{ is a solution.}$$

(c) If $y = x^2 e^{-2x}$, then $y' = (2x - 2x^2)e^{-2x}$ and $y'' = (4x^2 - 8x + 2)e^{-2x}$. So,

$$y'' + 4y' + 4y = (4x^2 - 8x + 2)e^{-2x} + 4(2x - 2x^2)e^{-2x} + 4(x^2 e^{-2x}) \neq 0, \text{ and } x^2 e^{-2x} \text{ is not a solution.}$$

(d) If $y = (x + 2)e^{-2x}$, then $y' = (-3 - 2x)e^{-2x}$ and $y'' = (4 + 4x)e^{-2x}$. So,

$$y'' + 4y' + 4y = (4 + 4x)e^{-2x} + 4(-3 - 2x)e^{-2x} + 4(x + 2)e^{-2x} = 0, \text{ and } (x + 2)e^{-2x} \text{ is a solution.}$$

6. (a) If $y = 3\cos x$, $y^{(4)} = 3\cos x$ and $y^{(4)} - 16y = -45\cos x \ne 0$. So, $3\cos x$ *is not* a solution of the equation.

(b) If $y = 3\cos 2x$, then $y^{(4)} = 48\cos 2x$ and $y^{(4)} - 16y = 0$. So, $3\cos 2x$ *is* a solution of the equation.

(c) If $y = e^{-2x}$, then $y^{(4)} = 16e^{-2x}$ and $y^{(4)} - 16y = 0$. So, e^{-2x} *is* a solution of the equation.

(d) If $y = 3e^{2x} - 4\sin 2x$, then $y^{(4)} = 48e^{2x} - 64\sin 2x$ and $y^{(4)} - 16y = 0$. So, $3e^{2x} - 4\sin 2x$ *is* a solution of the equation.

8. (a) If $y = e^{x-x^2}$, then $y' = (1 - 2x)e^{x-x^2}$ and $y' + (2x - 1)y = 0$. So, e^{x-x^2} *is* a solution of the equation.

(b) If $y = 2e^{x-x^2}$, then $y' = (2 - 4x)e^{x-x^2}$ and $y' + (2x - 1)y = 0$. So, $2e^{x-x^2}$ *is* a solution of the equation.

(c) If $y = 3e^{x-x^2}$, then $y' = (3 - 6x)e^{x-x^2}$ and $y' + (2x - 1)y = 0$. So, $3e^{x-x^2}$ *is* a solution of the equation.

(d) If $y = 4e^{x-x^2}$, then $y' = (4 - 8x)e^{x-x^2}$ and $y' + (2x - 1)y = 0$. So, $4e^{x-x^2}$ *is* a solution of the equation.

10. (a) If $y = x$, then $y' = 1$ and $y'' = 0$. So, $xy'' + 2y' = x(0) + 2(1) \ne 0$, and $y = x$ *is not* a solution.

(b) If $y = \dfrac{1}{x}$, then $y' = -\dfrac{1}{x^2}$ and $y'' = \dfrac{2}{x^3}$. So, $xy'' + 2y' = x\left(\dfrac{2}{x^3}\right) + -2\left(-\dfrac{1}{x^2}\right) = 0$, and $y = \dfrac{1}{x}$ *is* a solution.

(c) If $y = xe^x$, then $y' = xe^x + e^x$ and $y'' = xe^x + 2e^x$. So, $xy'' + 2y' = x(xe^x + 2e^x) + 2(xe^x + e^x) \ne 0$, and $y = xe^x$ *is not* a solution.

(d) If $y = xe^{-x}$, then $y' = e^{-x} - xe^{-x}$ and $y'' = xe^{-x} - 2e^{-x}$. So, $xy'' + 2y' = x(xe^{-x} - 2e^{-x}) + 2(e^{-x} - xe^{-x}) \ne 0$, and $y = xe^{-x}$ *is not* a solution.

12. (a) If $y = 3e^{x^2}$, then $y' = 6xe^{x^2}$. So, $y' - 2xy = 6xe^{x^2} - 2x(3e^{x^2}) = 0$, and $y = 3e^{x^2}$ *is* a solution.

(b) If $y = xe^{x^2}$, then $y' = 2x^2e^{x^2} + e^{x^2}$. So, $y' - 2xy = 2x^2e^{x^2} + e^{x^2} - 2x(xe^{x^2}) \ne 0$, and $y = xe^{x^2}$ *is not* a solution.

(c) If $y = x^2e^x$, then $y' = x^2e^x + 2xe^x$. So, $y' - 2xy = x^2e^x + 2xe^x - 2x(x^2e^x) \ne 0$, and $y = x^2e^x$ *is not* a solution.

(d) If $y = xe^{-x}$, then $y' = e^{-x} - xe^{-x}$. So, $y' - 2xy = e^{-x} - xe^{-x} - 2x(xe^{-x}) \ne 0$, and $y = xe^{-x}$ *is not* a solution.

14. $W(e^{2x}, \cos 3x) = \begin{vmatrix} e^{2x} & \cos 3x \\ 2e^{2x} & -3\sin 3x \end{vmatrix}$

$\qquad = -3e^{2x} - \sin 3x - 2e^{2x}\cos 3x$

16. $W(e^{x^2}, e^{-x^2}) = \begin{vmatrix} e^{x^2} & e^{-x^2} \\ 2xe^{x^2} & -2xe^{-x^2} \end{vmatrix} = -4x$

18. $W(x, -\sin x, \cos x) = \begin{vmatrix} x & -\sin x & \cos x \\ 1 & -\cos x & -\sin x \\ 0 & \sin x & -\cos x \end{vmatrix} = x$

20. $W(x, e^{-x}, e^x) = \begin{vmatrix} x & e^{-x} & e^x \\ 1 & -e^{-x} & e^x \\ 0 & e^{-x} & e^x \end{vmatrix} = -2x$

22. $W(x^2, e^{x^2}, x^2e^x) = \begin{vmatrix} x^2 & e^{x^2} & x^2e^x \\ 2x & 2xe^{x^2} & 2xe^x + x^2e^x \\ 2 & 2e^{x^2} + 4x^2e^{x^2} & 2e^x + 4xe^x + x^2e^x \end{vmatrix} = -2x^2e^{x^2+x}(2x^4 - x^3 - 3x^2 + x + 3)$

24. $W(x, x^2, e^x, e^{-x}) = \begin{vmatrix} x & x^2 & e^x & e^{-x} \\ 1 & 2x & e^x & -e^{-x} \\ 0 & 2 & e^x & e^{-x} \\ 0 & 0 & e^x & -e^{-x} \end{vmatrix} = \begin{vmatrix} x & x^2 & 1 & 1 \\ 1 & 2x & 1 & -1 \\ 0 & 2 & 1 & 1 \\ 0 & 0 & 1 & -1 \end{vmatrix} = \begin{vmatrix} x & x^2 & 2 & 1 \\ 1 & 2x & 0 & -1 \\ 0 & 2 & 2 & 1 \\ 0 & 0 & 0 & -1 \end{vmatrix} = -1(4x^2 + 4 - 2x^2) = -2x^2 - 4$

26. $W(x, e^x, \sin x, \cos x) = \begin{vmatrix} x & e^x & \sin x & \cos x \\ 1 & e^x & \cos x & -\sin x \\ 0 & e^x & -\sin x & -\cos x \\ 0 & e^x & -\cos x & \sin x \end{vmatrix}$

$= \begin{vmatrix} x & 2e^x & 0 & 0 \\ 1 & 2e^x & 0 & 0 \\ 0 & e^x & -\sin x & -\cos x \\ 0 & e^x & -\cos x & \sin x \end{vmatrix}$

$= x \begin{vmatrix} 2e^x & 0 & 0 \\ e^x & -\sin x & -\cos x \\ e^x & -\cos x & \sin x \end{vmatrix} - 1 \begin{vmatrix} 2e^x & 0 & 0 \\ e^x & -\sin x & -\cos x \\ e^x & -\cos x & \sin x \end{vmatrix}$

$= 2xe^x(-\sin^2 x - \cos^2 x) - 2e^x(-\sin^2 x - \cos^2 x)$

$= -2xe^x + 2e^x$

28. (a) $y = e^x \Rightarrow y' = e^x, y'' = e^x \Rightarrow y'' - 2y' + y = 0$

$y = xe^x \Rightarrow y' = (x + 1)e^x, y'' = (x + 2)e^x \Rightarrow y'' - 2y' + y = 0$

(b) Because $W(e^x, xe^x) = \begin{vmatrix} e^x & xe^x \\ e^x & (x + 1)e^x \end{vmatrix} = (x + 1)e^{2x} - xe^{2x} = e^{2x} \neq 0$, the set is linearly independent.

(c) $y = C_1 e^x + C_2 x e^x$

30. (a) $y = 2 \Rightarrow y' = y''' = 0 \Rightarrow y''' + 4y' = 0$

$y = 2\sin 2x \Rightarrow y' = 4\cos 2x, y''' = -16\cos 2x \Rightarrow y''' + 4y' = 0$

$y = 1 + \sin 2x \Rightarrow y' = 2\cos 2x, y''' = -8\cos 2x \Rightarrow y''' + 4y' = 0$

(b) Because $W(2, 2\sin 2x, 1 + \sin 2x) = \begin{vmatrix} 2 & 2\sin 2x & 1 + \sin 2x \\ 0 & 4\cos 2x & 2\cos 2x \\ 0 & -8\sin 2x & -4\sin 2x \end{vmatrix} = 2(-16\sin 2x \cos 2x + 16\sin 2x \cos 2x) = 0$,

the set is linearly dependent.

32. (a) $y = e^{-x} \Rightarrow y' = -e^{-x}, y'' = e^{-x}, y''' = -e^{-x} \Rightarrow y''' + 3y'' + 3y' + y = 0$

$y = xe^{-x} \Rightarrow y' = (1 - x)e^{-x}, y'' = (x - 2)e^{-x}, y''' = (3 - x)e^{-x} \Rightarrow y''' + 3y'' + 3y' + y = 0$

$y = x^2 e^{-x} \Rightarrow y' = (2x - x^2)e^{-x}, y'' = (x^2 - 4x + 2)e^{-x}, y''' = (-x^2 + 6x - 6)e^{-x} \Rightarrow y''' + 3y'' + 3y' + y = 0$

(b) Because

$W(e^{-x}, xe^{-x}, x^2 e^{-x}) = \begin{vmatrix} e^{-x} & xe^{-x} & x^2 e^{-x} \\ -e^{-x} & (1 - x)e^{-x} & (2x - x^2)e^{-x} \\ e^{-x} & (x - 2)e^{-x} & (x^2 - 4x + 2)e^{-x} \end{vmatrix}$

$= e^{-3x} \begin{vmatrix} 1 & x & x^2 \\ -1 & 1 - x & 2x - x^2 \\ 1 & x - 2 & x^2 - 4x + 2 \end{vmatrix}$

$= e^{-3x} \begin{vmatrix} 1 & x & x^2 \\ 0 & 1 & 2x \\ 0 & -2 & -4x + 2 \end{vmatrix}$

$= 2e^{-3x} \neq 0$,

the set is linearly independent.

(c) $y = C_1 e^{-x} + C_2 x e^{-x} + C_3 x^2 e^{-x}$

34. (a) $y = 1 \Rightarrow y'' = y''' = y^{(4)} = 0 \Rightarrow y^{(4)} - 2y''' + y'' = 0$

$y = x \Rightarrow y'' = y''' = y^{(4)} = 0 \Rightarrow y^{(4)} - 2y''' + y'' = 0$

$y = e^x \Rightarrow y'' = y''' = y^{(4)} = e^x \Rightarrow y^{(4)} - 2y''' + y'' = 0$

$y = xe^x \Rightarrow y'' = (x + 2)e^x, \; y''' = (x + 3)e^x, \; y^{(4)} = (x + 4)e^x \Rightarrow y^{(4)} - 2y''' + y'' = 0$

(b) Because

$$W\left(1, x, e^x, xe^x\right) = \begin{vmatrix} 1 & x & e^x & xe^x \\ 0 & 1 & e^x & (x+1)e^x \\ 0 & 0 & e^x & (x+2)e^x \\ 0 & 0 & e^x & (x+3)e^x \end{vmatrix} = \begin{vmatrix} e^x & (x+2)e^x \\ e^x & (x+3)e^x \end{vmatrix} = e^{2x}(x+3) - e^{2x}(x+2) = e^{2x} \neq 0,$$

the set is linearly independent.

(c) $y = C_1 + C_2x + C_3e^x + C_4xe^x$

36. Clearly $\cos ax$ and $\sin ax$ satisfy the differential equation $y'' + a^2y = 0$. Because $W(\cos ax, \sin ax) = a \neq 0$, they are linearly independent. So, the general solution is $y = C_1 \cos ax + C_2 \sin ax$.

38. First calculate the Wronskian of the two functions.

$$W\left(e^{ax}, xe^{ax}\right) = \begin{vmatrix} e^{ax} & xe^{ax} \\ ae^{ax} & (ax+1)e^{ax} \end{vmatrix} = (ax+1)e^{2ax} - axe^{2ax} = e^{2ax}$$

Because $W\left(e^{ax}, xe^{ax}\right) \neq 0$ and the functions are solutions to $y'' - 2ay' + a^2y = 0$, they are linearly independent.

40. Proving that $\{y_1, y_2\}$ is linearly independent if and only if $W(y_1, y_2) \neq 0$ is equivalent to proving that $\{y_1, y_2\}$ is linearly dependent if and only if $W(y_1, y_2) = 0$.

To prove one direction, assume $\{y_1, y_2\}$ is linearly dependent. By the Corollary to Theorem 4.8 on page 177, one of the functions is a scalar multiple of the other. So, $y_1 = cy_2$. Then

$$W(y_1, y_2) = W(y_1, cy_1) = \begin{vmatrix} y_1 & cy_1 \\ y_1' & cy_1' \end{vmatrix} = 0.$$

To prove the other direction, assume $W(y_1, y_2) = 0$. Then the column vectors $\begin{bmatrix} y_1 \\ y_1' \end{bmatrix}$ and $\begin{bmatrix} y_2 \\ y_2' \end{bmatrix}$ are linearly dependent (see Summary of Equivalent Conditions for Square Matrices, page 198). So, $\begin{bmatrix} y_1 \\ y_1' \end{bmatrix} = c \begin{bmatrix} y_2 \\ y_2' \end{bmatrix} \Rightarrow y_1 = cy_2$, and $\{y_1, y_2\}$ is linearly dependent.

42. No. For instance, consider the nonhomogeneous differential equation $y'' = 1$. Clearly, $y = x^2/2$ is a solution, whereas the scalar multiple $2(x^2/2)$ is not.

44. The graph of this equation is a parabola $x = -\dfrac{y^2}{8}$, opening to the left, with the vertex at the origin.

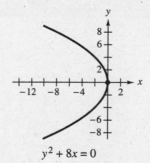

$$y^2 + 8x = 0$$

46. By rewriting the equation as

$$\frac{x^2}{3} + \frac{y^2}{5} = 1$$

you see that this is the equation of an ellipse centered at the origin with major axis falling along the y-axis.

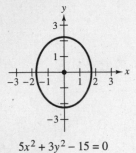

$$5x^2 + 3y^2 - 15 = 0$$

48. The graph of this equation is a hyperbola centered at the origin with transverse axis along the x-axis.

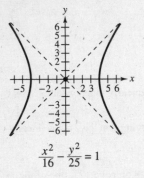

$$\frac{x^2}{16} - \frac{y^2}{25} = 1$$

50. The graph of this equation is a parabola

$(y - 3)^2 = 4(x - 3)$, opening to the right, with the

vertex at $(3, 3)$.

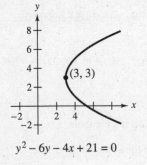

$$y^2 - 6y - 4x + 21 = 0$$

52. The graph of this equation is an ellipse

$$\frac{(x - 1)^2}{\frac{1}{4}} + y^2 = 1 \text{ with the center at } (1, 0).$$

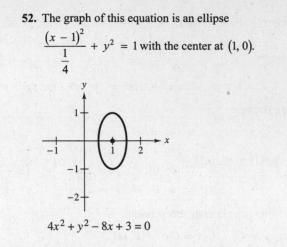

$$4x^2 + y^2 - 8x + 3 = 0$$

54. The graph of this equation is a hyperbola

$$\frac{\left(y - \frac{1}{2}\right)^2}{2} - \frac{(x + 2)^2}{4} = 1 \text{ centered at } \left(-2, \frac{1}{2}\right), \text{ with a}$$

vertical transverse axis.

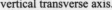
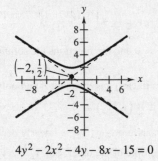

$$4y^2 - 2x^2 - 4y - 8x - 15 = 0$$

56. The graph of this equation is a circle $(x - 3)^2 + y^2 = \frac{1}{4}$

with the center at $(3, 0)$ and a radius of $\frac{1}{2}$.

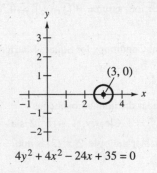

$$4y^2 + 4x^2 - 24x + 35 = 0$$

58. The graph of this equation is a hyperbola

$$\frac{\left(x + \frac{1}{2}\right)^2}{\frac{1}{4}} - \frac{(y - 1)^2}{1} = 1 \text{ centered at } \left(-\frac{1}{2}, 1\right), \text{ with a}$$

horizontal transverse axis.

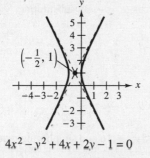

$$4x^2 - y^2 + 4x + 2y - 1 = 0$$

60. Complete the square to find the standard form.

$$(y + 3)^2 = 4(-2)(x + 2)$$

You see that this is the equation of a parabola, opening to the left, with vertex at $(-2, -3)$.

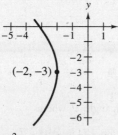

$$y^2 + 8x + 6y + 25 = 0$$

62. $-2x^2 + 3xy + 2y^2 + 3 = 0$

$$B^2 - 4AC = (3)^2 - 4(-2)(2) = 25 \Rightarrow$$

The graph is a hyperbola.

$$\cot 2\theta = \frac{A - C}{B} = -\frac{4}{3} \Rightarrow \theta \approx -18.43°$$

Matches graph (b).

64. $x^2 - 4xy + 4y^2 + 10x - 30 = 0$

$$A = 1, B = -4, C = 4$$

$$B^2 - 4AC = (-4)^2 - 4(1)(4) = 0$$

The graph is a parabola.

$$\cot 2\theta = \frac{A - C}{B} = \frac{1 - 4}{-4} = \frac{3}{4} \Rightarrow \theta \approx 26.57°$$

Matches graph (d).

66. Begin by finding the rotation angle θ, where

$$\cot 2\theta = \frac{a - c}{b} = \frac{0 - 0}{1} = 0 \Rightarrow \theta = \frac{\pi}{4}.$$

So, $\sin \theta = 1/\sqrt{2}$ and $\cos \theta = 1/\sqrt{2}$. By substituting

$$x = x' \cos \theta - y' \sin \theta = \frac{1}{\sqrt{2}}(x' - y')$$

and

$$y = x' \sin \theta + y' \cos \theta = \frac{1}{\sqrt{2}}(x' + y')$$

into

$$xy - 2 = 0 \text{ and simplifying, you obtain}$$

$$(x')^2 - (y')^2 - 4 = 0.$$

In standard form, $\dfrac{(x')^2}{4} - \dfrac{(y')^2}{4} = 1$.

This is the equation of a hyperbola with a transverse axis along the x'-axis.

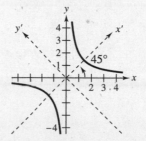

68. Begin by finding the rotation angle θ, where

$$\cot 2\theta = \frac{a - c}{b} = \frac{1 - 1}{2} = 0 \Rightarrow \theta = \frac{\pi}{4}.$$

So, $\sin \theta = \dfrac{1}{\sqrt{2}}$ and $\cos \theta = \dfrac{1}{\sqrt{2}}$. By substituting

$$x = x' \cos \theta - y' \sin \theta = \frac{1}{\sqrt{2}}(x' - y')$$

and

$$y = x' \sin \theta + y' \cos \theta = \frac{1}{\sqrt{2}}(x' + y')$$

into

$$x^2 + 2xy + y^2 - 8x + 8y = 0 \text{ and simplifying, you}$$

obtain $(x')^2 = -4\sqrt{2}y'$ or $y' = \dfrac{-1}{4\sqrt{2}}(x')^2$, which is a

parabola.

70. Begin by finding the rotation angle θ, where

$$\cot 2\theta = \frac{5 - 5}{-2} = 0, \text{ implying that } \theta = \frac{\pi}{4}.$$

So, $\sin \theta = 1/\sqrt{2}$ and $\cos \theta = 1/\sqrt{2}$. By substituting

$$x = x' \cos \theta - y' \sin \theta = \frac{1}{\sqrt{2}}(x' - y')$$

and

$$y = x' \sin \theta + y' \cos \theta = \frac{1}{\sqrt{2}}(x' + y')$$

into

$$5x^2 - 2xy + 5y^2 - 24 = 0 \text{ and simplifying, you obtain}$$

$$4(x')^2 + 6(y')^2 - 24 = 0.$$

In standard form, $\dfrac{(x')^2}{6} + \dfrac{(y')^2}{4} = 1.$

This is the equation of an ellipse with major axis along the x'-axis.

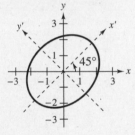

72. Begin by finding the rotation angle θ, where

$$\cot 2\theta = \frac{a - c}{b} = \frac{5 - 5}{-6} = 0, \text{ implying that } \theta = \frac{\pi}{4}.$$

So, $\sin \theta = 1/\sqrt{2}$ and $\cos \theta = 1/\sqrt{2}$. By substituting

$$x = x' \cos \theta - y' \sin \theta = \frac{1}{\sqrt{2}}(x' - y')$$

and

$$y = x' \sin \theta + y' \cos \theta = \frac{1}{\sqrt{2}}(x' + y')$$

into

$$5x^2 - 6xy + 5y^2 - 12 = 0 \text{ and simplifying, you obtain}$$

$$2(x')^2 + 2(y')^2 - 12 = 0.$$

In standard form, $(x')^2 + (y')^2 = 6.$

This is an equation of a circle with the center at $(0, 0)$ and a radius of $\sqrt{6}.$

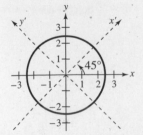

74. Begin by finding the rotation angle θ, where

$$\cot 2\theta = \frac{a - c}{b} = \frac{7 - 5}{-2\sqrt{3}} = \frac{-1}{\sqrt{3}} \Rightarrow 2\theta = \frac{2\pi}{3},$$

implying that $\theta = \dfrac{\pi}{3}.$

So, $\sin \theta = \dfrac{\sqrt{3}}{2}$ and $\cos \theta = \dfrac{1}{2}.$ By substituting

$$x = x' \cos \theta - y' \sin \theta = \frac{1}{2}x' - \frac{\sqrt{3}}{2}y'$$

and

$$y = x' \sin \theta + y' \cos \theta = \frac{\sqrt{3}}{2}x' + \frac{1}{2}y'$$

into $7x^2 - 2\sqrt{3}xy + 5y^2 = 16$ and simplifying, you

obtain $\dfrac{(x')^2}{4} + \dfrac{(y')^2}{2} = 1,$ which is an ellipse with

major axis along the x'-axis.

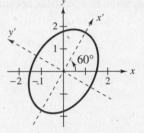

76. Begin by finding the rotation angle θ, where

$$\cot 2\theta = \frac{1 - 3}{2\sqrt{3}} = -\frac{1}{\sqrt{3}}, \text{ implying that } \theta = \frac{\pi}{3}.$$

So, $\sin \theta = \sqrt{3}/2$ and $\cos \theta = 1/2.$ By substituting

$$x = x' \cos \theta - y' \sin \theta = \frac{1}{2}(x' - \sqrt{3}y')$$

and

$$y = x' \sin \theta + y' \cos \theta = \frac{1}{2}(\sqrt{3}x' + y')$$

into $x^2 + 2\sqrt{3}xy + 3y^2 - 2\sqrt{3}x + 2y + 16 = 0$

and simplifying, you obtain

$$4(x')^2 + 4y' + 16 = 0.$$

In standard form, $y' + 4 = -(x')^2.$

This is the equation of a parabola with axis on the y'-axis.

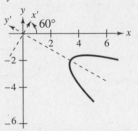

78. Begin by finding the rotation angle θ, where

$$\cot 2\theta = \frac{a-c}{b} = \frac{5-5}{-2} = 0, \text{ implying that } \theta = \frac{\pi}{4}.$$

So, $\sin \theta = \dfrac{1}{\sqrt{2}}$ and $\cos \theta = \dfrac{1}{\sqrt{2}}$. By substituting

$$x = x' \cos \theta - y' \sin \theta = \frac{1}{\sqrt{2}}(x' - y')$$

and

$$y = x' \sin \theta + y' \cos \theta = \frac{1}{\sqrt{2}}(x' + y') \text{ into}$$

$5x^2 - 2xy + 5y^2 = 0$ and simplifying, you obtain

$4(x')^2 + 6(y')^2 = 0$, which is a single point, $(0, 0)$.

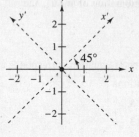

80. Begin by finding the rotation angle θ, where

$$\cot 2\theta = \frac{a-c}{b} = \frac{1-1}{-10} = 0, \text{ implying that } \theta = \frac{\pi}{4}.$$

So, $\sin \theta = 1/\sqrt{2}$ and $\cos \theta = 1/\sqrt{2}$. By substituting

$$x = x' \cos \theta - y' \sin \theta = \frac{1}{\sqrt{2}}(x' - y')$$

and

$$y = x' \sin \theta + y' \cos \theta = \frac{1}{\sqrt{2}}(x' + y')$$

into

$x^2 - 10xy + y^2 = 0$ and simplifying, you obtain

$$6(y')^2 - 4(x')^2 = 0.$$

The graph of this equation is two lines $y' = \pm\dfrac{\sqrt{6}}{3}x'$.

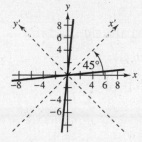

82. Let θ satisfy $\cot 2\theta = (a - c)/b$. Substitute $x = x' \cos \theta - y' \sin \theta$ and $y = x' \sin \theta + y' \cos \theta$ into the equation

$ax^2 + bxy + cy^2 + dx + ey + f = 0$. To show that the xy-term will be eliminated, analyze the first three terms under this substitution.

$$\begin{aligned}
ax^2 + bxy + cy^2 &= a(x' \cos \theta - y' \sin \theta)^2 + b(x' \cos \theta - y' \sin \theta)(x' \sin \theta + y' \cos \theta) + c(x' \sin \theta + y' \cos \theta)^2 \\
&= a(x')^2 \cos^2 \theta + a(y')^2 \sin^2 \theta - 2ax'y' \cos \theta \sin \theta \\
&\quad + b(x')^2 \cos \theta \sin \theta + bx'y' \cos^2 \theta - bx'y' \sin^2 \theta - b(y')^2 \cos \theta \sin \theta \\
&\quad + c(x')^2 \sin^2 \theta + c(y')^2 \cos^2 \theta + 2cx'y' \sin \theta \cos \theta.
\end{aligned}$$

So, the new xy-terms are

$$-2ax'y' \cos \theta \sin \theta + bx'y'(\cos^2 \theta - \sin^2 \theta) + 2cx'y' \sin \theta \cos \theta = x'y'[-a \sin 2\theta + b \cos 2\theta + c \sin 2\theta]$$

$$= -x'y'[(a - c) \sin 2\theta - b \cos 2\theta].$$

But, $\cot 2\theta = \dfrac{\cos 2\theta}{\sin 2\theta} = \dfrac{a-c}{b} \Rightarrow b \cos 2\theta = (a - c) \sin 2\theta$, which shows that the coefficient is zero.

84. (a) Set up the Wronskian with the given solutions and their derivatives. Then find the determinant. If the determinant is nonzero, the solutions are linearly independent.

(b) Use the substitutions $x = x' \cos \theta - y' \sin \theta$ and $y = x' \sin \theta + y' \cos \theta$, where θ is found by using the coefficients of the original equation in the formula $\cot 2\theta = \dfrac{a-c}{b}$.

Review Exercises for Chapter 4

2. (a) $\mathbf{u} + \mathbf{v} = (-1, 2, 1) + (0, 1, 1) = (-1, 3, 2)$

(b) $2\mathbf{v} = 2(0, 1, 1) = (0, 2, 2)$

(c) $\mathbf{u} - \mathbf{v} = (-1, 2, 1) - (0, 1, 1) = (-1, 1, 0)$

(d) $3\mathbf{u} - 2\mathbf{v} = 3(-1, 2, 1) - 2(0, 1, 1)$

$\qquad = (-3, 6, 3) - (0, 2, 2) = (-3, 4, 1)$

4. (a) $\mathbf{u} + \mathbf{v} = (0, 1, -1, 2) + (1, 0, 0, 2) = (1, 1, -1, 4)$

(b) $2\mathbf{v} = 2(1, 0, 0, 2) = (2, 0, 0, 4)$

(c) $\mathbf{u} - \mathbf{v} = (0, 1, -1, 2) - (1, 0, 0, 2) = (-1, 1, -1, 0)$

(d) $3\mathbf{u} - 2\mathbf{v} = 3(0, 1, -1, 2) - 2(1, 0, 0, 2)$

$\qquad = (0, 3, -3, 6) - (2, 0, 0, 4) = (-2, 3, -3, 2)$

6. $\mathbf{x} = \frac{1}{3}[-2\mathbf{u} + \mathbf{v} - 2\mathbf{w}]$

$\quad = \frac{1}{3}\left[-2(1, -1, 2) + (0, 2, 3) - 2(0, 1, 1)\right]$

$\quad = \frac{1}{3}\left[(-2, 2, -4) + (0, 0, 1)\right]$

$\quad = \frac{1}{3}(-2, 2, -3) = \left(-\frac{2}{3}, \frac{2}{3}, -1\right)$

8. $2\mathbf{u} + 3\mathbf{x} = 2\mathbf{v} - \mathbf{w}$

$\quad 3\mathbf{x} = -2\mathbf{u} + 2\mathbf{v} - \mathbf{w}$

$\quad \mathbf{x} = -\frac{2}{3}\mathbf{u} + \frac{2}{3}\mathbf{v} - \frac{1}{3}\mathbf{w}$

$\quad = -\frac{2}{3}(1, -1, 2) + \frac{2}{3}(0, 2, 3) - \frac{1}{3}(0, 1, 1)$

$\quad = \left(-\frac{2}{3}, \frac{2}{3}, -\frac{4}{3}\right) + \left(0, \frac{4}{3}, 2\right) - \left(0, \frac{1}{3}, \frac{1}{3}\right)$

$\quad = \left(-\frac{2}{3} + 0 - 0, \frac{2}{3} + \frac{4}{3} - \frac{1}{3}, -\frac{4}{3} + 2 - \frac{1}{3}\right)$

$\quad = \left(-\frac{2}{3}, \frac{5}{3}, \frac{1}{3}\right)$

10. To write $\mathbf{v}$ as a linear combination of $\mathbf{u}_1, \mathbf{u}_2,$ and $\mathbf{u}_3$, solve the equation

$$c_1\mathbf{u}_1 + c_2\mathbf{u}_2 + c_3\mathbf{u}_3 = \mathbf{v}$$

for $c_1, c_2,$ and c_3. This vector equation corresponds to the system

$$c_1 - 2c_2 + c_3 = 4$$
$$2c_1 \qquad\qquad = 4$$
$$3c_1 + \ c_2 \qquad = 5.$$

The solution of this system is $c_1 = 2, c_2 = -1,$ and $c_3 = 0$. So, $\mathbf{v} = 2\mathbf{u}_1 - \mathbf{u}_2$.

12. To write $\mathbf{v}$ as a linear combination of $\mathbf{u}_1, \mathbf{u}_2,$ and $\mathbf{u}_3$, solve the equation

$$c_1\mathbf{u}_1 + c_2\mathbf{u}_2 + c_3\mathbf{u}_3 = \mathbf{v}$$

for $c_1, c_2,$ and c_3. This vector equation corresponds to the system of linear equations

$$c_1 - \ c_2 \qquad\quad = 4$$
$$-2c_1 + 2c_2 - c_3 = -13$$
$$c_1 + 3c_2 - c_3 = -5$$
$$c_1 + 2c_2 - c_3 = -4.$$

The solution of this system is $c_1 = 3, c_2 = -1,$ and $c_3 = 5$. So, $\mathbf{v} = 3\mathbf{u}_1 - \mathbf{u}_2 + 5\mathbf{u}_3$.

14. The zero vector is the zero polynomial $p(x) = 0$. The additive inverse of a vector in P_8 is

$$-\left(a_0 + a_1x + a_2x^2 + \cdots + a_8x^8\right) = -a_0 - a_1x - a_2x^2 - \cdots - a_8x^8.$$

16. The zero vector is

$$\begin{bmatrix} 0 & 0 & 0 \\ 0 & 0 & 0 \end{bmatrix}.$$

The additive inverse of

$$\begin{bmatrix} a_{11} & a_{12} & a_{13} \\ a_{21} & a_{22} & a_{23} \end{bmatrix} \text{ is } \begin{bmatrix} -a_{11} & -a_{12} & -a_{13} \\ -a_{21} & -a_{22} & -a_{23} \end{bmatrix}.$$

18. W is not a subspace of R^2. For instance, $(2, 1) \in W$ and $(3, 2) \in W$, but their sum $(5, 3) \in W$. So, W is not closed under addition (nor scalar multiplication).

20. W is not a subspace of R^2. For instance $(1, 3) \in W$ and $(2, 12) \in W$, but their sum $(3, 15) \notin W$. So, W is not closed under addition (nor scalar multiplication).

22. W is not a subspace of R^3, because it is not closed under scalar multiplication. For instance $(1, 1, 1) \in W$ and $-2 \in R$, but $-2(1, 1, 1) = (-2, -2, -2) \notin W$.

24. Because W is a nonempty subset of $C[-1, 1]$, you need only check that W is closed under addition and scalar multiplication. If f and g are in W, then

$f(-1) = g(-1) = 0$, and

$(f + g)(-1) = f(-1) + g(-1) = 0$, which implies that $f + g \in W$. Similarly, if c is a scalar, then

$cf(-1) = c0 = 0$, which implies that $cf \in W$. So, W is a subspace of $C[-1, 1]$.

26. (a) W is a subspace of R^3, because W is nonempty

$\big((0, 0, 0) \in W\big)$ and W is closed under addition and scalar multiplication.

For if (x_1, x_2, x_3) and (y_1, y_2, y_3) are in W, then $x_1 + x_2 + x_3 = 0$ and $y_1 + y_2 + y_3 = 0$. Because

$(x_1, x_2, x_3) + (y_1, y_2, y_3) = (x_1 + y_1, x_2 + y_2, x_3 + y_3)$ satisfies $(x_1 + y_1) + (x_2 + y_2) + (x_3 + y_3) = 0$, W is closed under addition. Similarly, $c(x_1, x_2, x_3) = (cx_1, cx_2, cx_3)$ satisfies $cx_1 + cx_2 + cx_3 = 0$, showing that W is closed under scalar multiplication.

(b) W is not closed under addition or scalar multiplication, so it is not a subspace of R^3. For example, $(1, 0, 0) \in W$, and yet

$2(1, 0, 0) = (2, 0, 0) \notin W$.

28. (a) To find out whether S spans R^3, form the vector equation

$c_1(4, 0, 1) + c_2(0, -3, 2) + c_3(5, 10, 0) = (u_1, u_2, u_3)$.

This yields the system of equations

$$\begin{aligned} 4c_1 \quad\quad + 5c_3 &= u_1 \\ -3c_2 + 10c_3 &= u_2 \\ c_1 + 2c_2 \quad\quad &= u_3. \end{aligned}$$

This system has a unique solution for every (u_1, u_2, u_3) because the determinant of the coefficient matrix is not zero. So, S spans R^3.

(b) Solving the same system in (a) with $(u_1, u_2, u_3) = (0, 0, 0)$ yields the trivial solution. So, S is linearly independent.

(c) Because S is linearly independent and spans R^3, it is a basis for R^3.

30. (a) To find out whether S spans R^3, form the vector equation

$c_1(2, 0, 1) + c_2(2, -1, 1)) + c_3(4, 2, 0) = (u_1, u_2, u_3)$.

This yields the system of linear equations

$$\begin{aligned} 2c_1 + 2c_2 + 4c_3 &= u_1 \\ -c_2 + 2c_3 &= u_2 \\ c_1 + c_2 \quad\quad &= u_3. \end{aligned}$$

This system has a unique solution for every (u_1, u_2, u_3) because the determinant of the coefficient matrix is not zero. So, S spans R^3.

(b) Solving the same system in part (a) with $(u_1, u_2, u_3) = (0, 0, 0)$ yields the trivial solution. So, S is linearly independent.

(c) Because S is linearly independent and S spans R^3, it is a basis for R^3.

32. (a) The set

$S = \{(1, 0, 0), (0, 1, 0), (0, 0, 1), (2, -1, 0)\}$ spans R^3

because any vector $\mathbf{u} = (u_1, u_2, u_3)$ in R^3 can be written as

$$\begin{aligned} \mathbf{u} &= u_1(1, 0, 0) + u_2(0, 1, 0) + u_3(0, 0, 1) \\ &= (u_1, u_2, u_3). \end{aligned}$$

(b) S is not linearly independent because

$2(1, 0, 0) - (0, 1, 0) + 0(0, 0, 1) = (2, -1, 0)$.

(c) S is not a basis for R^3 because S is not linearly independent.

34. S has three vectors, so you need only check that S is linearly independent.

Form the vector equation

$c_1(1) + c_2(t) + c_3(1 + t^2) = 0 + 0t + 0t^2$

which yields the homogeneous system of linear equations

$$\begin{aligned} c_1 \quad + c_3 &= 0 \\ c_2 \quad\quad &= 0 \\ c_3 &= 0. \end{aligned}$$

This system has only the trivial solution. So, S is linearly independent and S is a basis for P_2.

36. S has four vectors, so you need only check that S is linearly independent.

Form the vector equation

$$c_1\begin{bmatrix} 1 & 0 \\ 0 & 1 \end{bmatrix} + c_2\begin{bmatrix} -1 & 0 \\ 1 & 1 \end{bmatrix} + c_3\begin{bmatrix} 2 & 1 \\ 1 & 0 \end{bmatrix} + c_4\begin{bmatrix} 1 & 1 \\ 0 & 1 \end{bmatrix} = \begin{bmatrix} 0 & 0 \\ 0 & 0 \end{bmatrix}$$

which yields the homogeneous system of linear equations

$$\begin{aligned} c_1 - c_2 + 2c_3 + c_4 &= 0 \\ c_3 + c_4 &= 0 \\ c_2 + c_3 \quad\quad &= 0 \\ c_1 + c_2 \quad\quad + c_4 &= 0. \end{aligned}$$

This system has only the trivial solution. So, S is linearly independent and S is a basis for $M_{2,2}$.

38. (a) The system given by $A\mathbf{x} = \mathbf{0}$ has only the trivial solution $(0, 0)$. So, the solution space is $\{(0, 0)\}$, which does not have a basis.

(b) The nullity is 0.

Note that $\text{rank}(A) + \text{nullity}(A) = 2 + 0 = 2 = n$.

(c) The rank of A is 2 (the number of nonzero row vectors in the reduced row-echelon matrix).

40. (a) The system given by $A\mathbf{x} = \mathbf{0}$ has solutions of the form $(2t, 5t, t, t)$, where t is any real number. So, a basis for the solution space of $A\mathbf{x} = \mathbf{0}$ is $\{(2, 5, 1, 1)\}$.

(b) The nullity of A is 1.

Note that $\text{rank}(A) + \text{nullity}(A) = 3 + 1 = 4 = n$.

(c) The rank of A is 3 (the number of nonzero row vectors in the reduced row-echelon matrix).

42. (a) The system given by $A\mathbf{x} = \mathbf{0}$ has only the trivial solution $(0, 0, 0, 0)$. So, the solution space is $\{(0, 0, 0, 0)\}$, which does not have a basis.

(b) The nullity is 0.

Note that $\text{rank}(A) + \text{nullity}(A) = 4 + 0 = 4 = n$.

(c) The rank of A is 4 (the number of nonzero row vectors in the reduced row-echelon matrix).

44. (a) This system has solutions of the form $\left(3t, -\frac{1}{2}t, -4t, t\right)$, where t is any real number. A basis for the solution space is $\left\{\left(3, -\frac{1}{2}, -4, 1\right)\right\}$.

(b) The dimension of the solution space is 1, the number of vectors in the basis.

46. (a) This system has solutions of the form $\left(0, -\frac{3}{2}t, -t, t\right)$, where t is any real number. A basis for the solution space is $\left\{\left(0, -\frac{3}{2}, -1, 1\right)\right\}$.

(b) The dimension of the solution space is 1, the number of vectors in a basis.

48. (a) Using Gauss-Jordan elimination, the matrix reduces to
$$\begin{bmatrix} 1 & 0 & \frac{26}{11} \\ 0 & 1 & \frac{8}{11} \\ 0 & 0 & 0 \end{bmatrix}.$$
So, the rank is 2.

(b) A basis for the row space is $\left\{\left(1, 0, \frac{26}{11}\right), \left(0, 1, \frac{8}{11}\right)\right\}$.

50. (a) Because the matrix is already row reduced, its rank is 1.

(b) A basis for the row space is $\{(1, 2, -1)\}$.

52. (a) Using Gauss-Jordan elimination, the matrix reduces to
$$\begin{bmatrix} 1 & 0 & 0 \\ 0 & 1 & 0 \\ 0 & 0 & 1 \end{bmatrix}.$$
So, the rank is 3.

(b) A basis for the row space is $\{(1, 0, 0), (0, 1, 0), (0, 0, 1)\}$.

54. Because $[\mathbf{x}]_B = \begin{bmatrix} 1 \\ 1 \end{bmatrix}$, write $\mathbf{x}$ as

$\mathbf{x} = 1(2, 0) + 1(3, 3) = (5, 3)$. Because

$(5, 3) = 5(1, 0) + 3(0, 1)$, the coordinate vector of $\mathbf{x}$ relative to the standard basis is

$$[\mathbf{x}]_S = \begin{bmatrix} 5 \\ 3 \end{bmatrix}.$$

56. Because $[\mathbf{x}]_B = \begin{bmatrix} 2 \\ 1 \end{bmatrix}$, write $\mathbf{x}$ as

$\mathbf{x} = 2(4, 2) + 1(1, -1) = (9, 3)$.

Because $(9, 3) = 9(1, 0) + 3(0, 1)$, the coordinate vector of $\mathbf{x}$ relative to the standard basis is

$$[\mathbf{x}]_S = \begin{bmatrix} 9 \\ 3 \end{bmatrix}.$$

58. Because $[\mathbf{x}]_B = \begin{bmatrix} 4 \\ 0 \\ 2 \end{bmatrix}$, write $\mathbf{x}$ as

$\mathbf{x} = 4(1, 0, 1) + 0(0, 1, 0) + 2(0, 1, 1) = (4, 2, 6)$.

Because $(4, 2, 6) = 4(1, 0, 0) + 2(0, 1, 0) + 6(0, 0, 1)$, the coordinate vector of $\mathbf{x}$ relative to the standard basis is

$$[\mathbf{x}]_S = \begin{bmatrix} 4 \\ 2 \\ 6 \end{bmatrix}.$$

60. To find $[\mathbf{x}]_{B'} = \begin{bmatrix} c_1 \\ c_2 \end{bmatrix}$, solve the equation

$c_1(1, 1) + c_2(0, -2) = (2, -1)$.

The resulting system of linear equations is

$c_1 \qquad\quad = 2$

$c_1 - 2c_2 = -1.$

So, $c_1 = 2$ and $c_2 = \frac{3}{2}$, and you have

$$[\mathbf{x}]_{B'} = \begin{bmatrix} 2 \\ \frac{3}{2} \end{bmatrix}.$$

62. To find $[\mathbf{x}]_{B'} = \begin{bmatrix} c_1 \\ c_2 \\ c_3 \end{bmatrix}$, solve the equation

$$c_1(1, 0, 0) + c_2(0, 1, 0) + c_3(1, 1, 1) = (4, -2, 9).$$

Forming the corresponding linear system, the solution is $c_1 = -5, c_2 = -11,$ and $c_3 = 9.$ So,

$$[\mathbf{x}]_{B'} = \begin{bmatrix} -5 \\ -11 \\ 9 \end{bmatrix}.$$

64. To find $[\mathbf{x}]_{B'} = \begin{bmatrix} c_1 \\ c_2 \\ c_3 \\ c_4 \end{bmatrix}$, solve the equation

$$c_1(1, -1, 2, 1) + c_2(1, 1, -4, 3) + c_3(1, 2, 0, 3) + c_4(1, 2, -2, 0) = (5, 3, -6, 2).$$

The resulting system of linear equations is

$$
\begin{aligned}
c_1 + c_2 + c_3 + c_4 &= 5 \\
-c_1 + c_2 + 2c_3 + 2c_4 &= 3 \\
2c_1 - 4c_2 \qquad - 2c_4 &= -6 \\
c_1 + 3c_2 + 3c_3 \qquad &= 2.
\end{aligned}
$$

So, $c_1 = 2, c_2 = 1, c_3 = -1,$ and $c_4 = 3,$ and you have

$$[\mathbf{x}]_{B'} = \begin{bmatrix} 2 \\ 1 \\ -1 \\ 3 \end{bmatrix}.$$

66. Begin by forming

$$[B' \ B] = \begin{bmatrix} 1 & -1 & 1 & 3 \\ 2 & 0 & -1 & 1 \end{bmatrix}.$$

Then use Gauss-Jordan elimination to obtain

$$[I_2 \ P^{-1}] = \begin{bmatrix} 1 & 0 & -\frac{1}{2} & \frac{1}{2} \\ 0 & 1 & -\frac{3}{2} & -\frac{5}{2} \end{bmatrix}.$$

So,

$$P^{-1} = \begin{bmatrix} -\frac{1}{2} & \frac{1}{2} \\ -\frac{3}{2} & -\frac{5}{2} \end{bmatrix}.$$

68. Begin by forming

$$[B' \ B] = \begin{bmatrix} 1 & 0 & 1 & 1 & 1 & 1 \\ 2 & 1 & 0 & 1 & 1 & 0 \\ 3 & 0 & 1 & 1 & 0 & 0 \end{bmatrix}.$$

Then use Gauss-Jordan elimination to obtain

$$[I_3 \ P^{-1}] = \begin{bmatrix} 1 & 0 & 0 & 0 & -\frac{1}{2} & -\frac{1}{2} \\ 0 & 1 & 0 & 1 & 2 & 1 \\ 0 & 0 & 1 & 1 & \frac{3}{2} & \frac{3}{2} \end{bmatrix}.$$

So,

$$P^{-1} = \begin{bmatrix} 0 & -\frac{1}{2} & -\frac{1}{2} \\ 1 & 2 & 1 \\ 1 & \frac{3}{2} & \frac{3}{2} \end{bmatrix}.$$

70. (a) $\begin{bmatrix} B' & B \end{bmatrix} = \begin{bmatrix} 1 & 1 & 1 & 1 \\ 1 & -1 & 0 & -1 \end{bmatrix} \Rightarrow \begin{bmatrix} 1 & 0 & \frac{1}{2} & 0 \\ 0 & 1 & \frac{1}{2} & 1 \end{bmatrix} = \begin{bmatrix} I & P^{-1} \end{bmatrix}$

   (b) $\begin{bmatrix} B & B' \end{bmatrix} = \begin{bmatrix} 1 & 1 & 1 & 1 \\ 0 & -1 & 1 & -1 \end{bmatrix} \Rightarrow \begin{bmatrix} 1 & 0 & 2 & 0 \\ 0 & 1 & -1 & 1 \end{bmatrix} = \begin{bmatrix} I & P \end{bmatrix}$

   (c) $P^{-1} P = \begin{bmatrix} \frac{1}{2} & 0 \\ \frac{1}{2} & 1 \end{bmatrix} \begin{bmatrix} 2 & 0 \\ -1 & 1 \end{bmatrix} = \begin{bmatrix} 1 & 0 \\ 0 & 1 \end{bmatrix}$

   (d) $[\mathbf{x}]_{B'} = P^{-1}[\mathbf{x}]_B = \begin{bmatrix} \frac{1}{2} & 0 \\ \frac{1}{2} & 1 \end{bmatrix} \begin{bmatrix} 2 \\ -2 \end{bmatrix} = \begin{bmatrix} 1 \\ -1 \end{bmatrix}$

72. (a) $\begin{bmatrix} B' & B \end{bmatrix} = \begin{bmatrix} 1 & 2 & 2 & 1 & 1 & 1 \\ -1 & 2 & 2 & 1 & 1 & -1 \\ 2 & -1 & 2 & -1 & 0 & 0 \end{bmatrix} \Rightarrow \begin{bmatrix} 1 & 0 & 0 & 0 & 0 & 1 \\ 0 & 1 & 0 & \frac{2}{3} & \frac{1}{3} & \frac{2}{3} \\ 0 & 0 & 1 & -\frac{1}{6} & \frac{1}{6} & -\frac{2}{3} \end{bmatrix} = \begin{bmatrix} I & P^{-1} \end{bmatrix}$

   (b) $\begin{bmatrix} B & B' \end{bmatrix} = \begin{bmatrix} 1 & 1 & 1 & 1 & 2 & 2 \\ 1 & 1 & -1 & -1 & 2 & 2 \\ -1 & 0 & 0 & 2 & -1 & 2 \end{bmatrix} \Rightarrow \begin{bmatrix} 1 & 0 & 0 & -2 & 1 & -2 \\ 0 & 1 & 0 & 2 & 1 & 4 \\ 0 & 0 & 1 & 1 & 0 & 0 \end{bmatrix} = \begin{bmatrix} I & P \end{bmatrix}$

   (c) $P^{-1} P = \begin{bmatrix} 0 & 0 & 1 \\ \frac{2}{3} & \frac{1}{3} & \frac{2}{3} \\ -\frac{1}{6} & \frac{1}{6} & -\frac{2}{3} \end{bmatrix} \begin{bmatrix} -2 & 1 & -2 \\ 2 & 1 & 4 \\ 1 & 0 & 0 \end{bmatrix} = \begin{bmatrix} 1 & 0 & 0 \\ 0 & 1 & 0 \\ 0 & 0 & 1 \end{bmatrix}$

   (d) $[\mathbf{x}]_{B'} = P^{-1}[\mathbf{x}]_B = \begin{bmatrix} 0 & 0 & 1 \\ \frac{2}{3} & \frac{1}{3} & \frac{2}{3} \\ -\frac{1}{6} & \frac{1}{6} & -\frac{2}{3} \end{bmatrix} \begin{bmatrix} 2 \\ 2 \\ -1 \end{bmatrix} = \begin{bmatrix} -1 \\ \frac{4}{3} \\ \frac{2}{3} \end{bmatrix}$

74. (a) Because W is a nonempty subset of V, you need to only check that W is closed under addition and scalar multiplication. If $f, g \in W$, then $f' = 3f$ and $g' = 3g$. So,

$$(f + g)' = f' + g' = 3f + 3g = 3(f + g),$$

which shows that $f + g \in W$. Finally, if c is a scalar, then $(cf)' = (cf') = c(3f) = 3(cf)$, which implies that $cf \in W$.

   (b) V is not closed under addition nor scalar multiplication. For instance, let $f = e^x - 1 \in U$. Note that $2f = 2e^x - 2 \notin U$ because

$$(2f)' = 2e^x \neq (2f) + 1 = 2e^x - 1.$$

76. Suppose, on the contrary, that A and B are linearly dependent. Then $B = cA$ for some scalar c. So,

$(cA)^T = B^T = -B$, which implies that $cA = -B$. So, $B = O$, a contradiction.

78. Because $-(\mathbf{v}_1 - 2\mathbf{v}_2) - (2\mathbf{v}_2 - 3\mathbf{v}_3) = 3\mathbf{v}_3 - \mathbf{v}_1$, the set is linearly dependent.

80. S is a nonempty subset of R^n, so you need only show closure under addition and scalar multiplication. Let $\mathbf{x}, \mathbf{y} \in S$. Then $A\mathbf{x} = \lambda\mathbf{x}$ and $A\mathbf{y} = \lambda\mathbf{y}$. So,

$A(\mathbf{x} + \mathbf{y}) = A\mathbf{x} + A\mathbf{y} = \lambda\mathbf{x} + \lambda\mathbf{y} = \lambda(\mathbf{x} + \mathbf{y})$, which implies that $\mathbf{x} + \mathbf{y} \in S$. Finally, for any scalar c, $A(c\mathbf{x}) = c(A\mathbf{x}) = c(\lambda\mathbf{x}) = \lambda(c\mathbf{x})$, which implies that $c\mathbf{x} \in S$.

If $\lambda = 3$, then solve for $\mathbf{x}$ in the equation

$A\mathbf{x} = \lambda\mathbf{x} = 3\mathbf{x}$, or $A\mathbf{x} - 3\mathbf{x} = \mathbf{0}$, or $(A - 3I_3)\mathbf{x} = \mathbf{0}$.

$$\left(\begin{bmatrix} 3 & 1 & 0 \\ 0 & 3 & 0 \\ 0 & 0 & 1 \end{bmatrix} - 3 \begin{bmatrix} 1 & 0 & 0 \\ 0 & 1 & 0 \\ 0 & 0 & 1 \end{bmatrix} \right) \begin{bmatrix} x_1 \\ x_2 \\ x_3 \end{bmatrix} = \begin{bmatrix} 0 \\ 0 \\ 0 \end{bmatrix}$$

$$\begin{bmatrix} 0 & 1 & 0 \\ 0 & 0 & 0 \\ 0 & 0 & -2 \end{bmatrix} \begin{bmatrix} x_1 \\ x_2 \\ x_3 \end{bmatrix} = \begin{bmatrix} 0 \\ 0 \\ 0 \end{bmatrix}$$

The solution to this homogeneous system is $x_1 = t$, $x_2 = 0$, and $x_3 = 0$, where t is any real number. So, a basis for S is $\{(1, 0, 0)\}$, and the dimension of S is 1.

82. From Exercise 79, you see that a set of functions $\{f_1, \ldots, f_n\}$ can be linearly independent in $C[a, b]$ and linearly dependent in $C[c, d]$, where $[a, b]$ and $[c, d]$ are different domains.

84. (a) False. This set is not closed under addition or scalar multiplication:

$(0, 1, 1) \in W$, but $2(0, 1, 1) = (0, 2, 2)$ is not in W.

(b) True. See "Definition of Basis," on page 180.

(c) False. For example, let $A = I_3$ be the 3×3 identity matrix. It is invertible and the rows of A form the standard basis for R^3 and, in particular, the rows of A are linearly independent.

86. (a) True. It is a nonempty subset of R^2, and it is closed under addition and scalar multiplication.

(b) False. These operations only preserve the linear relationships among the columns.

88. (a) Because $y' = y'' = y''' = y'''' = e^x$, you have

$y'''' - y = e^x - e^x = 0.$

Therefore, e^x is a solution.

(b) Because $y' = -e^{-x}, y'' = e^{-x}, y''' = -e^{-x}$ and $y'''' = e^{-x}$, you have

$y'''' - y = e^{-x} - e^{-x} = 0.$

Therefore e^{-x} is a solution.

(c) Because

$y' = -\sin x, y'' = -\cos x, y''' = \sin x, y'''' = \cos x,$

you have

$y'''' - y = \cos x - \cos x = 0.$

Therefore, $\cos x$ is a solution.

(d) Because

$y' = \cos x, y'' = -\sin x, y''' = -\cos x, y'''' = \sin x,$

you have

$y'''' - y = \sin x - \sin x = 0.$

Therefore, $\sin x$ is a solution.

90. (a) Because $y'' = -9 \cos 3x - 9 \sin 3x$, you have

$$y'' + 9y = -9 \cos 3x - 9 \sin 3x + 9(\sin 3x + \cos 3x)$$
$$= -9 \cos 3x - 9 \sin 3x + 9 \sin 3x + 9 \cos 3x$$
$$= 0.$$

Therefore, $\sin 3x + \cos 3x$ is a solution.

(b) Because $y'' = -3 \cos x - 3 \sin x$, you have

$$y'' + 9y = -3 \cos x - 3 \sin x + 9(3 \sin x + 3 \cos x)$$
$$= -3 \cos x - 3 \sin x + 27 \sin x + 27 \cos x$$
$$\neq 0.$$

Therefore, $3 \sin x + 3 \cos x$ is not a solution.

(c) Because $y'' = -9 \sin 3x$, you have

$$y'' + 9y = -9 \sin 3x + 9(\sin 3x) = -9 \sin 3x + 9 \sin 3x = 0.$$

Therefore, $\sin 3x$ is a solution.

(d) Because $y'' = -9 \cos 3x$, you have

$$y'' + 9y = -9 \cos 3x + 9(\cos 3x) = -9 \cos 3x + 9 \cos 3x = 0.$$

Therefore, $\cos 3x$ is a solution.

92. $W(1, x, 2 + x) = \begin{vmatrix} 1 & x & (2 + x) \\ 0 & 1 & 1 \\ 0 & 0 & 0 \end{vmatrix} = 0$

94. $W(x_1 \sin^2 x_1 \cos^2 x) = \begin{vmatrix} x & \sin^2 x & \cos^2 x \\ 1 & 2 \sin x \cos x & -2 \sin x \cos x \\ 0 & 4 \cos^2 x - 2 & 2 - 4 \cos^2 x \end{vmatrix} = 4 \cos^2 x - 2$

96. (a) $y = e^{-3x} \Rightarrow y' = -3e^{-3x}, y'' = 9e^{-3x} \Rightarrow y'' + 6y' + 9y = 0$

$y = 3e^{-3x} \Rightarrow y' = -9e^{-3x}, y'' = 27e^{-3x} \Rightarrow y'' + 6y' + 9y = 0$

(b) The Wronskian of this set is

$$W\left(e^{-3x}, 3e^{-3x}\right) = \begin{vmatrix} e^{-3x} & 3e^{-3x} \\ -3x^{-3x} & -9e^{-3x} \end{vmatrix} = -9e^{-6x} + 9e^{-6x} = 0 = 0.$$

Because $W\left(e^{-3x}, 3e^{-3x}\right) = 0$, the set is linearly dependent.

98. (a) $y = \sin 2x \Rightarrow y'' = -4 \sin 2x \Rightarrow y'' + 4y = 0$

$y = \cos 2x \Rightarrow y'' = -4 \cos 2x \Rightarrow y'' + 4y = 0$

(b) The Wronskian of this set is

$$W\left(\sin 2x, \cos 2x\right) = \begin{vmatrix} \sin 2x & \cos 2x \\ 2 \cos 2x & -2 \sin 2x \end{vmatrix} = -2 \sin^2 2x - 2 \cos^2 2x = -2.$$

Because $W\left(\sin 2x, \cos 2x\right) \neq 0$ the set is linearly independent.

(c) $y = C_1 \sin 2x + C_2 \cos 2x$

100. Begin by completing the square.

$$9x^2 + 18x + 9y^2 - 18y = -14$$
$$9\left(x^2 + 2x + 1\right) + 9\left(y^2 - 2y + 1\right) = -14 + 9 + 9$$
$$\left(x + 1\right)^2 + \left(y - 1\right)^2 = \frac{4}{9}$$

This is the equation of a circle centered at $(-1, 1)$ with a radius of $\frac{2}{3}$.

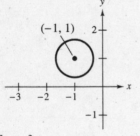

$9x^2 + 9y^2 + 18x - 18y + 14 = 0$

102. Begin by completing the square.

$$4x^2 + 8x - y^2 - 6y = -4$$
$$4\left(x^2 + 2x + 1\right) - \left(y^2 + 6y + 9\right) = -4 + 4 - 9$$
$$\frac{\left(y + 3\right)^2}{9} - \frac{\left(x + 1\right)^2}{\frac{9}{4}} = 1$$

This is the equation of a hyperbola centered at $(-1, -3)$.

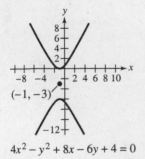

$4x^2 - y^2 + 8x - 6y + 4 = 0$

104. $y^2 - 4x - 4 = 0$

$$y^2 = 4x + 4$$
$$y^2 = 4(x + 1)$$

This is the equation of a parabola with vertex $(-1, 0)$.

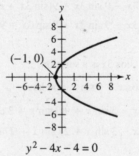

$y^2 - 4x - 4 = 0$

106. Begin by completing the square.

$$16x^2 - 32x + 25y^2 - 50y = -16$$
$$16\left(x^2 - 2x + 1\right) + 25\left(y^2 - 2y + 1\right) = -16 + 16 + 25$$
$$\frac{\left(x - 1\right)^2}{\frac{25}{16}} + \left(y - 1\right)^2 = 1$$

This is the equation of an ellipse centered at $(1, 1)$.

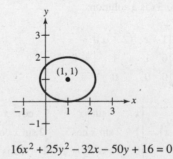

$16x^2 + 25y^2 - 32x - 50y + 16 = 0$

108. From the equation

$$\cot 2\theta = \frac{a-c}{b} = \frac{9-9}{4} = 0,$$

you find that the angle of rotation is $\theta = \frac{\pi}{4}$. Therefore,

$$\sin \theta = \frac{1}{\sqrt{2}} \text{ and } \cos \theta = \frac{1}{\sqrt{2}}.$$

By substituting

$$x = x' \cos \theta - y' \sin \theta = \frac{1}{\sqrt{2}}(x' - y')$$

and

$$y = x' \sin \theta + y' \cos \theta = \frac{1}{\sqrt{2}}(x' + y')$$

Into $9x^2 + 4xy + 9y^2 - 20 = 0$, you obtain

$$11(x')^2 + 7(y')^2 = 20.$$

In standard form,

$$\frac{(x')^2}{\frac{20}{11}} + \frac{(y')^2}{\frac{20}{7}} = 1$$

which is the equation of an ellipse with major axis along the y'-axis.

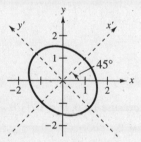

110. From the equation

$$\cot 2\theta = \frac{a-c}{b} = \frac{7-13}{6\sqrt{3}} = \frac{-6}{6\sqrt{3}} = -\frac{\sqrt{3}}{3}$$

you find the angle of rotation to be $\theta = -\frac{\pi}{6}$.

Therefore, $\sin \theta = -1/2$ and $\cos \theta = \sqrt{3/2}$.

By substituting

$$x = x' \cos \theta - y' \sin \theta = \frac{1}{2}\left(\sqrt{3}x' + y'\right)$$

and

$$y = x' \sin \theta + y' \cos \theta = \frac{1}{2}\left(\sqrt{3}y' - x'\right)$$

into $7x^2 + 6\sqrt{3}xy + 13y^2 - 16 = 0$, you obtain

$$4(x')^2 + 16(y')^2 = 16.$$ In standard form,

$$\frac{(x')^2}{4} + (y')^2 = 1$$

which is the equation of an ellipse centered at $(0, 0)$, with the major axis along the x'-axis.

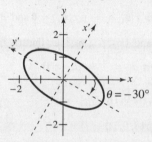

Project Solutions for Chapter 4

1 Solutions of Linear Systems

1. Because $(-2, -1, 1, 1)$ is a solution of $A\mathbf{x} = \mathbf{0}$, so is any multiple $-2(-2, -1, 1, 1) = (4, 2, -2, -2)$ because the solution space is a subspace.

2. The solutions of $A\mathbf{x} = \mathbf{0}$ form a subspace, so any linear combination $2\mathbf{x}_1 - 3\mathbf{x}_2$ of solutions $\mathbf{x}_1$ and $\mathbf{x}_2$ is again a solution.

3. Let the first system be $A\mathbf{x} = \mathbf{b}_1$. Because it is consistent, $\mathbf{b}_1$ is in the column space of A. The second system is $A\mathbf{x} = \mathbf{b}_2$, and $\mathbf{b}_2$ is a multiple of $\mathbf{b}_1$, so it is in the column space of A as well. So, the second system is consistent.

4. $2\mathbf{x}_1 - 3\mathbf{x}_2$ is *not* a solution (unless $\mathbf{b} = \mathbf{0}$). The set of solutions to a nonhomogeneous system is not a subspace. If $A\mathbf{x}_1 = \mathbf{b}$ and $A\mathbf{x}_2 = \mathbf{b}$, then

$$A(2\mathbf{x}_1 - 3\mathbf{x}_2) = 2A\mathbf{x}_1 - 3A\mathbf{x}_2 = 2\mathbf{b} - 3\mathbf{b} = -\mathbf{b} \neq \mathbf{b}.$$

5. Yes, $\mathbf{b}_1$ and $\mathbf{b}_2$ are in the column space of A, therefore so is $\mathbf{b}_1 + \mathbf{b}_2$.

2 Direct Sum

1. Basis for U: $\{(1, 0, 1), (0, 1, -1)\}$

   Basis for W: $\{(1, 0, 1)\}$

   Basis for Z: $\{(1, 1, 1)\}$

   $U + W = U$ because $W \subseteq U$

   $U + Z = R^3$ because $\{(1, 0, 1), (0, 1, -1), (1, 1, 1)\}$ is a basis for R^3.

   $W + Z = \text{span}\{(1, 0, 1), (1, 1, 1)\} = \text{span}\{(1, 0, 1), (0, 1, 0)\}$

2. Suppose $\mathbf{u}_1 + \mathbf{w}_1 = \mathbf{u}_2 + \mathbf{w}_2$, which implies $\mathbf{u}_1 - \mathbf{u}_2 = \mathbf{w}_2 - \mathbf{w}_1$.

   Because $\mathbf{u}_1 - \mathbf{u}_2 \in U \cap W$ and $\mathbf{w}_2 - \mathbf{w}_1 \in U \cap W$, and $U \cap W = \{\mathbf{0}\}$, $\mathbf{u}_1 = \mathbf{u}_2$ and $\mathbf{w}_1 = \mathbf{w}_2$.

   $U \oplus Z$ and $W \oplus Z$ are direct sums.

3. Let $\mathbf{v} \in V$, then $\mathbf{v} = \mathbf{u} + \mathbf{w}, \mathbf{u} \in U, \mathbf{w} \in W$. Then $\mathbf{v} = (c_1\mathbf{u}_1 + \cdots + c_k\mathbf{u}_k) + (d_1\mathbf{w}_1 + \cdots + d_m\mathbf{w}_m)$,

   and $\mathbf{v}$ is in the span of $\{\mathbf{u}_1, \ldots, \mathbf{u}_k, \mathbf{w}_1, \ldots, \mathbf{w}_m\}$. To show that this set is linearly independent, suppose

   $c_1\mathbf{u}_1 + \cdots + c_k\mathbf{u}_k + d_1\mathbf{w}_1 + \cdots + d_m\mathbf{w}_m = \mathbf{0}$

   $\Rightarrow c_1\mathbf{u}_1 + \cdots + c_k\mathbf{u}_k = -(d_1\mathbf{w}_1 + \cdots + d_m\mathbf{w}_m)$

   But $U \cap W \neq \{\mathbf{0}\} \Rightarrow c_1\mathbf{u}_1 + \cdots + c_k\mathbf{u}_k = \mathbf{0}$ and $d_1\mathbf{w}_1 + \cdots + d_m\mathbf{w}_m = \mathbf{0}$.

   Because $\{\mathbf{u}_1, \ldots, \mathbf{u}_k\}$ and $\{\mathbf{w}_1, \ldots, \mathbf{w}_m\}$ are linearly independent,

   $c_1 = \cdots = c_k = 0$ and $d_1 = \cdots = d_m = 0$.

4. Basis for U: $\{(1, 0, 0), (0, 0, 1)\}$

   Basis for W: $\{(0, 1, 0), (0, 0, 1)\}$

   $U + W$ is spanned by $\{(1, 0, 0), (0, 0, 1), (0, 1, 0)\} \Rightarrow U + W = R^3$. This is not a direct sum because $(0, 0, 1) \in U \cap W$.

   $\dim U = 2, \dim W = 2, \dim(U \cap W) = 1$

   $\dim U + \dim W = \dim(U + W) + \dim(U \cap W)$.
   $\quad 2 \quad + \quad 2 \quad = \quad\quad 3 \quad\quad + \quad\quad 1$

   In general, $\dim U + \dim W = \dim(U + W) + \dim(U \cap W)$.

5. No, $\dim U + \dim W = 2 + 2 = 4$, then $\dim(U + W) + \dim(U \cap W) = \dim(U + W) = 4$, which is impossible in R^3.

CHAPTER 5
Inner Product Spaces

CHAPTER 5
Inner Product Spaces

Section 5.1   Length and Dot Product in R^n

2. $\|\mathbf{v}\| = \sqrt{0^2 + 1^2} = \sqrt{1} = 1$

4. $\|\mathbf{v}\| = \sqrt{2^2 + 0^2 + (-5)^2 + 5^2} = \sqrt{54} = 3\sqrt{6}$

6. (a) $\|\mathbf{u}\| = \sqrt{1^2 + \left(\dfrac{1}{2}\right)^2} = \sqrt{\dfrac{5}{4}} = \dfrac{1}{2}\sqrt{5}$

  (b) $\|\mathbf{v}\| = \sqrt{2^2 + \left(-\dfrac{1}{2}\right)^2} = \sqrt{\dfrac{17}{4}} = \dfrac{1}{2}\sqrt{17}$

  (c) $\|\mathbf{u} + \mathbf{v}\| = \|(3, 0)\| = \sqrt{3^2 + 0^2} = \sqrt{9} = 3$

8. (a) $\|\mathbf{u}\| = \sqrt{0^2 + 1^2 + (-1)^2 + 2^2} = \sqrt{6}$

  (b) $\|\mathbf{v}\| = \sqrt{1^2 + 1^2 + 3^2 + 0^2} = \sqrt{11}$

  (c) $\|\mathbf{u} + \mathbf{v}\| = \|(1, 2, 2, 2)\|$
  $= \sqrt{1^2 + 2^2 + 2^2 + 2^2} = \sqrt{13}$

10. (a) A unit vector $\mathbf{v}$ in the direction of $\mathbf{u}$ is given by

  $\mathbf{v} = \dfrac{\mathbf{u}}{\|\mathbf{u}\|} = \dfrac{1}{\sqrt{1^2 + (-1)^2}}(1, -1)$

  $= \dfrac{1}{\sqrt{2}}(1, -1) = \left(\dfrac{1}{\sqrt{2}}, -\dfrac{1}{\sqrt{2}}\right)$.

  (b) A unit vector in the direction opposite that of $\mathbf{u}$ is given by

  $-\mathbf{v} = -\left(\dfrac{1}{\sqrt{2}}, -\dfrac{1}{\sqrt{2}}\right) = \left(-\dfrac{1}{\sqrt{2}}, \dfrac{1}{\sqrt{2}}\right)$.

12. (a) A unit vector $\mathbf{v}$ in the direction of $\mathbf{u}$ is given by

  $\mathbf{v} = \dfrac{\mathbf{u}}{\|\mathbf{u}\|} = \dfrac{1}{\sqrt{(-1)^2 + 3^2 + 4^2}}(-1, 3, 4)$

  $= \dfrac{1}{\sqrt{26}}(-1, 3, 4) = \left(-\dfrac{1}{\sqrt{26}}, \dfrac{3}{\sqrt{26}}, \dfrac{4}{\sqrt{26}}\right)$

  (b) A unit vector in the direction opposite that of $\mathbf{u}$ is given by

  $-\mathbf{v} = -\left(-\dfrac{1}{\sqrt{26}}, \dfrac{3}{\sqrt{26}}, \dfrac{4}{\sqrt{26}}\right)$

  $= \left(\dfrac{1}{\sqrt{26}}, -\dfrac{3}{\sqrt{26}}, -\dfrac{4}{\sqrt{26}}\right)$.

14. First find a unit vector in the direction of $\mathbf{u}$.

  $\dfrac{\mathbf{u}}{\|\mathbf{u}\|} = \dfrac{1}{\sqrt{(-1)^2 + 1^2}}(-1, 1) = \dfrac{1}{\sqrt{2}}(-1, 1) = \left(-\dfrac{1}{\sqrt{2}}, \dfrac{1}{\sqrt{2}}\right)$

  Then $\mathbf{v}$ is four times this vector.

  $\mathbf{v} = 4\dfrac{\mathbf{u}}{\|\mathbf{u}\|} = 4\left(-\dfrac{1}{\sqrt{2}}, \dfrac{1}{\sqrt{2}}\right)$

  $= \left(-\dfrac{4}{\sqrt{2}}, \dfrac{4}{\sqrt{2}}\right) = \left(-2\sqrt{2}, 2\sqrt{2}\right)$

16. First find a unit vector in the direction of $\mathbf{u}$.

  $\dfrac{\mathbf{u}}{\|\mathbf{u}\|} = \dfrac{1}{\sqrt{0 + 4 + 1 + 1}}(0, 2, 1, -1) = \dfrac{1}{\sqrt{6}}(0, 2, 1, -1)$

  Then $\mathbf{v}$ is three times this vector.

  $\mathbf{v} = 3\dfrac{1}{\sqrt{6}}(0, 2, 1, -1) = \left(0, \dfrac{6}{\sqrt{6}}, \dfrac{3}{\sqrt{6}}, -\dfrac{3}{\sqrt{6}}\right)$

18. Solve the equation for c as follows.

  $\|c(1, 2, 3)\| = 1$

  $|c|\,\|(1, 2, 3)\| = 1$

  $|c| = \dfrac{1}{\|(1, 2, 3)\|} = \dfrac{1}{\sqrt{14}}$

  $c = \pm\dfrac{1}{\sqrt{14}}$

20. $d(\mathbf{u}, \mathbf{v}) = \|\mathbf{u} - \mathbf{v}\| = \|(2, -2, 2)\|$
  $= \sqrt{2^2 + (-2)^2 + 2^2} = 2\sqrt{3}$

22. $d(\mathbf{u}, \mathbf{v}) = \|\mathbf{u} - \mathbf{v}\| = \|(-1, 0, -3, 0)\|$
  $= \sqrt{(-1)^2 + 0^2 + (-3)^2 + 0^2}$
  $= \sqrt{10}$

24. (a) $\mathbf{u} \cdot \mathbf{v} = (-1)(2) + (2)(-2) = -2 - 4 = -6$

  (b) $\mathbf{v} \cdot \mathbf{v} = 2(2) + (-2)(-2) = 4 + 4 = 8$

  (c) $\|\mathbf{u}\|^2 = \mathbf{u} \cdot \mathbf{u} = (-1)(-1) + (2)(2) = 1 + 4 = 5$

  (d) $(\mathbf{u} \cdot \mathbf{v})\mathbf{v} = -6(2, -2) = (-12, 12)$

  (e) $\mathbf{u} \cdot (5\mathbf{v}) = 5(\mathbf{u} \cdot \mathbf{v}) = 5(-6) = -30$

26. (a) $\mathbf{u} \cdot \mathbf{v} = 4(0) + 0(2) + (-3)(5) + (5)(4)$
$$= 0 + 0 - 15 + 20$$
$$= 5$$

(b) $\mathbf{v} \cdot \mathbf{v} = 0(0) + 2(2) + 5(5) + 4(4)$
$$= 0 + 4 + 25 + 16$$
$$= 45$$

(c) $\|\mathbf{u}\|^2 = \mathbf{u} \cdot \mathbf{u} = 4(4) + 0(0) + (-3)(-3) + 5(5)$
$$= 16 + 0 + 9 + 25$$
$$= 50$$

(d) $(\mathbf{u} \cdot \mathbf{v})\mathbf{v} = 5(0, 2, 5, 4)$
$$= (0, 10, 25, 20)$$

(e) $\mathbf{u} \cdot (5\mathbf{v}) = 5(\mathbf{u} \cdot \mathbf{v}) = 5(5) = 25$

28. $(3\mathbf{u} - \mathbf{v}) \cdot (\mathbf{u} - 3\mathbf{v}) = 3\mathbf{u} \cdot (\mathbf{u} - 3\mathbf{v}) - \mathbf{v} \cdot (\mathbf{u} - 3\mathbf{v})$
$$= 3\mathbf{u} \cdot \mathbf{u} - 9\mathbf{u} \cdot \mathbf{v} - \mathbf{v} \cdot \mathbf{u} + 3\mathbf{v} \cdot \mathbf{v}$$
$$= 3\mathbf{u} \cdot \mathbf{u} - 10\mathbf{u} \cdot \mathbf{v} + 3\mathbf{v} \cdot \mathbf{v}$$
$$= 3(8) - 10(7) + 3(6)$$
$$= -28$$

30. $\mathbf{u} = \left(-1, \frac{1}{2}, \frac{1}{4}\right)$ and $\mathbf{v} = \left(0, \frac{1}{4}, -\frac{1}{2}\right)$

(a) $\|\mathbf{u}\| = 1.1456$ and $\|\mathbf{v}\| = 0.5590$

(b) $\frac{1}{\|\mathbf{v}\|}\mathbf{v} = (0, 0.4472, -0.8944)$

(c) $-\frac{1}{\|\mathbf{u}\|}\mathbf{u} = (0.8729, -0.4364, -0.2182)$

(d) $\mathbf{u} \cdot \mathbf{v} = 0$

(e) $\mathbf{u} \cdot \mathbf{u} = 1.3125$

(f) $\mathbf{v} \cdot \mathbf{v} = 0.3125$

38. The cosine of the angle θ between $\mathbf{u}$ and $\mathbf{v}$ is given by
$$\cos\theta = \frac{\mathbf{u} \cdot \mathbf{v}}{\|\mathbf{u}\|\|\mathbf{v}\|} = \frac{2(2) - 1(0)}{\sqrt{2^2 + (-1)^2}\sqrt{2^2 + 0^2}} = \frac{4}{2\sqrt{5}} = \frac{2\sqrt{5}}{5}.$$

So, $\theta = \cos^{-1}\left(\frac{2\sqrt{5}}{5}\right) \approx 0.4636$ radians (26.57°).

40. The cosine of the angle θ between $\mathbf{u}$ and $\mathbf{v}$ is given by
$$\cos\theta = \frac{\mathbf{u} \cdot \mathbf{v}}{\|\mathbf{u}\|\|\mathbf{v}\|} = \frac{\cos\frac{\pi}{3}\left(\cos\frac{\pi}{4}\right) + \sin\frac{\pi}{3}\left(\sin\frac{\pi}{4}\right)}{\sqrt{\left(\cos\frac{\pi}{3}\right)^2 + \left(\sin\frac{\pi}{3}\right)^2}\sqrt{\left(\cos\frac{\pi}{4}\right)^2 + \left(\sin\frac{\pi}{4}\right)^2}} = \frac{\cos\left(\frac{\pi}{3} - \frac{\pi}{4}\right)}{1 \cdot 1} = \cos\left(\frac{\pi}{12}\right).$$

So, $\theta = \frac{\pi}{12}$ radians (15°).

32. $\mathbf{u} = \left(-1, \sqrt{3}, 2\right)$ and $\mathbf{v} = \left(\sqrt{2}, -1, -\sqrt{2}\right)$

(a) $\|\mathbf{u}\| = 2.8284$ and $\|\mathbf{v}\| = 2.2361$

(b) $\frac{1}{\|\mathbf{v}\|}\mathbf{v} = (0.6325, -0.4472, -0.6325)$

(c) $-\frac{1}{\|\mathbf{u}\|}\mathbf{u} = (0.3536, -0.6124, -0.7071)$

(d) $\mathbf{u} \cdot \mathbf{v} = -5.9747$

(e) $\mathbf{u} \cdot \mathbf{u} = 8$

(f) $\mathbf{v} \cdot \mathbf{v} = 5$

34. You have
$$\mathbf{u} \cdot \mathbf{v} = -1(1) + 0(1) = -1,$$
$$\|\mathbf{u}\| = \sqrt{(-1)^2 + 0^2} = \sqrt{1} = 1, \text{ and}$$
$$\|\mathbf{v}\| = \sqrt{1^2 + 1^2} = \sqrt{2}. \text{ So,}$$
$$|\mathbf{u} \cdot \mathbf{v}| \leq \|\mathbf{u}\|\|\mathbf{v}\|$$
$$|-1| \leq 1\sqrt{2}$$
$$1 \leq \sqrt{2}.$$

36. You have
$$\mathbf{u} \cdot \mathbf{v} = 1(0) - 1(1) + 0(-1) = -1,$$
$$\|\mathbf{u}\| = \sqrt{1^2 + (-1)^2 + 0^2} = \sqrt{2}, \text{ and}$$
$$\|\mathbf{v}\| = \sqrt{0^2 + 1^2 + (-1)^2} = \sqrt{2}. \text{ So,}$$
$$|\mathbf{u} \cdot \mathbf{v}| \leq \|\mathbf{u}\|\|\mathbf{v}\|$$
$$|-1| \leq \sqrt{2} \cdot \sqrt{2}$$
$$1 \leq 2.$$

136 *Chapter 5   Inner Product Spaces*

42. The cosine of the angle θ between $\mathbf{u}$ and $\mathbf{v}$ is given by

$$\cos\theta = \frac{\mathbf{u}\cdot\mathbf{v}}{\|\mathbf{u}\|\|\mathbf{v}\|} = \frac{2(-3)+3(2)+1(0)}{\|\mathbf{u}\|\|\mathbf{v}\|} = 0.$$

So, $\theta = \dfrac{\pi}{2}$ radians (90°).

44. The cosine of the angle θ between $\mathbf{u}$ and $\mathbf{v}$ is given by

$$\cos\theta = \frac{\mathbf{u}\cdot\mathbf{v}}{\|\mathbf{u}\|\|\mathbf{v}\|} = \frac{1(-1)-1(2)+0(-1)+1(0)}{\sqrt{1^2+(-1)^2+0^2+1^2}\sqrt{(-1)^2+2^2+(-1)^2+0^2}} = \frac{-3}{\sqrt{3}\sqrt{6}} = -\frac{3}{3\sqrt{2}} = -\frac{\sqrt{2}}{2}.$$

So, $\theta = \cos^{-1}\left(-\dfrac{\sqrt{2}}{2}\right) \approx \dfrac{3\pi}{4}$ radians (135°).

46. Because $\mathbf{u}\cdot\mathbf{v} = (4,3)\cdot\left(\frac{1}{2},-\frac{2}{3}\right) = 2-2 = 0,$ the vectors $\mathbf{u}$ and $\mathbf{v}$ are orthogonal.

48. Because $\mathbf{u}\cdot\mathbf{v} = 1(0)-1(-1) = 1 \neq 0,$ the vectors $\mathbf{u}$ and $\mathbf{v}$ are not orthogonal. Moreover, because one is not a scalar multiple of the other, they are not parallel.

50. Because $\mathbf{u}\cdot\mathbf{v} = 0(1)+1(-2)+6(-1) = -8 \neq 0,$ the vectors $\mathbf{u}$ and $\mathbf{v}$ are not orthogonal. Moreover, because one is not a scalar multiple of the other, they are not parallel.

52. Because

$$\mathbf{u}\cdot\mathbf{v} = 4(-2)+\tfrac{3}{2}\left(-\tfrac{3}{4}\right)+(-1)\left(\tfrac{1}{2}\right)+\tfrac{1}{2}\left(-\tfrac{1}{4}\right) = -\tfrac{39}{4} \neq 0,$$

the vectors are not orthogonal. Moreover, because one vector is a scalar multiple of the other, they are parallel.

54. $\mathbf{u}\cdot\mathbf{v} = 0$

$(2,7)\cdot(v_1,v_2) = 0$

$2v_1 + 7v_2 = 0$

So, $\mathbf{v} = (-7t, 2t)$, where t is any real number.

56. $\mathbf{u}\cdot\mathbf{v} = 0$

$(4,-1,0)\cdot(v_1,v_2,v_3) = 0$

$4v_1 + (-1)v_2 + 0v_3 = 0$

$4v_1 - v_2 = 0$

So, $\mathbf{v} = (t, 4t, s)$, where s and t are any real numbers.

58. Because $\mathbf{u}+\mathbf{v} = (-1,1)+(2,0) = (1,1)$, you have

$\|\mathbf{u}+\mathbf{v}\| \leq \|\mathbf{u}\|+\|\mathbf{v}\|$

$\|(1,1)\| \leq \|(-1,1)\|+\|(2,0)\|$

$\sqrt{2} \leq \sqrt{2}+2.$

60. Because $\mathbf{u}+\mathbf{v} = (1,-1,0)+(0,1,2) = (1,0,2)$, you have

$\|\mathbf{u}+\mathbf{v}\| \leq \|\mathbf{u}\|+\|\mathbf{v}\|$

$\|(1,0,2)\| \leq \|(1,-1,0)\|+\|(0,1,2)\|$

$\sqrt{5} \leq \sqrt{2}+\sqrt{5}.$

62. First note that $\mathbf{u}$ and $\mathbf{v}$ are orthogonal, because

$\mathbf{u}\cdot\mathbf{v} = (3,-2)\cdot(4,6) = 0.$

Then note

$\|\mathbf{u}+\mathbf{v}\|^2 = \|\mathbf{u}\|^2 + \|\mathbf{v}\|^2$

$\|(7,4)\|^2 = \|(3,-2)\|^2 + \|(4,6)\|^2$

$65 = 13 + 52$

$65 = 65.$

64. First note that $\mathbf{u}$ and $\mathbf{v}$ are orthogonal, because

$\mathbf{u}\cdot\mathbf{v} = (4,1,-5)\cdot(2,-3,1) = 0.$

Then note

$\|\mathbf{u}+\mathbf{v}\|^2 = \|\mathbf{u}\|^2 + \|\mathbf{v}\|^2$

$\|(6,-2,-4)\|^2 = \|(4,1,-5)\|^2 + \|(2,-3,1)\|^2$

$56 = 42 + 14$

$56 = 56.$

66. (a) $\mathbf{u} \cdot \mathbf{v} = \mathbf{u}^T\mathbf{v} = \begin{bmatrix} -1 & 2 \end{bmatrix}\begin{bmatrix} 2 \\ -2 \end{bmatrix} = \left[(-1)(2) + (2)(-2)\right] = \begin{bmatrix} -2 & -4 \end{bmatrix} = -6$

(b) $\mathbf{v} \cdot \mathbf{v} = \mathbf{v}^T\mathbf{v} = \begin{bmatrix} 2 & -2 \end{bmatrix}\begin{bmatrix} 2 \\ -2 \end{bmatrix} = \left[2(2) + (-2)(-2)\right] = \begin{bmatrix} 4 + 4 \end{bmatrix} = 8$

(c) $\|\mathbf{u}\|^2 = \mathbf{u}^T\mathbf{u} = \begin{bmatrix} -1 & 2 \end{bmatrix}\begin{bmatrix} -1 \\ 2 \end{bmatrix} = \left[(-1)(-1) + 2(2)\right] = \begin{bmatrix} 1 + 4 \end{bmatrix} = 5$

(d) $(\mathbf{u} \cdot \mathbf{v})\mathbf{v} = (\mathbf{u}^T\mathbf{v})\mathbf{v} = \left(\begin{bmatrix} -1 & 2 \end{bmatrix}\begin{bmatrix} 2 \\ -2 \end{bmatrix}\right)\begin{bmatrix} 2 \\ -2 \end{bmatrix} = -6\begin{bmatrix} 2 \\ -2 \end{bmatrix} = \begin{bmatrix} -12 \\ 12 \end{bmatrix}$

(e) $\mathbf{u} \cdot (5\mathbf{v}) = 5(\mathbf{u}^T\mathbf{v}) = 5\left(\begin{bmatrix} -1 & 2 \end{bmatrix}\begin{bmatrix} 2 \\ -2 \end{bmatrix}\right) = 5(-6) = -30$

68. (a) $\mathbf{u} \cdot \mathbf{v} = \mathbf{u}^T\mathbf{v} = \begin{bmatrix} 4 & 0 & -3 & 5 \end{bmatrix}\begin{bmatrix} 0 \\ 2 \\ 5 \\ 4 \end{bmatrix} = \left[4(0) + 0(2) + (-3)(5) + (5)(4)\right] = \begin{bmatrix} 0 + 0 - 15 + 20 \end{bmatrix} = 5$

(b) $\mathbf{v} \cdot \mathbf{v} = \mathbf{v}^T\mathbf{v} = \begin{bmatrix} 0 & 2 & 5 & 4 \end{bmatrix}\begin{bmatrix} 0 \\ 2 \\ 5 \\ 4 \end{bmatrix} = \left[0(0) + 2(2) + 5(5) + 4(4)\right] = \begin{bmatrix} 0 + 4 + 25 + 16 \end{bmatrix} = 45$

(c) $\|\mathbf{u}\|^2 = \mathbf{u}^T\mathbf{u} = \begin{bmatrix} 4 & 0 & -3 & 5 \end{bmatrix}\begin{bmatrix} 4 \\ 0 \\ -3 \\ 5 \end{bmatrix} = \left[4(4) + 0(0) + (-3)(-3) + 5(5)\right] = \begin{bmatrix} 16 + 0 + 9 + 25 \end{bmatrix} = 50$

(d) $(\mathbf{u} \cdot \mathbf{v})\mathbf{v} = (\mathbf{u}^T\mathbf{v})\mathbf{v} = \left(\begin{bmatrix} 4 & 0 & -3 & 5 \end{bmatrix}\begin{bmatrix} 0 \\ 2 \\ 5 \\ 4 \end{bmatrix}\right)\begin{bmatrix} 0 \\ 2 \\ 5 \\ 4 \end{bmatrix} = 5\begin{bmatrix} 0 \\ 2 \\ 5 \\ 4 \end{bmatrix} = \begin{bmatrix} 0 \\ 10 \\ 25 \\ 20 \end{bmatrix}$

(e) $\mathbf{u} \cdot (5\mathbf{v}) = 5(\mathbf{u}^T\mathbf{v}) = 5\left(\begin{bmatrix} 4 & 0 & -3 & 5 \end{bmatrix}\begin{bmatrix} 0 \\ 2 \\ 5 \\ 4 \end{bmatrix}\right) = 5(5) = 25$

70. Because $\mathbf{u} \cdot \mathbf{v} = -\sin\theta \sin\theta + \cos\theta(-\cos\theta) + 1(0)$

$\qquad = -(\sin\theta)^2 - (\cos\theta)^2$

$\qquad = -(\sin^2\theta + \cos^2\theta)$

$\qquad = -1 \neq 0,$

the vectors $\mathbf{u}$ and $\mathbf{v}$ are not orthogonal. Moreover, because one is not a scalar multiple of the other, they are not parallel.

72. (a) False. The unit vector in the direction of $\mathbf{v}$ is given by $\dfrac{\mathbf{v}}{\|\mathbf{v}\|}$.

(b) False. If $\mathbf{u} \cdot \mathbf{v} < 0$ then the angle between them lies between $\dfrac{\pi}{2}$ and π, because

$\cos\theta < 0 \Rightarrow \dfrac{\pi}{2} < \theta < \pi.$

74. (a) $(\mathbf{u} \cdot \mathbf{v}) \cdot \mathbf{u}$ is meaningless because $\mathbf{u} \cdot \mathbf{v}$ is a scalar.

(b) $c \cdot (\mathbf{u} \cdot \mathbf{v})$ is meaningless because c is a scalar, as well as $\mathbf{u} \cdot \mathbf{v}$.

76. $\mathbf{v} = (v_1, v_2) = (8, 15), (v_2, -v_1) = (15, -8)$

$(8, 15) \cdot (15, -8) = 8(15) + 15(-8) = 120 - 120 = 0$

So, $(v_2, -v_1)$ is orthogonal to $\mathbf{v}$.

Two unit vectors orthogonal to $\mathbf{v}$:

$-1(15, -8) = (-15, 8): (8, 15) \cdot (-15, 8) = 8(-15) + 15(8)$

$= -120 + 120$

$= 0$

$3(15, -8) = (45, -24): (8, 15) \cdot (45, -24) = 8(45) + (15)(-24)$

$= 360 - 360$

$= 0$

(Answer is not unique.)

78. $\mathbf{u} \cdot \mathbf{v} = (4600, 4290, 5250) \cdot (79.99, 89.99, 99.99)$

$= 4600(79.99) + 4290(89.99) + 5250(99.99)$

$= \$1{,}278{,}958.60$

This represents the total revenue earned from selling the three models of cellular phones.

80. Let $\mathbf{v} = (t, t, t)$ be the diagonal of the cube, and $\mathbf{u} = (t, t, 0)$ the diagonal of one of its sides. Then,

$$\cos \theta = \frac{\mathbf{u} \cdot \mathbf{v}}{\|\mathbf{u}\|\|\mathbf{v}\|} = \frac{2t^2}{(\sqrt{2}\,t)(\sqrt{3}\,t)} = \frac{2}{\sqrt{6}} = \frac{\sqrt{6}}{3}$$

and $\theta = \cos^{-1}\left(\dfrac{\sqrt{6}}{3}\right) \approx 35.26°.$

82. $\frac{1}{4}\|\mathbf{u} + \mathbf{v}\|^2 - \frac{1}{4}\|\mathbf{u} - \mathbf{v}\|^2 = \frac{1}{4}\left[(\mathbf{u} + \mathbf{v}) \cdot (\mathbf{u} + \mathbf{v}) - (\mathbf{u} - \mathbf{v}) \cdot (\mathbf{u} - \mathbf{v})\right]$

$= \frac{1}{4}\left[\mathbf{u} \cdot \mathbf{u} + 2\mathbf{u} \cdot \mathbf{v} + \mathbf{v} \cdot \mathbf{v} - (\mathbf{u} \cdot \mathbf{u} - 2\mathbf{u} \cdot \mathbf{v} + \mathbf{v} \cdot \mathbf{v})\right]$

$= \frac{1}{4}[4\mathbf{u} \cdot \mathbf{v}] = \mathbf{u} \cdot \mathbf{v}$

84. If $\mathbf{u}$ and $\mathbf{v}$ have the same direction, then $\mathbf{u} = c\mathbf{v}, c > 0$, and

$\|\mathbf{u} + \mathbf{v}\| = \|c\mathbf{v} + \mathbf{v}\| = (c + 1)\|\mathbf{v}\|$

$= c\|\mathbf{v}\| + \|\mathbf{v}\| = \|c\mathbf{v}\| + \|\mathbf{v}\|$

$= \|\mathbf{u}\| + \|\mathbf{v}\|.$

On the other hand, if

$\|\mathbf{u} + \mathbf{v}\| = \|\mathbf{u}\| + \|\mathbf{v}\|$, then

$\|\mathbf{u} + \mathbf{v}\|^2 = (\|\mathbf{u}\| + \|\mathbf{v}\|)^2$

$(\mathbf{u} + \mathbf{v}) \cdot (\mathbf{u} + \mathbf{v}) = \|\mathbf{u}\|^2 + \|\mathbf{v}\|^2 + 2\|\mathbf{u}\|\|\mathbf{v}\|$

$\|\mathbf{u}\|^2 + \|\mathbf{v}\|^2 + 2\mathbf{u} \cdot \mathbf{v} = \|\mathbf{u}\|^2 + \|\mathbf{v}\|^2 + 2\|\mathbf{u}\|\|\mathbf{v}\|$

$2\mathbf{u} \cdot \mathbf{v} = 2\|\mathbf{u}\|\|\mathbf{v}\|$

$\Rightarrow \cos \theta = \dfrac{\mathbf{u} \cdot \mathbf{v}}{\|\mathbf{u}\|\|\mathbf{v}\|} = 1 \quad \Rightarrow \quad \theta = 0 \quad \Rightarrow \quad \mathbf{u}$ and $\mathbf{v}$ have the same direction.

86. (a) When $\mathbf{u} \cdot \mathbf{v} = 0$, the vectors $\mathbf{u}$ and $\mathbf{v}$ are orthogonal $(\theta = 90°)$.

(b) When $\mathbf{u} \cdot \mathbf{v} > 0$, the vectors form an acute angle for $\theta \left(0° \leq \theta < 90° \text{ or } 0 \leq \theta < \dfrac{\pi}{2}\right).$

(c) When $\mathbf{u} \cdot \mathbf{v} < 0$, the vectors form an obtuse angle for $\theta \left(90° < \theta \leq 180° \text{ or } \dfrac{\pi}{2} < \theta \leq \pi\right).$

Section 5.2   Inner Product Spaces

2. 1. Since the product of real numbers is commutative,

$$\langle \mathbf{u}, \mathbf{v} \rangle = u_1 v_1 + 5 u_2 v_2 = v_1 u_1 + 5 v_2 u_2 = \langle \mathbf{v}, \mathbf{u} \rangle.$$

2. Let $\mathbf{w} = (w_1, w_2)$. Then,

$$\begin{aligned}
\langle \mathbf{u}, \mathbf{v} + \mathbf{w} \rangle &= u_1(v_1 + w_1) + 5 u_2(v_2 + w_2) \\
&= u_1 v_1 + u_1 w_1 + 5 u_2 v_2 + 5 u_2 w_2 \\
&= u_1 v_1 + 5 u_2 v_2 + u_1 w_1 + 5 u_2 w_2 \\
&= \langle \mathbf{u}, \mathbf{v} \rangle + \langle \mathbf{u}, \mathbf{w} \rangle.
\end{aligned}$$

3. If c is any scalar, then

$$c\langle \mathbf{u}, \mathbf{v} \rangle = c(u_1 v_1 + 5 u_2 v_2) = (c u_1)v_1 + 5(c u_2)v_2 = \langle c\mathbf{u}, \mathbf{v} \rangle.$$

4. Since the square of a real number is nonnegative, $\langle \mathbf{v}, \mathbf{v} \rangle = v_1^2 + 5 v_2^2 \geq 0$. Moreover, this expression is equal to zero if and only if $\mathbf{v} = \mathbf{0}$ (that is, if and only if $v_1 = v_2 = 0$).

4. 1. Since the product of real numbers is commutative,

$$\langle \mathbf{u}, \mathbf{v} \rangle = 2 u_1 v_2 + u_2 v_1 + u_1 v_2 + 2 u_2 v_2 = 2 v_2 u_1 + v_1 u_2 + v_2 u_1 + 2 v_2 u_2 = \langle \mathbf{v}, \mathbf{u} \rangle.$$

2. Let $\mathbf{w} = (w_1, w_2)$. Then,

$$\begin{aligned}
\langle \mathbf{u}, \mathbf{v} + \mathbf{w} \rangle &= 2 u_1(v_2 + w_2) + u_2(v_1 + w_1) + u_1(v_2 + w_2) + 2 u_2(v_2 + w_2) \\
&= 2 u_1 v_2 + 2 u_1 w_2 + u_2 v_1 + u_2 w_1 + u_1 v_2 + u_1 w_2 + 2 u_2 v_2 + 2 u_2 w_2 \\
&= 2 u_1 v_2 + u_2 v_1 + u_1 v_2 + 2 u_2 v_2 + 2 u_1 w_2 + u_2 w_1 + u_1 w_2 + 2 u_2 w_2 \\
&= \langle \mathbf{u}, \mathbf{v} \rangle + \langle \mathbf{u}, \mathbf{w} \rangle.
\end{aligned}$$

3. If c is any scalar, then

$$c\langle \mathbf{u}, \mathbf{v} \rangle = c(2 u_1 v_2 + u_2 v_1 + u_1 v_2 + 2 u_2 v_2) = 2(c u_1)v_2 + (c u_2)v_1 + (c u_1)v_2 + 2(c u_2)v_2 = \langle c\mathbf{u}, \mathbf{v} \rangle.$$

4. Since the square of a real number is nonnegative, $\langle \mathbf{v}, \mathbf{v} \rangle = 2 v_2^2 + v_1^2 + v_2^2 + 2 v_2^2 \geq 0$. Moreover, this expression is equal to zero if and only if $\mathbf{v} = \mathbf{0}$ (that is, if and only if $v_1 = v_2 = 0$).

6. 1. Since the product of real numbers is commutative,

$$\langle \mathbf{u}, \mathbf{v} \rangle = u_1 v_1 + 2 u_2 v_2 + u_3 v_3 = v_1 u_1 + 2 v_2 u_2 + v_3 u_3 = \langle \mathbf{v}, \mathbf{u} \rangle.$$

2. Let $\mathbf{w} = (w_1, w_2, w_3)$. Then,

$$\begin{aligned}
\langle \mathbf{u}, \mathbf{v} + \mathbf{w} \rangle &= u_1(v_1 + w_1) + 2 u_2(v_2 + w_2) + u_3(v_3 + w_3) \\
&= u_1 v_1 + u_1 w_1 + 2 u_2 v_2 + 2 u_2 w_2 + u_3 v_3 + u_3 w_3 \\
&= u_1 v_1 + 2 u_2 v_2 + u_3 v_3 + u_1 w_1 + 2 u_2 w_2 + u_3 w_3 \\
&= \langle \mathbf{u}, \mathbf{v} \rangle + \langle \mathbf{u}, \mathbf{w} \rangle.
\end{aligned}$$

3. If c is any scalar, then

$$c\langle \mathbf{u}, \mathbf{v} \rangle = c(u_1 v_1 + 2 u_2 v_2 + u_3 v_3) = (c u_1)v_1 + 2(c u_2)v_2 + (c u_3)v_3 = \langle c\mathbf{u}, \mathbf{v} \rangle.$$

4. Since the square of a real number is nonnegative, $\langle \mathbf{v}, \mathbf{v} \rangle = v_1^2 + 2 v_2^2 + v_3^2 \geq 0$. Moreover, this expression is equal to zero if and only if $\mathbf{v} = \mathbf{0}$ (that is, if and only if $v_1 = v_2 = v_3 = 0$).

8. 1. Since the product of real numbers is commutative,

$$\langle \mathbf{u}, \mathbf{v} \rangle = \tfrac{1}{2}u_1v_1 + \tfrac{1}{4}u_2v_2 + \tfrac{1}{2}u_3v_3 = \tfrac{1}{2}v_1u_1 + \tfrac{1}{4}v_2u_2 + \tfrac{1}{2}v_3u_3 = \langle \mathbf{v}, \mathbf{u} \rangle.$$

2. Let $\mathbf{w} = (w_1, w_2, w_3)$. Then

$$\langle \mathbf{u}, \mathbf{v} + \mathbf{w} \rangle = \tfrac{1}{2}u_1(v_1 + w_1) + \tfrac{1}{4}u_2(v_2 + w_2) + \tfrac{1}{2}u_3(v_3 + w_3)$$

$$= \tfrac{1}{2}u_1v_1 + \tfrac{1}{2}u_1w_1 + \tfrac{1}{4}u_2v_2 + \tfrac{1}{4}u_2w_2 + \tfrac{1}{2}u_3v_3 + \tfrac{1}{2}u_3w_3$$

$$= \tfrac{1}{2}u_1v_1 + \tfrac{1}{4}u_2v_2 + \tfrac{1}{2}u_3v_3 + \tfrac{1}{2}u_1w_1 + \tfrac{1}{4}u_2w_2 + \tfrac{1}{2}u_3w_3$$

$$= \langle \mathbf{u}, \mathbf{v} \rangle + \langle \mathbf{u}, \mathbf{w} \rangle.$$

3. If c is any scalar, then

$$c\langle \mathbf{u}, \mathbf{v} \rangle = c\left(\tfrac{1}{2}u_1v_1 + \tfrac{1}{4}u_2v_2 + \tfrac{1}{2}u_3v_3\right) = \tfrac{1}{2}(cu_1)v_1 + \tfrac{1}{4}(cu_2)v_2 + \tfrac{1}{2}(cu_3)v_3 = \langle c\mathbf{u}, \mathbf{v} \rangle.$$

4. Since the square of a real number is nonnegative, $\langle \mathbf{v}, \mathbf{v} \rangle = \tfrac{1}{2}v_1^2 + \tfrac{1}{4}v_2^2 + \tfrac{1}{2}v_3^2 \geq 0$. Moreover, this expression is equal to zero if and only if $\mathbf{v} = \mathbf{0}$ (that is, if and only if $v_1 = v_2 = 0$).

10. The product $\langle \mathbf{u}, \mathbf{v} \rangle$ is not an inner product because Axiom 4 is not satisfied. For example, let $\mathbf{v} = (1, 1)$. Then

$$\langle \mathbf{v}, \mathbf{v} \rangle = (1)(1) - 2(1)(1) = -1, \text{ which is less than zero.}$$

12. The product $\langle \mathbf{u}, \mathbf{v} \rangle$ is not an inner product because it is not commutative. For example, if $\mathbf{u} = (1, 2)$, and $\mathbf{v} = (2, 3)$, then

$$\langle \mathbf{u}, \mathbf{v} \rangle = 3(1)(3) - 2(2) = 5 \text{ while } \langle \mathbf{v}, \mathbf{u} \rangle = 3(2)(2) - 3(1) = 9.$$

14. The product $\langle \mathbf{u}, \mathbf{v} \rangle$ is not an inner product because nonzero vectors can have a norm of zero. For example, if $\mathbf{v} = (1, 1, 0)$, then

$$\langle (1, 1, 0), (1, 1, 0) \rangle = 0.$$

16. The product $\langle \mathbf{u}, \mathbf{v} \rangle$ is not an inner product because Axiom 2 is not satisfied. For example, let $\mathbf{u} = (1, 0, 0)$, $\mathbf{v} = (1, 1, 1)$, and $\mathbf{w} = (2, 1, 2)$.

$$\langle \mathbf{u}, \mathbf{v} + \mathbf{w} \rangle = 1(0) + 3(2) + 0(3) = 6$$

$$\langle \mathbf{u}, \mathbf{v} \rangle + \langle \mathbf{u}, \mathbf{w} \rangle = 1(0) + 1(1) + 0(1) + 1(0) + 2(1) + 0(2) = 3$$

So, $\langle \mathbf{u}, \mathbf{v} + \mathbf{w} \rangle \neq \langle \mathbf{u}, \mathbf{v} \rangle + \langle \mathbf{u}, \mathbf{w} \rangle.$

18. (a) $\langle \mathbf{u}, \mathbf{v} \rangle = \mathbf{u} \cdot \mathbf{v} = 1(7) + 1(9) = 16$

(b) $\|\mathbf{u}\| = \sqrt{\langle \mathbf{u}, \mathbf{u} \rangle} = \sqrt{1^2 + 1^2} = \sqrt{2}$

(c) $\|\mathbf{v}\| = \sqrt{\langle \mathbf{v}, \mathbf{v} \rangle} = \sqrt{7^2 + 9^2} = \sqrt{130}$

(d) $d(\mathbf{u}, \mathbf{v}) = \|\mathbf{u} - \mathbf{v}\| = \|(-6, -8)\| = \sqrt{(-6)^2 + (-8)^2} = \sqrt{100} = 10$

20. (a) $\langle \mathbf{u}, \mathbf{v} \rangle = \mathbf{u} \cdot \mathbf{v} = 0(-1) + 2(-6)(1) = -12$

(b) $\|\mathbf{u}\| = \sqrt{\langle \mathbf{u}, \mathbf{u} \rangle} = \sqrt{0(0) + 2(-6)(-6)} = 6\sqrt{2}$

(c) $\|\mathbf{v}\| = \sqrt{\langle \mathbf{v}, \mathbf{v} \rangle} = \sqrt{(-1)(-1) + 2(1)(1)} = \sqrt{3}$

(d) $d(\mathbf{u}, \mathbf{v}) = \|\mathbf{u} - \mathbf{v}\| = \|(1, -7)\| = \sqrt{1(1) + 2(-7)(-7)} = \sqrt{99} = 3\sqrt{11}$

22. (a) $\langle \mathbf{u}, \mathbf{v} \rangle = \mathbf{u} \cdot \mathbf{v} = 0(1) + 1(2) + 2(0) = 2$

(b) $\|\mathbf{u}\| = \sqrt{\langle \mathbf{u}, \mathbf{u} \rangle} = \sqrt{0^2 + 1^2 + 2^2} = \sqrt{5}$

(c) $\|\mathbf{v}\| = \sqrt{\langle \mathbf{v}, \mathbf{v} \rangle} = \sqrt{1^2 + 2^2 + 0^2} = \sqrt{5}$

(d) $d(\mathbf{u}, \mathbf{v}) = \|\mathbf{u} - \mathbf{v}\| = \|(-1, -1, 2)\| = \sqrt{(-1)^2 + (-1)^2 + 2^2} = \sqrt{6}$

24. (a) $\langle \mathbf{u}, \mathbf{v} \rangle = \mathbf{u} \cdot \mathbf{v} = (1)(2) + 2(1)(5) + (1)(2) = 14$

  (b) $\|\mathbf{u}\| = \sqrt{\langle \mathbf{u}, \mathbf{u} \rangle} = \sqrt{(1)^2 + 2(1)^2 + (1)^2} = 2$

  (c) $\|\mathbf{v}\| = \sqrt{\langle \mathbf{v}, \mathbf{v} \rangle} = \sqrt{(2)^2 + 2(5)^2 + (2)^2} = \sqrt{58}$

  (d) $d(\mathbf{u}, \mathbf{v}) = \|\mathbf{u} - \mathbf{v}\| = \|(1,1,1) - (2,5,2)\| = \|(-1,-4,-1)\| = \sqrt{(-1)^2 + 2(-4)^2 + (-1)^2} = \sqrt{34}$

26. (a) $\langle \mathbf{u}, \mathbf{v} \rangle = \mathbf{u} \cdot \mathbf{v} = 1(2) + (-1)(1) + 2(0) + 0(-1) = 1$

  (b) $\|\mathbf{u}\| = \sqrt{\langle \mathbf{u}, \mathbf{u} \rangle} = \sqrt{1^2 + (-1)^2 + 2^2 + 0^2} = \sqrt{6}$

  (c) $\|\mathbf{v}\| = \sqrt{\langle \mathbf{v}, \mathbf{v} \rangle} = \sqrt{2^2 + 1^2 + 0^2 + (-1)^2} = \sqrt{6}$

  (d) $d(\mathbf{u}, \mathbf{v}) = \|\mathbf{u} - \mathbf{v}\| = \|(-1,-2,2,1)\| = \sqrt{(-1)^2 + (-2)^2 + 2^2 + 1^2} = \sqrt{10}$

28. 1. Since the product of real numbers within a matrix is commutative,

$$\langle A, B \rangle = 2a_{11}b_{11} + a_{21}b_{21} + a_{12}b_{12} + 2a_{22}b_{22}$$
$$= 2b_{11}a_{11} + b_{21}a_{21} + b_{12}a_{12} + 2b_{22}a_{22}$$
$$= \langle B, A \rangle.$$

  2. Let $W = \begin{bmatrix} w_{11} & w_{12} \\ w_{21} & w_{22} \end{bmatrix}$. Then,

$$\langle A, B + W \rangle = 2a_{11}(b_{11} + w_{11}) + a_{21}(b_{21} + w_{21}) + a_{12}(b_{12} + w_{12}) + 2a_{22}(b_{22} + w_{22})$$
$$= 2a_{11}b_{11} + 2a_{11}w_{11} + a_{21}b_{21} + a_{21}w_{21} + a_{12}b_{12} + a_{12}w_{12} + 2a_{22}b_{22} + 2a_{22}w_{22}$$
$$= 2a_{11}b_{11} + a_{21}b_{21} + a_{12}b_{12} + 2a_{22}b_{22} + 2a_{11}w_{11} + a_{21}w_{21} + a_{12}w_{12} + 2a_{22}w_{22}$$
$$= \langle A, B \rangle + \langle A, W \rangle.$$

  3. If c is any scalar, then

$$c\langle A, B \rangle = c(2a_{11}b_{11} + a_{21}b_{21} + a_{12}b_{12} + 2a_{22}b_{22})$$
$$= 2(ca_{11})b_{11} + (ca_{21})b_{21} + (ca_{12})b_{12} + 2(ca_{22})b_{22}$$
$$= \langle CA, B \rangle$$

  4. Since the square of a real number is nonnegative, $\langle B, B \rangle = 2b_{11}^2 + b_{21}^2 + b_{12}^2 + 2b_{22}^2 \geq 0$. Moreover, this expression is equal to zero if and only if $B = 0$ (that is, if and only if $b_{11} = b_{12} = b_{21} = b_{22} = 0$).

30. (a) $\langle A, B \rangle = 2(1)(0) + (0)(1) + (0)(1) + 2(1)(0) = 0$

  (b) $\|A\|^2 = \langle A, A \rangle = 2(1)^2 + 0^2 + 0^2 + 2(1)^2 = 4$

  $\|A\| = \sqrt{\langle A, A \rangle} = 2$

  (c) $\|B\|^2 = \langle B, B \rangle = 2 \cdot 0^2 + 1^2 + 1^2 + 2 \cdot 0^2 = 2$

  $\|B\| = \sqrt{\langle B, B \rangle} = \sqrt{2}$

  (d) Use the fact that $d(A, B) = \|A - B\|$. Because

  $A - B = \begin{bmatrix} 1 & -1 \\ -1 & 1 \end{bmatrix}$, you have

  $\langle A - B, A - B \rangle = 2(1)^2 + (-1)^2 + (-1)^2 + 2(1)^2 = 6.$

  $d(A, B) = \sqrt{\langle A - B, A - B \rangle} = \sqrt{6}$

32. (a) $\langle A, B \rangle = 2(1)(1) + (0)(0) + (0)(1) + 2(-1)(-1) = 4$

(b) $\|A\|^2 = \langle A, A \rangle = 2(1)^2 + 0^2 + 0^2 + 2(-1)^2 = 4$

$\|A\| = \sqrt{\langle A, A \rangle} = \sqrt{4} = 2$

(c) $\|B\|^2 = \langle B, B \rangle = 2(1)^2 + 0^2 + 1^2 + 2(-1)^2 = 5$

$\|B\| = \sqrt{\langle B, B \rangle} = \sqrt{5}$

(d) Use the fact that $d(A, B) = \|A - B\|$. Because $A - B = \begin{bmatrix} 0 & -1 \\ 0 & 0 \end{bmatrix}$, you have

$\langle A - B, A - B \rangle = 2(0)^2 + 0^2 + (-1)^2 + 2(0)^2 = 1.$

$d(A, B) = \sqrt{\langle A - B, A - B \rangle} = \sqrt{1} = 1$

34. 1. Since the product of real numbers is commutative,

$\langle p, q \rangle = a_0 b_0 + a_1 b_1 + \cdots + a_n b_n = b_0 a_0 + b_1 a_1 + \cdots + b_n a_n = \langle q, p \rangle.$

2. Let $\mathbf{w} = w_0 + w_1 x + \cdots + w_n x^n$, then

$\langle p, q + w \rangle = a_0(b_0 + w_0) + a_1(b_1 + w_1)x + \cdots + a_n(b_n + w_n)x^n$

$= a_0 b_0 + a_0 w_0 + a_1 b_1 x + a_1 w_1 x + \cdots + a_n b_n x^n + a_n w_n x^n$

$= a_0 b_0 + a_1 b_1 x + \cdots + a_n b_n x^n + a_0 w_0 + a_1 w_1 x + \cdots + a_n w_n x^n$

$= \langle p, q \rangle + \langle p, w \rangle.$

3. If c is any scalar, then

$c\langle p, q \rangle = c\left(a_0 b_0 + a_1 b_1 x + \cdots + a_n b_n x^n\right)$

$= (ca_0)b_0 + (ca_1)b_1 x + \cdots + (ca_n)b_n x^n$

$= \langle cp, q \rangle.$

4. Since the square of a real number is nonnegative, $\langle q, q \rangle = b_0^2 + b_1^2 x^2 + \cdots + b_n^2 x^{2n} \geq 0$. Moreover, this expression is equal to zero if and only if $q = 0$ (that is, if and only if $q_0 = \cdots = q_n = 0$).

36. (a) $\langle p, q \rangle = 1(1) + 1(0) + \frac{1}{2}(2) = 2$

(b) $\|p\|^2 = \langle p, p \rangle = 1^2 + 1^2 + \left(\frac{1}{2}\right)^2 = \frac{9}{4}$

$\|p\| = \sqrt{\langle p, p \rangle} = \sqrt{\frac{9}{4}} = \frac{3}{2}$

(c) $\|q\|^2 = \langle q, q \rangle = 1^2 + 0^2 + 2^2 = 5$

$\|q\| = \sqrt{\langle q, q \rangle} = \sqrt{5}$

(d) Use the fact that $d(p, q) = \|p - q\|$. Because

$p - q = x - \frac{3}{2}x^2$, you have

$\langle p - q, p - q \rangle = 0^2 + 1^2 + \left(-\frac{3}{2}\right)^2 = \frac{13}{4}.$

$d(p, q) = \sqrt{\langle p - q, p - q \rangle} = \sqrt{\frac{13}{4}} = \frac{\sqrt{13}}{2}$

38. (a) $\langle p, q \rangle = 1(0) + (-2)(1) + (-1)(-1) = -1$

(b) $\|p\|^2 = \langle p, p \rangle = 1^2 + (-2)^2 + (-1)^2 = 6$

$\|p\| = \sqrt{\langle p, p \rangle} = \sqrt{6}$

(c) $\|q\|^2 = \langle q, q \rangle = 0^2 + 1^2 + (-1)^2 = 2$

$\|q\| = \sqrt{\langle q, q \rangle} = \sqrt{2}$

(d) Use the fact that $d(p, q) = \|p - q\|$. Because

$p - q = 1 - 3x$, you have

$\langle p - q, p - q \rangle = 1^2 + (-3)^2 + 0^2 = 10.$

$d(p, q) = \sqrt{\langle p - q, p - q \rangle} = \sqrt{10}$

40. (a) $\langle f, g \rangle = \int_{-1}^{1} f(x)g(x)dx = \int_{-1}^{1} (-x)(x^2 - x + 2)dx = \int_{-1}^{1} (-x^3 + x^2 - 2x)dx = \left[-\frac{x^4}{4} + \frac{x^3}{3} - x^2 \right]_{-1}^{1} = \frac{2}{3}$

(b) $\|f\|^2 = \langle f, f \rangle = \int_{-1}^{1} (-x)(-x)dx = \frac{x^3}{3} \Big]_{-1}^{1} = \frac{2}{3}$

$\|f\| = \sqrt{\frac{2}{3}}$

(c) $\|g\|^2 = \langle g, g \rangle = \int_{-1}^{1} (x^2 - x + 2)^2 dx = \int_{-1}^{1} (x^4 - 2x^3 + 5x^2 - 4x + 4)dx = \left[\frac{x^5}{5} - \frac{x^4}{2} + \frac{5x^3}{3} - 2x^2 + 4x \right]_{-1}^{1} = \frac{176}{15}$

$\|g\| = \sqrt{\frac{176}{15}}$

(d) Use the fact that $d(f, g) = \|f - g\|$. Because $f - g = -x - (x^2 - x + 2) = -x^2 - 2$, you have

$\langle f - g, f - g \rangle = \langle -x^2 - 2, -x^2 - 2 \rangle = \int_{-1}^{1} (x^4 + 4x^2 + 4)dx = \left[\frac{x^5}{5} + \frac{4x^3}{3} + 4x \right]_{-1}^{1} = \frac{166}{15}.$

$d(f, g) = \sqrt{\langle f - g, f - g \rangle} = \sqrt{\frac{166}{15}}.$

42. (a) $\langle f, g \rangle = \int_{-1}^{1} xe^{-x}dx = -e^{-x}(x + 1) \Big]_{-1}^{1} = -2e^{-1} + 0 = -\frac{2}{e}$

(b) $\|f\|^2 = \langle f, f \rangle = \int_{-1}^{1} x^2 dx = \frac{x^3}{3} \Big]_{-1}^{1} = \frac{1}{3} + \frac{1}{3} = \frac{2}{3}$

$\|f\| = \sqrt{\frac{2}{3}} = \frac{\sqrt{6}}{3}$

(c) $\|g\|^2 = \langle g, g \rangle = \int_{-1}^{1} e^{-2x}dx = -\frac{e^{-2x}}{2} \Big]_{-1}^{1} = \frac{1}{2}(-e^{-2} + e^2)$

$\|g\| = \sqrt{\frac{1}{2}(-e^{-2} + e^2)}$

(d) Use the fact that $d(f, g) = \|f - g\|$. Because $f - g = x - e^{-x}$, you have

$\langle f - g, f - g \rangle = \int_{-1}^{1} (x - e^{-x})^2 dx$

$= \int_{-1}^{1} (x^2 - 2e^{-x} + e^{-2x})dx$

$= \left[\frac{x^3}{3} + 2e^{-x}(x + 1) - \frac{e^{-2x}}{2} \right]_{-1}^{1}$

$= \frac{2}{3} + 4e^{-1} - \frac{e^{-2}}{2} + \frac{e^2}{2}.$

$d(f, g) = \sqrt{\langle f - g, f - g \rangle} = \sqrt{\frac{2}{3} + 4e^{-1} - \frac{e^{-2}}{2} + \frac{e^2}{2}}$

44. Because $\langle \mathbf{u}, \mathbf{v} \rangle = (2)\left(\frac{1}{2}\right) + (-1)(1) = 0$, the angle between $\mathbf{u}$ and $\mathbf{v}$ is $\frac{\pi}{2}$.

46. Because $\langle \mathbf{u}, \mathbf{v} \rangle = 2\left(\frac{1}{4}\right)(2) + (-1)(1) = 0$, the angle between $\mathbf{u}$ and $\mathbf{v}$ is $\frac{\pi}{2}$.

48. Because $\dfrac{\langle u+v\rangle}{\|u\|\|v\|} = \dfrac{(0)(1)+(1)(2)+(-1)(3)}{\sqrt{(0)^2+(1)^2+(-1)^2}\sqrt{(1)^2+(2)^2+(3)^2}} = \dfrac{-1}{\sqrt{2}\cdot\sqrt{14}} = -\dfrac{1}{2\sqrt{7}}$,

the angle between u and v is $\cos^{-1}\left(-\dfrac{1}{2\sqrt{7}}\right) \approx 1.761$ radians $(100.89°)$.

50. Because $\dfrac{\langle p,q\rangle}{\|p\|\|q\|} = \dfrac{(1)(0)+2(0)(1)+(1)(-1)}{\sqrt{(1)^2+2(0)^2+(1)^2}\sqrt{(0)^2+2(1)^2+(-1)^2}} = \dfrac{-1}{\sqrt{2}\sqrt{3}} = -\dfrac{1}{\sqrt{6}}$,

the angle between p and q is $\cos^{-1}\left(-\dfrac{1}{\sqrt{6}}\right) \approx 1.991\,(114.09°)$.

52. First compute

$$\langle f,g\rangle = \langle 1,x^2\rangle = \int_{-1}^{1} x^2\,dx = \dfrac{x^3}{3}\bigg]_{-1}^{1} = \dfrac{2}{3}$$

$$\|f\|^2 = \langle 1,1\rangle = \int_{-1}^{1} 1\,dx = x\bigg]_{-1}^{1} = 2 \Rightarrow \|f\| = \sqrt{2}$$

$$\|g\|^2 = \langle x^2,x^2\rangle = \int_{-1}^{1} x^4\,dx = \dfrac{x^5}{5}\bigg]_{-1}^{1} = \dfrac{2}{5} \Rightarrow \|g\| = \sqrt{\dfrac{2}{5}}.$$

So,

$$\dfrac{\langle f,g\rangle}{\|f\|\|g\|} = \dfrac{2/3}{\sqrt{2}\sqrt{2/5}} = \dfrac{\sqrt{5}}{3}$$

and the angle between f and g is $\cos^{-1}\left(\dfrac{\sqrt{5}}{3}\right) \approx 0.73$ radians $(41.81°)$.

54. (a) To verify the Cauchy-Schwarz Inequality, observe

$$|\langle u,v\rangle| \le \|u\|\|v\|$$
$$|(-1)(1)+(1)(-1)| \le \sqrt{(-1)^2+(1)^2}\cdot\sqrt{(1)^2+(-1)^2}$$
$$|-2| \le \sqrt{2}\cdot\sqrt{2}$$
$$2 \le 2.$$

(b) To verify the Triangle Inequality, observe

$$\|u+v\| \le \|u\|+\|v\|$$
$$\sqrt{(0)^2+(0)^2} \le \sqrt{(-1)^2+(1)^2}+\sqrt{(1)^2+(-1)^2}$$
$$0 \le \sqrt{2}+\sqrt{2}$$
$$0 \le 2\sqrt{2}.$$

56. (a) To verify the Cauchy-Schwarz Inequality, observe

$$|\langle u,v\rangle| \le \|u\|\|v\|$$
$$|(1)(1)+(0)(2)+(2)(0)| \le \sqrt{(1)^2+(0)^2+(2)^2}\cdot\sqrt{(1)^2+(2)^2+(0)^2}$$
$$|1| \le \sqrt{5}\cdot\sqrt{5}$$
$$1 \le 5.$$

(b) To verify the Triangle Inequality, observe

$$\|u+v\| \le \|u\|+\|v\|$$
$$\sqrt{(2)^2+(2)^2+(2)^2} \le \sqrt{(1)^2+(0)^2+(2)^2}+\sqrt{(1)^2+(2)^2+(0)^2}$$
$$\sqrt{12} \le \sqrt{5}+\sqrt{5}$$
$$2\sqrt{3} \le 2\sqrt{5}.$$

58. (a) To verify the Cauchy-Schwarz Inequality, observe

$$|\langle p, q \rangle| \le \|p\|\,\|q\|$$

$$|(0)(1) + 2(1)(0) + (0)(-1)| \le \sqrt{(0)^2 + 2(1)^2 + (0)^2} \cdot \sqrt{(1)^2 + 2(0)^2 + (-1)^2}$$

$$|0| \le \sqrt{2} \cdot \sqrt{2}$$

$$0 \le 2.$$

(b) To verify the Triangle Inequality, observe

$$\|p + q\| \le \|p\| + \|q\|$$

$$\sqrt{(1)^2 + 2(1)^2 + (-1)^2} \le \sqrt{(0)^2 + 2(1)^2 + (0)^2} + \sqrt{(1)^2 + 2(0)^2 + (-1)^2}$$

$$\sqrt{4} \le \sqrt{2} + \sqrt{2}$$

$$2 \le 2\sqrt{2}.$$

60. (a) To verify the Cauchy-Schwarz Inequality, observe

$$|\langle A, B \rangle| \le \|A\|\,\|B\|$$

$$|(0)(1) + (1)(1) + (2)(2) + (-1)(-2)| \le \sqrt{(0)^2 + (1)^2 + (2)^2 + (-1)^2} \cdot \sqrt{(1)^2 + (1)^2 + (2)^2 + (-2)^2}$$

$$|7| \le \sqrt{6} \cdot \sqrt{10}$$

$$7 \le \sqrt{60}$$

$$7 \le 7.746.$$

(b) To verify the Triangle Inequality, observe

$$\|A + B\| \le \|A\| + \|B\|$$

$$\sqrt{(1)^2 + (2)^2 + (4)^2 + (-3)^2} \le \sqrt{(0)^2 + (1)^2 + (2)^2 + (-1)^2} + \sqrt{(1)^2 + (1)^2 + (2)^2 + (-2)^2}$$

$$\sqrt{30} \le \sqrt{6} + \sqrt{10}$$

$$5.477 \le 5.612.$$

62. (a) To verify the Cauchy-Schwarz Inequality, observe

$$\langle f, g \rangle = \langle 1, \cos \pi x \rangle = \int_0^2 \cos \pi x \, dx = \frac{\sin \pi x}{\pi} \Big]_0^2 = 0$$

$$\|f\|^2 = \langle 1, 1 \rangle = \int_0^2 1 \, dx = x \Big]_0^2 = 2 \implies \|f\| = \sqrt{2}$$

$$\|g\|^2 = \langle \cos \pi x, \cos \pi x \rangle = \int_0^2 \cos^2 \pi x \, dx = \int_0^2 \frac{1 + \cos 2\pi x}{2} dx = \left[\frac{1}{2}x + \frac{\sin 2\pi x}{4\pi}\right]_0^2 = 1 \implies \|g\| = 1$$

and observe that

$$|f, g| \le \|f\|\,\|g\|$$

$$0 \le \sqrt{2}(1).$$

(b) To verify the Triangle Inequality, observe

$$\|f + g\|^2 = \|1 + \cos \pi x\|^2 = \int_0^2 (1 + \cos \pi x)^2 dx = \left[x + \cos^2 \pi x + 2 \cos \pi x\right]_0^2 = 3 \implies \|f + g\| = \sqrt{3}.$$

So, $\|f + g\| \le \|f\| + \|g\|$

$$\sqrt{3} \le \sqrt{2} + 1.$$

64. (a) To verify the Cauchy-Schwarz Inequality, compute

$$\langle f, g \rangle = \langle x, e^{-x} \rangle = \int_0^1 xe^{-x}\,dx = -e^{-x}(x+1)\Big]_0^1 = 1 - 2e^{-1}$$

$$\|f\|^2 = \langle x, x \rangle = \int_0^1 x^2\,dx = \frac{x^3}{3}\Big]_0^1 = \frac{1}{3} \Rightarrow \|f\| = \frac{\sqrt{3}}{3}$$

$$\|g\|^2 = \langle e^{-x}, e^{-x} \rangle = \int_0^1 e^{-2x}\,dx = -\frac{e^{-2x}}{2}\Big]_0^1 = -\frac{e^{-2}}{2} + \frac{1}{2} \Rightarrow \|g\| = \sqrt{-\frac{e^{-2}}{2} + \frac{1}{2}}$$

and observe that

$$|\langle f, g \rangle| \le \|f\|\,\|g\|$$

$$\left|1 - 2e^{-1}\right| \le \left(\frac{\sqrt{3}}{3}\right)\left(\sqrt{-\frac{e^{-2}}{2} + \frac{1}{2}}\right)$$

$$0.264 \le 0.380.$$

(b) To verify the Triangle Inequality, compute

$$\|f + g\|^2 = \langle x + e^{-x}, x + e^{-x} \rangle = \int_0^1 \left(x + e^{-x}\right)^2 dx = \left[-2e^{-x}(x+1) - \frac{e^{-2x}}{2} + \frac{x^3}{3}\right]_0^1$$

$$= \left[-4e^{-1} - \frac{e^{-2}}{2} + \frac{1}{3}\right] - \left[-2 - \frac{1}{2} + 0\right]$$

$$= -4e^{-1} - \frac{e^{-2}}{2} + \frac{17}{6} \Rightarrow \|f + g\| = \sqrt{-4e^{-1} - \frac{e^{-2}}{2} + \frac{17}{6}}$$

and observe that

$$\|f + g\| \le \|f\| + \|g\|$$

$$\sqrt{-4e^{-1} - \frac{e^{-2}}{2} + \frac{17}{6}} \le \frac{\sqrt{3}}{3} + \sqrt{-\frac{e^{-2}}{2} + \frac{1}{2}}$$

$$1.138 \le 1.235.$$

66. The functions $f(x) = x$ and $g(x) = \frac{1}{2}(3x^2 - 1)$ are orthogonal because

$$\langle f, g \rangle = \int_{-1}^1 x\frac{1}{2}(3x^2 - 1)\,dx = \frac{1}{2}\int_{-1}^1 (3x^3 - x)\,dx = \frac{1}{2}\left(\frac{3x^4}{4} - \frac{x^2}{2}\right)\Big]_{-1}^1 = 0.$$

68. The functions $f(x) = 1$ and $g(x) = \cos(2nx)$ are orthogonal because $\langle f, g \rangle = \int_0^\pi \cos(2nx)\,dx = \frac{1}{2n}\sin(2nx)\Big]_0^\pi = 0.$

70. (a) $\text{proj}_{\mathbf{v}}\mathbf{u} = \dfrac{\langle \mathbf{u}, \mathbf{v} \rangle}{\langle \mathbf{v}, \mathbf{v} \rangle}\mathbf{v} = \dfrac{(-1)(4) + (-2)(2)}{(4)^2 + (2)^2}(4, 2) = \dfrac{-8}{20}(4, 2) = \left(-\dfrac{8}{5}, -\dfrac{4}{5}\right)$

(b) $\text{proj}_{\mathbf{u}}\mathbf{v} = \dfrac{\langle \mathbf{v}, \mathbf{u} \rangle}{\langle \mathbf{u}, \mathbf{u} \rangle}\mathbf{u} = \dfrac{(4)(-1) + (2)(-2)}{(-1)^2 + (-2)^2}(-1, -2) = \dfrac{-8}{5}(-1, -2) = \left(\dfrac{8}{5}, \dfrac{16}{5}\right)$

(c)

72. (a) $\text{proj}_{\mathbf{v}}\mathbf{u} = \dfrac{\langle \mathbf{u}, \mathbf{v} \rangle}{\langle \mathbf{v}, \mathbf{v} \rangle}\mathbf{v} = \dfrac{(2)(3) + (-2)(1)}{(3)^2 + (1)^2}(3, 1) = \dfrac{4}{10}(3, 1) = \left(\dfrac{6}{5}, \dfrac{2}{5} \right)$

(b) $\text{proj}_{\mathbf{u}}\mathbf{v} = \dfrac{\langle \mathbf{v}, \mathbf{u} \rangle}{\langle \mathbf{u}, \mathbf{u} \rangle}\mathbf{u} = \dfrac{(3)(2) + (1)(-2)}{(2)^2 + (-2)^2}(2, -2) = \dfrac{4}{8}(2, -2) = (1, -1)$

(c)

74. (a) $\text{proj}_{\mathbf{v}}\mathbf{u} = \dfrac{\langle \mathbf{u}, \mathbf{v} \rangle}{\langle \mathbf{v}, \mathbf{v} \rangle}\mathbf{v} = \dfrac{(1)(-1) + (2)(2) + (-1)(-1)}{(-1)^2 + (2)^2 + (-1)^2}(-1, 2, -1) = \dfrac{4}{6}(-1, 2, -1) = \left(-\dfrac{2}{3}, \dfrac{4}{3}, -\dfrac{2}{3} \right)$

(b) $\text{proj}_{\mathbf{u}}\mathbf{v} = \dfrac{\langle \mathbf{v}, \mathbf{u} \rangle}{\langle \mathbf{u}, \mathbf{u} \rangle}\mathbf{u} = \dfrac{(-1)(1) + (2)(2) + (-1)(-1)}{(1)^2 + (2)^2 + (-1)^2}(1, 2, -1) = \dfrac{4}{6}(1, 2, -1) = \left(\dfrac{2}{3}, \dfrac{4}{3}, -\dfrac{2}{3} \right)$

76. (a) $\text{proj}_{\mathbf{v}}\mathbf{u} = \dfrac{\langle \mathbf{u}, \mathbf{v} \rangle}{\langle \mathbf{v}, \mathbf{v} \rangle}\mathbf{v} = \dfrac{(-1)(2) + (4)(-1) + (-2)(2) + (3)(-1)}{(2)^2 + (-1)^2 + (2)^2 + (-1)^2}(2, -1, 2, -1)$

$= \dfrac{-13}{10}(2, -1, 2, -1) = \left(-\dfrac{13}{5}, \dfrac{13}{10}, -\dfrac{13}{5}, \dfrac{13}{10} \right)$

(b) $\text{proj}_{\mathbf{u}}\mathbf{v} = \dfrac{\langle \mathbf{v}, \mathbf{u} \rangle}{\langle \mathbf{u}, \mathbf{u} \rangle}\mathbf{u} = \dfrac{(2)(-1) + (-1)(4) + (2)(-2) + (-1)(3)}{(-1)^2 + (4)^2 + (-2)^2 + (3)^2}(-1, 4, -2, 3)$

$= \dfrac{-13}{30}(-1, 4, -2, 3) = \left(\dfrac{13}{30}, -\dfrac{26}{15}, \dfrac{13}{15}, -\dfrac{13}{10} \right)$

78. The inner products $\langle f, g \rangle$ and $\langle g, g \rangle$ are as follows.

$\langle f, g \rangle = \displaystyle\int_{-1}^{1}(x^3 - x)(2x - 1)\,dx = \int_{-1}^{1}(2x^4 - x^3 - 2x^2 + x)\,dx = \left[\dfrac{2x^5}{5} - \dfrac{x^4}{4} - \dfrac{2x^3}{3} + \dfrac{x^2}{2} \right]_{-1}^{1} = -\dfrac{8}{15}$

$\langle g, g \rangle = \displaystyle\int_{-1}^{1}(2x - 1)^2\,dx = \int_{-1}^{1}(4x^2 - 4x + 1)\,dx = \left[\dfrac{4x^3}{3} - 2x^2 + x \right]_{-1}^{1} = \dfrac{14}{3}$

So, the projection of f onto g is $\text{proj}_{g}f = \dfrac{\langle f, g \rangle}{\langle g, g \rangle}g = \dfrac{-8/15}{14/3}(2x - 1) = -\dfrac{4}{35}(2x - 1)$.

80. The inner products $\langle f, g \rangle$ and $\langle g, g \rangle$ are as follows.

$\langle f, g \rangle = \displaystyle\int_{0}^{1} xe^{-x}\,dx = \left[-e^{-x}(x + 1) \right]_{0}^{1} = -2e^{-1} + 1$

$\langle g, g \rangle = \displaystyle\int_{0}^{1} e^{-2x}\,dx = \left. \dfrac{-e^{-2x}}{2} \right]_{0}^{1} = \dfrac{-e^{-2}}{2} + \dfrac{1}{2} = \dfrac{1 - e^{-2}}{2}$

So, the projection of f onto g is $\text{proj}_{g}f = \dfrac{\langle f, g \rangle}{\langle g, g \rangle}g = \dfrac{-2e^{-1} + 1}{\dfrac{1 - e^{-2}}{2}}(e^{-x}) = \dfrac{-4e^{-1} + 2}{1 - e^{-2}}(e^{-x}) = \dfrac{-4e^{-x-1} + 2e^{-x}}{1 - e^{-2}}$.

82. The inner product $\langle f, g \rangle$ is

$$\langle f, g \rangle = \int_{-\pi}^{\pi} \sin 2x \sin 3x \, dx = \int_{-\pi}^{\pi} \frac{1}{2}(\cos x - \cos 5x) \, dx = \frac{1}{2}\left(\sin x - \frac{\sin 5x}{5} \right)\Bigg]_{-\pi}^{\pi} = 0$$

which implies that $\text{proj}_g f = 0$.

84. The inner product $\langle f, g \rangle$ is $\langle f, g \rangle = \int_{-\pi}^{\pi} x \cos 2x \, dx = \left[\frac{\cos 2x}{4} + \frac{x \sin 2x}{2} \right]_{-\pi}^{\pi} = \frac{1}{4} - \frac{1}{4} = 0$

which implies that $\text{proj}_g f = 0$.

86. (a) False. The norm of a vector $\mathbf{u}$ is defined as a square root of $\langle \mathbf{u}, \mathbf{u} \rangle$.

(b) False. The angle between $a\mathbf{v}$ and $\mathbf{v}$ is zero if $a > 0$ and it is π if $a < 0$.

88. $\|\mathbf{u} + \mathbf{v}\|^2 + \|\mathbf{u} - \mathbf{v}\|^2 = \langle \mathbf{u} + \mathbf{v}, \mathbf{u} + \mathbf{v} \rangle + \langle \mathbf{u} - \mathbf{v}, \mathbf{u} - \mathbf{v} \rangle$

$$= (\langle \mathbf{u}, \mathbf{u} \rangle + 2\langle \mathbf{u}, \mathbf{v} \rangle + \langle \mathbf{v}, \mathbf{v} \rangle) + (\langle \mathbf{u}, \mathbf{u} \rangle - 2\langle \mathbf{u}, \mathbf{v} \rangle + \langle \mathbf{v}, \mathbf{v} \rangle)$$

$$= 2\|\mathbf{u}\|^2 + 2\|\mathbf{v}\|^2$$

90. To prove that $\mathbf{u} - \text{proj}_\mathbf{v}\mathbf{u}$ is orthogonal to $\mathbf{v}$, you calculate their inner product as follows

$$\langle \mathbf{u} - \text{proj}_\mathbf{v}\mathbf{u}, \mathbf{v} \rangle = \langle \mathbf{u}, \mathbf{v} \rangle - \langle \text{proj}_\mathbf{v}\mathbf{u}, \mathbf{v} \rangle = \langle \mathbf{u}, \mathbf{v} \rangle - \left\langle \frac{\langle \mathbf{u}, \mathbf{v} \rangle}{\langle \mathbf{v}, \mathbf{v} \rangle}\mathbf{v}, \mathbf{v} \right\rangle = \langle \mathbf{u}, \mathbf{v} \rangle - \frac{\langle \mathbf{u}, \mathbf{v} \rangle}{\langle \mathbf{v}, \mathbf{v} \rangle}\langle \mathbf{v}, \mathbf{v} \rangle = \langle \mathbf{u}, \mathbf{v} \rangle - \langle \mathbf{u}, \mathbf{v} \rangle = 0.$$

92. You have from the definition of inner product $\langle \mathbf{u}, c\mathbf{v} \rangle = \langle c\mathbf{v}, \mathbf{u} \rangle = c\langle \mathbf{v}, \mathbf{u} \rangle = c\langle \mathbf{u}, \mathbf{v} \rangle$.

94. Let $W = \{(c, 2c, 3c) : c \in R\}$. Then

$$W^\perp = \{\mathbf{v} \in R^3 : \mathbf{v} \cdot (c, 2c, 3c) = 0\} = \{(x, y, z) \in R^3 : (x, y, z) \cdot (1, 2, 3) = 0\}.$$

You need to solve $x + 2y + 3z = 0$. Choosing y and z as free variables, you obtain the solution $x = -2t - 3s, y = t, z = s$ for any real numbers t and s. Therefore,

$$W^\perp = \{t(-2, 1, 0) + s(-3, 0, 1) : t, s \in R\} = \text{span}\{(-2, 1, 0), (-3, 0, 1)\}.$$

96. (a) All four axioms of the definition of an inner product must be satisfied.

(i) $\langle \mathbf{u}, \mathbf{v} \rangle = \langle \mathbf{v}, \mathbf{u} \rangle$

(ii) $\langle \mathbf{u}, \mathbf{v} + \mathbf{w} \rangle = \langle \mathbf{u}, \mathbf{v} \rangle + \langle \mathbf{u}, \mathbf{w} \rangle$

(iii) $c\langle \mathbf{u}, \mathbf{v} \rangle = \langle c\mathbf{u}, \mathbf{v} \rangle$

(iv) $\langle \mathbf{v}, \mathbf{v} \rangle \geq 0$, and $\langle \mathbf{v}, \mathbf{v} \rangle = 0$ if and only if $\mathbf{v} = \mathbf{0}$.

(b) To find an orthogonal projection, find $\langle \mathbf{u}, \mathbf{v} \rangle$ and $\langle \mathbf{v}, \mathbf{v} \rangle$, and have $\mathbf{v} \neq \mathbf{0}$ so that

$$\text{proj}_\mathbf{v}\mathbf{u} = \frac{\langle \mathbf{u}, \mathbf{v} \rangle}{\langle \mathbf{v}, \mathbf{v} \rangle}\mathbf{v}.$$

98. Let $\mathbf{u} = (x, y)$. Then $\|\mathbf{u}\| = \sqrt{c_1 x^2 + c_2 y^2} = 1$. Since the equation of the graph is $\frac{1}{4}x^2 + \frac{1}{9}y^2 = 1$, $c_1 = \frac{1}{4}$ and $c_2 = \frac{1}{9}$.

100. Let $\mathbf{u} = (x, y)$. Then $\|\mathbf{u}\| = \sqrt{c_1 x^2 + c_2 y^2} = 1$. Since the equation of the graph is $\frac{1}{25}x^2 + \frac{1}{9}y^2 = 1$, $c_1 = \frac{1}{25}$ and $c_2 = \frac{1}{9}$.

Section 5.3   Orthonormal Bases: Gram-Schmidt Process

2. (a) The set is orthogonal since
$$(3, -2) \cdot (-4, -6) = 3(-4) - 2(-6) = 0.$$

(b) This set is *not* orthonormal since
$$\|(3, -2)\| = \sqrt{3^2 + (-2)^2} = \sqrt{13} \neq 1.$$

(c) Because the two vectors are not scalar multiples of each other, by the Corollary to Theorem 4.8 they are linearly independent. By Theorem 4.12, they form a basis for R^2.

4. (a) The set is *not* orthogonal since
$$(11, 4) \cdot (8, -3) = 88 - 12 = 76 \neq 0.$$

(b) The set is *not* orthonormal since
$$\|(11, 4)\| = \sqrt{11^2 + 4^2} = \sqrt{137} \neq 1.$$

(c) Because the two vectors are not scalar multiples of each other, by the Corollary to Theorem 4.8 they are linearly independent. By Theorem 4.12, they form a basis for R^2.

6. (a) The set is orthogonal since $(1, 2) \cdot \left(\frac{-2}{5}, \frac{1}{5}\right) = \frac{-2}{5} + \frac{2}{5} = 0.$

(b) The set is *not* orthonormal since $\|(1, 2)\| = \sqrt{1^2 + 2^2} = \sqrt{5} \neq 1.$

(c) Because the vectors are not scalar multiples of each other, by the Corollary to Theorem 4.8 they are linearly independent. By Theorem 4.12, they form a basis for R^2.

8. (a) The set is orthogonal since $(2, -4, 2) \cdot (0, 2, 4) = 0 - 8 + 8 = 0,$ $(2, -4, 2) \cdot (-10, -4, 2) = -20 + 16 + 4 = 0,$ and $(0, 2, 4) \cdot (-10, -4, 2) = 0 - 8 + 8 = 0.$

(b) The set is *not* orthonormal since $\|(2, -4, 2)\| = \sqrt{2^2 + (-4)^2 + 2^2} = \sqrt{24} \neq 1.$

(c) Because the three vectors do not lie in the same plane, they span R^3. By Theorem 4.12, they form a basis for R^3.

10. (a) The set is *not* orthogonal since $\left(\frac{\sqrt{2}}{3}, 0, \frac{-\sqrt{2}}{6}\right) \cdot \left(0, \frac{2\sqrt{5}}{5}, \frac{-\sqrt{5}}{5}\right) = \frac{\sqrt{10}}{30} \neq 0.$

(b) The set is *not* orthonormal since $\left\|\left(\frac{\sqrt{2}}{3}, 0, \frac{-\sqrt{2}}{6}\right)\right\| = \sqrt{\left(\frac{\sqrt{2}}{3}\right)^2 + 0^2 + \left(\frac{-\sqrt{2}}{6}\right)^2} = \sqrt{\frac{2}{9} + 0 + \frac{2}{36}} \neq 1.$

(c) Because the three vectors do not lie in the same plane, they span R^3. By Theorem 4.12, they form a basis for R^3.

12. (a) The set is orthogonal since $(-6, 3, 2, 1) \cdot (2, 0, 6, 0) = -12 + 12 = 0.$

(b) The set is *not* orthonormal since $\|(-6, 3, 2, 1)\| = \sqrt{36 + 9 + 4 + 1} = \sqrt{50} \neq 1.$

(c) Since there aren't enough vectors, the set is *not* a basis for R^4.

14. (a) The set is orthogonal since

$$\left(\frac{\sqrt{10}}{10}, 0, 0, \frac{3\sqrt{10}}{10}\right) \cdot (0, 0, 1, 0) = 0,$$

$$\left(\frac{\sqrt{10}}{10}, 0, 0, \frac{3\sqrt{10}}{10}\right) \cdot (0, 1, 0, 0) = 0,$$

$$\left(\frac{\sqrt{10}}{10}, 0, 0, \frac{3\sqrt{10}}{10}\right) \cdot \left(\frac{-3\sqrt{10}}{10}, 0, 0, \frac{\sqrt{10}}{10}\right) = \frac{-3}{10} + \frac{3}{10} = 0,$$

$$(0, 0, 1, 0) \cdot (0, 1, 0, 0) = 0,$$

$$(0, 0, 1, 0) \cdot \left(\frac{-3\sqrt{10}}{10}, 0, 0, \frac{\sqrt{10}}{10}\right) = 0,$$

and $(0, 1, 0, 0) \cdot \left(\frac{-3\sqrt{10}}{10}, 0, 0, \frac{\sqrt{10}}{10}\right) = 0.$

(b) The set is orthonormal since $\left\|\left(\dfrac{\sqrt{10}}{10}, 0, 0, \dfrac{3\sqrt{10}}{10}\right)\right\| = \dfrac{1}{10} + \dfrac{9}{10} = 1, \|(0, 0, 1, 0)\| = 1, \|(0, 1, 0, 0)\| = 1,$ and

$$\left\|\left(\dfrac{-3\sqrt{10}}{10}, 0, 0, \dfrac{\sqrt{10}}{10}\right)\right\| = \dfrac{9}{10} + \dfrac{1}{10} = 1.$$

(c) By the Corollary to Theorem 5.10, the set of four vectors is a basis for R^4.

16. (a) The set is orthogonal since $(2, -5) \cdot (10, 4) = 20 - 20 = 0$.

(b) Since $\|(2, -5)\| = \sqrt{2^2 + (-5)^2} = \sqrt{29}$, normalizing the set produces an orthonormal set.

$$\mathbf{u}_1 = \dfrac{\mathbf{v}_1}{\|\mathbf{v}_1\|} = \dfrac{1}{\sqrt{29}}(2, -5) = \left(\dfrac{2\sqrt{29}}{29}, -\dfrac{5\sqrt{29}}{29}\right)$$

$$\mathbf{u}_2 = \dfrac{\mathbf{v}_2}{\|\mathbf{v}_2\|} = \dfrac{1}{2\sqrt{29}}(10, 4) = \left(\dfrac{5\sqrt{29}}{29}, \dfrac{2\sqrt{29}}{29}\right)$$

18. (a) The set is orthogonal since $\left(\dfrac{-2}{15}, \dfrac{1}{15}, \dfrac{2}{15}\right) \cdot \left(\dfrac{1}{15}, \dfrac{2}{15}, 0\right) = \dfrac{-2}{225} + \dfrac{2}{225} + 0 = 0.$

(b) Since $\left\|\left(\dfrac{-2}{15}, \dfrac{1}{15}, \dfrac{2}{15}\right)\right\| = \sqrt{\left(\dfrac{-2}{15}\right)^2 + \left(\dfrac{1}{15}\right)^2 + \left(\dfrac{2}{15}\right)^2} = \dfrac{1}{5}$, normalizing the set produces an orthonormal set.

$$\mathbf{u}_1 = \dfrac{\mathbf{v}_1}{\|\mathbf{v}_1\|} = \dfrac{1}{\dfrac{1}{5}}\left(\dfrac{-2}{5}, \dfrac{1}{15}, \dfrac{2}{15}\right) = 5\left(\dfrac{-2}{5}, \dfrac{1}{15}, \dfrac{2}{15}\right) = \left(-2, \dfrac{1}{3}, \dfrac{2}{3}\right)$$

$$\mathbf{u}_2 = \dfrac{\mathbf{v}_2}{\|\mathbf{v}_2\|} = \dfrac{1}{\sqrt{\dfrac{1}{45}}}\left(\dfrac{1}{15}, \dfrac{2}{15}, 0\right) = 3\sqrt{5}\left(\dfrac{1}{15}, \dfrac{2}{15}, 0\right) = \left(\dfrac{\sqrt{5}}{5}, \dfrac{2\sqrt{5}}{5}, 0\right)$$

20. The set $\{(\sin \theta, \cos \theta), (\cos \theta, -\sin \theta)\}$ is orthogonal because

$(\sin \theta, \cos \theta) \cdot (\cos \theta, -\sin \theta) = \sin \theta \cos \theta - \cos \theta \sin \theta = 0.$

Furthermore, the set is orthonormal because

$\|(\sin \theta, \cos \theta)\| = \sin^2 \theta + \cos^2 \theta = 1$

$\|(\cos \theta, -\sin \theta)\| = \cos^2 \theta + (-\sin \theta)^2 = 1.$

So, the set forms an orthonormal basis for R^2.

22. Use Theorem 5.11 to find the coordinates of $\mathbf{x} = (-3, 4)$ relative to B.

$$(-3, 4) \cdot \left(\dfrac{\sqrt{5}}{5}, \dfrac{2\sqrt{5}}{5}\right) = -\dfrac{3\sqrt{5}}{5} + \dfrac{8\sqrt{5}}{5} = \sqrt{5}$$

$$(-3, 4) \cdot \left(-\dfrac{2\sqrt{5}}{5}, \dfrac{\sqrt{5}}{5}\right) = \dfrac{6\sqrt{5}}{5} + \dfrac{4\sqrt{5}}{5} = 2\sqrt{5}$$

So, $[\mathbf{x}]_B = \left[\left(\sqrt{5}, 2\sqrt{5}\right)\right]^T.$

24. Use Theorem 5.11 to find the coordinates of $\mathbf{x} = (3, -5, 11)$ relative to B.

$(3, -5, 11) \cdot (1, 0, 0) = 3$

$(3, -5, 11) \cdot (0, 1, 0) = -5$

$(3, -5, 11) \cdot (0, 0, 1) = 11$

So, $[\mathbf{x}]_B = [(3, -5, 11)]^T.$

26. Use Theorem 5.11 to find the coordinates of $\mathbf{x} = (2, -1, 4, 3)$ relative to B.

$$(2, -1, 4, 3) \cdot \left(\tfrac{5}{13}, 0, \tfrac{12}{13}, 0\right) = \tfrac{10}{13} + \tfrac{48}{13} = \tfrac{58}{13}$$

$$(2, -1, 4, 3) \cdot (0, 1, 0, 0) = -1$$

$$(2, -1, 4, 3) \cdot \left(-\tfrac{12}{13}, 0, \tfrac{5}{13}, 0\right) = -\tfrac{24}{13} + \tfrac{20}{13} = -\tfrac{4}{13}$$

$$(2, -1, 4, 3) \cdot (0, 0, 0, 1) = 3$$

So, $[\mathbf{x}]_B = \left[\left(\tfrac{58}{13}, -1, -\tfrac{4}{13}, 3\right)\right]^T$.

28. First, orthogonalize each vector in B.

$$\mathbf{w}_1 = \mathbf{v}_1 = (1, 2)$$

$$\mathbf{w}_2 = \mathbf{v}_2 - \frac{\langle \mathbf{v}_2, \mathbf{w}_1 \rangle}{\langle \mathbf{w}_1, \mathbf{w}_1 \rangle}\mathbf{w}_1 = (-1, 0) - \frac{(-1)(1) + 0(2)}{1^2 + 2^2}(1, 2) = (-1, 0) + \frac{1}{5}(1, 2) = \left(-\frac{4}{5}, \frac{2}{5}\right)$$

Then, normalize the vectors.

$$\mathbf{u}_1 = \frac{\mathbf{w}_1}{\|\mathbf{w}_1\|} = \frac{1}{\sqrt{1^2 + 2^2}}(1, 2) = \left(\frac{\sqrt{5}}{5}, \frac{2\sqrt{5}}{5}\right)$$

$$\mathbf{u}_2 = \frac{\mathbf{w}_2}{\|\mathbf{w}_2\|} = \frac{1}{\sqrt{\left(-\frac{4}{5}\right)^2 + \left(\frac{2}{5}\right)^2}}\left(-\frac{4}{5}, \frac{2}{5}\right) = \left(-\frac{2\sqrt{5}}{5}, \frac{\sqrt{5}}{5}\right)$$

So, the orthonormal basis is $B' = \left\{\left(\frac{\sqrt{5}}{5}, \frac{2\sqrt{5}}{5}\right), \left(-\frac{2\sqrt{5}}{5}, \frac{\sqrt{5}}{5}\right)\right\}$.

30. First, orthogonalize each vector in B.

$$\mathbf{w}_1 = \mathbf{v}_1 = (4, -3)$$

$$\mathbf{w}_2 = \mathbf{v}_2 - \frac{\langle \mathbf{v}_2, \mathbf{w}_1 \rangle}{\langle \mathbf{w}_1, \mathbf{w}_1 \rangle}\mathbf{w}_1$$

$$= (3, 2) - \frac{3(4) + 2(-3)}{4^2 + (-3)^2}(4, -3)$$

$$= (3, 2) - \frac{6}{25}(4, -3)$$

$$= \left(\frac{51}{25}, \frac{68}{25}\right)$$

Then, normalize the vectors.

$$\mathbf{u}_1 = \frac{\mathbf{w}_1}{\|\mathbf{w}_1\|} = \frac{1}{\sqrt{4^2 + (-3)^2}}(4, -3) = \left(\frac{4}{5}, -\frac{3}{5}\right)$$

$$\mathbf{u}_2 = \frac{\mathbf{w}_2}{\|\mathbf{w}_2\|} = \frac{1}{\sqrt{\left(\frac{51}{25}\right)^2 + \left(\frac{68}{25}\right)^2}}\left(\frac{51}{25}, \frac{68}{25}\right) = \left(\frac{3}{5}, \frac{4}{5}\right)$$

So, the orthonormal basis is $B' = \left\{\left(\frac{4}{5}, -\frac{3}{5}\right), \left(\frac{3}{5}, \frac{4}{5}\right)\right\}$.

32. First, orthogonalize each vector in B.

$$\mathbf{w}_1 = \mathbf{v}_1 = (1, 0, 0)$$

$$\mathbf{w}_2 = \mathbf{v}_2 - \frac{\langle \mathbf{v}_2, \mathbf{w}_1 \rangle}{\langle \mathbf{w}_1, \mathbf{w}_1 \rangle}\mathbf{w}_1$$

$$= (1, 1, 1) - \frac{1}{1}(1, 0, 0)$$

$$= (0, 1, 1)$$

$$\mathbf{w}_3 = \mathbf{v}_3 - \frac{\langle \mathbf{v}_3, \mathbf{w}_1 \rangle}{\langle \mathbf{w}_1, \mathbf{w}_1 \rangle}\mathbf{w}_1 - \frac{\langle \mathbf{v}_3, \mathbf{w}_2 \rangle}{\langle \mathbf{w}_2, \mathbf{w}_2 \rangle}\mathbf{w}_2$$

$$= (1, 1, -1) - \frac{1}{1}(1, 0, 0) - \frac{0}{2}(0, 1, 1)$$

$$= (0, 1, -1)$$

Then, normalize the vectors.

$$\mathbf{u}_1 = \frac{\mathbf{w}_1}{\|\mathbf{w}_1\|} = (1, 0, 0)$$

$$\mathbf{u}_2 = \frac{\mathbf{w}_2}{\|\mathbf{w}_2\|} = \frac{1}{\sqrt{2}}(0, 1, 1) = \left(0, \frac{1}{\sqrt{2}}, \frac{1}{\sqrt{2}}\right)$$

$$\mathbf{u}_3 = \frac{\mathbf{w}_3}{\|\mathbf{w}_3\|} = \frac{1}{\sqrt{2}}(0, 1, -1) = \left(0, \frac{1}{\sqrt{2}}, -\frac{1}{\sqrt{2}}\right)$$

So, the orthonormal basis is

$$\left\{(1, 0, 0), \left(0, \frac{1}{\sqrt{2}}, \frac{1}{\sqrt{2}}\right), \left(0, \frac{1}{\sqrt{2}}, -\frac{1}{\sqrt{2}}\right)\right\}.$$

34. First, orthogonalize each vector in B.

$$\mathbf{w}_1 = \mathbf{v}_1 = (0, 1, 2)$$

$$\mathbf{w}_2 = \mathbf{v}_2 - \frac{\langle \mathbf{v}_2, \mathbf{w}_1 \rangle}{\langle \mathbf{w}_1, \mathbf{w}_1 \rangle}\mathbf{w}_1 = (2, 0, 0) - 0(0, 1, 2) = (2, 0, 0)$$

$$\mathbf{w}_3 = \mathbf{v}_3 - \frac{\langle \mathbf{v}_3, \mathbf{w}_1 \rangle}{\langle \mathbf{w}_1, \mathbf{w}_1 \rangle}\mathbf{w}_1 - \frac{\langle \mathbf{v}_3, \mathbf{w}_2 \rangle}{\langle \mathbf{w}_2, \mathbf{w}_2 \rangle}\mathbf{w}_2 = (1, 1, 1) - \frac{3}{5}(0, 1, 2) - \frac{2}{4}(2, 0, 0) = \left(0, \frac{2}{5}, -\frac{1}{5}\right)$$

Then, normalize the vectors.

$$\mathbf{u}_1 = \frac{\mathbf{w}_1}{\|\mathbf{w}_1\|} = \frac{1}{\sqrt{5}}(0, 1, 2) = \left(0, \frac{1}{\sqrt{5}}, \frac{2}{\sqrt{5}}\right)$$

$$\mathbf{u}_2 = \frac{\mathbf{w}_2}{\|\mathbf{w}_2\|} = \frac{1}{2}(2, 0, 0) = (1, 0, 0)$$

$$\mathbf{u}_3 = \frac{\mathbf{w}_3}{\|\mathbf{w}_3\|} = \sqrt{5}\left(0, \frac{2}{5}, -\frac{1}{5}\right) = \left(0, \frac{2}{\sqrt{5}}, -\frac{1}{\sqrt{5}}\right)$$

So, the orthonormal basis is $\left\{\left(0, \frac{1}{\sqrt{5}}, \frac{2}{\sqrt{5}}\right), (1, 0, 0), \left(0, \frac{2}{\sqrt{5}}, -\frac{1}{\sqrt{5}}\right)\right\}$.

36. First, orthogonalize each vector in B.

$$\mathbf{w}_1 = \mathbf{v}_1 = (3, 4, 0, 0)$$

$$\mathbf{w}_2 = \mathbf{v}_2 - \frac{\langle \mathbf{v}_2, \mathbf{w}_1 \rangle}{\langle \mathbf{w}_1, \mathbf{w}_1 \rangle}\mathbf{w}_1 = (-1, 1, 0, 0) - \frac{1}{25}(3, 4, 0, 0) = \left(-\frac{28}{25}, \frac{21}{25}, 0, 0\right)$$

$$\mathbf{w}_3 = \mathbf{v}_3 - \frac{\langle \mathbf{v}_3, \mathbf{w}_1 \rangle}{\langle \mathbf{w}_1, \mathbf{w}_1 \rangle}\mathbf{w}_1 - \frac{\langle \mathbf{v}_3, \mathbf{w}_2 \rangle}{\langle \mathbf{w}_2, \mathbf{w}_2 \rangle}\mathbf{w}_2$$

$$= (2, 1, 0, -1) - \frac{10}{25}(3, 4, 0, 0) - \frac{-\frac{7}{5}}{\frac{49}{25}}\left(-\frac{28}{25}, \frac{21}{25}, 0, 0\right)$$

$$= (2, 1, 0, -1) - \left(\frac{6}{5}, \frac{8}{5}, 0, 0\right) + \left(-\frac{4}{5}, \frac{3}{5}, 0, 0\right) = (0, 0, 0, -1)$$

$$\mathbf{w}_4 = \mathbf{v}_4 - \frac{\langle \mathbf{v}_4, \mathbf{w}_1 \rangle}{\langle \mathbf{w}_1, \mathbf{w}_1 \rangle}\mathbf{w}_1 - \frac{\langle \mathbf{v}_4, \mathbf{w}_2 \rangle}{\langle \mathbf{w}_2, \mathbf{w}_2 \rangle}\mathbf{w}_2 - \frac{\langle \mathbf{v}_4, \mathbf{w}_3 \rangle}{\langle \mathbf{w}_3, \mathbf{w}_3 \rangle}\mathbf{w}_3$$

$$= (0, 1, 1, 0) - \frac{4}{25}(3, 4, 0, 0) - \frac{\frac{21}{25}}{\frac{49}{25}}\left(-\frac{28}{25}, \frac{21}{25}, 0, 0\right) - 0(0, 0, 0, -1)$$

$$= (0, 1, 1, 0) - \left(\frac{12}{25}, \frac{16}{25}, 0, 0\right) - \left(-\frac{12}{25}, \frac{9}{25}, 0, 0\right) = (0, 0, 1, 0)$$

Then, normalize the vectors.

$$\mathbf{u}_1 = \frac{\mathbf{w}_1}{\|\mathbf{w}_1\|} = \frac{1}{5}(3, 4, 0, 0) = \left(\frac{3}{5}, \frac{4}{5}, 0, 0\right)$$

$$\mathbf{u}_2 = \frac{\mathbf{w}_2}{\|\mathbf{w}_2\|} = \frac{5}{7}\left(-\frac{28}{25}, \frac{21}{25}, 0, 0\right) = \left(-\frac{4}{5}, \frac{3}{5}, 0, 0\right)$$

$$\mathbf{u}_3 = \frac{\mathbf{w}_3}{\|\mathbf{w}_3\|} = (0, 0, 0, -1)$$

$$\mathbf{u}_4 = \mathbf{w}_4 = (0, 0, 1, 0)$$

So, the orthonormal basis is $\left\{\left(\frac{3}{5}, \frac{4}{5}, 0, 0\right), \left(-\frac{4}{5}, \frac{3}{5}, 0, 0\right), (0, 0, 0, -1), (0, 0, 1, 0)\right\}$.

38. Because there is just one vector, you simply need to normalize it.

$$\mathbf{u}_1 = \frac{1}{\sqrt{4^2 + (-7) + 6^2}}(4, -7, 6) = \frac{1}{\sqrt{101}}(4, -7, 6) = \left(\frac{4}{\sqrt{101}}, -\frac{7}{\sqrt{101}}, \frac{6}{\sqrt{101}}\right)$$

40. First, orthogonalize each vector in B.

$$\mathbf{w}_1 = \mathbf{v}_1 = (1, 2, 0)$$

$$\mathbf{w}_2 = \mathbf{v}_2 - \frac{\langle \mathbf{v}_2, \mathbf{w}_1 \rangle}{\langle \mathbf{w}_1, \mathbf{w}_1 \rangle}\mathbf{w}_1 = (2, 0, -2) - \frac{2}{5}(1, 2, 0) = \left(\frac{8}{5}, -\frac{4}{5}, -2\right)$$

Then, normalize the vectors.

$$\mathbf{u}_1 = \frac{\mathbf{w}_1}{\|\mathbf{w}_1\|} = \frac{1}{\sqrt{5}}(1, 2, 0) = \left(\frac{1}{\sqrt{5}}, \frac{2}{\sqrt{5}}, 0\right)$$

$$\mathbf{u}_2 = \frac{\mathbf{w}_2}{\|\mathbf{w}_2\|} = \frac{1}{6/\sqrt{5}}\left(\frac{8}{5}, -\frac{4}{5}, -2\right) = \left(\frac{4}{3\sqrt{5}}, -\frac{2}{3\sqrt{5}}, -\frac{5}{3\sqrt{5}}\right)$$

So, the orthonormal basis is $\left\{\left(\frac{1}{\sqrt{5}}, \frac{2}{\sqrt{5}}, 0\right), \left(\frac{4}{3\sqrt{5}}, -\frac{2}{3\sqrt{5}}, -\frac{5}{3\sqrt{5}}\right)\right\}$.

42. First, normalize each vector in B.

$$\mathbf{w}_1 = \mathbf{v}_1 = (7, 24, 0, 0)$$

$$\mathbf{w}_2 = \mathbf{v}_2 - \frac{\langle \mathbf{v}_2, \mathbf{w}_1 \rangle}{\langle \mathbf{w}_1, \mathbf{w}_1 \rangle}\mathbf{w}_1 = (0, 0, 1, 1) - 0(7, 24, 0, 0) = (0, 0, 1, 1)$$

$$\mathbf{w}_3 = \mathbf{v}_3 - \frac{\langle \mathbf{v}_3, \mathbf{w}_1 \rangle}{\langle \mathbf{w}_1, \mathbf{w}_1 \rangle}\mathbf{w}_1 - \frac{\langle \mathbf{v}_3, \mathbf{w}_2 \rangle}{\langle \mathbf{w}_2, \mathbf{w}_2 \rangle}\mathbf{w}_2 = (0, 0, 1, -2) - 0(7, 24, 0, 0) - \frac{-1}{2}(0, 0, 1, 1) = \left(0, 0, \frac{3}{2}, -\frac{3}{2}\right)$$

Then, normalize the vectors.

$$\mathbf{u}_1 = \frac{\mathbf{w}_1}{\|\mathbf{w}_1\|} = \frac{1}{25}(7, 24, 0, 0) = \left(\frac{7}{25}, \frac{24}{25}, 0, 0\right)$$

$$\mathbf{u}_2 = \frac{\mathbf{w}_2}{\|\mathbf{w}_2\|} = \frac{1}{\sqrt{2}}(0, 0, 1, 1) = \left(0, 0, \frac{1}{\sqrt{2}}, \frac{1}{\sqrt{2}}\right)$$

$$\mathbf{u}_3 = \frac{\mathbf{w}_3}{\|\mathbf{w}_3\|} = \frac{1}{3/\sqrt{2}}\left(0, 0, \frac{3}{2}, -\frac{3}{2}\right) = \left(0, 0, \frac{1}{\sqrt{2}}, -\frac{1}{\sqrt{2}}\right)$$

So, the orthonormal basis is

$$\left\{\left(\frac{7}{25}, \frac{24}{25}, 0, 0\right), \left(0, 0, \frac{1}{\sqrt{2}}, \frac{1}{\sqrt{2}}\right), \left(0, 0, \frac{1}{\sqrt{2}}, -\frac{1}{\sqrt{2}}\right)\right\}.$$

44. The set $\left\{\left(\frac{2}{3}, -\frac{1}{3}\right), \left(\frac{\sqrt{2}}{6}, \frac{2\sqrt{2}}{3}\right)\right\}$ from Exercise 43 is not orthonormal using the Euclidean inner product because

$$\left\|\left(\frac{2}{3}, -\frac{1}{3}\right)\right\| = \sqrt{\frac{4}{9} + \frac{1}{9}} = \frac{\sqrt{5}}{3} \neq 1.$$

46. $\langle 1, 1 \rangle = \int_{-1}^{1} 1\, dx = x \Big]_{-1}^{1} = 1 - (-1) = 2$

48. $\langle x^2, x \rangle = \int_{-1}^{1} x^2 x\, dx = \int_{-1}^{1} x^3 dx = \frac{x^4}{4}\Big]_{-1}^{1} = \frac{1}{4} - \left(\frac{1}{4}\right) = 0$

50. $\left\langle x^2 - \dfrac{1}{3}, x^2 - \dfrac{1}{3} \right\rangle = \displaystyle\int_{-1}^{1}\left(x^2 - \dfrac{1}{3} \right)\left(x^2 - \dfrac{1}{3} \right) dx$

$\qquad\qquad\qquad\quad = \displaystyle\int_{-1}^{1}\left(x^4 - \dfrac{1}{3}x^2 - \dfrac{1}{3}x^2 + \dfrac{1}{9} \right) dx$

$\qquad\qquad\qquad\quad = \displaystyle\int_{-1}^{1}\left(x^4 - \dfrac{2}{3}x^2 + \dfrac{1}{9} \right) dx$

$\qquad\qquad\qquad\quad = \dfrac{x^5}{5} - \dfrac{2}{9}x^3 + \dfrac{1}{9}x \Big]_{-1}^{1}$

$\qquad\qquad\qquad\quad = \left[\dfrac{1}{5}(1)^5 - \dfrac{2}{9}(1)^3 + \dfrac{1}{9}(1) \right] - \left[\dfrac{1}{5}(-1)^5 - \dfrac{2}{9}(-1)^3 + \dfrac{1}{9}(-1) \right]$

$\qquad\qquad\qquad\quad = \dfrac{8}{45}$

52. The solutions of the homogeneous system are of the form $\left(s + t, 0, s, t \right)$, where s and t are any real numbers. So, a basis for the solution space is $\left\{ (1, 0, 1, 0), (1, 0, 0, 1) \right\}$.

Orthogonalize this basis as follows.

$\mathbf{w}_1 = \mathbf{v}_1 = (1, 0, 1, 0)$

$\mathbf{w}_2 = \mathbf{v}_2 - \dfrac{\langle \mathbf{v}_2, \mathbf{w}_1 \rangle}{\langle \mathbf{w}_1, \mathbf{w}_1 \rangle}\mathbf{w}_1 = (1, 0, 0, 1) - \dfrac{1}{2}(1, 0, 1, 0) = \left(\dfrac{1}{2}, 0, -\dfrac{1}{2}, 1 \right)$

Then, normalize these vectors.

$\mathbf{u}_1 = \dfrac{\mathbf{w}_1}{\|\mathbf{w}_1\|} = \dfrac{1}{\sqrt{2}}(1, 0, 1, 0) = \left(\dfrac{\sqrt{2}}{2}, 0, \dfrac{\sqrt{2}}{2}, 0 \right)$

$\mathbf{u}_2 = \dfrac{\mathbf{w}_2}{\|\mathbf{w}_2\|} = \dfrac{1}{\sqrt{3/2}}\left(\dfrac{1}{2}, 0, -\dfrac{1}{2}, 1 \right) = \left(\dfrac{\sqrt{6}}{6}, 0, -\dfrac{\sqrt{6}}{6}, \dfrac{\sqrt{6}}{3} \right)$

So, an orthonormal basis for the solution space is $\left\{ \left(\dfrac{\sqrt{2}}{2}, 0, \dfrac{\sqrt{2}}{2}, 0 \right), \left(\dfrac{\sqrt{6}}{6}, 0, -\dfrac{\sqrt{6}}{6}, \dfrac{\sqrt{6}}{3} \right) \right\}$.

54. The solutions of the homogeneous system are of the form $\left(-3s + 3t, s, t \right)$, where s and t are any real numbers. So, a basis for the solution space is $\left\{ (-3, 1, 0), (3, 0, 1) \right\}$.

Orthogonalize this basis as follows.

$\mathbf{w}_1 = \mathbf{v}_1 = (-3, 1, 0)$

$\mathbf{w}_2 = \mathbf{v}_2 - \dfrac{\langle \mathbf{v}_2, \mathbf{w}_1 \rangle}{\langle \mathbf{w}_1, \mathbf{w}_1 \rangle}\mathbf{w}_1 = (3, 0, 1) + \dfrac{9}{10}(-3, 1, 0) = \left(\dfrac{3}{10}, \dfrac{9}{10}, 1 \right)$

Then, normalize these vectors.

$\mathbf{u}_1 = \dfrac{\mathbf{w}_1}{\|\mathbf{w}_1\|} = \dfrac{1}{\sqrt{10}}(-3, 1, 0) = \left(-\dfrac{3\sqrt{10}}{10}, \dfrac{\sqrt{10}}{10}, 0 \right)$

$\mathbf{u}_2 = \dfrac{\mathbf{w}_2}{\|\mathbf{w}_2\|} = \dfrac{1}{\sqrt{19/10}}\left(\dfrac{3}{10}, \dfrac{9}{10}, 1 \right) = \left(\dfrac{3\sqrt{190}}{190}, \dfrac{9\sqrt{190}}{190}, \dfrac{\sqrt{190}}{19} \right)$

So, an orthonormal basis for the solution space is

$\left\{ \left(-\dfrac{3\sqrt{10}}{10}, \dfrac{\sqrt{10}}{10}, 0 \right), \left(\dfrac{3\sqrt{190}}{190}, \dfrac{9\sqrt{190}}{190}, \dfrac{\sqrt{190}}{19} \right) \right\}$.

56. To form an orthonormal basis B' for V, follow these steps:

    (i)   Begin with a basis for the inner product space. It need not be orthogonal nor consist of unit vectors.

    (ii) Convert the given basis to an orthogonal basis.

    (iii) Normalize each vector in the orthogonal basis to form an orthonormal basis.

58. (a) True. See definition on page 248.

    (b) True. See Theorem 5.10 on page 251.

60. Let $p(x) = \sqrt{2}(x^2 - 1)$ and $q(x) = \sqrt{2}(x^2 + x + 2)$. Because $\langle p, q \rangle = \sqrt{2}\sqrt{2} + 0(\sqrt{2}) + (-\sqrt{2})(2\sqrt{2}) = -2 \neq 0$, the set is not orthogonal.

Orthogonalize the set as follows.

$$\mathbf{w}_1 = p = \sqrt{2}(x^2 - 1)$$

$$\mathbf{w}_2 = q - \frac{\langle q, \mathbf{w}_1 \rangle}{\langle \mathbf{w}_1, \mathbf{w}_1 \rangle}\mathbf{w}_1 = \sqrt{2}(x^2 + x + 2) - \frac{-2}{4}\left(\sqrt{2}(x^2 - 1)\right) = \frac{3\sqrt{2}}{2}x^2 + \sqrt{2}x + \frac{3\sqrt{2}}{2}$$

Then, normalize the vectors.

$$\mathbf{u}_1 = \frac{\mathbf{w}_1}{\|\mathbf{w}_1\|} = \frac{1}{2}\sqrt{2}(x^2 - 1) = \frac{\sqrt{2}}{2}x^2 - \frac{\sqrt{2}}{2}$$

$$\mathbf{u}_2 = \frac{\mathbf{w}_2}{\|\mathbf{w}_2\|} = \frac{1}{\sqrt{11}}\left(\frac{3\sqrt{2}}{2}x^2 + \sqrt{2}x + \frac{3\sqrt{2}}{2}\right) = \frac{3}{\sqrt{22}}x^2 + \frac{2}{\sqrt{22}}x + \frac{3}{\sqrt{22}}$$

So, the orthonormal set is $\left\{ \dfrac{\sqrt{2}}{2}x^2 - \dfrac{\sqrt{2}}{2}, \dfrac{3}{\sqrt{22}}x^2 + \dfrac{2}{\sqrt{22}}x + \dfrac{3}{\sqrt{22}} \right\}$.

62. The set $\{1, x, x^2\}$ of polynomials is orthonormal. (see Example 2)

64. Let $p(x) = x^2 - 1$ and $q(x) = x - 1$. Then, because $\langle p, q \rangle = 1 \neq 0$, the set is not orthogonal. Orthogonalize the set as follows.

$$\mathbf{w}_1 = p = x^2 - 1$$

$$\mathbf{w}_2 = q - \frac{\langle q, \mathbf{w}_1 \rangle}{\langle \mathbf{w}_1, \mathbf{w}_1 \rangle}\mathbf{w}_1 = (x - 1) - \frac{1}{2}(x^2 - 1) = -\frac{1}{2}x^2 + x - \frac{1}{2}$$

Then, normalize the vectors.

$$\mathbf{u}_1 = \frac{\mathbf{w}_1}{\|\mathbf{w}_1\|} = \frac{1}{\sqrt{2}}(x^2 - 1) = \frac{\sqrt{2}}{2}(x^2 - 1)$$

$$\mathbf{u}_2 = \frac{\mathbf{w}_2}{\|\mathbf{w}_2\|} = \frac{1}{\sqrt{3/2}}\left(-\frac{1}{2}x^2 + x - \frac{1}{2}\right) = \frac{\sqrt{6}}{3}\left(-\frac{1}{2}x^2 + x - \frac{1}{2}\right) = \frac{-\sqrt{6}}{6}(x^2 - 2x + 1)$$

So, the orthonormal set is $\left\{ \dfrac{\sqrt{2}}{2}(x^2 - 1), -\dfrac{\sqrt{6}}{6}(x^2 - 2x + 1) \right\}$.

66. Let $\mathbf{v} = c_1\mathbf{v}_1 + \cdots + c_n\mathbf{v}_n$ be an arbitrary linear combination of vectors in S. Then

$$\langle \mathbf{w}, \mathbf{v} \rangle = \langle \mathbf{w}, c_1\mathbf{v}_1 + \cdots + c_n\mathbf{v}_n \rangle$$

$$= \langle \mathbf{w}, c_1\mathbf{v}_1 \rangle + \cdots + \langle \mathbf{w}, c_n\mathbf{v}_n \rangle$$

$$= c_1\langle \mathbf{w}, \mathbf{v}_1 \rangle + \cdots + c_n\langle \mathbf{w}, \mathbf{v}_n \rangle = c_1 \cdot 0 + \cdots + c_n \cdot 0 = 0.$$

Because $c_1, \ldots, c_n$ are arbitrary real numbers, you conclude that $\mathbf{w}$ is orthogonal to *any* linear combination of vectors in S.

68. Let $\mathbf{v} \in W \cap W^\perp$. Then $\mathbf{v} \cdot \mathbf{w} = 0$ for all $\mathbf{w}$ in W. In particular, since $\mathbf{v} \in W$, $\mathbf{v} \cdot \mathbf{v} = 0$, which implies that $\mathbf{v} = \mathbf{0}$.

70. $A = \begin{bmatrix} 0 & 1 & -1 \\ 0 & -2 & 2 \\ 0 & -1 & 1 \end{bmatrix} \Rightarrow \begin{bmatrix} 0 & 1 & -1 \\ 0 & 0 & 0 \\ 0 & 0 & 0 \end{bmatrix}$

$A^T = \begin{bmatrix} 0 & 0 & 1 \\ 1 & -2 & -1 \\ -1 & 2 & 1 \end{bmatrix} \Rightarrow \begin{bmatrix} 1 & -2 & -1 \\ 0 & 0 & 0 \\ 0 & 0 & 0 \end{bmatrix}$

$N(A) = \text{span} \left\{ \begin{bmatrix} 1 \\ 0 \\ 0 \end{bmatrix}, \begin{bmatrix} 0 \\ 1 \\ 1 \end{bmatrix} \right\}$

$N(A^T) = \text{span} \left\{ \begin{bmatrix} 2 \\ 1 \\ 0 \end{bmatrix}, \begin{bmatrix} 1 \\ 0 \\ 1 \end{bmatrix} \right\}$

$R(A) = \text{span} \left\{ \begin{bmatrix} 1 \\ -2 \\ -1 \end{bmatrix} \right\}$

$R(A^T) = \text{span} \left\{ \begin{bmatrix} 0 \\ 1 \\ -1 \end{bmatrix} \right\}$

$N(A) = R(A^T)^\perp$ and $N(A^T) = R(A)^\perp$

72. Note that $\mathbf{v}_1$ and $\mathbf{v}_2$ are orthogonal unit vectors. Furthermore, a vector (c_1, c_2, c_3, c_4) orthogonal to $\mathbf{v}_1$ and $\mathbf{v}_2$ satisfies the homogeneous system of linear equations

$$\frac{1}{\sqrt{2}}c_1 \qquad + \frac{1}{\sqrt{2}}c_3 \qquad = 0$$

$$-\frac{1}{\sqrt{2}}c_2 \qquad + \frac{1}{\sqrt{2}}c_4 = 0,$$

which has solutions of the form $(-s, t, s, t)$, where s and t are any real numbers. A basis for the solution set is $\{(1, 0, -1, 0), (0, 1, 0, 1)\}$. Because $(1, 0, -1, 0)$ and $(0, 1, 0, 1)$ are already orthogonal, you simply normalize them to yield $\left(\frac{1}{\sqrt{2}}, 0, -\frac{1}{\sqrt{2}}, 0\right)$ and $\left(0, \frac{1}{\sqrt{2}}, 0, \frac{1}{\sqrt{2}}\right)$.
So,

$$\left\{ \left(\frac{1}{\sqrt{2}}, 0, \frac{1}{\sqrt{2}}, 0\right), \left(0, -\frac{1}{\sqrt{2}}, 0, \frac{1}{\sqrt{2}}\right), \right.$$

$$\left. \left(\frac{1}{\sqrt{2}}, 0, -\frac{1}{\sqrt{2}}, 0\right), \left(0, \frac{1}{\sqrt{2}}, 0, \frac{1}{\sqrt{2}}\right) \right\}$$

is an orthonormal basis.

Section 5.4   Mathematical Models and Least Squares Analysis

2. The system

$$c_0 \qquad = 0$$
$$c_0 + 3c_1 = 1$$
$$c_0 + 4c_1 = 2$$

has no solution. The points are *not* collinear.

4. The system

$$c_0 - c_1 = 5$$
$$c_0 + c_1 = -1$$
$$c_0 + 2c_1 = -4$$

has no solution. The points are *not* collinear.

6. Orthogonal: $\begin{bmatrix} -3 \\ 0 \\ 1 \end{bmatrix} \cdot \begin{bmatrix} 2 \\ 1 \\ 6 \end{bmatrix} = \begin{bmatrix} -3 \\ 0 \\ 1 \end{bmatrix} \cdot \begin{bmatrix} 0 \\ 1 \\ 0 \end{bmatrix} = 0$

8. Not orthogonal: $\begin{bmatrix} 0 \\ 0 \\ 1 \\ -2 \end{bmatrix} \cdot \begin{bmatrix} 0 \\ 1 \\ -2 \\ 2 \end{bmatrix} = -6 \neq 0$

10. (a) Because $S = \left\{ [x, y, 0, 0, z]^T \right\}$,

$$S^\perp = \text{span} \left\{ \begin{bmatrix} 0 \\ 0 \\ 1 \\ 0 \\ 0 \end{bmatrix}, \begin{bmatrix} 0 \\ 0 \\ 0 \\ 1 \\ 0 \end{bmatrix} \right\}.$$

(b) Since $S^\perp = \text{span} \left\{ \begin{bmatrix} 1 \\ 0 \\ 0 \\ 0 \\ 0 \end{bmatrix}, \begin{bmatrix} 0 \\ 1 \\ 0 \\ 0 \\ 0 \end{bmatrix}, \begin{bmatrix} 0 \\ 0 \\ 0 \\ 0 \\ 1 \end{bmatrix} \right\}$, you can see that

$$S \oplus S^\perp = R^5.$$

12. (a) $A^T = \begin{bmatrix} 0 & 1 & -1 & 1 \end{bmatrix} \Rightarrow S^\perp = \text{span} \left\{ \begin{bmatrix} 1 \\ 0 \\ 0 \\ 0 \end{bmatrix}, \begin{bmatrix} 0 \\ 1 \\ 1 \\ 0 \end{bmatrix}, \begin{bmatrix} 0 \\ 1 \\ 0 \\ -1 \end{bmatrix} \right\}$

(b) Since $S = \text{span} \left\{ \begin{bmatrix} 0 \\ 1 \\ -1 \\ 1 \end{bmatrix} \right\}$, you can see that

$$S \oplus S^\perp = R^4.$$

14. The orthogonal complement of

$$S^\perp = \text{span}\left\{ \begin{bmatrix} 1 \\ 0 \\ 0 \\ 0 \end{bmatrix}, \begin{bmatrix} 0 \\ 1 \\ 1 \\ 0 \end{bmatrix}, \begin{bmatrix} 0 \\ 1 \\ 0 \\ -1 \end{bmatrix} \right\}$$

is

$$\left(S^\perp\right)^\perp = S = \text{span}\left\{ \begin{bmatrix} 0 \\ 1 \\ -1 \\ 0 \end{bmatrix} \right\}.$$

16. Using the Gram-Schmidt process, an orthogonal basis for S is

$$\left\{ \begin{bmatrix} -\frac{1}{\sqrt5} \\ \frac{2}{\sqrt5} \\ 0 \\ 0 \end{bmatrix}, \begin{bmatrix} 0 \\ 0 \\ 1 \\ 0 \end{bmatrix}, \begin{bmatrix} 0 \\ 0 \\ 0 \\ 1 \end{bmatrix} \right\}.$$

$$\text{proj}_S \mathbf{v} = (\mathbf{u}_1 \cdot \mathbf{v})\mathbf{u}_1 + (\mathbf{u}_2 \cdot \mathbf{v})\mathbf{u}_2 + (\mathbf{u}_3 \cdot \mathbf{v})\mathbf{u}_3$$

$$= \frac{1}{\sqrt5}\begin{bmatrix} -\frac{1}{\sqrt5} \\ \frac{2}{\sqrt5} \\ 0 \\ 0 \end{bmatrix} + 1\begin{bmatrix} 0 \\ 0 \\ 1 \\ 0 \end{bmatrix} + 1\begin{bmatrix} 0 \\ 0 \\ 0 \\ 1 \end{bmatrix} = \begin{bmatrix} -\frac{1}{5} \\ \frac{2}{5} \\ 1 \\ 1 \end{bmatrix}$$

18. Using the Gram-Schmidt process, an orthonormal basis for S is

$$\left\{ \begin{bmatrix} \frac{1}{2} \\ \frac{1}{2} \\ \frac{1}{2} \\ \frac{1}{2} \end{bmatrix}, \begin{bmatrix} 0 \\ \frac{1}{\sqrt2} \\ -\frac{1}{\sqrt2} \\ 0 \end{bmatrix}, \begin{bmatrix} -\frac{1}{2} \\ \frac{1}{2} \\ \frac{1}{2} \\ -\frac{1}{2} \end{bmatrix} \right\}.$$

$$\text{proj}_S \mathbf{v} = (\mathbf{u}_1 \cdot \mathbf{v})\mathbf{u}_1 + (\mathbf{u}_2 \cdot \mathbf{v})\mathbf{u}_2 + (\mathbf{u}_3 \cdot \mathbf{v})\mathbf{u}_3$$

$$= 5\begin{bmatrix} \frac{1}{2} \\ \frac{1}{2} \\ \frac{1}{2} \\ \frac{1}{2} \end{bmatrix} + \frac{-1}{\sqrt2}\begin{bmatrix} 0 \\ \frac{1}{\sqrt2} \\ -\frac{1}{\sqrt2} \\ 0 \end{bmatrix} + 0\begin{bmatrix} -\frac{1}{2} \\ \frac{1}{2} \\ \frac{1}{2} \\ -\frac{1}{2} \end{bmatrix} = \begin{bmatrix} \frac{5}{2} \\ 2 \\ 3 \\ \frac{5}{2} \end{bmatrix}$$

20. $A = \begin{bmatrix} 0 & -1 & 1 \\ 1 & 2 & 0 \\ 1 & 1 & 1 \end{bmatrix} \Rightarrow \begin{bmatrix} 1 & 0 & 2 \\ 0 & 1 & -1 \\ 0 & 0 & 0 \end{bmatrix}$

$A^T = \begin{bmatrix} 0 & 1 & 1 \\ -1 & 2 & 1 \\ 1 & 0 & 1 \end{bmatrix} \Rightarrow \begin{bmatrix} 1 & 0 & 1 \\ 0 & 1 & 1 \\ 0 & 0 & 0 \end{bmatrix}$

$N(A) = \text{span}\left\{ \begin{bmatrix} -2 \\ 1 \\ 1 \end{bmatrix} \right\}$

$N(A^T) = \text{span}\left\{ \begin{bmatrix} -1 \\ -1 \\ 1 \end{bmatrix} \right\}$

$R(A) = \text{span}\left\{ \begin{bmatrix} 0 \\ 1 \\ 1 \end{bmatrix}, \begin{bmatrix} -1 \\ 2 \\ 1 \end{bmatrix} \right\}$

$R(A^T) = \text{span}\left\{ \begin{bmatrix} 0 \\ -1 \\ 1 \end{bmatrix}, \begin{bmatrix} 1 \\ 2 \\ 0 \end{bmatrix} \right\}$

22. $A = \begin{bmatrix} 1 & 0 & -1 \\ 0 & -1 & 1 \\ 1 & 1 & 0 \\ 1 & 0 & 1 \end{bmatrix} \Rightarrow \begin{bmatrix} 1 & 0 & 0 \\ 0 & 1 & 0 \\ 0 & 0 & 1 \\ 0 & 0 & 0 \end{bmatrix}$

$A^T = \begin{bmatrix} 1 & 0 & 1 & 1 \\ 0 & -1 & 1 & 0 \\ -1 & 1 & 0 & 1 \end{bmatrix} \Rightarrow \begin{bmatrix} 1 & 0 & 0 & 0 \\ 0 & 1 & 0 & 1 \\ 0 & 0 & 1 & 1 \end{bmatrix}$

$N(A) = \left\{ \begin{bmatrix} 0 \\ 0 \\ 0 \end{bmatrix} \right\}$

$N(A^T) = \text{span}\left\{ \begin{bmatrix} 0 \\ -1 \\ -1 \\ 1 \end{bmatrix} \right\}$

$R(A) = \text{span}\left\{ \begin{bmatrix} 1 \\ 0 \\ 1 \\ 1 \end{bmatrix}, \begin{bmatrix} 0 \\ -1 \\ 1 \\ 0 \end{bmatrix}, \begin{bmatrix} -1 \\ 1 \\ 0 \\ 1 \end{bmatrix} \right\}$

$R(A^T) = \text{span}\left\{ \begin{bmatrix} 1 \\ 0 \\ -1 \end{bmatrix}, \begin{bmatrix} 0 \\ -1 \\ 1 \end{bmatrix}, \begin{bmatrix} 1 \\ 1 \\ 0 \end{bmatrix} \right\} \quad \left(R(A^T) = R^3\right)$

24. $A^T A = \begin{bmatrix} 1 & 1 & 0 & 1 \\ -1 & 1 & 1 & 0 \\ 1 & 1 & 1 & 1 \end{bmatrix} \begin{bmatrix} 1 & -1 & 1 \\ 1 & 1 & 1 \\ 0 & 1 & 1 \\ 1 & 0 & 1 \end{bmatrix} = \begin{bmatrix} 3 & 0 & 3 \\ 0 & 3 & 1 \\ 3 & 1 & 4 \end{bmatrix}$

$A^T \mathbf{b} = \begin{bmatrix} 1 & 1 & 0 & 1 \\ -1 & 1 & 1 & 0 \\ 1 & 1 & 1 & 1 \end{bmatrix} \begin{bmatrix} 2 \\ 1 \\ 0 \\ 2 \end{bmatrix} = \begin{bmatrix} 5 \\ -1 \\ 5 \end{bmatrix}$

$\begin{bmatrix} 3 & 0 & 3 & 5 \\ 0 & 3 & 1 & -1 \\ 3 & 1 & 4 & 5 \end{bmatrix} \Rightarrow \begin{bmatrix} 1 & 0 & 0 & \frac{7}{6} \\ 0 & 1 & 0 & -\frac{1}{2} \\ 0 & 0 & 1 & \frac{1}{2} \end{bmatrix} \Rightarrow \mathbf{x} = \begin{bmatrix} \frac{7}{6} \\ -\frac{1}{2} \\ \frac{1}{2} \end{bmatrix}$

26. $A^T A = \begin{bmatrix} 0 & 1 & 2 & 1 & 0 \\ 2 & 1 & 1 & 1 & 2 \\ 1 & -1 & 0 & 1 & -1 \end{bmatrix} \begin{bmatrix} 0 & 2 & 1 \\ 1 & 1 & -1 \\ 2 & 1 & 0 \\ 1 & 1 & 1 \\ 0 & 2 & -1 \end{bmatrix} = \begin{bmatrix} 6 & 4 & 0 \\ 4 & 11 & 0 \\ 0 & 0 & 4 \end{bmatrix}$

$A^T \mathbf{b} = \begin{bmatrix} 0 & 1 & 2 & 1 & 0 \\ 2 & 1 & 1 & 1 & 2 \\ 1 & -1 & 0 & 1 & -1 \end{bmatrix} \begin{bmatrix} 1 \\ 0 \\ 1 \\ -1 \\ 0 \end{bmatrix} = \begin{bmatrix} 1 \\ 2 \\ 0 \end{bmatrix}$

$\begin{bmatrix} 6 & 4 & 0 & 1 \\ 4 & 11 & 0 & 2 \\ 0 & 0 & 4 & 0 \end{bmatrix} \Rightarrow \begin{bmatrix} 1 & 0 & 0 & \frac{3}{50} \\ 0 & 1 & 0 & \frac{4}{25} \\ 0 & 0 & 1 & 0 \end{bmatrix} \Rightarrow \mathbf{x} = \begin{bmatrix} \frac{3}{50} \\ \frac{4}{25} \\ 0 \end{bmatrix}$

28. $A^T A = \begin{bmatrix} 0 & 1 & 1 \\ 2 & 1 & 3 \end{bmatrix} \begin{bmatrix} 0 & 2 \\ 1 & 1 \\ 1 & 3 \end{bmatrix} = \begin{bmatrix} 2 & 4 \\ 4 & 14 \end{bmatrix}$

$A^T \mathbf{b} = \begin{bmatrix} 0 & 1 & 1 \\ 2 & 1 & 3 \end{bmatrix} \begin{bmatrix} 2 \\ -2 \\ 1 \end{bmatrix} = \begin{bmatrix} -1 \\ 5 \end{bmatrix}$

The normal equations are

$$A^T A \mathbf{x} = A^T \mathbf{b}$$

$$\begin{bmatrix} 2 & 4 \\ 4 & 14 \end{bmatrix} \begin{bmatrix} x_1 \\ x_2 \end{bmatrix} = \begin{bmatrix} -1 \\ 5 \end{bmatrix}$$

The solution is

$$\mathbf{x} = \begin{bmatrix} x_1 \\ x_2 \end{bmatrix} = \begin{bmatrix} -\frac{17}{6} \\ \frac{7}{6} \end{bmatrix}.$$

Finally, the projection of $\bar{\mathbf{b}}$ onto S is

$$A\mathbf{x} = \begin{bmatrix} 0 & 2 \\ 1 & 1 \\ 1 & 3 \end{bmatrix} \begin{bmatrix} -\frac{17}{6} \\ \frac{7}{6} \end{bmatrix} = \begin{bmatrix} \frac{7}{3} \\ -\frac{5}{3} \\ \frac{2}{3} \end{bmatrix}.$$

30. $A^T A = \begin{bmatrix} 1 & 1 & 1 \\ 1 & 2 & 4 \end{bmatrix} \begin{bmatrix} 1 & 1 \\ 1 & 2 \\ 1 & 4 \end{bmatrix} = \begin{bmatrix} 3 & 7 \\ 7 & 21 \end{bmatrix}$

$A^T \mathbf{b} = \begin{bmatrix} 1 & 1 & 1 \\ 1 & 2 & 4 \end{bmatrix} \begin{bmatrix} 1 \\ 3 \\ 5 \end{bmatrix} = \begin{bmatrix} 9 \\ 27 \end{bmatrix}$

$\begin{bmatrix} 3 & 7 & 9 \\ 7 & 21 & 27 \end{bmatrix} \Rightarrow \begin{bmatrix} 1 & 0 & 0 \\ 0 & 1 & \frac{9}{7} \end{bmatrix} \Rightarrow \mathbf{x} = \begin{bmatrix} 0 \\ \frac{9}{7} \end{bmatrix}$

line: $y = \frac{9}{7}x$

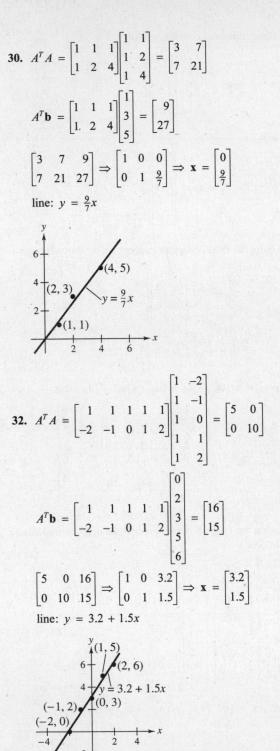

32. $A^T A = \begin{bmatrix} 1 & 1 & 1 & 1 & 1 \\ -2 & -1 & 0 & 1 & 2 \end{bmatrix} \begin{bmatrix} 1 & -2 \\ 1 & -1 \\ 1 & 0 \\ 1 & 1 \\ 1 & 2 \end{bmatrix} = \begin{bmatrix} 5 & 0 \\ 0 & 10 \end{bmatrix}$

$A^T \mathbf{b} = \begin{bmatrix} 1 & 1 & 1 & 1 & 1 \\ -2 & -1 & 0 & 1 & 2 \end{bmatrix} \begin{bmatrix} 0 \\ 2 \\ 3 \\ 5 \\ 6 \end{bmatrix} = \begin{bmatrix} 16 \\ 15 \end{bmatrix}$

$\begin{bmatrix} 5 & 0 & 16 \\ 0 & 10 & 15 \end{bmatrix} \Rightarrow \begin{bmatrix} 1 & 0 & 3.2 \\ 0 & 1 & 1.5 \end{bmatrix} \Rightarrow \mathbf{x} = \begin{bmatrix} 3.2 \\ 1.5 \end{bmatrix}$

line: $y = 3.2 + 1.5x$

34. $A^TA = \begin{bmatrix} 1 & 1 & 1 & 1 \\ 0 & 1 & 2 & 3 \\ 0 & 1 & 4 & 9 \end{bmatrix}\begin{bmatrix} 1 & 0 & 0 \\ 1 & 1 & 1 \\ 1 & 2 & 4 \\ 1 & 3 & 9 \end{bmatrix} = \begin{bmatrix} 4 & 6 & 14 \\ 6 & 14 & 36 \\ 14 & 36 & 98 \end{bmatrix}$

$A^T\mathbf{b} = \begin{bmatrix} 1 & 1 & 1 & 1 \\ 0 & 1 & 2 & 3 \\ 0 & 1 & 4 & 9 \end{bmatrix}\begin{bmatrix} 2 \\ \frac{3}{2} \\ \frac{5}{2} \\ 4 \end{bmatrix} = \begin{bmatrix} 10 \\ \frac{37}{2} \\ \frac{95}{2} \end{bmatrix}$

$\begin{bmatrix} 4 & 6 & 14 & 10 \\ 6 & 14 & 36 & \frac{37}{2} \\ 14 & 36 & 98 & \frac{95}{2} \end{bmatrix} \Rightarrow \begin{bmatrix} 1 & 0 & 0 & \frac{39}{20} \\ 0 & 1 & 0 & -\frac{4}{5} \\ 0 & 0 & 1 & \frac{1}{2} \end{bmatrix} \Rightarrow \mathbf{x} = \begin{bmatrix} \frac{39}{20} \\ -\frac{4}{5} \\ \frac{1}{2} \end{bmatrix}$

Quadratic Polynomial: $y = \frac{39}{20} - \frac{4}{5}x + \frac{1}{2}x^2$

36. $A^TA = \begin{bmatrix} 1 & 1 & 1 & 1 & 1 \\ -2 & -1 & 0 & 1 & 2 \\ 4 & 1 & 0 & 1 & 4 \end{bmatrix}\begin{bmatrix} 1 & -2 & 4 \\ 1 & -1 & 1 \\ 1 & 0 & 0 \\ 1 & 1 & 1 \\ 1 & 2 & 4 \end{bmatrix} = \begin{bmatrix} 5 & 0 & 10 \\ 0 & 10 & 0 \\ 10 & 0 & 34 \end{bmatrix}$

$A^T\mathbf{b} = \begin{bmatrix} 1 & 1 & 1 & 1 & 1 \\ -2 & -1 & 0 & 1 & 2 \\ 4 & 1 & 0 & 1 & 4 \end{bmatrix}\begin{bmatrix} 6 \\ 5 \\ \frac{7}{2} \\ 2 \\ -1 \end{bmatrix} = \begin{bmatrix} \frac{31}{2} \\ -17 \\ 27 \end{bmatrix}$

$\begin{bmatrix} 5 & 0 & 10 & \frac{31}{2} \\ 0 & 10 & 0 & -17 \\ 10 & 0 & 34 & 27 \end{bmatrix} \Rightarrow \begin{bmatrix} 1 & 0 & 0 & \frac{257}{70} \\ 0 & 1 & 0 & -\frac{17}{10} \\ 0 & 0 & 1 & -\frac{2}{7} \end{bmatrix} \Rightarrow \mathbf{x} = \begin{bmatrix} \frac{257}{70} \\ -\frac{17}{10} \\ -\frac{2}{7} \end{bmatrix}$

Quadratic Polynomial: $y = \frac{257}{70} - \frac{17}{10}x - \frac{2}{7}x^2$

38. Substitute the data points
$(5, 21.2), (6, 24.1), (7, 27.2), (8, 29.3), (9, 32.0),$ and
$(10, 32.5)$ into the quadratic polynomial

$y = c_0 + c_1t + c_2t^2$. You then obtain the system of linear equations

$c_0 + 5c_1 + 25c_2 = 21.2$

$c_0 + 6c_1 + 36c_2 = 24.1$

$c_0 + 7c_1 + 49c_2 = 27.2$

$c_0 + 8c_1 + 64c_2 = 29.3$

$c_0 + 9c_1 + 81c_2 = 32.0$

$c_0 + 10c_1 + 100c_2 = 32.5.$

This produces the least squares problem

$$A\mathbf{t} = \mathbf{b}$$

$\begin{bmatrix} 1 & 5 & 25 \\ 1 & 6 & 36 \\ 1 & 7 & 49 \\ 1 & 8 & 64 \\ 1 & 9 & 81 \\ 1 & 10 & 100 \end{bmatrix}\begin{bmatrix} c_0 \\ c_1 \\ c_2 \end{bmatrix} = \begin{bmatrix} 21.2 \\ 24.1 \\ 27.2 \\ 29.3 \\ 32.0 \\ 32.5 \end{bmatrix}.$

The normal equations are

$$A^TA\mathbf{t} = A^T\mathbf{b}$$

$\begin{bmatrix} 6 & 45 & 355 \\ 45 & 355 & 2925 \\ 355 & 2925 & 24{,}979 \end{bmatrix}\begin{bmatrix} c_0 \\ c_1 \\ c_2 \end{bmatrix} = \begin{bmatrix} 166.3 \\ 1288.4 \\ 10{,}447.6 \end{bmatrix}$

and the solution is $\mathbf{t} = \begin{bmatrix} c_0 \\ c_1 \\ c_2 \end{bmatrix} = \begin{bmatrix} -2.9 \\ 5.99 \\ -0.243 \end{bmatrix}.$

The least squares quadratic is

$y = -2.9 + 5.99t - 0.243t^2$. Substitute the same data points into the cubic polynomial

$y = c_0 + c_1t + c_2t^2 + c_3t^3$. You then obtain the system of linear equations

$c_0 + 5c_1 + 25c_2 + 125c_3 = 21.2$

$c_0 + 6c_1 + 36c_2 + 216c_3 = 24.1$

$c_0 + 7c_1 + 49c_2 + 343c_3 = 27.2$

$c_0 + 8c_1 + 64c_2 + 512c_3 = 29.3$

$c_0 + 9c_1 + 81c_2 + 729c_3 = 32.0$

$c_0 + 10c_1 + 100c_2 + 1000c_3 = 32.5.$

This produces the least squares problem

$$A\mathbf{t} = \mathbf{b}$$

$\begin{bmatrix} 1 & 5 & 25 & 125 \\ 1 & 6 & 36 & 216 \\ 1 & 7 & 49 & 343 \\ 1 & 8 & 64 & 512 \\ 1 & 9 & 81 & 729 \\ 1 & 10 & 100 & 1000 \end{bmatrix}\begin{bmatrix} c_0 \\ c_1 \\ c_2 \\ c_3 \end{bmatrix} = \begin{bmatrix} 21.2 \\ 24.1 \\ 27.2 \\ 29.3 \\ 32.0 \\ 32.5 \end{bmatrix}.$

The normal equations are

$$A^T A t = A^T b$$

$$\begin{bmatrix} 6 & 45 & 355 & 2925 \\ 45 & 355 & 2925 & 24{,}979 \\ 355 & 2925 & 24{,}979 & 219{,}525 \\ 2925 & 24{,}979 & 219{,}525 & 1{,}973{,}515 \end{bmatrix} \begin{bmatrix} c_0 \\ c_1 \\ c_2 \\ c_3 \end{bmatrix} = \begin{bmatrix} 166.3 \\ 1288.4 \\ 10{,}447.6 \\ 88{,}014.8 \end{bmatrix}$$

and the solution is $t = \begin{bmatrix} c_0 \\ c_1 \\ c_2 \\ c_3 \end{bmatrix} = \begin{bmatrix} 22.7 \\ -4.92 \\ 1.257 \\ -0.0667 \end{bmatrix}$.

The least squares regression cubic is

$$y = 22.7 - 4.92t + 1.257t^2 - 0.0667t^3.$$

2015 (quadratic):

$$y = -2.9 + 5.99(15) - 0.243(15)^2 \approx \$32.3 \text{ billion}$$

2015 (cubic):

$$y = 22.7 - 4.92(15) + 1.257(15)^2 - 0.0667(15)^3$$

$$\approx \$6.6 \text{ billion}$$

Because the original data increased from 2005 to 2010, with the revenue leveling off in 2010, you can expect the revenue to increase or stay about the same for future years. Because the quadratic polynomial predicts the revenue to be about $32.3 billion in 2015, this model is more accurate for predicting future revenues.

40. The vector Ax that minimizes $\|Ax - b\|$ for a given vector b is $Ax = proj_S b$, where $S = R(A)$. Since $Ax - b = proj_S b - b$, $(Ax - b) \in S^\perp$. Then $(Ax - b) \in N(A^T)$, because $S^\perp = R(A)^\perp N(A^T)$. So

$$A^T(Ax - b) = 0$$
$$A^T Ax - A^T b = 0$$
$$A^T Ax = A^T b.$$

These equations are used to find b and solve the least squares problem.

42. (a) False. They are orthogonal subspaces of R^m not R^n.

(b) True. See the "Definition of Orthogonal Complement" on page 260.

(c) True. See page 259 for the definition of the "Least Squares Problem."

44. Let S be a subspace of R^n and $S^\perp$ its orthogonal complement. $S^\perp$ contains the zero vector. If $v_1, v_2 \in S^\perp$, then for all $w \in S$,

$$(v_1 + v_2) \cdot w = v_1 \cdot w + v_2 \cdot w = 0 + 0 = 0 \Rightarrow v_1 + v_2 \in S^\perp$$

and for any scalar c,

$$(cv_1) \cdot w = c(v_1 \cdot w) = c0 = 0 \Rightarrow cv_1 \in S^\perp.$$

46. Let $x \in S_1 \cap S_2$, where $R^n = S_1 \oplus S_2$. Then $x = v_1 + v_2$, $v_1 \in S_1$ and $v_2 \in S_2$. But, $x \in S_1 \Rightarrow x = x + 0, x \in S_1, 0 \in S_2$, and $x \in S_2 \Rightarrow x = 0 + x, 0 \in S_1, x \in S_2$. So, $x = 0$ by the uniqueness of direct sum representation.

Section 5.5 Applications of Inner Product Spaces

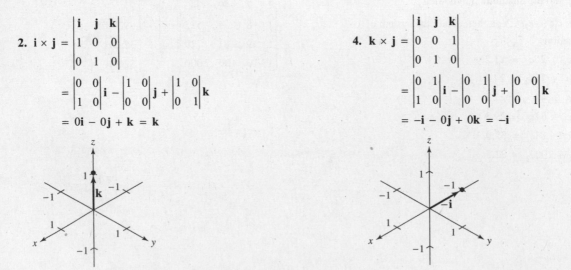

2. $i \times j = \begin{vmatrix} i & j & k \\ 1 & 0 & 0 \\ 0 & 1 & 0 \end{vmatrix}$

$$= \begin{vmatrix} 0 & 0 \\ 1 & 0 \end{vmatrix} i - \begin{vmatrix} 1 & 0 \\ 0 & 0 \end{vmatrix} j + \begin{vmatrix} 1 & 0 \\ 0 & 1 \end{vmatrix} k$$

$$= 0i - 0j + k = k$$

4. $k \times j = \begin{vmatrix} i & j & k \\ 0 & 0 & 1 \\ 0 & 1 & 0 \end{vmatrix}$

$$= \begin{vmatrix} 0 & 1 \\ 1 & 0 \end{vmatrix} i - \begin{vmatrix} 0 & 1 \\ 0 & 0 \end{vmatrix} j + \begin{vmatrix} 0 & 0 \\ 0 & 1 \end{vmatrix} k$$

$$= -i - 0j + 0k = -i$$

6. $\mathbf{k} \times \mathbf{i} = \begin{vmatrix} \mathbf{i} & \mathbf{j} & \mathbf{k} \\ 0 & 0 & 1 \\ 1 & 0 & 0 \end{vmatrix}$

$= \begin{vmatrix} 0 & 1 \\ 0 & 0 \end{vmatrix} \mathbf{i} - \begin{vmatrix} 0 & 1 \\ 1 & 0 \end{vmatrix} \mathbf{j} + \begin{vmatrix} 0 & 0 \\ 1 & 0 \end{vmatrix} \mathbf{k}$

$= 0\mathbf{i} + \mathbf{j} + 0\mathbf{k} = \mathbf{j}$

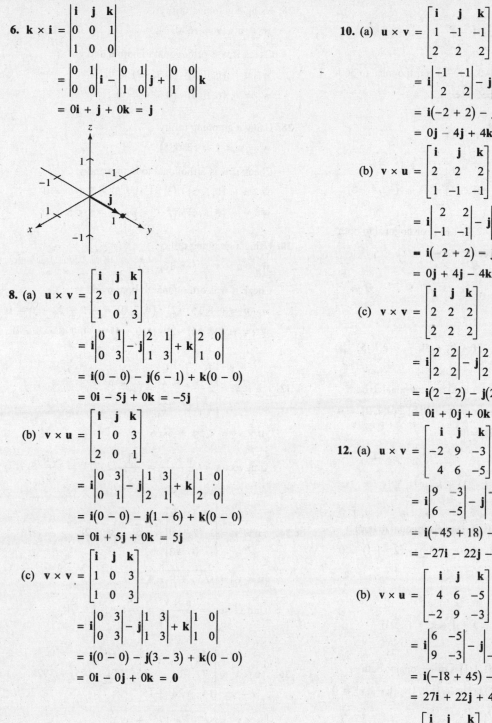

8. (a) $\mathbf{u} \times \mathbf{v} = \begin{bmatrix} \mathbf{i} & \mathbf{j} & \mathbf{k} \\ 2 & 0 & 1 \\ 1 & 0 & 3 \end{bmatrix}$

$= \mathbf{i} \begin{vmatrix} 0 & 1 \\ 0 & 3 \end{vmatrix} - \mathbf{j} \begin{vmatrix} 2 & 1 \\ 1 & 3 \end{vmatrix} + \mathbf{k} \begin{vmatrix} 2 & 0 \\ 1 & 0 \end{vmatrix}$

$= \mathbf{i}(0 - 0) - \mathbf{j}(6 - 1) + \mathbf{k}(0 - 0)$

$= 0\mathbf{i} - 5\mathbf{j} + 0\mathbf{k} = -5\mathbf{j}$

(b) $\mathbf{v} \times \mathbf{u} = \begin{bmatrix} \mathbf{i} & \mathbf{j} & \mathbf{k} \\ 1 & 0 & 3 \\ 2 & 0 & 1 \end{bmatrix}$

$= \mathbf{i} \begin{vmatrix} 0 & 3 \\ 0 & 1 \end{vmatrix} - \mathbf{j} \begin{vmatrix} 1 & 3 \\ 2 & 1 \end{vmatrix} + \mathbf{k} \begin{vmatrix} 1 & 0 \\ 2 & 0 \end{vmatrix}$

$= \mathbf{i}(0 - 0) - \mathbf{j}(1 - 6) + \mathbf{k}(0 - 0)$

$= 0\mathbf{i} + 5\mathbf{j} + 0\mathbf{k} = 5\mathbf{j}$

(c) $\mathbf{v} \times \mathbf{v} = \begin{bmatrix} \mathbf{i} & \mathbf{j} & \mathbf{k} \\ 1 & 0 & 3 \\ 1 & 0 & 3 \end{bmatrix}$

$= \mathbf{i} \begin{vmatrix} 0 & 3 \\ 0 & 3 \end{vmatrix} - \mathbf{j} \begin{vmatrix} 1 & 3 \\ 1 & 3 \end{vmatrix} + \mathbf{k} \begin{vmatrix} 1 & 0 \\ 1 & 0 \end{vmatrix}$

$= \mathbf{i}(0 - 0) - \mathbf{j}(3 - 3) + \mathbf{k}(0 - 0)$

$= 0\mathbf{i} - 0\mathbf{j} + 0\mathbf{k} = \mathbf{0}$

10. (a) $\mathbf{u} \times \mathbf{v} = \begin{bmatrix} \mathbf{i} & \mathbf{j} & \mathbf{k} \\ 1 & -1 & -1 \\ 2 & 2 & 2 \end{bmatrix}$

$= \mathbf{i} \begin{vmatrix} -1 & -1 \\ 2 & 2 \end{vmatrix} - \mathbf{j} \begin{vmatrix} 1 & -1 \\ 2 & 2 \end{vmatrix} + \mathbf{k} \begin{vmatrix} 1 & -1 \\ 2 & 2 \end{vmatrix}$

$= \mathbf{i}(-2 + 2) - \mathbf{j}(2 + 2) + \mathbf{k}(2 + 2)$

$= 0\mathbf{j} - 4\mathbf{j} + 4\mathbf{k} = -4\mathbf{j} + 4\mathbf{k}$

(b) $\mathbf{v} \times \mathbf{u} = \begin{bmatrix} \mathbf{i} & \mathbf{j} & \mathbf{k} \\ 2 & 2 & 2 \\ 1 & -1 & -1 \end{bmatrix}$

$= \mathbf{i} \begin{vmatrix} 2 & 2 \\ -1 & -1 \end{vmatrix} - \mathbf{j} \begin{vmatrix} 2 & 2 \\ 1 & -1 \end{vmatrix} + \mathbf{k} \begin{vmatrix} 2 & 2 \\ 1 & -1 \end{vmatrix}$

$= \mathbf{i}(-2 + 2) - \mathbf{j}(-2 - 2) + \mathbf{k}(-2 - 2)$

$= 0\mathbf{j} + 4\mathbf{j} - 4\mathbf{k} = 4\mathbf{j} - 4\mathbf{k}$

(c) $\mathbf{v} \times \mathbf{v} = \begin{bmatrix} \mathbf{i} & \mathbf{j} & \mathbf{k} \\ 2 & 2 & 2 \\ 2 & 2 & 2 \end{bmatrix}$

$= \mathbf{i} \begin{vmatrix} 2 & 2 \\ 2 & 2 \end{vmatrix} - \mathbf{j} \begin{vmatrix} 2 & 2 \\ 2 & 2 \end{vmatrix} + \mathbf{k} \begin{vmatrix} 2 & 2 \\ 2 & 2 \end{vmatrix}$

$= \mathbf{i}(2 - 2) - \mathbf{j}(2 - 2) + \mathbf{k}(2 - 2)$

$= 0\mathbf{i} + 0\mathbf{j} + 0\mathbf{k} = \mathbf{0}$

12. (a) $\mathbf{u} \times \mathbf{v} = \begin{bmatrix} \mathbf{i} & \mathbf{j} & \mathbf{k} \\ -2 & 9 & -3 \\ 4 & 6 & -5 \end{bmatrix}$

$= \mathbf{i} \begin{vmatrix} 9 & -3 \\ 6 & -5 \end{vmatrix} - \mathbf{j} \begin{vmatrix} -2 & -3 \\ 4 & -5 \end{vmatrix} + \mathbf{k} \begin{vmatrix} -2 & 9 \\ 4 & 6 \end{vmatrix}$

$= \mathbf{i}(-45 + 18) - \mathbf{j}(10 + 12) + \mathbf{k}(-12 - 36)$

$= -27\mathbf{i} - 22\mathbf{j} - 48\mathbf{k}$

(b) $\mathbf{v} \times \mathbf{u} = \begin{bmatrix} \mathbf{i} & \mathbf{j} & \mathbf{k} \\ 4 & 6 & -5 \\ -2 & 9 & -3 \end{bmatrix}$

$= \mathbf{i} \begin{vmatrix} 6 & -5 \\ 9 & -3 \end{vmatrix} - \mathbf{j} \begin{vmatrix} 4 & -5 \\ -2 & -3 \end{vmatrix} + \mathbf{k} \begin{vmatrix} 4 & 6 \\ -2 & 9 \end{vmatrix}$

$= \mathbf{i}(-18 + 45) - \mathbf{j}(-12 - 10) + \mathbf{k}(36 + 12)$

$= 27\mathbf{i} + 22\mathbf{j} + 48\mathbf{k}$

(c) $\mathbf{v} \times \mathbf{v} = \begin{bmatrix} \mathbf{i} & \mathbf{j} & \mathbf{k} \\ 4 & 6 & -5 \\ 4 & 6 & -5 \end{bmatrix}$

$= \mathbf{i} \begin{vmatrix} 6 & -5 \\ 6 & -5 \end{vmatrix} - \mathbf{j} \begin{vmatrix} 4 & -5 \\ 4 & -5 \end{vmatrix} + \mathbf{k} \begin{vmatrix} 4 & 6 \\ 4 & 6 \end{vmatrix}$

$= \mathbf{i}(-30 + 30) - \mathbf{j}(-20 + 20) + \mathbf{k}(24 - 24)$

$= 0\mathbf{i} + 0\mathbf{j} + 0\mathbf{k} = \mathbf{0}$

14. $\mathbf{u} \times \mathbf{v} = \begin{vmatrix} \mathbf{i} & \mathbf{j} & \mathbf{k} \\ -1 & 1 & 2 \\ 0 & 1 & -1 \end{vmatrix} = -3\mathbf{i} - \mathbf{j} - \mathbf{k} = (-3, -1, -1)$

Furthermore, $\mathbf{u} \times \mathbf{v} = (-3, -1, -1)$ is orthogonal to both

$(-1, 1, 2)$ and $(0, 1, -1)$ because

$(-3, -1, -1) \cdot (-1, 1, 2) = 0$ and

$(-3, -1, -1) \cdot (0, 1, -1) = 0.$

16. $\mathbf{u} \times \mathbf{v} = \begin{vmatrix} \mathbf{i} & \mathbf{j} & \mathbf{k} \\ -2 & 1 & 1 \\ 4 & 2 & 0 \end{vmatrix} = -2\mathbf{i} + 4\mathbf{j} - 8\mathbf{k} = (-2, 4, -8)$

Furthermore, $\mathbf{u} \times \mathbf{v} = (-2, 4, -8)$ is orthogonal to both

$(-2, 1, 1)$ and $(4, 2, 0)$ because

$(-2, 4, -8) \cdot (-2, 1, 1) = 0$ and

$(-2, 4, -8) \cdot (4, 2, 0) = 0.$

18. $\mathbf{u} \times \mathbf{v} = \begin{vmatrix} \mathbf{i} & \mathbf{j} & \mathbf{k} \\ 4 & 1 & 0 \\ 3 & 2 & -2 \end{vmatrix} = -2\mathbf{i} + 8\mathbf{j} + 5\mathbf{k} = (-2, 8, 5)$

Furthermore, $\mathbf{u} \times \mathbf{v} = (-2, 8, 5)$ is orthogonal to both

$(4, 1, 0)$ and $(3, 2, -2)$ because $(-2, 8, 5) \cdot (4, 1, 0) = 0$

and $(-2, 8, 5) \cdot (3, 2, -2) = 0.$

20. $\mathbf{u} \times \mathbf{v} = \begin{vmatrix} \mathbf{i} & \mathbf{j} & \mathbf{k} \\ 2 & -1 & 1 \\ 3 & -1 & 0 \end{vmatrix} = \mathbf{i} + 3\mathbf{j} + \mathbf{k} = (1, 3, 1)$

Furthermore, $\mathbf{u} \times \mathbf{v} = (1, 3, 1)$ is orthogonal to both

$(2, -1, 1)$ and $(3, -1, 0)$ because $(1, 3, 1) \cdot (2, -1, 1) = 0$

and $(1, 3, 1) \cdot (3, -1, 0) = 0.$

22. $\mathbf{u} \times \mathbf{v} = \begin{vmatrix} \mathbf{i} & \mathbf{j} & \mathbf{k} \\ 1 & -2 & 1 \\ -1 & 3 & -2 \end{vmatrix} = \mathbf{i} + \mathbf{j} + \mathbf{k} = (1, 1, 1)$

Furthermore, $\mathbf{u} \times \mathbf{v} = (1, 1, 1)$ is orthogonal to both

$(1, -2, 1)$ and $(-1, 3, -2)$ because $(1, 1, 1) \cdot (1, -2, 1) = 0$

and $(1, 1, 1) \cdot (-1, 3, -2) = 0.$

24. Using a graphing utility:

$\mathbf{w} = \mathbf{u} \times \mathbf{v} = (7, 1, 3)$

Check if $\mathbf{w}$ is orthogonal to both $\mathbf{u}$ and $\mathbf{v}$:

$\mathbf{w} \cdot \mathbf{u} = (7, 1, 3) \cdot (1, 2, -3) = 7 + 2 - 9 = 0$

$\mathbf{w} \cdot \mathbf{v} = (7, 1, 3) \cdot (-1, 1, 2) = -7 + 1 + 6 = 0$

26. Using a graphing utility:

$\mathbf{w} = \mathbf{u} \times \mathbf{v} = (6, 0, 0)$

Check if $\mathbf{w}$ is orthogonal to both $\mathbf{u}$ and $\mathbf{v}$:

$\mathbf{w} \cdot \mathbf{u} = (6, 0, 0) \cdot (0, 1, -2) = 0$

$\mathbf{w} \cdot \mathbf{v} = (6, 0, 0) \cdot (0, 1, 4) = 0$

28. Using a graphing utility:

$\mathbf{w} = \mathbf{u} \times \mathbf{v} = (0, 5, 5)$

Check if $\mathbf{w}$ is orthogonal to both $\mathbf{u}$ and $\mathbf{v}$:

$\mathbf{w} \cdot \mathbf{u} = (0, 5, 5) \cdot (3, -1, 1) = 0 - 5 + 5 = 0$

$\mathbf{w} \cdot \mathbf{v} = (0, 5, 5) \cdot (2, 1, -1) = 0 + 5 - 5 = 0$

30. Using a graphing utility:

$\mathbf{w} = \mathbf{u} \times \mathbf{v} = (-8, 16, -2)$

Check if $\mathbf{w}$ is orthogonal to both $\mathbf{u}$ and $\mathbf{v}$:

$\mathbf{w} \cdot \mathbf{u} = (-8, 16, -2) \cdot (4, 2, 0) = -32 + 32 + 0 = 0$

$\mathbf{w} \cdot \mathbf{v} = (-8, 16, -2) \cdot (1, 0, -4) = -8 + 0 + 8 = 0$

32. $\mathbf{u} \times \mathbf{v} = \begin{vmatrix} \mathbf{i} & \mathbf{j} & \mathbf{k} \\ 2 & -1 & 3 \\ 1 & 0 & -2 \end{vmatrix} = \langle 2, 7, 1 \rangle$

$\|\mathbf{u} \times \mathbf{v}\| = \sqrt{54} = 3\sqrt{6}$

Unit vector $= \dfrac{\mathbf{u} \times \mathbf{v}}{\|\mathbf{u} \times \mathbf{v}\|} = \dfrac{1}{3\sqrt{6}} \langle 2, 7, 1 \rangle = \dfrac{\sqrt{6}}{18} \langle 2, 7, 1 \rangle$

34. $\mathbf{u} \times \mathbf{v} = \begin{vmatrix} \mathbf{i} & \mathbf{j} & \mathbf{k} \\ 1 & 2 & 0 \\ 1 & 0 & -3 \end{vmatrix} = -6\mathbf{i} + 3\mathbf{j} - 2\mathbf{k}$

$\|\mathbf{u} \times \mathbf{v}\| = \sqrt{36 + 9 + 4} = 7$

Unit vector $= \dfrac{\mathbf{u} \times \mathbf{v}}{\|\mathbf{u} \times \mathbf{v}\|} = -\dfrac{6}{7}\mathbf{i} + \dfrac{3}{7}\mathbf{j} - \dfrac{2}{7}\mathbf{k}$

36. $\mathbf{u} \times \mathbf{v} = \begin{vmatrix} \mathbf{i} & \mathbf{j} & \mathbf{k} \\ 7 & -14 & 5 \\ 14 & 28 & -15 \end{vmatrix} = 70\mathbf{i} + 175\mathbf{j} + 392\mathbf{k}$

$\|\mathbf{u} \times \mathbf{v}\| = \sqrt{70^2 + 175^2 + 392^2}$

$= \sqrt{189,189} = 21\sqrt{429}$

Unit vector $= \dfrac{\mathbf{u} \times \mathbf{v}}{\|\mathbf{u} \times \mathbf{v}\|} = \dfrac{1}{21\sqrt{249}} \langle 70, 175, 392 \rangle$

$= \dfrac{1}{3\sqrt{429}} \langle 10, 25, 56 \rangle$

$= \dfrac{\sqrt{429}}{1287} \langle 10, 25, 56 \rangle$

38. $\mathbf{u} \times \mathbf{v} = \begin{vmatrix} \mathbf{i} & \mathbf{j} & \mathbf{k} \\ 1 & -2 & 2 \\ 2 & -1 & -2 \end{vmatrix} = 6\mathbf{i} + 6\mathbf{j} + 3\mathbf{k}$

$\|\mathbf{u} \times \mathbf{v}\| = \sqrt{36 + 36 + 9} = 9$

Unit vector $= \dfrac{\mathbf{u} \times \mathbf{v}}{\|\mathbf{u} \times \mathbf{v}\|} = \dfrac{1}{9}(6\mathbf{i} + 6\mathbf{j} + 3\mathbf{k})$

$\qquad\qquad = \dfrac{2}{3}\mathbf{i} + \dfrac{2}{3}\mathbf{j} + \dfrac{1}{3}\mathbf{k}$

40. Because

$\mathbf{u} \times \mathbf{v} = \begin{vmatrix} \mathbf{i} & \mathbf{j} & \mathbf{k} \\ 1 & 1 & 1 \\ 0 & 1 & 1 \end{vmatrix} = -\mathbf{j} + \mathbf{k} = (0, -1, 1),$

the area of the parallelogram is

$\|\mathbf{u} \times \mathbf{v}\| = \|(0, -1, 1)\| = \sqrt{2}.$

42. Because

$\mathbf{u} \times \mathbf{v} = \begin{vmatrix} \mathbf{i} & \mathbf{j} & \mathbf{k} \\ 2 & -1 & 0 \\ -1 & 2 & 0 \end{vmatrix} = 3\mathbf{k} = (0, 0, 3),$

the area of the parallelogram is

$\|(0, 0, 3)\| = 3.$

44. $(5, 1, 4) - (2, -1, 1) = (3, 2, 3)$

$(3, 3, 4) - (0, 1, 1) = (3, 2, 3)$

$(3, 3, 4) - (5, 1, 4) = (-2, 2, 0)$

$(0, 1, 1) - (2, -1, 1) = (-2, 2, 0)$

$\mathbf{u} = (3, 2, 3)$ and $\mathbf{v} = (-2, 2, 0)$

Because

$\mathbf{u} \times \mathbf{v} = \begin{vmatrix} \mathbf{i} & \mathbf{j} & \mathbf{k} \\ 3 & 2 & 3 \\ -2 & 2 & 0 \end{vmatrix} = -6\mathbf{i} - 6\mathbf{j} + 10\mathbf{k},$

the area of the parallelogram is

$\|\mathbf{u} \times \mathbf{v}\| = \sqrt{(-6)^2 + (-6)^2 + 10^2} = \sqrt{172} = 2\sqrt{43}.$

46. Because

$\mathbf{v} \times \mathbf{w} = \begin{vmatrix} \mathbf{i} & \mathbf{j} & \mathbf{k} \\ 0 & -1 & 0 \\ 0 & 0 & 1 \end{vmatrix} = -\mathbf{i} = (-1, 0, 0),$

the triple scalar product of $\mathbf{u}$, $\mathbf{v}$, and $\mathbf{w}$ is

$\mathbf{u} \cdot (\mathbf{v} \times \mathbf{w}) = (-1, 0, 0) \cdot (-1, 0, 0) = 1.$

48. Because

$\mathbf{v} \times \mathbf{w} = \begin{vmatrix} \mathbf{i} & \mathbf{j} & \mathbf{k} \\ 0 & 3 & 0 \\ 0 & 0 & 1 \end{vmatrix} = 3\mathbf{i} = (3, 0, 0),$

the triple scalar product is

$\mathbf{u} \cdot (\mathbf{v} \times \mathbf{w}) = (2, 0, 1) \cdot (3, 0, 0) = 6.$

50. (a) Because

$\mathbf{v} \times \mathbf{w} = \begin{vmatrix} \mathbf{i} & \mathbf{j} & \mathbf{k} \\ 0 & 1 & 1 \\ 1 & 0 & 2 \end{vmatrix} = (2, 1, -1),$

The volume is given by

$|\mathbf{u} \cdot (\mathbf{v} \times \mathbf{w})| = |(1, 1, 0) \cdot (2, 1, \ -1)|$

$\qquad\qquad = 1(2) + 1(1) + 0(-1) = 3.$

(b) Because

$\mathbf{v} \times \mathbf{w} = \begin{vmatrix} \mathbf{i} & \mathbf{j} & \mathbf{k} \\ 0 & 1 & 1 \\ 1 & 0 & 1 \end{vmatrix} = \mathbf{i} + \mathbf{j} - \mathbf{k} = (1, 1, -1),$

The volume is given by

$|\mathbf{u} \cdot (\mathbf{v} \times \mathbf{w})| = |(1, 1, 0) \cdot (1, 1, \ -1)| = 2.$

(c) $\mathbf{u} \cdot (\mathbf{v} \times \mathbf{w}) = \begin{vmatrix} 0 & 2 & 2 \\ 0 & 0 & -2 \\ 3 & 0 & 2 \end{vmatrix} = 0 - 2(6) + 2(0) = -12$

Volume $= |\mathbf{u} \cdot (\mathbf{v} \times \mathbf{w})| = 12$ cubic units

(d) $\mathbf{u} \cdot (\mathbf{v} \times \mathbf{w}) = \begin{vmatrix} 1 & 2 & -1 \\ -1 & 2 & 2 \\ 2 & 0 & 1 \end{vmatrix}$

$\qquad\qquad = 1(2) - 2(-1 - 4) - 1(0 - 4) = 16$

Volume $= |\mathbf{u} \cdot (\mathbf{v} \times \mathbf{w})| = 16$ cubic units

52. $(0, 1, 2) - (2, -3, 4) = (-2, 4, -2)$

$(0, 1, 2) - (-1, 2, 0) = (1, -1, 2)$

Because

$\mathbf{u} \times \mathbf{v} = \begin{vmatrix} \mathbf{i} & \mathbf{j} & \mathbf{k} \\ -2 & 4 & -2 \\ 1 & -1 & 2 \end{vmatrix} = 6\mathbf{i} + 2\mathbf{j} - 2\mathbf{k} = (6, 2, -2),$

the area of the triangle is

$A = \dfrac{1}{2}\|\mathbf{u} \times \mathbf{v}\| = \dfrac{1}{2}\sqrt{6^2 + 2^2 + (-2)^2} = \dfrac{1}{2}\sqrt{44} = \sqrt{11}.$

54. $c\mathbf{u} \times \mathbf{v} = \begin{vmatrix} \mathbf{i} & \mathbf{j} & \mathbf{k} \\ cu_1 & cu_2 & cu_3 \\ v_1 & v_2 & v_3 \end{vmatrix} = c\begin{vmatrix} \mathbf{i} & \mathbf{j} & \mathbf{k} \\ u_1 & u_2 & u_3 \\ v_1 & v_2 & v_3 \end{vmatrix} = c(\mathbf{u} \times \mathbf{v}) = \begin{vmatrix} \mathbf{i} & \mathbf{j} & \mathbf{k} \\ u_1 & u_2 & u_3 \\ cv_1 & cv_2 & cv_3 \end{vmatrix} = \mathbf{u} \times (c\mathbf{v})$

56. $\mathbf{u} \times \mathbf{u} = \begin{vmatrix} \mathbf{i} & \mathbf{j} & \mathbf{k} \\ u_1 & u_2 & u_3 \\ u_1 & u_2 & u_3 \end{vmatrix} = 0$, because two rows are the same.

58. Because $\mathbf{u} \times \mathbf{v} = (u_2v_3 - v_2u_3)\mathbf{i} - (u_1v_3 - u_3v_1)\mathbf{j} + (u_1v_2 - v_1u_2)\mathbf{k}$

you see that

$$\mathbf{u} \cdot (\mathbf{u} \times \mathbf{v}) = (u_1, u_2, u_3) \cdot (u_2v_3 - v_2u_3, -u_1v_3 + u_3v_1, u_1v_2 - v_1u_2)$$

$$= (u_1u_2v_3 - u_1v_2u_3 - u_2u_1v_3 + u_2u_3v_1 + u_3u_1v_2 - u_3v_1u_2) = 0,$$

which shows that $\mathbf{u}$ is orthogonal to $\mathbf{u} \times \mathbf{v}$. A similar computation shows that $\mathbf{v} \cdot (\mathbf{u} \times \mathbf{v}) = 0$. [Note that

$\mathbf{v} \cdot (\mathbf{u} \times \mathbf{v}) = -\mathbf{v} \cdot (\mathbf{v} \times \mathbf{u}) = 0$ by the above with the roles of $\mathbf{u}$ and $\mathbf{v}$ reversed.]

60. You have the following equivalences.

$\mathbf{u} \times \mathbf{v} = \mathbf{0} \Leftrightarrow \|\mathbf{u} \times \mathbf{v}\| = 0 \Leftrightarrow \|\mathbf{u}\|\|\mathbf{v}\|\sin\theta = 0 \,(\text{Theorem } 5.18\,(2)) \Leftrightarrow \sin\theta = 0 \Leftrightarrow \theta = 0 \Leftrightarrow \mathbf{u} \text{ and } \mathbf{v} \text{ are parallel.}$

62. (a) $\mathbf{u} \times (\mathbf{v} \times \mathbf{w}) = \mathbf{u} \times \begin{vmatrix} \mathbf{i} & \mathbf{j} & \mathbf{k} \\ v_1 & v_2 & v_3 \\ w_1 & w_2 & w_3 \end{vmatrix}$

$$= \mathbf{u} \times \left[(v_2w_3 - w_2v_3)\mathbf{i} - (v_1w_3 - w_1v_3)\mathbf{j} + (v_1w_2 - v_2w_1)\mathbf{k} \right]$$

$$= \begin{vmatrix} \mathbf{i} & \mathbf{j} & \mathbf{k} \\ u_1 & u_2 & u_3 \\ (v_2w_3 - w_2v_3) & (w_1v_3 - v_1w_3) & (v_1w_2 - v_2w_1) \end{vmatrix}$$

$$= \left[(u_2(v_1w_2 - v_2w_1)) - u_3(w_1v_3 - v_1w_3) \right]\mathbf{i} - \left[u_1(v_1w_2 - v_2w_1) - u_3(v_2w_3 - w_2v_3) \right]\mathbf{j}$$

$$+ \left[u_1(w_1v_3 - v_1w_3) - u_2(v_2w_3 - w_2v_3) \right]\mathbf{k}$$

$$= (u_2w_2v_1 + u_3w_3v_1 - u_2v_2w_1 - u_3v_3w_1, u_1w_1v_2 + u_3w_3v_2 - u_1v_1w_2 - u_3v_3w_2,$$

$$u_1w_1v_3 + u_2w_2v_3 - u_1v_1w_3 - u_2v_2w_3)$$

$$= (u_1w_1 + u_2w_2 + u_3w_3)(v_1, v_2, v_3) - (u_1v_1 + u_2v_2 + u_3v_3)(w_1, w_2, w_3)$$

$$= (\mathbf{u} \cdot \mathbf{w})\mathbf{v} - (\mathbf{u} \cdot \mathbf{v})\mathbf{w}$$

(b) Let

$\mathbf{u} = (1, 0, 0), \mathbf{v} = (0, 1, 0)$ and $\mathbf{w} = (1, 1, 1)$.

Then

$\mathbf{v} \times \mathbf{w} = (1, 0, -1)$ and $\mathbf{u} \times \mathbf{v} = (0, 0, 1)$.

So

$\mathbf{u} \times (\mathbf{v} \times \mathbf{w}) = (1, 0, 0) \times (1, 0, -1) = (0, 1, 0),$

while

$(\mathbf{u} \times \mathbf{v}) \times \mathbf{w} = (0, 0, 1) \times (1, 1, 1) = (-1, 1, 0),$

which are not equal.

64. (a) The standard basis for P_1 is $\{1, x\}$. Applying the Gram-Schmidt orthonormalization process produces the orthonormal basis

$$B = \{\mathbf{w}_1, \mathbf{w}_2\} = \left\{\frac{1}{\sqrt{3}}, \frac{1}{3}(2x - 5)\right\}.$$

The least squares approximating function is given by $g(x) = \langle f, \mathbf{w}_1 \rangle \mathbf{w}_1 + \langle f, \mathbf{w}_2 \rangle \mathbf{w}_2$.

Find the inner products

$$\langle f_1, \mathbf{w}_1 \rangle = \int_1^4 \sqrt{x}\,\frac{1}{\sqrt{3}}dx = \frac{2}{3\sqrt{3}}x^{3/2}\bigg]_1^4 = \frac{14}{3\sqrt{3}}$$

$$\langle f, \mathbf{w}_2 \rangle = \int_1^4 \sqrt{x}\left(\frac{1}{3}\right)(2x - 5)dx = \left[\frac{4}{15}x^{5/2} - \frac{10}{9}x^{3/2}\right]_1^4 = \frac{22}{45}$$

and conclude that

$$g(x) = \langle f, \mathbf{w}_1 \rangle \mathbf{w}_1 + \langle f, \mathbf{w}_2 \rangle \mathbf{w}_2 = \frac{14}{3\sqrt{3}}\frac{1}{\sqrt{3}} + \frac{22}{45}\left(\frac{1}{3}\right)(2x - 5) \doteq \frac{44}{135}x + \frac{20}{27} = \frac{4}{135}(25 + 11x).$$

(b)

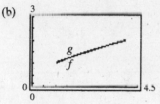

66. (a) The standard basis for P_1 is $\{1, x\}$. Applying the Gram-Schmidt orthonormalization process produces the orthonormal basis

$$B = \{\mathbf{w}_1, \mathbf{w}_2\} = \left\{1, \sqrt{3}(2x - 1)\right\}.$$

The least squares approximating function is then given by $g(x) = \langle f, \mathbf{w}_1 \rangle \mathbf{w}_1 + \langle f, \mathbf{w}_2 \rangle \mathbf{w}_2$.

Find the inner products

$$\langle f, \mathbf{w}_1 \rangle = \int_0^1 e^{-2x}dx = -\tfrac{1}{2}e^{-2x}\bigg]_0^1 = -\tfrac{1}{2}(e^{-2} - 1)$$

$$\langle f, \mathbf{w}_2 \rangle = \int_0^1 e^{-2x}\sqrt{3}(2x - 1)dx = -\sqrt{3} \times e^{-2x}\bigg]_0^1 = -\sqrt{3}e^{-2}$$

and conclude that

$$g(x) = \langle f, \mathbf{w}_1 \rangle \mathbf{w}_1 + \langle f, \mathbf{w}_2 \rangle \mathbf{w}_2 = -\tfrac{1}{2}(e^{-2} - 1) - \sqrt{3}e^{-2}\left(\sqrt{3}(2x - 1)\right) = -6e^{-2}x + \tfrac{1}{2}(5e^{-2} + 1) \approx -0.812x + 0.8383.$$

(b)

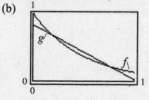

68. (a) The standard basis for P_1, is $\{1, x\}$. Applying the Gram-Schmidt orthonormalization process produces the orthonormal basis

$$B = \{\mathbf{w}_1, \mathbf{w}_2\} = \left\{ \frac{\sqrt{2\pi}}{\pi}, \frac{\sqrt{6\pi}}{\pi^2}(4x - \pi) \right\}.$$

The least squares approximating function is then given by $g(x) = \langle f, \mathbf{w}_1 \rangle \mathbf{w}_1 + \langle f, \mathbf{w}_2 \rangle \mathbf{w}_2$.

Find the inner products

$$\langle f, \mathbf{w}_1 \rangle = \int_0^{\pi/2} (\sin x) \left(\frac{\sqrt{2\pi}}{\pi} \right) dx = -\frac{\sqrt{2\pi}}{\pi} \cos x \Big]_0^{\pi/2} = \frac{\sqrt{2\pi}}{\pi}$$

$$\langle f, \mathbf{w}_2 \rangle = \int_0^{\pi/2} (\sin x) \left[\frac{\sqrt{6\pi}}{\pi^2}(4x - \pi) \right] dx = \frac{\sqrt{6\pi}}{\pi^2}[-4x \cos x + 4 \sin x + \pi \cos x]_0^{\pi/2} = \frac{\sqrt{6\pi}}{\pi^2}(4 - \pi)$$

and conclude that

$$\begin{aligned}
g(x) &= \langle f, \mathbf{w}_1 \rangle \mathbf{w}_1 + \langle f, \mathbf{w}_2 \rangle \mathbf{w}_2 \\
&= \frac{\sqrt{2\pi}}{\pi} \left(\frac{\sqrt{2\pi}}{\pi} \right) + \frac{\sqrt{6\pi}}{\pi^2}(4 - \pi) \left[\frac{\sqrt{6\pi}}{\pi^2}(4x - \pi) \right] \\
&= \frac{2}{\pi} + \frac{6}{\pi^3}(4 - \pi)(4x - \pi) \\
&= \frac{24(4 - \pi)}{\pi^3} x - \frac{8(3 - \pi)}{\pi^2} \approx 0.6644x + 0.1148.
\end{aligned}$$

(b)

70. (a) The standard basis for P_2 is $\{1, x, x^2\}$. Applying the Gram-Schmidt orthonormalization process produces the orthonormal basis

$$B = \{\mathbf{w}_1, \mathbf{w}_2, \mathbf{w}_3\} = \left\{ \frac{1}{\sqrt{3}}, \frac{1}{3}(2x - 5), \frac{2\sqrt{5}}{3\sqrt{3}} \left(x^2 - 5x + \frac{11}{2} \right) \right\}.$$

The least squares approximating function is then given by $g(x) = \langle f, \mathbf{w}_1 \rangle \mathbf{w}_1 + \langle f, \mathbf{w}_2 \rangle \mathbf{w}_2 + \langle f, \mathbf{w}_3 \rangle \mathbf{w}_3$.

Find the inner products

$$\langle f, \mathbf{w}_1 \rangle = \int_1^4 \sqrt{x} \frac{1}{\sqrt{3}} dx = \frac{14}{3\sqrt{3}} \text{ (see Exercise 51)}$$

$$\langle f, \mathbf{w}_2 \rangle = \int_1^4 \sqrt{x} \frac{1}{3}(2x - 5) dx = \frac{22}{45} \text{ (see Exercise 51)}$$

$$\langle f, \mathbf{w}_3 \rangle = \int_1^4 \sqrt{x} \frac{2\sqrt{5}}{3\sqrt{3}} \left(x^2 - 5x + \frac{11}{2} \right) dx = \frac{2\sqrt{5}}{3\sqrt{3}} \int_1^4 \left(x^{5/2} - 5x^{3/2} + \frac{11}{2}x^{1/2} \right) dx = \frac{2\sqrt{5}}{3\sqrt{3}} \left[\frac{2}{7}x^{7/2} - 2x^{5/2} + \frac{11}{3}x^{3/2} \right]_1^4 = \frac{-2\sqrt{5}}{63\sqrt{3}}$$

and conclude that g is given by

$$\begin{aligned}
g(x) &= \frac{14}{3\sqrt{3}} \left(\frac{1}{\sqrt{3}} \right) + \frac{22}{45} \left(\frac{1}{3}(2x - 5) \right) - \frac{2\sqrt{5}}{63\sqrt{3}} \cdot \frac{2\sqrt{5}}{3\sqrt{3}} \left(x^2 - 5x + \frac{11}{2} \right) \\
&= \frac{14}{9} + \frac{44x}{135} - \frac{22}{27} - \frac{20}{567}x^2 + \frac{100}{567}x - \frac{110}{567} = -\frac{20}{567}x^2 + \frac{1424}{2835}x + \frac{310}{567}.
\end{aligned}$$

(b)

72. (a) The standard basis for P_2 is $\{1, x, x^2\}$. Applying the Gram-Schmidt orthonormalization process produces the orthonormal

basis $B = \{\mathbf{w}_1, \mathbf{w}_2, \mathbf{w}_3\} = \left\{\dfrac{1}{\sqrt{\pi}}, \dfrac{2\sqrt{3}}{\pi^{3/2}}x, \dfrac{6\sqrt{5}}{\pi^{5/2}}\left(x^2 - \dfrac{\pi^2}{12}\right)\right\}.$

The least squares approximating function is then given by $g(x) = \langle f, \mathbf{w}\rangle\mathbf{w}_1 + \langle f, \mathbf{w}_2\rangle\mathbf{w}_2 + \langle f, \mathbf{w}_3\rangle\mathbf{w}_3.$

Find the inner products

$$\langle f, \mathbf{w}_1\rangle = \int_{-\pi/2}^{\pi/2} \frac{1}{\sqrt{\pi}}\cos x \, dx = \frac{\sin x}{\sqrt{\pi}}\Big]_{-\pi/2}^{\pi/2} = \frac{2}{\sqrt{\pi}}$$

$$\langle f, \mathbf{w}_2\rangle = \int_{-\pi/2}^{\pi/2} \frac{2\sqrt{3}}{\pi^{3/2}}x \cos x \, dx = \left[\frac{2\sqrt{3}\cos x}{\pi^{3/2}} + \frac{2\sqrt{3}x\sin x}{\pi^{3/2}}\right]_{-\pi/2}^{\pi/2} = 0$$

$$\langle f, \mathbf{w}_3\rangle = \int_{-\pi/2}^{\pi/2} \frac{6\sqrt{5}}{\pi^{3/2}}\left(x^2 - \frac{\pi^2}{12}\right)\cos x \, dx = \left[\frac{12\sqrt{5}x\cos x}{\pi^{5/2}} + \frac{\sqrt{5}\left(12x^2 - \pi^2 - 24\right)\sin x}{2\pi^{5/2}}\right]_{-\pi/2}^{\pi/2} = \frac{2\sqrt{5}\left(\pi^2 - 12\right)}{\pi^{5/2}}$$

and conclude that

$$g(x) = \langle f, \mathbf{w}_1\rangle\mathbf{w}_1 + \langle f, \mathbf{w}_2\rangle\mathbf{w}_2 + \langle f, \mathbf{w}_3\rangle\mathbf{w}_3$$

$$= \left(\frac{2}{\sqrt{\pi}}\right)\left(\frac{1}{\sqrt{\pi}}\right) + (0)\left(\frac{2\sqrt{3}}{\pi^{3/2}}x\right) + \left(\frac{2\sqrt{5}\left(\pi^2 - 12\right)}{\pi^{5/2}}\right)\left(\frac{6\sqrt{5}}{\pi^{5/2}}\left(x^2 - \frac{\pi^2}{12}\right)\right)$$

$$= \frac{2}{\pi} + \frac{60\pi^2 - 720}{\pi^5}\left(x^2 - \frac{\pi^2}{12}\right) = \left(\frac{60\left(\pi^2 - 12\right)}{\pi^5}\right)x^2 + \frac{60 - 3\pi^2}{\pi^3} \approx -0.4177x^2 + 0.9802.$$

74. The fourth order Fourier approximation of $f(x) = \pi - x$ is of the form

$$g(x) = \frac{a_0}{2} + a_1\cos x + b_1\sin x + a_2\cos 2x + b_2\sin 2x + a_3\cos 3x + b_3\sin 3x + a_4\cos 4x + b_4\sin 4x.$$

In Exercise 63, you determined a_0 and the general form of the coefficients a_j and b_j.

$a_0 = 0$

$a_j = 0, \quad j = 1, 2, 3, \ldots$

$b_j = \dfrac{2}{j}, \quad j = 1, 2, 3, \ldots$

So, the approximation is $g(x) = 2\sin x + \sin 2x + \dfrac{2}{3}\sin 3x + \dfrac{1}{2}\sin 4x.$

76. The fourth order Fourier approximation of $f(x) = (x - \pi)^2$ is of the form

$$g(x) = \frac{a_0}{2} + a_1\cos x + b_1\sin x + a_2\cos 2x + b_2\sin 2x + a_3\cos 3x + b_3\sin 3x + a_4\cos 4x + b_4\sin 4x.$$

In Exercise 65, you determined a_0 and the general form of the coefficients a_j and b_j.

$a_0 = \dfrac{2\pi^2}{3}$

$a_j = \dfrac{4}{j^2}, \quad j = 1, 2, \ldots$

$b_j = 0, \quad j = 1, 2, \ldots$

So, the approximation is $g(x) = \dfrac{\pi^2}{3} + 4\cos x + \cos 2x + \dfrac{4}{9}\cos 3x + \dfrac{1}{4}\cos 4x.$

78. The second order Fourier approximation of $f(x) = e^{-x}$ is of the form

$$g(x) = \frac{a_0}{2} + a_1 \cos x + b_1 \sin x + a_2 \cos 2x + b_2 \sin 2x.$$

In Exercise 67, found that

$a_0 = \left(1 - e^{-2\pi}\right)/\pi$

$a_1 = \left(1 - e^{-2\pi}\right)/2\pi$

$b_1 = \left(1 - e^{-2\pi}\right)/2\pi.$

So, you need to determine a_2 and b_2.

$$a_2 = \frac{1}{\pi}\int_0^{2\pi} f(x) \cos 2x \, dx = \frac{1}{\pi}\int_0^{2\pi} e^{-x} \cos 2x \, dx$$

$$= \frac{1}{\pi}\left[\frac{1}{5}\left(-e^{-x}\cos 2x + 2e^{-x}\sin 2x\right)\right]_0^{2\pi} = \frac{1}{5\pi}\left(1 - e^{-2\pi}\right)$$

$$b_2 = \frac{1}{\pi}\int_0^{2\pi} f(x) \sin 2x \, dx = \frac{1}{\pi}\int_0^{2\pi} e^{-x} \sin 2x \, dx$$

$$= \frac{1}{\pi}\left[\frac{1}{5}\left(-e^{-x}\sin 2x - 2e^{-x}\cos 2x\right)\right]_0^{2\pi} = \frac{2}{5\pi}\left(1 - e^{-2\pi}\right)$$

So, the approximation is

$$g(x) = \frac{1 - e^{-2\pi}}{2\pi} + \frac{1 - e^{-2\pi}}{2\pi}\cos x + \frac{1 - e^{-2\pi}}{2\pi}\sin x + \frac{1 - e^{-2\pi}}{5\pi}\cos 2x + \frac{1 - e^{-2\pi}}{5\pi}2\sin 2x$$

$$= \frac{1}{10\pi}\left(1 - e^{-2\pi}\right)\left(5 + 5\cos x + 5\sin x + 2\cos 2x + 4\sin 2x\right).$$

80. The second order Fourier approximation of $f(x) = e^{-2x}$ is of the form

$$g(x) = \frac{a_0}{2} + a_1 \cos x + b_1 \sin x + a_2 \cos 2x + b_2 \cos 2x.$$

In Exercise 69, you found that

$$a_0 = \frac{1 - e^{-4\pi}}{2\pi}$$

$$a_1 = 2\left(\frac{1 - e^{-4\pi}}{5\pi}\right)$$

$$b_1 = \frac{1 - e^{-4\pi}}{5\pi}.$$

So, you need to determine a_2 and b_2.

$$a_2 = \frac{1}{\pi}\int_0^{2\pi} f(x) \cos 2x \, dx = \frac{1}{\pi}\int_0^{2\pi} e^{-2x} \cos 2x \, dx = \left[\frac{1}{4\pi}e^{-2x}\sin 2x - \frac{1}{4\pi}e^{-2x}\cos 2x\right]_0^{2\pi} = \frac{1 - e^{-4\pi}}{4\pi}$$

$$b_2 = \frac{1}{\pi}\int_0^{2\pi} f(x) \sin 2x \, dx = \frac{1}{\pi}\int_0^{2\pi} e^{-2x} \sin 2x \, dx = \left[-\frac{1}{4\pi}e^{-2x}\sin 2x - \frac{1}{4\pi}e^{-2x}\cos 2x\right]_0^{2\pi} = \frac{1 - e^{-4\pi}}{4\pi}$$

So, the approximation is

$$g(x) = \frac{1 - e^{-4\pi}}{4\pi} + 2\left(\frac{1 - e^{-4\pi}}{5\pi}\right)\cos x + \frac{1 - e^{-4\pi}}{5\pi}\sin x + \frac{1 - e^{-4\pi}}{4\pi}\cos 2x + \frac{1 - e^{-4\pi}}{4\pi}\sin 2x$$

$$= 5\left(\frac{1 - e^{-4\pi}}{20\pi}\right) + 8\left(\frac{1 - e^{-4\pi}}{20\pi}\right)\cos x + 4\left(\frac{1 - e^{-4\pi}}{20\pi}\right)\sin x + 5\left(\frac{1 - e^{-4\pi}}{20\pi}\right)\cos 2x + 5\left(\frac{1 - e^{-4\pi}}{20\pi}\right)\sin 2x$$

$$= \left(\frac{1 - e^{-4\pi}}{20\pi}\right)\left(5 + 8\cos x + 4\sin x + 5\cos 2x + 5\sin 2x\right).$$

82. The fourth order Fourier approximation of $f(x) = 1 + x$ is of the form

$$g(x) = \frac{a_0}{2} + a_1 \cos x + b_1 \sin x + a_2 \cos 2x + b_2 \sin 2x + a_3 \cos 3x + b_3 \sin 3x + a_4 \cos 4x + b_4 \sin 4x.$$

In Exercise 67, you found that

$a_0 = 2 + 2\pi$

$a_j = 0, \ j = 1, 2, \ldots$

$b_j = \dfrac{-2}{j}, \ j = 1, 2, \ldots$

So, the approximation is $g(x) = (1 + \pi) - 2 \sin x - \sin 2x - \frac{2}{3} \sin 3x - \frac{1}{2} \sin 4x.$

84. Because $f(x) = \sin^2 x = \frac{1}{2} - \frac{1}{2} \cos 2x$, you see that the fourth order Fourier approximation is simply $g(x) = \frac{1}{2} - \frac{1}{2} \cos 2x.$

86. Because

$$a_0 = \frac{2\pi^2}{3}, a_j = \frac{4}{j^2}\,(j = 1, 2, \ldots), b_j = 0\,(j = 1, 2, \ldots),$$

the nth order Fourier approximation is

$$g(x) = \frac{\pi^2}{3} + 4 \cos x + \cos 2x + \frac{4}{9} \cos 3x + \frac{4}{16} \cos 4x + \cdots + \frac{4}{n^2} \cos nx.$$

88. (a) If $\mathbf{u} = (u_1, u_2, u_3)$ and $\mathbf{v} = (v_1, v_2, v_3)$, then the cross product of $\mathbf{u}$ and $\mathbf{v}$ is the vector

$\mathbf{u} \times \mathbf{v} = (u_2 v_3 - u_3 v_2, u_3 v_1 - u_1 v_3, u_1 v_2 - u_2 v_1).$

(b) For a continuous function f on $[a,b]$ and a finite-dimensional subspace W of $C[a,b]$, the least squares approximating function of f with respect to W is given by $g = \langle f, \mathbf{w}_1 \rangle + \langle f, \mathbf{w}_2 \rangle \mathbf{w}_2 + \cdots + \langle f, \mathbf{w}_n \rangle \mathbf{w}_n$, where $B = \{\mathbf{w}_1, \mathbf{w}_2, \ldots, \mathbf{w}_n\}$ is an orthonormal basis for W.

(c) On the interval $[0, 2\pi]$, the least squares approximation of a continuous function f with respect to the vector space spanned by $\{1, \cos x, \ldots, \cos nx, \sin x, \ldots, \sin nx\}$ is

$$g(x) = \frac{a_0}{2} + a_1 \cos x + \cdots + a_n \cos nx + b_1 \sin x + \cdots + b_n \sin nx, \text{ where the Fourier coefficients}$$

$a_0, a_1, \ldots, a_n, b_1, \ldots, b_n$ are

$a_0 = \dfrac{1}{\pi} \displaystyle\int_0^{2\pi} f(x)\,dx$

$a_j = \dfrac{1}{\pi} \displaystyle\int_0^{2\pi} f(x) \cos jx \, dx, \ j = 1, 2, \ldots n$

$b_j = \dfrac{1}{\pi} \displaystyle\int_0^{2\pi} f(x) \sin jx \, dx, \ j = 1, 2, \ldots n.$

Review Exercises for Chapter 5

2. (a) $\|\mathbf{u}\| = \sqrt{(-1)^2 + 2^2} = \sqrt{5}$

(b) $\|\mathbf{v}\| = \sqrt{2^2 + 3^2} = \sqrt{13}$

(c) $\mathbf{u} - \mathbf{v} = -1(2) + 2(3) = 4$

(d) $d(\mathbf{u}, \mathbf{v}) = \|\mathbf{u} - \mathbf{v}\| = \|(-3, -1)\| = \sqrt{(-3)^2 + (-1)^2} = \sqrt{10}$

4. $\mathbf{u} = (1, -1, 2)$ and $\mathbf{v} = (2, 3, 1)$

$$\|\mathbf{u}\| = \sqrt{1^2 + (-1)^2 + 2^2} = \sqrt{6}$$

$$\|\mathbf{v}\| = \sqrt{2^2 + 3^2 + 1^2} = \sqrt{14}$$

$$\mathbf{u} \cdot \mathbf{v} = 1(2) + (-1)(3) + 2(1) = 1$$

$$\begin{aligned} d(\mathbf{u}, \mathbf{v}) &= \|\mathbf{u} - \mathbf{v}\| \\ &= \|(-1, -4, 1)\| \\ &= \sqrt{(-1)^2 + (-4)^2 + 1^2} = \sqrt{18} \end{aligned}$$

6. (a) $\|\mathbf{u}\| = \sqrt{1^2 + (-2)^2 + 2^2 + 0^2} = \sqrt{9} = 3$

(b) $\|\mathbf{v}\| = \sqrt{2^2 + (-1)^2 + 0^2 + 2^2} = \sqrt{9} = 3$

(c) $\mathbf{u} \cdot \mathbf{v} = 1(2) + (-2)(-1) + 2(0) + (0)(2) = 4$

(d) $\begin{aligned} d(\mathbf{u}, \mathbf{v}) &= \|\mathbf{u} - \mathbf{v}\| \\ &= \|(-1, -1, 2, -2)\| \\ &= \sqrt{(-1)^2 + (-1)^2 + 2^2 + (-2)^2} = \sqrt{10} \end{aligned}$

8. (a) $\|\mathbf{u}\| = \sqrt{1^2 + (-1)^2 + 0^2 + 1^2 + 1^2} = \sqrt{4} = 2$

(b) $\|\mathbf{v}\| = \sqrt{0^2 + 1^2 + (-2)^2 + 2^2 + 1^2} = \sqrt{10}$

(c) $\mathbf{u} \cdot \mathbf{v} = 1(0) + (-1)(1) + 0(-2) + 1(2) + 1(1) = 2$

(d) $\begin{aligned} d(\mathbf{u}, \mathbf{v}) &= \|\mathbf{u} - \mathbf{v}\| \\ &= \|(1, -2, 2, -1, 0)\| \\ &= \sqrt{1^2 + (-2)^2 + 2^2 + (-1)^2} = \sqrt{10} \end{aligned}$

10. The norm of $\mathbf{v}$ is

$$\|\mathbf{v}\| = \sqrt{1^2 + (-2)^2 + 1^2} = \sqrt{6}.$$

So, a unit vector in the direction of $\mathbf{v}$ is

$$\mathbf{u} = \frac{1}{\|\mathbf{v}\|}\mathbf{v} = \frac{1}{\sqrt{6}}(1, -2, 1) = \left(\frac{1}{\sqrt{6}}, \frac{-2}{\sqrt{6}}, \frac{1}{\sqrt{6}}\right).$$

12. The norm of $\mathbf{v}$ is

$$\|\mathbf{v}\| = \sqrt{0^2 + 2^2 + (-1)^2} = \sqrt{5}.$$

So, a unit vector in the direction of $\mathbf{v}$ is

$$\mathbf{u} = \frac{1}{\|\mathbf{v}\|}\mathbf{v} = \frac{1}{\sqrt{5}}(0, 2, -1) = \left(0, \frac{2}{\sqrt{5}}, \frac{-1}{\sqrt{5}}\right).$$

14. Solve the equation for c as follows.

$$\|c(2, 2, -1)\| = 3$$

$$|c|\|(2, 2, -1)\| = 3$$

$$|c|\sqrt{2^2 + 2^2 + (-1)^2} = 3$$

$$|c|3 = 3 \Rightarrow c = \pm 1$$

16. The cosine of the angle θ between $\mathbf{u}$ and $\mathbf{v}$ is given by

$$\cos\theta = \frac{\mathbf{u} \cdot \mathbf{v}}{\|\mathbf{u}\|\|\mathbf{v}\|} = \frac{1(0) + (-1)(1)}{\sqrt{1^2 + (-1)^2}\sqrt{0^2 + 1^2}} = \frac{-1}{\sqrt{2}\sqrt{1}} = \frac{-1}{\sqrt{2}}$$

which implies that $\theta = \cos^{-1}\left(\frac{-1}{\sqrt{2}}\right) = \frac{3\pi}{4}$ radians (135°).

18. The cosine of the angle θ between $\mathbf{u}$ and $\mathbf{v}$ is given by

$$\cos\theta = \frac{\mathbf{u} \cdot \mathbf{v}}{\|\mathbf{u}\|\|\mathbf{v}\|} = \frac{\cos\frac{\pi}{6}\cos\frac{5\pi}{6} + \sin\frac{\pi}{6}\sin\frac{5\pi}{6}}{\sqrt{\cos^2\frac{\pi}{6} + \sin^2\frac{\pi}{6}}\sqrt{\cos^2\frac{5\pi}{6} + \sin^2\frac{5\pi}{6}}} = \frac{\frac{\sqrt{3}}{2}\left(-\frac{\sqrt{3}}{2}\right) + \frac{1}{2}\left(\frac{1}{2}\right)}{\sqrt{\left(\frac{\sqrt{3}}{2}\right)^2 + \left(\frac{1}{2}\right)^2}\sqrt{\left(-\frac{\sqrt{3}}{2}\right)^2 + \left(\frac{1}{2}\right)^2}} = \frac{-\frac{1}{2}}{\sqrt{1}\cdot\sqrt{1}} = -\frac{1}{2}$$

which implies that $\theta = \cos^{-1}\left(-\frac{1}{2}\right) = \frac{2\pi}{3}$ radians (120°).

20. The cosine of the angle θ between **u** and **v** is given by

$$\cos\theta = \frac{\mathbf{u}\cdot\mathbf{v}}{\|\mathbf{u}\|\|\mathbf{v}\|} = \frac{2-3}{\sqrt{10}\sqrt{10}} = -\frac{1}{10}.$$

which implies that $\theta = \cos^{-1}\left(\frac{-1}{10}\right) \approx 1.67$ radians $(95.7°)$.

22. A vector $\mathbf{v} = (v_1, v_2, v_3)$ that is orthogonal to **u** must satisfy the equation $\mathbf{u}\cdot\mathbf{v} = v_1 - v_2 + 2v_3 = 0$.

This equation has solutions of the form

$\mathbf{v} = \left(s, t, \frac{1}{2}t - \frac{1}{2}s\right)$, where s and t are any real numbers.

28. Verify the Triangle Inequality as follows.

$$\|\mathbf{u}+\mathbf{v}\| \le \|\mathbf{u}\|+\|\mathbf{v}\|$$

$$\left\|\left(\frac{4}{3}, 4, -\frac{8}{3}\right)\right\| \le \sqrt{9 + 2\left(\frac{1}{9}\right)} + \sqrt{2\left(\frac{16}{9}\right) + 1 + 18}$$

$$\sqrt{2\left(\frac{4}{3}\right)^2 + 4^2 + 2\left(-\frac{8}{3}\right)^2} \le 3.037 + 4.749$$

$$5.812 \le 7.786$$

Verify the Cauchy-Schwarz Inequality as follows.

$$|\langle\mathbf{u},\mathbf{v}\rangle| \le \|\mathbf{u}\|\|\mathbf{v}\|$$

$$\left|(3)(1) + 2\left(\frac{1}{3}\right)(-3)\right| \le (3.037)(4.749)$$

$$1 \le 14.423$$

30. (a) $\langle f, g\rangle = \int_0^1 x\,4x^2\,dx = x^4\Big]_0^1 = 1$

(b) The vectors are not orthogonal.

(c) Because $\|f\| = \sqrt{\frac{1}{3}}$ and $\|g\| = \frac{4}{\sqrt{5}}$, verify the Cauchy-Schwarz Inequality as follows

$$|\langle f, g\rangle| \le \|f\|\|g\|$$

$$1 \le \sqrt{\frac{1}{3}}\frac{4}{\sqrt{5}} \approx 1.0328.$$

32. The projection of **u** onto **v** is given by

$$\text{proj}_\mathbf{v}\mathbf{u} = \frac{\mathbf{u}\cdot\mathbf{v}}{\mathbf{v}\cdot\mathbf{v}}\mathbf{v}$$

$$= \frac{2(0) + 3(4)}{0^2 + 4^2}(0, 4)$$

$$= \frac{12}{16}(0, 4)$$

$$= (0, 3).$$

24. A vector $\mathbf{v} = (v_1, v_2, v_3, v_4)$ that is orthogonal to **u** must satisfy the equation $\mathbf{u}\cdot\mathbf{v} = 0v_1 + v_2 + 2v_3 - v_4 = 0$.

This equation has solutions of the form

$\mathbf{v} = \left(r, s, \frac{1}{2}t - \frac{1}{2}s, t\right)$, where r, s, and t are any real numbers.

26. (a) $\langle\mathbf{u},\mathbf{v}\rangle = 2(0)\left(\frac{4}{3}\right) + (3)(1) + 2\left(\frac{1}{3}\right)(-3) = 1$

(b) $d(\mathbf{u},\mathbf{v}) = \|\mathbf{u}-\mathbf{v}\| = \sqrt{\langle\mathbf{u}-\mathbf{v}, \mathbf{u}-\mathbf{v}\rangle}$

$$= \sqrt{2\left(-\frac{4}{3}\right)^2 + 2^2 + 2\left(\frac{10}{3}\right)^2}$$

$$= \frac{\sqrt{268}}{3} = \frac{2}{3}\sqrt{67}$$

34. The projection of **u** onto **v** is given by

$$\text{proj}_\mathbf{v}\mathbf{u} = \frac{\mathbf{u}\cdot\mathbf{v}}{\mathbf{v}\cdot\mathbf{v}}\mathbf{v}$$

$$= \frac{2(0) + 5(5)}{0^2 + 5^2}(0, 5)$$

$$= \frac{25}{25}(0, 5)$$

$$= (0, 5).$$

36. The projection of **u** onto **v** is given by

$$\text{proj}_\mathbf{v}\mathbf{u} = \frac{\mathbf{u}\cdot\mathbf{v}}{\mathbf{v}\cdot\mathbf{v}}\mathbf{v}$$

$$= \frac{1(0) + 2(2) + (-1)(3)}{0^2 + 2^2 + 3^2}(0, 2, 3)$$

$$= \frac{1}{13}(0, 2, 3)$$

$$= \left(0, \frac{2}{13}, \frac{3}{13}\right).$$

38. Orthogonalize the vectors in B.

$\mathbf{w}_1 = (3, 4)$

$\mathbf{w}_2 = (1, 2) - \dfrac{11}{25}(3, 4) = \left(-\dfrac{8}{25}, \dfrac{6}{25}\right)$

Then normalize each vector.

$\mathbf{u}_1 = \dfrac{1}{\|\mathbf{w}_1\|}\mathbf{w}_1 = \dfrac{1}{5}(3, 4) = \left(\dfrac{3}{5}, \dfrac{4}{5}\right)$

$\mathbf{u}_2 = \dfrac{1}{\|\mathbf{w}_2\|}\mathbf{w}_2 = \dfrac{1}{2/5}\left(-\dfrac{8}{25}, \dfrac{6}{25}\right) = \left(-\dfrac{4}{5}, \dfrac{3}{5}\right)$

So, an orthonormal basis for R^2 is $\left\{\left(\dfrac{3}{5}, \dfrac{4}{5}\right), \left(-\dfrac{4}{5}, \dfrac{3}{5}\right)\right\}$.

40. Orthogonalize the vectors in B.

$\mathbf{w}_1 = (0, 0, 2)$

$\mathbf{w}_2 = (0, 1, 1) - \dfrac{2}{4}(0, 0, 2) = (0, 1, 0)$

$\mathbf{w}_3 = (1, 1, 1) - \dfrac{2}{4}(0, 0, 2) - \dfrac{1}{1}(0, 1, 0) = (1, 0, 0)$

Then normalize each vector to obtain the orthonormal basis for R^3.

$\{(0, 0, 1), (0, 1, 0), (1, 0, 0)\}.$

42. (a) To find $\mathbf{x} = (-3, 4, 4)$ as a linear combination of the vectors in

$B = \{(-1, 2, 2), (1, 0, 0)\}$ solve the vector equation

$c_1(-1, 2, 2) + c_2(1, 0, 0) = (-3, 4, 4).$

The solution to the corresponding system of equations is $c_1 = 2$ and $c_2 = -1$.

So, $[\mathbf{x}]_B = (2, -1)$, and you can write

$(-3, 4, 4) = 2(-1, 2, 2) - (1, 0, 0).$

(b) To apply the Gram-Schmidt orthonormalization process, first orthogonalize each vector in B.

$\mathbf{w}_1 = (-1, 2, 2)$

$\mathbf{w}_2 = (1, 0, 0) - \dfrac{-1}{9}(-1, 2, 2) = \left(\dfrac{8}{9}, \dfrac{2}{9}, \dfrac{2}{9}\right)$

Then normalize $\mathbf{w}_1$ and $\mathbf{w}_2$ as follows

$\mathbf{u}_1 = \dfrac{1}{\|\mathbf{w}_1\|}\mathbf{w}_1 = \dfrac{1}{3}(-1, 2, 2) = \left(-\dfrac{1}{3}, \dfrac{2}{3}, \dfrac{2}{3}\right)$

$\mathbf{u}_2 = \dfrac{1}{\|\mathbf{w}_2\|}\mathbf{w}_2 = \dfrac{1}{2\sqrt{2}/3}\left(\dfrac{8}{9}, \dfrac{2}{9}, \dfrac{2}{9}\right) = \left(\dfrac{4}{3\sqrt{2}}, \dfrac{1}{3\sqrt{2}}, \dfrac{1}{3\sqrt{2}}\right).$

So, $B' = \left\{\left(-\dfrac{1}{3}, \dfrac{2}{3}, \dfrac{2}{3}\right), \left(\dfrac{4}{3\sqrt{2}}, \dfrac{1}{3\sqrt{2}}, \dfrac{1}{3\sqrt{2}}\right)\right\}.$

(c) The coordinates of $\mathbf{x}$ relative to B' are found by calculating

$\langle \mathbf{x}, \mathbf{u}_1 \rangle = (-3, 4, 4) \cdot \left(-\dfrac{1}{3}, \dfrac{2}{3}, \dfrac{2}{3}\right) = \dfrac{19}{3}$

$\langle \mathbf{x}, \mathbf{u}_2 \rangle = (-3, 4, 4) \cdot \left(\dfrac{4}{3\sqrt{2}}, \dfrac{1}{3\sqrt{2}}, \dfrac{1}{3\sqrt{2}}\right) = \dfrac{-4}{3\sqrt{2}}.$

So,

$(-3, 4, 4) = \dfrac{19}{3}\left(-\dfrac{1}{3}, \dfrac{2}{3}, \dfrac{2}{3}\right) - \dfrac{4}{3\sqrt{2}}\left(\dfrac{4}{3\sqrt{2}}, \dfrac{1}{3\sqrt{2}}, \dfrac{1}{3\sqrt{2}}\right).$

44. These functions are orthogonal because $\langle f, g \rangle = \displaystyle\int_{-1}^{1} \sqrt{1 - x^2}\, 2x\sqrt{1 - x^2}\, dx$

$$= \int_{-1}^{1} \left(2x - 2x^3\right) dx = \left[x^2 - \dfrac{x^4}{2}\right]_{-1}^{1} = 0.$$

46. (a) $\langle f, g \rangle = \int_0^1 f(x)g(x)\,dx = \int_0^1 (x+2)(15x-8)\,dx = \int_0^1 (15x^2 + 22x - 16)\,dx = \left[5x^3 + 11x^2 - 16x \right]_0^1 = 0$

(b) $\langle -4f, g \rangle = -4\langle f, g \rangle = -4(0) = 0$

(c) $\|f\|^2 = \langle f, f \rangle = \int_0^1 (x+2)^2\,dx = \int_0^1 (x^2 + 4x + 4)\,dx = \left[\dfrac{x^3}{3} + 2x^2 + 4x \right]_0^1 = \dfrac{19}{3}$

$\|f\| = \sqrt{\langle f, f \rangle} = \sqrt{\dfrac{19}{3}}$

(d) Because f and g are already orthogonal, you only need to normalize them. You know $\|f\| = \sqrt{\dfrac{19}{3}}$ and so you compute $\|g\|$.

$\|g\|^2 = \langle g, g \rangle = \int_0^1 (15x-8)^2\,dx = \int_0^1 (225x^2 - 240x + 64)\,dx = \left[75x^3 - 120x^2 + 64x \right]_0^1 = 19$

$\|g\| = \sqrt{19}$

So,

$\mathbf{u}_1 = \dfrac{1}{\|f\|} f = \dfrac{1}{\sqrt{\dfrac{19}{3}}}(x+2) = \sqrt{\dfrac{3}{19}}(x+2)$

$\mathbf{u}_2 = \dfrac{1}{\|g\|} g = \dfrac{1}{\sqrt{19}}(15x - 8).$

The orthonormal set is

$B' = \left\{ \left(\sqrt{\dfrac{3}{19}}x + 2\sqrt{\dfrac{3}{19}} \right), \left(\dfrac{15}{\sqrt{19}}x - \dfrac{8}{\sqrt{19}} \right) \right\}.$

48. The solution space of the homogeneous system consists of vectors of the form $(-t, s, s, t)$, where s and t are any real numbers. So, a basis for the solution space is $B = \{(-1, 0, 0, 1), (0, 1, 1, 0)\}$. Because these vectors are orthogonal, and their length is $\sqrt{2}$, you normalize them to obtain the orthonormal basis

$\left\{ \left(-\dfrac{\sqrt{2}}{2}, 0, 0, \dfrac{\sqrt{2}}{2} \right), \left(0, \dfrac{\sqrt{2}}{2}, \dfrac{\sqrt{2}}{2}, 0 \right) \right\}.$

50. $\|\mathbf{u} + \mathbf{v}\|^2 + \|\mathbf{u} - \mathbf{v}\|^2 = (\mathbf{u} + \mathbf{v}) \cdot (\mathbf{u} + \mathbf{v}) + (\mathbf{u} - \mathbf{v}) \cdot (\mathbf{u} - \mathbf{v})$

$= (\mathbf{u} \cdot \mathbf{u} + \mathbf{v} \cdot \mathbf{v} + 2\mathbf{u} \cdot \mathbf{v}) + (\mathbf{u} \cdot \mathbf{u} + \mathbf{v} \cdot \mathbf{v} - 2\mathbf{u} \cdot \mathbf{v})$

$= 2\|\mathbf{u}\|^2 + 2\|\mathbf{v}\|^2$

52. Use the Triangle Inequality

$\|\mathbf{u} + \mathbf{w}\| \le \|\mathbf{u}\| + \|\mathbf{w}\|$ with $\mathbf{w} = \mathbf{v} - \mathbf{u}$

$\|\mathbf{u} + \mathbf{w}\| = \|\mathbf{u} + (\mathbf{v} - \mathbf{u})\| = \|\mathbf{v}\| \le \|\mathbf{u}\| + \|\mathbf{v} - \mathbf{u}\|$

and so, $\|\mathbf{v}\| - \|\mathbf{u}\| \le \|\mathbf{v} - \mathbf{u}\|$. By symmetry, you also have $\|\mathbf{u}\| - \|\mathbf{v}\| \le \|\mathbf{u} - \mathbf{v}\| = \|\mathbf{v} - \mathbf{u}\|$.

So, $\big| \|\mathbf{u}\| - \|\mathbf{v}\| \big| \le \|\mathbf{u} - \mathbf{v}\|$. To complete the proof, first observe that the Triangle Inequality implies that

$\|\mathbf{u} - \mathbf{w}\| \le \|\mathbf{u}\| + \|-\mathbf{w}\| = \|\mathbf{u}\| + \|\mathbf{w}\|$. Letting $\mathbf{w} = \mathbf{u} + \mathbf{v}$, you have

$\|\mathbf{u} - \mathbf{w}\| = \|\mathbf{u} - (\mathbf{u} + \mathbf{v})\| = \|-\mathbf{v}\| = \|\mathbf{v}\| \le \|\mathbf{u}\| + \|\mathbf{u} + \mathbf{v}\|$ and so $\|\mathbf{v}\| - \|\mathbf{u}\| \le \|\mathbf{u} + \mathbf{v}\|$.

Similarly, $\|\mathbf{u}\| - \|\mathbf{v}\| \le \|\mathbf{u} + \mathbf{v}\|$, and $\big| \|\mathbf{u}\| - \|\mathbf{v}\| \big| \le \|\mathbf{u} + \mathbf{v}\|$. In conclusion, $\big| \|\mathbf{u}\| - \|\mathbf{v}\| \big| \le \|\mathbf{u} \pm \mathbf{v}\|$.

54. Extend the V-basis $\{(0, 1, 0, 1), (0, 2, 0, 0)\}$ to a basis of R^4.

$B = \{(0, 1, 0, 1), (0, 2, 0, 0), (1, 0, 0, 0), (0, 0, 1, 0)\}$

Now, $(1, 1, 1, 1) = (0, 1, 0, 1) + (1, 0, 1, 0) = \mathbf{v} + \mathbf{w}$

where $\mathbf{v} \in V$ and $\mathbf{w}$ is orthogonal to every vector in V.

56. $(x_1 + x_2 + \cdots + x_n)^2 = (x_1 + x_2 + \cdots + x_n)(x_1 + x_2 + \cdots + x_n)$

$= (x_1, \ldots, x_n) \cdot (x_1, \ldots, x_n) + (x_2, \ldots, x_n, x_1) \cdot (x_1, \ldots, x_n)$

$+ \cdots + (x_n, x_1, \ldots, x_{n-1}) \cdot (x_1, \ldots, x_n)$

$\leq \left(x_1^2 + \cdots + x_n^2\right)^{\frac{1}{2}}\left(x_1^2 + \cdots + x_n^2\right)^{\frac{1}{2}}$

$+ \left(x_2^2 + \cdots + x_n^2 + x_1^2\right)^{\frac{1}{2}}\left(x_1^2 + \cdots + x_n^2\right)^{\frac{1}{2}} + \cdots$

$+ \left(x_n^2 + x_1^2 + \cdots + x_{n-1}^2\right)^{\frac{1}{2}}\left(x_1^2 + \cdots + x_n^2\right)^{\frac{1}{2}}$

$= n\left(x_1^2 + \cdots + x_n^2\right)$

58. Let $\{\mathbf{u}_1, \mathbf{u}_2, \ldots, \mathbf{u}_n\}$ be a dependent set of vectors, and assume $\mathbf{u}_k$ is a linear combination of $\mathbf{u}_1, \mathbf{u}_2, \ldots, \mathbf{u}_{k-1}$, which are linearly independent. The Gram-Schmidt process will orthonormalize $\mathbf{u}_1, \ldots, \mathbf{u}_{k-1}$, but then $\mathbf{u}_k$ will be a linear combination of $\mathbf{u}_1, \ldots, \mathbf{u}_{k-1}$.

60. An orthonormal basis for S is

$$\left\{ \begin{bmatrix} 0 \\ -\dfrac{1}{\sqrt{2}} \\ \dfrac{1}{\sqrt{2}} \end{bmatrix}, \begin{bmatrix} 0 \\ \dfrac{1}{\sqrt{2}} \\ \dfrac{1}{\sqrt{2}} \end{bmatrix} \right\}$$

$\text{proj}_s\mathbf{v} = (\mathbf{v} \cdot \mathbf{u}_1)\mathbf{u}_1 + (\mathbf{v} \cdot \mathbf{u}_2)\mathbf{u}_2$

$$= \left(-\dfrac{2}{\sqrt{2}}\right)\begin{bmatrix} 0 \\ -\dfrac{1}{\sqrt{2}} \\ \dfrac{1}{\sqrt{2}} \end{bmatrix} + \left(-\dfrac{2}{\sqrt{2}}\right)\begin{bmatrix} 0 \\ \dfrac{1}{\sqrt{2}} \\ \dfrac{1}{\sqrt{2}} \end{bmatrix}$$

$$= \begin{bmatrix} 0 \\ 0 \\ -2 \end{bmatrix}.$$

62. $A^T A = \begin{bmatrix} 1 & 1 & 1 & 1 \\ -2 & -1 & 0 & 1 \end{bmatrix}\begin{bmatrix} 1 & -2 \\ 1 & -1 \\ 1 & 0 \\ 1 & 1 \end{bmatrix} = \begin{bmatrix} 4 & -2 \\ -2 & 6 \end{bmatrix}$

$A^T\mathbf{b} = \begin{bmatrix} 1 & 1 & 1 & 1 \\ -2 & -1 & 0 & 1 \end{bmatrix}\begin{bmatrix} 2 \\ 1 \\ 1 \\ 3 \end{bmatrix} = \begin{bmatrix} 7 \\ -2 \end{bmatrix}$

$A^T A\mathbf{x} = A^T\mathbf{b} \Rightarrow \mathbf{x} = \begin{bmatrix} 1.9 \\ 0.3 \end{bmatrix}$

line: $y = 0.3x + 1.9$

64. Substitute the data points
$(3, 1.5), (4, 3.2), (5, 6.1), (6, 10.6), (7, 16.6), (8, 21.8),$
$(9, 23.7),$ and $(10, 29.3)$ into the quadratic polynomial
$y = c_0 + c_1 t + c_2 t^2.$ You then obtain the system of
linear equations

$$c_0 + 3c_1 + 9c_2 = 1.5$$
$$c_0 + 4c_1 + 16c_2 = 3.2$$
$$c_0 + 5c_1 + 25c_2 = 6.1$$
$$c_0 + 6c_1 + 36c_2 = 10.6$$
$$c_0 + 7c_1 + 49c_2 = 16.6$$
$$c_0 + 8c_1 + 64c_2 = 21.8$$
$$c_0 + 9c_1 + 81c_2 = 23.7$$
$$c_0 + 10c_1 + 100c_2 = 29.3.$$

This produces the least squares problem

$$A t = b$$

$$\begin{bmatrix} 1 & 3 & 9 \\ 1 & 4 & 16 \\ 1 & 5 & 25 \\ 1 & 6 & 36 \\ 1 & 7 & 49 \\ 1 & 8 & 64 \\ 1 & 9 & 81 \\ 1 & 10 & 100 \end{bmatrix} \begin{bmatrix} c_0 \\ c_1 \\ c_2 \end{bmatrix} = \begin{bmatrix} 1.5 \\ 3.2 \\ 6.1 \\ 10.6 \\ 16.6 \\ 21.8 \\ 23.7 \\ 29.3 \end{bmatrix}.$$

The normal equations are

$$A^T A t = A^T b$$

$$\begin{bmatrix} 8 & 52 & 380 \\ 52 & 380 & 3016 \\ 380 & 3016 & 25{,}316 \end{bmatrix} \begin{bmatrix} c_0 \\ c_1 \\ c_2 \end{bmatrix} = \begin{bmatrix} 112.8 \\ 908.3 \\ 7657.1 \end{bmatrix}$$

and the solution is $t = \begin{bmatrix} c_0 \\ c_1 \\ c_2 \end{bmatrix} = \begin{bmatrix} -8.0 \\ 2.40 \\ 0.136 \end{bmatrix}.$ The least

squares quadratic is $y = -8.0 + 2.40t + 0.136t^2.$
Substitute the same data points into the cubic polynomial
$y = c_0 + c_1 t_1 + c_2 t^2 + c_3 t^3.$ You then obtain the system
of linear equations

$$c_0 + 3c_1 + 9c_2 + 27c_3 = 1.5$$
$$c_0 + 4c_1 + 16c_2 + 64c_3 = 3.2$$
$$c_0 + 5c_1 + 25c_2 + 125c_3 = 6.1$$
$$c_0 + 6c_1 + 36c_2 + 216c_3 = 10.6$$
$$c_0 + 7c_1 + 49c_2 + 343c_3 = 16.6$$
$$c_0 + 8c_1 + 64c_2 + 512c_3 = 21.8$$
$$c_0 + 9c_1 + 81c_2 + 729c_3 = 23.7$$
$$c_0 + 10c_1 + 100c_2 + 1000c_3 = 29.3.$$

This produces the least squares problem

$$A t = b$$

$$\begin{bmatrix} 1 & 3 & 9 & 27 \\ 1 & 4 & 16 & 64 \\ 1 & 5 & 25 & 125 \\ 1 & 6 & 36 & 216 \\ 1 & 7 & 49 & 343 \\ 1 & 8 & 64 & 512 \\ 1 & 9 & 81 & 729 \\ 1 & 10 & 100 & 1000 \end{bmatrix} \begin{bmatrix} c_0 \\ c_1 \\ c_2 \\ c_3 \end{bmatrix} = \begin{bmatrix} 1.5 \\ 3.2 \\ 6.1 \\ 10.6 \\ 16.6 \\ 21.8 \\ 23.7 \\ 29.3 \end{bmatrix}.$$

The normal equations are

$$A^T A t = A^T b$$

$$\begin{bmatrix} 8 & 52 & 380 & 3016 \\ 52 & 380 & 3016 & 25{,}316 \\ 380 & 3016 & 25{,}316 & 220{,}792 \\ 3016 & 25{,}316 & 220{,}792 & 1{,}978{,}340 \end{bmatrix} \begin{bmatrix} c_0 \\ c_1 \\ c_2 \\ c_3 \end{bmatrix} = \begin{bmatrix} 112.8 \\ 908.3 \\ 7657.1 \\ 66{,}730.1 \end{bmatrix}$$

and the solution is $t = \begin{bmatrix} c_0 \\ c_1 \\ c_2 \\ c_3 \end{bmatrix} = \begin{bmatrix} 11.4 \\ -8.22 \\ 1.899 \\ -0.0904 \end{bmatrix}.$

The least squares cubic is
$y = 11.4 - 8.22t + 1.899t^2 - 0.0904t^3.$

2015 (quadratic):
$y = -8.0 + 2.40(15) + 0.136(15)^2 = \$58.6 \text{ billion}$

2015 (cubic):
$y = 11.4 - 8.22(15) + 1.899(15)^2 - 0.0904(15)^3$
$\approx \$10.3 \text{ billion}$

Because the original data increased from 2003 to 2010,
you can expect the revenue to continue to increase.
Because the predicted value given by the quadratic
polynomial is greater than the actual value for 2010, this
model is more accurate for predicting future revenues.

66. The cross product is

$$\mathbf{u} \times \mathbf{v} = \begin{vmatrix} \mathbf{i} & \mathbf{j} & \mathbf{k} \\ 1 & -1 & 1 \\ 0 & 1 & 1 \end{vmatrix} = -2\mathbf{i} - \mathbf{j} + \mathbf{k} = (-2, -1, 1).$$

Furthermore, $\mathbf{u} \times \mathbf{v}$ is orthogonal to both $\mathbf{u}$ and $\mathbf{v}$
because

$$\mathbf{u} \cdot (\mathbf{u} \times \mathbf{v}) = 1(-2) + (1)(-1) + 1(1) = 0$$

and

$$\mathbf{v} \cdot (\mathbf{u} \times \mathbf{v}) = 0(-2) + 1(-1) + 1(1) = 0.$$

68. The cross product is

$$\mathbf{u} \times \mathbf{v} = \begin{vmatrix} \mathbf{i} & \mathbf{j} & \mathbf{k} \\ 2 & 0 & -1 \\ 1 & 1 & -1 \end{vmatrix} = \mathbf{i} + \mathbf{j} + 2\mathbf{k} = (1, 1, 2).$$

Furthermore, $\mathbf{u} \times \mathbf{v}$ is orthogonal to both $\mathbf{u}$ and $\mathbf{v}$ because

$$\mathbf{u} \cdot (\mathbf{u} \times \mathbf{v}) = 2(1) + 0(1) + (-1)(2) = 0$$

and

$$\mathbf{v} \cdot (\mathbf{u} \times \mathbf{v}) = 1(1) + 1(1) + (-1)(2) = 0.$$

70. Because

$$\mathbf{v} \times \mathbf{w} = \begin{vmatrix} \mathbf{i} & \mathbf{j} & \mathbf{k} \\ -1 & -1 & 0 \\ 3 & 4 & -1 \end{vmatrix} = \mathbf{i} - \mathbf{j} - \mathbf{k} = (1, -1, -1),$$

the volume is

$$\left| \mathbf{u} \cdot (\mathbf{v} \times \mathbf{w}) \right| = \left| (1, 2, 1) \cdot (1, -1, -1) \right| = \left| -2 \right| = 2.$$

72. $\mathbf{u} \cdot (\mathbf{v} \times \mathbf{w}) = \begin{vmatrix} 1 & 1 & 3 \\ 0 & 3 & 3 \\ 3 & 0 & 3 \end{vmatrix} = 1(9) + 3(-9) = -9$

Volume $= \left| \mathbf{u} \cdot (\mathbf{v} \times \mathbf{w}) \right| = \left| -9 \right| = 9$ cubic units

74. Because $\|\mathbf{u} \times \mathbf{v}\| = \|\mathbf{u}\|\,\|\mathbf{v}\|\sin\theta$, you see that $\mathbf{u}$ and $\mathbf{v}$ are orthogonal if and only if $\sin\theta = 1$, which means

$\|\mathbf{u} \times \mathbf{v}\| = \|\mathbf{u}\|\,\|\mathbf{v}\|.$

76. (a) The standard basis for P_1 is $\{1, x\}$. In the interval $[0, 2]$, the Gram-Schmidt orthonormalization process yields the orthonormal basis $\left\{ \dfrac{1}{\sqrt{2}}, \dfrac{\sqrt{3}}{\sqrt{2}}(x - 1) \right\}$.

Because

$$\langle f, \mathbf{w}_1 \rangle = \int_0^2 x^3 \frac{1}{\sqrt{2}}\,dx = \frac{4}{\sqrt{2}}$$

$$\langle f, \mathbf{w}_2 \rangle = \int_0^2 x^3 \frac{\sqrt{3}}{\sqrt{2}}(x - 1)\,dx$$

$$= \frac{\sqrt{3}}{\sqrt{2}} \int_0^2 \left(x^4 - x^3 \right) dx$$

$$= \frac{\sqrt{3}}{\sqrt{2}} \left(\frac{x^5}{5} - \frac{x^4}{5} \right) \Big]_0^2$$

$$= \frac{\sqrt{3}}{\sqrt{2}} \left(\frac{32}{5} - 4 \right)$$

$$= \frac{\sqrt{3}}{\sqrt{2}} \left(\frac{12}{5} \right),$$

g is given by

$$g(x) = \langle f, \mathbf{w}_1 \rangle + \langle f, \mathbf{w}_2 \rangle \mathbf{w}_2$$

$$= \frac{4}{\sqrt{2}} \left(\frac{1}{\sqrt{2}} \right) + \frac{\sqrt{3}}{\sqrt{2}} \left(\frac{12}{5} \right) \frac{\sqrt{3}}{\sqrt{2}}(x - 1)$$

$$= \frac{18}{5}x - \frac{8}{5}.$$

(b)

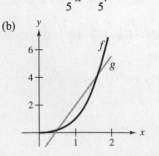

78. (a) The standard basis for P_1 is $\{1, x\}$. In the interval $[0, \pi]$ the Gram-Schmidt orthonormalization process yields the orthonormal basis $\left\{ \dfrac{1}{\sqrt{\pi}}, \dfrac{\sqrt{3}}{\pi^{3/2}}(2x - \pi) \right\}$.

Because

$$\langle f, \mathbf{w}_1 \rangle = \int_0^\pi \sin x \cos x \left(\frac{1}{\sqrt{\pi}} \right) dx = 0$$

$$\langle f, \mathbf{w}_2 \rangle = \int_0^\pi \sin x \cos x \left(\frac{\sqrt{3}}{\pi^{3/2}} \right)(2x - \pi)\,dx$$

$$= -\frac{\sqrt{3}}{2\pi^{1/2}},$$

g is given by

$$g(x) = \langle f, \mathbf{w}_1 \rangle \mathbf{w}_1 + \langle f, \mathbf{w}_2 \rangle \mathbf{w}_2$$

$$= 0 \left(\frac{1}{\sqrt{\pi}} \right) + \left(-\frac{\sqrt{3}}{2\pi^{1/2}} \right) \left(\frac{\sqrt{3}}{\pi^{3/2}}(2x - \pi) \right)$$

$$= -\frac{3x}{\pi^2} + \frac{3}{2\pi}.$$

(b)

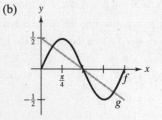

80. (a) The standard basis for P_2 is $\{1, x, x^2\}$. In the interval $[1, 2]$, the Gram-Schmidt orthonormalization process yields the orthonormal basis

$$\left\{1, 2\sqrt{3}\left(x - \frac{3}{2}\right), \frac{30}{\sqrt{5}}\left(x^2 - 3x + \frac{13}{6}\right)\right\}.$$

Because

$$\langle f, \mathbf{w}_1 \rangle = \int_0^2 \frac{1}{x}\, dx = \ln 2$$

$$\langle f, \mathbf{w}_2 \rangle = \int_1^2 \frac{1}{x} 2\sqrt{3}\left(x - \frac{3}{2}\right) dx = 2\sqrt{3}\int_1^2 \left(1 - \frac{3}{2x}\right) dx = 2\sqrt{3}\left(1 - \frac{3}{2}\ln 2\right)$$

$$\langle f, \mathbf{w}_3 \rangle = \int_1^2 \frac{1}{x}\frac{30}{\sqrt{5}}\left(x^2 - 3x + \frac{13}{6}\right) dx = \frac{30}{\sqrt{5}}\int_1^2 \left(x - 3 + \frac{13}{6x}\right) dx = \frac{30}{\sqrt{5}}\left(\frac{13}{6}\ln 2 - \frac{3}{2}\right),$$

g is given by $g(x) = \langle f, \mathbf{w}_1 \rangle \mathbf{w}_1 + \langle f, \mathbf{w}_2 \rangle \mathbf{w}_2 + \langle f, \mathbf{w}_3 \rangle \mathbf{w}_3$

$$= (\ln 2) + 2\sqrt{3}\left(1 - \frac{3}{2}\ln 2\right)2\sqrt{3}\left(x - \frac{3}{2}\right) + \frac{30}{\sqrt{5}}\left(\frac{13}{6}\ln 2 - \frac{3}{2}\right)\frac{30}{\sqrt{5}}\left(x^2 - 3x + \frac{13}{6}\right)$$

$$= \ln 2 + 12\left(1 - \frac{3}{2}\ln 2\right)\left(x - \frac{3}{2}\right) + 180\left(\frac{13}{6}\ln 2 - \frac{3}{2}\right)\left(x^2 - 3x + \frac{13}{6}\right) = .3274x^2 - 1.459x + 2.1175.$$

(b)

82. Find the coefficients as follows

$$a_0 = \frac{1}{\pi}\int_{-\pi}^{\pi} f(x)\,dx = \frac{1}{\pi}\int_{-\pi}^{\pi} x\,dx = 0$$

$$a_j = \frac{1}{\pi}\int_{-\pi}^{\pi} x\cos(jx)\,dx = \frac{1}{\pi}\left[\frac{1}{j^2}\cos(jx) + \frac{x}{j}\sin(jx)\right]_{-\pi}^{\pi} = 0, \; j = 1, 2 \ldots$$

$$b_j = \frac{1}{\pi}\int_{-\pi}^{\pi} x\sin(jx) = \frac{1}{\pi}\left[\frac{1}{j^2}\sin(jx) - \frac{x}{j}\cos(jx)\right]_{-\pi}^{\pi} = -\frac{2}{j}\cos(\pi j) \; j = 1, 2, \ldots$$

So, the approximation is $g(x) = \dfrac{a_0}{2} + a_1\cos x + a_2\cos 2x + b_1\sin x + b_2\sin 2x = 2\sin x - \sin 2x.$

84. (a) True. See note following Theorem 5.17, page 272.

(b) True. See Theorem 5.18, part 3, page 273.

(c) True. See discussion starting on page 279.

Project Solutions for Chapter 5

1 The *QR*-factorization

1. (a) $A = \begin{bmatrix} 1 & 1 \\ 0 & 1 \\ 1 & 0 \end{bmatrix} = \begin{bmatrix} .7071 & .4082 \\ 0 & .8165 \\ .7071 & -.4082 \end{bmatrix} \begin{bmatrix} 1.4142 & 0.7071 \\ 0 & 1.2247 \end{bmatrix} = QR$

(b) $A = \begin{bmatrix} 1 & 0 \\ 0 & 0 \\ 1 & 1 \\ 1 & 2 \end{bmatrix} = \begin{bmatrix} .5774 & -.7071 \\ 0 & 0 \\ .5774 & 0 \\ .5774 & .7071 \end{bmatrix} \begin{bmatrix} 1.7321 & 1.7321 \\ 0 & 1.4142 \end{bmatrix} = QR$

(c) $A = \begin{bmatrix} 1 & 0 & -1 \\ 1 & 2 & 0 \\ 1 & 2 & 0 \\ 1 & 0 & 0 \end{bmatrix} = \begin{bmatrix} .5 & -.5 & -.7071 \\ .5 & .5 & 0 \\ .5 & .5 & 0 \\ .5 & -.5 & .7071 \end{bmatrix} \begin{bmatrix} 2 & 2 & -.5 \\ 0 & 2 & .5 \\ 0 & 0 & .7071 \end{bmatrix} = QR$

2. The normal equations simplify using $A = QR$ as follows

$$A^T A \mathbf{x} = A^T \mathbf{b}$$
$$(QR)^T QR\mathbf{x} = (QR)^T \mathbf{b}$$
$$R^T Q^T QR\mathbf{x} = R^T Q^T \mathbf{b}$$
$$R^T R\mathbf{x} = R^T Q^T \mathbf{b} \quad (Q^T Q = I)$$
$$R\mathbf{x} = Q^T \mathbf{b}.$$

Because R is upper triangular, only back-substitution is needed.

3. $A = \begin{bmatrix} 1 & 1 \\ 0 & 1 \\ 1 & 0 \end{bmatrix} = \begin{bmatrix} .7071 & .4082 \\ 0 & .8165 \\ .7071 & -.4082 \end{bmatrix} \begin{bmatrix} 1.4142 & 0.7071 \\ 0 & 1.2247 \end{bmatrix} = QR.$

$$R\mathbf{x} = Q^T \mathbf{b} \begin{bmatrix} 1.4142 & 0.7071 \\ 0 & 1.2247 \end{bmatrix} \begin{bmatrix} x_1 \\ x_2 \end{bmatrix}$$

$$= \begin{bmatrix} .7071 & 0 & .7071 \\ .4082 & .8165 & -.4082 \end{bmatrix} \begin{bmatrix} -1 \\ 1 \\ -1 \end{bmatrix} = \begin{bmatrix} -1.4142 \\ 0.8165 \end{bmatrix}$$

$$\begin{bmatrix} x_1 \\ x_2 \end{bmatrix} = \begin{bmatrix} -1.3333 \\ 0.6667 \end{bmatrix}.$$

2 Orthogonal Matrices and Change of Basis

1. $P^{-1} = \begin{bmatrix} -1 & 2 \\ -2 & 3 \end{bmatrix} \neq P^T$

2. $\begin{bmatrix} \cos \theta & -\sin \theta \\ \sin \theta & \cos \theta \end{bmatrix}^{-1} = \begin{bmatrix} \cos \theta & \sin \theta \\ -\sin \theta & \cos \theta \end{bmatrix} = \begin{bmatrix} \cos \theta & -\sin \theta \\ \sin \theta & \cos \theta \end{bmatrix}^T$

3. If $P^{-1} = P^T$, then $P^T P = I \Rightarrow$ columns of P are pairwise orthogonal.

4. If P is orthogonal, then $P^{-1} = P^T$ by definition of orthogonal matrix. Then $\left(P^{-1}\right)^{-1} = \left(P^T\right)^{-1} = \left(P^{-1}\right)^T$. The last equality

holds because $\left(A^T\right)^{-1} = \left(A^{-1}\right)^T$ for any invertible matrix A. So, P^{-1} is orthogonal.

5. No. For example, $\begin{bmatrix} 1 & 0 \\ 0 & 1 \end{bmatrix} + \begin{bmatrix} 1 & 0 \\ 0 & 1 \end{bmatrix} = \begin{bmatrix} 2 & 0 \\ 0 & 2 \end{bmatrix}$ is not orthogonal. The product of orthogonal matrices is orthogonal. If

$P^{-1} = P^T$ and $Q^{-1} = Q^T$, then $(PQ)^{-1} = Q^{-1}P^{-1} = Q^T P^T = (PQ)^T$.

6. $\|P\mathbf{x}\| = (P\mathbf{x})^T P\mathbf{x} = \mathbf{x}^T P^T P\mathbf{x} = \mathbf{x}^T \mathbf{x} = \|\mathbf{x}\|$

7. Let

$$P = \begin{bmatrix} -\dfrac{2}{\sqrt{5}} & \dfrac{1}{\sqrt{5}} \\[2mm] \dfrac{1}{\sqrt{5}} & \dfrac{2}{\sqrt{5}} \end{bmatrix}$$

be the change of basis matrix from B' to B. Because P is orthogonal, lengths are preserved.

CHAPTER 6
Linear Transformations

CHAPTER 6
Linear Transformations

Section 6.1   Introduction to Linear Transformations

2. (a) The image of $\mathbf{v}$ is

$$T(0, 6) = (2(6) - 0, 0, 6) = (12, 0, 6).$$

(b) If $T(v_1, v_2) = (2v_2 - v_1, v_1, v_2) = (3, 1, 2)$, then

$$2v_2 - v_1 = 3$$
$$v_1 = 1$$
$$v_2 = 2$$

which implies that the preimage of $\mathbf{w}$ is
$(v_1, v_2) = (1, 2)$.

4. (a) The image of $\mathbf{v}$ is

$$T(-4, 5, 1) = (2(-4) + 5, 2(5) - 3(-4), -4 - 1)$$
$$= (-3, 22, -5).$$

(b) If $T(v_1, v_2, v_3) = (2v_1 + v_2, 2v_2 - 3v_1, v_1 - v_3)$
$$= (4, 1, -1),$$

then

$$2v_1 + v_2 \qquad = 4$$
$$-3v_1 + 2v_2 \qquad = 1$$
$$v_1 \qquad - v_3 = -1$$

which implies that $v_1 = 1$, $v_2 = 2$ and $v_3 = 2$. So,
the preimage of $\mathbf{w}$ is $(1, 2, 2)$.

6. (a) The image of $\mathbf{v}$ is

$$T(2, 1, 4) = (2(2) + 1, 2 - 1) = (5, 1).$$

(b) If $T(v_1, v_2, v_3) = (2v_1 + v_2, v_1 - v_2) = (-1, 2)$, then

$$2v_1 + v_2 = -1$$
$$v_1 - v_2 = 2,$$

which implies that $v_1 = \frac{1}{3}$, $v_2 = -\frac{5}{3}$, and $v_3 = t$,

where t is any real number. So, the preimage of $\mathbf{w}$ is
$\left\{ \left(\frac{1}{3}, -\frac{5}{3}, t \right) : t \text{ is any real number} \right\}$.

8. (a) The image of $\mathbf{v}$ is

$$T(2, 4) = \left(\frac{\sqrt{3}}{2}(2) - \frac{1}{2}(4), 2 - 4, 4 \right)$$
$$= \left(\sqrt{3} - 2, -2, 4 \right).$$

(b) If $T(v_1, v_2) = \left(\frac{\sqrt{3}}{2}v_1 - \frac{1}{2}v_2, v_1 - v_2, v_2 \right)$
$$= \left(\sqrt{3}, 2, 0 \right),$$

then

$$\frac{\sqrt{3}}{2}v_1 - \frac{1}{2}v_2 = \sqrt{3}$$
$$v_1 - v_2 = 2$$
$$v_2 = 0$$

which implies that $v_1 = 2$ and $v_2 = 0$. So, the
preimage of $\mathbf{w}$ is $(2, 0)$.

10. T is *not* a linear transformation because it does not
preserve addition nor scalar multiplication.
For example,

$$T(1, 1) + T(1, 1) = (1, 1) + (1, 1)$$
$$= (2, 2) \neq (4, 2) = T(2, 2).$$

12. T is *not* a linear transformation because it does not
preserve addition. For example,

$$T(1, 1, 1) + T(1, 1, 1) = (2, 2, 2) + (2, 2, 2)$$
$$= (4, 4, 4)$$
$$\neq (3, 3, 3) = T(2, 2, 2).$$

14. T is *not* a linear transformation because it does not
preserve addition nor scalar multiplication. For example,

$$T(1, 1) + T(1, 1) = (1, 1, 1) + (1, 1, 1)$$
$$= (2, 2, 2) \neq (4, 4, 4) = T(2, 2).$$

16. T preserves addition.

$$T(A_1) + T(A_2) = T\left(\begin{bmatrix} a_1 & b_1 \\ c_1 & d_1 \end{bmatrix} \right) + T\left(\begin{bmatrix} a_2 & b_2 \\ c_2 & d_2 \end{bmatrix} \right)$$
$$= a_1 + b_1 + c_1 + d_1 + a_2 + b_2 + c_2 + d_2$$
$$= (a_1 + a_2) + (b_1 + b_2) + (c_1 + c_2) + (d_1 + d_2) = T(A_1 + A_2)$$

T preserves scalar multiplication.

$$T(kA) = ka + kb + kc + kd = k(a + b + c + d) = kT(A)$$

Therefore, T is a linear transformation.

181

18. T is *not* a linear transformation. T does *not* preserve addition.

$$T(A_1) + T(A_2) = T\left(\begin{bmatrix} a_1 & b_1 \\ c_1 & d_1 \end{bmatrix}\right) + T\left(\begin{bmatrix} a_2 & b_2 \\ c_2 & d_2 \end{bmatrix}\right) = b_1^2 + b_2^2 \neq (b_1 + b_2)^2 = T(A_1 + A_2)$$

20. Let A and B be two elements of $M_{3,3}$ (two 3×3 matrices) and let c be a scalar. First

$$T(A + B) = \begin{bmatrix} 1 & 0 & 0 \\ 0 & 1 & 0 \\ 0 & 0 & -1 \end{bmatrix}(A + B) = \begin{bmatrix} 1 & 0 & 0 \\ 0 & 1 & 0 \\ 0 & 0 & -1 \end{bmatrix}A + \begin{bmatrix} 1 & 0 & 0 \\ 0 & 1 & 0 \\ 0 & 0 & -1 \end{bmatrix}B = T(A) + T(B)$$

by Theorem 2.3, part 2. And

$$T(cA) = \begin{bmatrix} 1 & 0 & 0 \\ 0 & 1 & 0 \\ 0 & 0 & -1 \end{bmatrix}(cA) = c\begin{bmatrix} 1 & 0 & 0 \\ 0 & 1 & 0 \\ 0 & 0 & -1 \end{bmatrix}A = cT(A)$$

by Theorem 2.3, part 4. So, T is a linear transformation.

22. T preserves addition.

$$T\left(a_0 + a_1 x + a_2 x^2\right) + T\left(b_0 + b_1 x + b_2 x^2\right) = (a_1 + 2a_2 x) + (b_1 + 2b_2 x)$$
$$= (a_1 + b_1) + 2(a_2 + b_2)x$$
$$= T\left((a_0 + b_0) + (a_1 + b_1)x + (a_2 + b_2)x^2\right)$$

T preserves scalar multiplication.

$$T\left(c\left(a_0 + a_1 x + a_2 x^2\right)\right) = T\left(ca_0 + ca_1 x + ca_2 x^2\right) = ca_1 + 2ca_2 x = c(a_1 + 2a_2 x) = cT\left(a_0 + a_1 x + a_2 x^2\right)$$

Therefore, T *is* a linear transformation.

24. First express $(1, 0)$ in terms of $(1, 1)$ and $(1, -1)$: $(1, 0) = \frac{1}{2}(1, 1) + \frac{1}{2}(1, -1)$. Then,

$$T(1, 0) = T\left[\frac{1}{2}(1, 1) + \frac{1}{2}(1, -1)\right] = \frac{1}{2}T(1, 1) + \frac{1}{2}T(1, -1) = \frac{1}{2}(1, 0) + \frac{1}{2}(0, 1) = \left(\frac{1}{2}, \frac{1}{2}\right).$$

Similarly, express $(0, 2) = 1(1, 1) - 1(1, -1)$. Then,

$$T(0, 2) = T\left[(1, 1) - (1, -1)\right] = T(1, 1) - T(1, -1) = (1, 0) - (0, 1) = (1, -1).$$

26. Because $(2, -1, 0)$ can be written as

$$(2, -1, 0) = 2(1, 0, 0) - 1(0, 1, 0) + 0(0, 0, 1),$$

you can use Property 4 of Theorem 6.1 to write

$$T(2, -1, 0) = 2T(1, 0, 0) - T(0, 1, 0) + 0T(0, 0, 1)$$
$$= 2(2, 4, -1) - (1, 3, -2) + (0, 0, 0)$$
$$= (3, 5, 0).$$

28. Because $(-2, 4, -1)$ can be written as

$$(-2, 4, -1) = -2(1, 0, 0) + 4(0, 1, 0) - 1(0, 0, 1),$$

you can use Property 4 of Theorem 6.1 to write

$$T(-2, 4, -1) = -2T(1, 0, 0) + 4T(0, 1, 0) - T(0, 0, 1)$$
$$= -2(2, 4, -1) + 4(1, 3, -2) - (0, -2, 2)$$
$$= (0, 6, -8).$$

30. Because $(0, 2, -1)$ can be written as

$$(0, 2, -1) = \frac{3}{2}(1, 1, 1) - \frac{1}{2}(0, -1, 2) - \frac{3}{2}(1, 0, 1),$$ you can

use Property 4 of Theorem 6.1 to write

$$T(0, 2, -1) = \frac{3}{2}T(1, 1, 1) - \frac{1}{2}T(0, -1, 2) - \frac{3}{2}T(1, 0, 1)$$
$$= \frac{3}{2}(2, 0, -1) - \frac{1}{2}(-3, 2, -1) - \frac{3}{2}(1, 1, 0)$$
$$= \left(3, -\frac{5}{2}, -1\right).$$

32. Because $(-2, 1, 0)$ can be written as

$$(-2, 1, 0) = 2(1, 1, 1) + (0, -1, 2) - 4(1, 0, 1),$$ you can use

Property 4 of Theorem 6.1 to write

$$T(-2, 1, 0) = 2T(1, 1, 1) + T(0, -1, 2) - 4T(1, 0, 1)$$
$$= 2(2, 0, -1) + (-3, 2, -1) - 4(1, 1, 0)$$
$$= (-3, -2, -3).$$

34. Because the matrix has 2 columns, the dimension of R^n is 2. Because the matrix has 3 rows, the dimension of R^m is 3. So, $T: R^2 \to R^3$.

36. Because the matrix has five columns, the dimension of R^n is 5. Because the matrix has two rows, the dimension of R^m is 2. So, $T: R^5 \to R^2$.

38. Since the matrix has five columns, the dimension of R^n is 5.

Since the matrix has three rows, the dimension of R^m is 3.

So, $T : R^5 \to R^3$.

40. (a) $T(2, 4) = \begin{bmatrix} 1 & 2 \\ -2 & 4 \\ -2 & 2 \end{bmatrix} \begin{bmatrix} 2 \\ 4 \end{bmatrix} = \begin{bmatrix} 10 \\ 12 \\ 4 \end{bmatrix} = (10, 12, 4)$

(b) The preimage of $(-1, 2, 2)$ is given by solving the equation

$$T(v_1, v_2) = \begin{bmatrix} 1 & 2 \\ -2 & 4 \\ -2 & 2 \end{bmatrix} \begin{bmatrix} v_1 \\ v_2 \end{bmatrix} = \begin{bmatrix} -1 \\ 2 \\ 2 \end{bmatrix}$$

for $\mathbf{v} = (v_1, v_2)$. The equivalent system of linear equations

$$v_1 + 2v_2 = -1$$
$$-2v_1 + 4v_2 = 2$$
$$-2v_1 + 2v_2 = 2$$

has the solution $v_1 = -1$ and $v_2 = 0$. So, $(-1, 0)$ is the preimage of $(-1, 2, 2)$ under T.

(c) Because the system of linear equations represented by the equation

$$\begin{bmatrix} 1 & 2 \\ -2 & 4 \\ -2 & 2 \end{bmatrix} \begin{bmatrix} v_1 \\ v_2 \end{bmatrix} = \begin{bmatrix} 1 \\ 1 \\ 1 \end{bmatrix}$$

has no solution, $(1, 1, 1)$ has no preimage under T.

42. (a) $T(1, 0, -1, 3, 0) = \begin{bmatrix} -1 & 2 & 1 & 3 & 4 \\ 0 & 0 & 2 & -1 & 0 \end{bmatrix} \begin{bmatrix} 1 \\ 0 \\ -1 \\ 3 \\ 0 \end{bmatrix} = \begin{bmatrix} 7 \\ -5 \end{bmatrix} = (7, -5).$

(b) The preimage of $(-1, 8)$ is determined by solving the equation $T(v_1, v_2, v_3, v_4, v_5) = \begin{bmatrix} -1 & 2 & 1 & 3 & 4 \\ 0 & 0 & 2 & -1 & 0 \end{bmatrix} \begin{bmatrix} v_1 \\ v_2 \\ v_3 \\ v_4 \\ v_5 \end{bmatrix} = \begin{bmatrix} -1 \\ 8 \end{bmatrix}.$

The equivalent system of linear equations has the solution $v_1 = 5 + 2r + \frac{7}{2}s + 4t$, $v_2 = r$, $v_3 = 4 + \frac{1}{2}s$, $v_4 = s$, and $v_5 = t$, where r, s, and t are any real numbers. So, the preimage is given by the set of vectors

$$\left\{ \left(5 + 2r + \tfrac{7}{2}s + 4t, r, 4 + \tfrac{1}{2}s, s, t \right) : r, s, t \text{ are real numbers} \right\}.$$

44. (a) $T(1, 0, 1, 0, 1) = \begin{bmatrix} 0 & 1 & 0 & 1 & 0 \\ 1 & 0 & 2 & 0 & 1 \\ 1 & 1 & 1 & 1 & 1 \end{bmatrix} \begin{bmatrix} 1 \\ 0 \\ 1 \\ 0 \\ 1 \end{bmatrix} = \begin{bmatrix} 0 \\ 4 \\ 3 \end{bmatrix}$

(b) The preimage of $(0, 0, 0)$ is determined by solving the equation.

$$T(v_1, v_2, v_3, v_4, v_5) = \begin{bmatrix} 0 & 1 & 0 & 1 & 0 \\ 1 & 0 & 2 & 0 & 1 \\ 1 & 1 & 1 & 1 & 1 \end{bmatrix} \begin{bmatrix} v_1 \\ v_2 \\ v_3 \\ v_4 \\ v_5 \end{bmatrix} = \begin{bmatrix} 0 \\ 0 \\ 0 \end{bmatrix}$$

The equivalent system of linear equations has the solution $v_1 = -t$, $v_2 = -s$, $v_3 = 0$, $v_4 = s$, and $v_5 = t$, where s and t are any real numbers.

So, the preimage is given by the set of vectors $\{(-t, -s, 0, s, t)\}$.

(c) The preimage of $(1, 1, 1)$ is determined by solving the equation.

$$T(v_1, v_2, v_3, v_4, v_5) = \begin{bmatrix} 0 & 1 & 0 & 1 & 0 \\ 1 & 0 & 2 & 0 & 1 \\ 1 & 1 & 1 & 1 & 1 \end{bmatrix} \begin{bmatrix} v_1 \\ v_2 \\ v_3 \\ v_4 \\ v_5 \end{bmatrix} = \begin{bmatrix} 1 \\ 1 \\ 1 \end{bmatrix}$$

The equivalent system of linear equations has the solution $v_1 = -1 - t$, $v_2 = 1 - s$, $v_3 = 1$, $v_4 = s$, and $v_5 = t$, where s and t are real numbers.

So, the preimage is given by the set of vectors $\{(-1 - t, 1 - s, 1, s, t)\}$.

46. If $\theta = 45°$, then T is given by

$T(x, y) = (x \cos \theta - y \sin \theta, x \sin \theta + y \cos \theta)$

$= \left(\dfrac{\sqrt{2}}{2}x - \dfrac{\sqrt{2}}{2}y, \dfrac{\sqrt{2}}{2}x + \dfrac{\sqrt{2}}{2}y \right)$.

Solving $T(x, y) = \mathbf{v} = (1, 1)$, you have

$\dfrac{\sqrt{2}}{2}x - \dfrac{\sqrt{2}}{2}y = 1$ and $\dfrac{\sqrt{2}}{2}x + \dfrac{\sqrt{2}}{2}y = 1$.

So, $x = \sqrt{2}$ and $y = 0$, and the preimage of $\mathbf{v}$ is $(\sqrt{2}, 0)$.

48. $\begin{bmatrix} a & -b \\ b & a \end{bmatrix} \begin{bmatrix} 12 \\ 5 \end{bmatrix} = \begin{bmatrix} 13 \\ 0 \end{bmatrix}$

You then obtain the following system of equations.

$12a - 5b = 13$

$12b + 5a = 0$

Solving the second equation for a gives $a = \dfrac{-12}{5}b$.

Substituting this back into the first equation produces

$12\left(\dfrac{-12}{5}b \right) - 5b = 13$

$\dfrac{-144}{5}b - 5b = 13$

$\dfrac{-169}{5}b = 13$

$b = \dfrac{-5}{13}$.

Substituting $b = \dfrac{-5}{13}$ into $a = \dfrac{-12}{5}b$ you obtain

$a = \dfrac{12}{13}$.

50. If $\mathbf{v} = (x, y, z)$ is a vector into R^3, then $T(\mathbf{v}) = (0, y, z)$. In other words, T maps every vector in R^3 to its orthogonal projection in the yz-plane.

52. T is a linear transformation.

T preserves addition.

$T(A + B) = (A + B)X - X(A + B)$

$\quad = AX + BX - XA - XB$

$\quad = (AX - XA) + (BX - XB)$

$\quad = T(A) + T(B)$

T preserves scalar multiplication.

$T(cA) = (cA)X - X(cA)$

$\quad = c(AX) - c(XA)$

$\quad = c(AX - XA)$

$\quad = cT(A)$

54. T is *not* a linear transformation.

Consider $A = I_n$. Then $T(A) = 1$, but

$T(2A) = 2^n \neq 2T(A)$.

56. $T\left(\begin{bmatrix} 1 & 3 \\ -1 & 4 \end{bmatrix}\right) = T\begin{bmatrix} 1 & 0 \\ 0 & 0 \end{bmatrix} + 3T\begin{bmatrix} 0 & 1 \\ 0 & 0 \end{bmatrix} - T\begin{bmatrix} 0 & 0 \\ 1 & 0 \end{bmatrix} + 4T\begin{bmatrix} 0 & 0 \\ 0 & 1 \end{bmatrix} = \begin{bmatrix} 1 & -1 \\ 0 & 2 \end{bmatrix} + 3\begin{bmatrix} 0 & 2 \\ 1 & 1 \end{bmatrix} - \begin{bmatrix} 1 & 2 \\ 0 & 1 \end{bmatrix} + 4\begin{bmatrix} 3 & -1 \\ 1 & 0 \end{bmatrix} = \begin{bmatrix} 12 & -1 \\ 7 & 4 \end{bmatrix}$

58. This statement is true because D_x is a linear transformation and therefore preserves addition and scalar multiplication.

60. This statement is false because $\cos \dfrac{x}{2} \neq \dfrac{1}{2}\cos x$ for all x.

66. Solve the equation $\int_0^1 p(x)\,dx = 1$ for $p(x)$ in P_2.

$\int_0^1 \left(a_0 + a_1 x + a_2 x^2\right)dx = 1 \Rightarrow \left[a_0 x + a_1 \dfrac{x^2}{2} + a_2 \dfrac{x^3}{3}\right]_0^1 = 1 \Rightarrow a_0 + \dfrac{1}{2}a_1 + \dfrac{1}{3}a_2 = 1.$

Letting $a_2 = -3b$ and $a_1 = -2a$ be free variables, $a_0 = 1 + a + b$, and $p(x) = (1 + a + b) - 2ax - 3bx^2$.

68. (a) False. This function does not preserve addition nor scalar multiplication. For example,
$$f(3x) = 27x^3 \neq 3f(x).$$

(b) False. If $f: R \to R$ is given by $f(x) = ax + b$ for some $a, b \in R$, then it preserves addition and scalar multiplication if and only if $b = 0$.

70. (a) $T(x, y) = T\big[x(1, 0) + y(0, 1)\big]$
$= xT(1, 0) + yT(0, 1)$
$= x(0, 1) + y(1, 0) = (y, x)$

(b) T is a reflection about the line $y = x$.

72. Use the result of Exercise 61(a) as follows.

$T(3, 4) = \left(\dfrac{3+4}{2}, \dfrac{3+4}{2}\right) = \left(\dfrac{7}{2}, \dfrac{7}{2}\right)$

$T(T(3, 4)) = T\left(\dfrac{7}{2}, \dfrac{7}{2}\right)$

$= \left(\dfrac{1}{2}\left(\dfrac{7}{2} + \dfrac{7}{2}\right), \dfrac{1}{2}\left(\dfrac{7}{2} + \dfrac{7}{2}\right)\right) = \left(\dfrac{7}{2}, \dfrac{7}{2}\right)$

T is projection onto the line $y = x$.

62. If $D_x\big(g(x)\big) = e^x$, then $g(x) = e^x + C$.

64. If $D_x\big(g(x)\big) = \dfrac{1}{x}$, then $g(x) = \ln x + C$.

74. To show that $T : V \to W$ is a linear transformation, show that $T : V \to W$ preserves addition and scalar multiplication by using the definition:

(1) $T(u + v) = T(u) + T(v)$

and

(2) $T(cu) = cT(u)$,

where c is any nonzero constant.

76. (a) Because $T(0, 0) = (-h, -k) \neq (0, 0)$, a translation cannot be a linear transformation.

(b) $T(0, 0) = (0 - 2, 0 + 1) = (-2, 1)$
$T(2, -1) = (2 - 2, -1 + 1) = (0, 0)$
$T(5, 4) = (5 - 2, 4 + 1) = (3, 5)$

(c) Because $T(x, y) = (x - h, y - k) = (x, y)$ implies $x - h = x$ and $y - k = y$, a translation has no fixed points.

78. There are many possible examples. For instance, let $T: R^3 \to R^3$ be given by $T(x, y, z) = (0, 0, 0)$. Then if $\{v_1, v_2, v_3\}$ is any set of linearly independent vectors, their images $T(v_1), T(v_2), T(v_3)$ form a dependent set.

80. Let T be defined by $T(v) = \langle v, v_0\rangle$. Then because

$T(v + w) = \langle v + w, v_0\rangle = \langle v, v_0\rangle + \langle w, v_0\rangle = T(v) + T(w)$

and $T(cv) = \langle cv, v_0\rangle = c\langle v, v_0\rangle = cT(v)$, T is a linear transformation.

82. Because

$$T(\mathbf{u} + \mathbf{v}) = \langle \mathbf{u} + \mathbf{v}, \mathbf{w}_1 \rangle \mathbf{w}_1 + \cdots + \langle \mathbf{u} + \mathbf{v}, \mathbf{w}_n \rangle \mathbf{w}_n$$

$$= \left(\langle \mathbf{u}, \mathbf{w}_1 \rangle \mathbf{w}_1 + \langle \mathbf{v}, \mathbf{w}_1 \rangle \mathbf{w}_1 \right) + \cdots + \left(\langle \mathbf{u}, \mathbf{w}_n \rangle \mathbf{w}_n + \langle \mathbf{v}, \mathbf{w}_n \rangle \mathbf{w}_n \right)$$

$$= \left(\langle \mathbf{u}, \mathbf{w}_1 \rangle \mathbf{w}_1 + \cdots + \langle \mathbf{u}, \mathbf{w}_n \rangle \mathbf{w}_n \right) + \langle \mathbf{v}, \mathbf{w}_1 \rangle \mathbf{w}_1 + \cdots + \langle \mathbf{v}, \mathbf{w}_n \rangle \mathbf{w}_n = T(\mathbf{u}) + T(\mathbf{v})$$

and

$$T(c\mathbf{u}) = \langle c\mathbf{u}, \mathbf{w}_1 \rangle \mathbf{w}_1 + \cdots + \langle c\mathbf{u}, \mathbf{w}_n \rangle \mathbf{w}_n = c\langle \mathbf{u}, \mathbf{w}_1 \rangle \mathbf{w}_1 + \cdots + c\langle \mathbf{u}, \mathbf{w}_n \rangle \mathbf{w}_n = c \left[\langle \mathbf{u}, \mathbf{w}_1 \rangle \mathbf{w}_1 + \cdots + \langle \mathbf{u}, \mathbf{w}_n \rangle \mathbf{w}_n \right] = cT(\mathbf{u}),$$

T is a linear transformation.

84. Suppose first that T is a linear transformation. Then $T(a\mathbf{u} + b\mathbf{v}) = T(a\mathbf{u}) + T(b\mathbf{v}) = aT(\mathbf{u}) + bT(\mathbf{v})$.

Second, suppose $T(a\mathbf{u} + b\mathbf{v}) = aT(\mathbf{u}) + bT(\mathbf{v})$. Then $T(\mathbf{u} + \mathbf{v}) = T(1\mathbf{u} + 1\mathbf{v}) = T(\mathbf{u}) + T(\mathbf{v})$

and $T(c\mathbf{u}) = T(c\mathbf{u} + \mathbf{0}) = cT(\mathbf{u}) + T(\mathbf{0}) = cT(\mathbf{u})$.

Section 6.2 The Kernel and Range of a Linear Transformation

2. $T : R^3 \to R^3, T(x, y, z) = (x, 0, z)$

The kernel consists of all vectors lying on the y-axis. That is, $\ker(T) = \{(0, y, 0) : y \text{ is a real number}\}$.

4. $T : R^3 \to R^3, T(x, y, z) = (z, y, x)$

Solving the equation $T(x, y, z) = (z, y, x) = (0, 0, 0)$ yields that trivial solution $x = y = z = 0$. So,

$\ker(T) = \{(0, 0, 0)\}$.

6. $T : P_2 \to R, T(a_0 + a_1 x + a_2 x^2) = a_0$

Solving the equation $T(a_0 + a_1 x + a_2 x^2) = a_0 = 0$ yields solutions of the form $a_0 = 0$ and a_1 and a_2 are any real numbers. So,

$\ker(T) = \{a_1 x + a_2 x^2 : a_1, a_2 \in R\}$.

8. $T : P_3 \to P_2$,

$$T(a_0 + a_1 x + a_2 x^2 + a_3 x^3) = a_1 + 2a_2 x + 3a_3 x^2$$

Solving the equation

$$T(a_0 + a_1 + a_2 x^2 + a_3 x^3) = a_1 + 2a_2 x + 3a_3 x^2 = 0$$

yields solutions of the form $a_1 = a_2 = a_3 = 0$ and a_0 any real number. So, $\ker(T) = \{a_0 : a_0 \in R\}$.

10. $T : R^2 \to R^2, T(x, y) = (x - y, y - x)$

Solving the equation

$T(x, y) = (x - y, y - x) = (0, 0)$ yields solutions of the form $x = y$. So, $\ker(T) = \{(x, x) : x \in R\}$.

12. (a) Because

$$T(\mathbf{v}) = \begin{bmatrix} 1 & 2 \\ -2 & -4 \end{bmatrix} \begin{bmatrix} v_1 \\ v_2 \end{bmatrix} = \begin{bmatrix} 0 \\ 0 \end{bmatrix}$$

has solutions of the form $(-2t, t)$ where t is any real number, a basis for $\ker(T)$ is $\{(-2, 1)\}$.

(b) Transpose A and find the equivalent reduced row-echelon form

$$A^T = \begin{bmatrix} 1 & -2 \\ 2 & -4 \end{bmatrix} \Rightarrow \begin{bmatrix} 1 & -2 \\ 0 & 0 \end{bmatrix}.$$

So, a basis for range (T) is $\{(1, -2)\}$.

14. (a) Because

$$T(\mathbf{v}) = \begin{bmatrix} 1 & -2 & 1 \\ 0 & 2 & 1 \end{bmatrix} \begin{bmatrix} v_1 \\ v_2 \\ v_3 \end{bmatrix} = \begin{bmatrix} 0 \\ 0 \end{bmatrix}$$

has solutions of the form $\left(-2t, -\frac{1}{2}t, t\right)$ where t is any real number, a basis for $\ker(T)$ is $\left\{\left(-2, -\frac{1}{2}, 1\right)\right\}$.

(b) Transpose A and find the equivalent reduced row-echelon form

$$A^T = \begin{bmatrix} 1 & 0 \\ -2 & 2 \\ 1 & 1 \end{bmatrix} \Rightarrow \begin{bmatrix} 1 & 0 \\ 0 & 1 \\ 0 & 0 \end{bmatrix}$$

So, a basis for the range (T) is $\{(1, 0), (0, 1)\}$.

16. (a) Because

$$T(\mathbf{v}) = \begin{bmatrix} 1 & 1 \\ -1 & 2 \\ 0 & 1 \end{bmatrix}\begin{bmatrix} v_1 \\ v_2 \end{bmatrix} = \begin{bmatrix} 0 \\ 0 \end{bmatrix}$$

has only the trivial solution $v_1 = v_2 = 0$, the kernel is $\{(0, 0)\}$.

(b) Transpose A and find the equivalent reduced row-echelon form

$$A^T = \begin{bmatrix} 1 & -1 & 0 \\ 1 & 2 & 1 \end{bmatrix} \Rightarrow \begin{bmatrix} 1 & 0 & \frac{1}{3} \\ 0 & 1 & \frac{1}{3} \end{bmatrix}$$

So, a basis for the range (T) is $\left\{\left(1, 0, \frac{1}{3}\right), \left(0, 1, \frac{1}{3}\right)\right\}$.

18. (a) Because

$$T(\mathbf{v}) = \begin{bmatrix} -1 & 3 & 2 & 1 & 4 \\ 2 & 3 & 5 & 0 & 0 \\ 2 & 1 & 2 & 1 & 0 \end{bmatrix}\begin{bmatrix} v_1 \\ v_2 \\ v_3 \\ v_4 \\ v_5 \end{bmatrix} = \begin{bmatrix} 0 \\ 0 \\ 0 \end{bmatrix}$$

has solutions of the form
$(-10s - 4t, -15s - 24t, 13s + 16t, 9s, 9t)$, a basis
for $\ker(T)$ is

$$\{(-10, -15, 13, 9, 0), (-4, -24, 16, 0, 9)\}.$$

(b) Transpose A and find the equivalent reduced row-echelon form.

$$A^T = \begin{bmatrix} -1 & 2 & 2 \\ 3 & 3 & 1 \\ 2 & 5 & 2 \\ 1 & 0 & 1 \\ 4 & 0 & 0 \end{bmatrix} \Rightarrow \begin{bmatrix} 1 & 0 & 0 \\ 0 & 1 & 0 \\ 0 & 0 & 1 \\ 0 & 0 & 0 \\ 0 & 0 & 0 \end{bmatrix}$$

So, a basis for range (T) is
$\{(1, 0, 0), (0, 1, 0), (0, 0, 1)\}$, and the range of T is all
of R^3.

20. (a) The kernel of T is given by the solution to the
equation $T(\mathbf{x}) = \mathbf{0}$. So,
$\ker(T) = \{(2t, -3t) : t \text{ is any real number}\}$.

(b) nullity$(T) = \dim\big(\ker(T)\big) = 1$

(c) Transpose T and find the equivalent reduced row-echelon form.

$$A^T = \begin{bmatrix} 3 & -9 \\ 2 & -6 \end{bmatrix} \Rightarrow \begin{bmatrix} 1 & -3 \\ 0 & 0 \end{bmatrix}$$

So, range$(T) = \{(t, -3t) : t \text{ is any real number}\}$.

(d) rank$(T) = \dim\big(\text{range}(T)\big) = 1$

22. (a) Because $T(\mathbf{x}) = \mathbf{0}$ has only the trivial solution
$\mathbf{x} = (0, 0)$, the kernel of T is $\{(0, 0)\}$.

(b) nullity$(T) = \dim\big(\ker(T)\big) = 0$

(c) Transpose A and find the equivalent row-echelon form.

$$A^T = \begin{bmatrix} 4 & 0 & 2 \\ 1 & 0 & -3 \end{bmatrix} \Rightarrow \begin{bmatrix} 1 & 0 & 0 \\ 0 & 0 & 1 \end{bmatrix}$$

So, range$(T) = \{(t, 0, s) : s, t \in R\}$.

(d) rank$(T) = \dim\big(\text{range}(T)\big) = 2$

24. (a) The kernel of T is given by the solution to the
equation $T(\mathbf{x}) = \mathbf{0}$. So, $\ker(T) = \{(5t, t) : t \in R\}$.

(b) nullity$(T) = \dim\big(\ker(T)\big) = 1$

(c) Transpose A and find its equivalent row-echelon form.

$$A^T = \begin{bmatrix} \frac{1}{26} & -\frac{5}{26} \\ -\frac{5}{26} & \frac{25}{26} \end{bmatrix} \Rightarrow \begin{bmatrix} 1 & -5 \\ 0 & 0 \end{bmatrix}$$

So, range$(T) = \{(t, -5t) : t \in R\}$.

(d) rank$(T) = \dim\big(\text{range}(T)\big) = 1$

26. (a) The kernel of T is given by the solution to the
equation $T(\mathbf{x}) = \mathbf{0}$. So, $\ker(T) = \{(0, t, 0) : t \in R\}$.

(b) nullity$(T) = \dim\big(\ker(T)\big) = 1$

(c) Transpose A and find its equivalent row-echelon form.

$$A^T = \begin{bmatrix} 1 & 0 & 0 \\ 0 & 0 & 0 \\ 0 & 0 & 1 \end{bmatrix} \Rightarrow \begin{bmatrix} 1 & 0 & 0 \\ 0 & 0 & 1 \\ 0 & 0 & 0 \end{bmatrix}$$

So, range$(T) = \{(t, 0, s) : s, t \in R\}$.

(d) rank$(T) = \dim\big(\text{range}(T)\big) = 2$

28. (a) The kernel of T is given by the solution to the equation $T(\mathbf{x}) = \mathbf{0}$. So,

$$\ker(T) = \{(t, -t, s, -s) : s, t \in R\}.$$

(b) $\text{nullity}(T) = \dim(\ker(T)) = 2$

(c) Transpose A and find its equivalent row-echelon form.

$$A^T = \begin{bmatrix} 1 & 0 \\ 1 & 0 \\ 0 & 1 \\ 0 & 1 \end{bmatrix} \Rightarrow \begin{bmatrix} 1 & 0 \\ 0 & 1 \\ 0 & 0 \\ 0 & 0 \end{bmatrix}$$

So, $\text{range}(T) = R^2$.

(d) $\text{rank}(T) = \dim(\text{range}(T)) = 2$

30. (a) The kernel of T is given by the solution to the equation $T(\mathbf{x}) = \mathbf{0}$. So,

$$\ker(T) = \{(-t - s - 2r, 6t - 2s, r, s, t) : r, s, t \in R\}.$$

(b) $\text{nullity}(T) = \dim(\ker(T)) = 3$

(c) Transpose A and find its equivalent row-echelon form.

$$A^T = \begin{bmatrix} 3 & 4 & 2 \\ -2 & 3 & -3 \\ 6 & 8 & 4 \\ -1 & 10 & -4 \\ 15 & -14 & 20 \end{bmatrix} \Rightarrow \begin{bmatrix} 17 & 0 & 18 \\ 0 & 17 & -5 \\ 0 & 0 & 0 \\ 0 & 0 & 0 \\ 0 & 0 & 0 \end{bmatrix}$$

So, $\text{range}(T) = \{(17s, 17t, 18s - 5t) : s, t \in R\}$.

(d) $\text{rank}(T) = \dim(\text{range}(T)) = 2$

32. Because $\text{rank}(T) + \text{nullity}(T) = 3$, and you are given $\text{rank}(T) = 1$, then $\text{nullity}(T) = 2$. So, the kernel of T is a plane, and the range is a line.

34. Because $\text{rank}(T) + \text{nullity}(T) = 3$, and you are given $\text{rank}(T) = 3$, then $\text{nullity}(T) = 0$. So, the kernel of T is the single point $\{(0, 0, 0)\}$, and the range is all of R^3.

36. The kernel of T is determined by solving $T(x, y, z) = (-x, y, z) = (0, 0, 0)$, which implies that the kernel is the single point $\{(0, 0, 0)\}$. From the equation $\text{rank}(T) + \text{nullity}(T) = 3$, you see that the rank of T is 3. So, the range of T is all of R^3.

38. The kernel of T is determined by solving $T(x, y, z) = (x, y, 0) = (0, 0, 0)$, which implies that $x = y = 0$. So, the nullity of T is 1, and the kernel is a line (the z-axis). The range of T is found by observing that $\text{rank}(T) + \text{nullity}(T) = 3$. That is, the range of T is 2-dimensional, the xy-plane in R^3.

40. $\text{rank}(T) + \text{nullity}(T) = \dim R^5 \Rightarrow \text{nullity}(T) = 5 - 2 = 3$

42. $\text{rank}(T) + \text{nullity}(T) = \dim P_3 \Rightarrow \text{nullity}(T) = 4 - 2 = 2$

44. Because $|A| = -1 \neq 0$, the homogeneous equation $A\mathbf{x} = \mathbf{0}$ has only the trivial solution. So, $\ker(T) = \{(0, 0)\}$ and T is one-to-one (by Theorem 6.6). Furthermore, because $\text{rank}(T) = \dim(R^2) - \text{nullity}(T) = 2 - 0 = 2 = \dim(R^2)$, T is onto (by Theorem 6.7).

46. Because $|A| = -24 \neq 0$, the homogeneous equation $A\mathbf{x} = \mathbf{0}$ has only the trivial solution. So, $\ker(T) = \{(0, 0, 0)\}$ and T is one-to-one (by Theorem 6.6). Furthermore, because $\text{rank}(T) = \dim R^3 - \text{nullity}(T) = 3 - 0 = 3 = \dim(R^3)$, T is onto (by Theorem 6.7).

48. The matrix representation of $T : R^2 \to R^2$ is given by $A = \begin{bmatrix} 1 & -1 \\ -1 & 1 \end{bmatrix}$.

The matrix in row-echelon form is $A = \begin{bmatrix} 1 & -1 \\ 0 & 0 \end{bmatrix}$.

So, you have the following.

$\dim(\text{domain}) = 2, \text{rank}(T) = 1, \text{nullity}(T) = 1$

Because the rank of T is not equal to the dimension of R^2, T is not onto. Because $\ker(T) \neq \{\mathbf{0}\}$, T is not one-to-one.

50. $A = \begin{bmatrix} -1 & 3 & 2 & 1 & 4 \\ 2 & 3 & 5 & 0 & 0 \\ 2 & 1 & 2 & 1 & 0 \end{bmatrix} \Rightarrow \begin{bmatrix} 1 & 0 & 0 & \frac{10}{9} & \frac{4}{9} \\ 0 & 1 & 0 & \frac{5}{3} & \frac{8}{3} \\ 0 & 0 & 1 & \frac{-13}{9} & \frac{-16}{9} \end{bmatrix}$

So, you have the following.

$\dim(\text{domain}) = 5, \text{rank}(T) = 3, \text{nullity}(T) = 2$

Because the rank of T is equal to the dimension of R^3, T is onto. Because $\ker(T) \neq \{\mathbf{0}\}$, T is not one-to-one.

52. The vector spaces isomorphic to R^6 are those whose dimension is six. That is, (a) $M_{2,3}$ (d) $M_{6,1}$ (e) P_5 and

(f) $\{(x_1, x_2, x_3, 0, x_5, x_6, x_7) : x_i \in R\}$ are isomorphic to R^6.

54. Solve the equation $T(p) = \int_0^1 p(x)dx = \int_0^1 (a_0 + a_1x + a_2x^2)dx = 0$ yielding $a_0 + a_1/2 + a_2/3 = 0$.

Letting $a_2 = -3b, a_1 = -2a$, you have $a_0 = -a_1/2 - a_2/3 = a + b$, and $\ker(T) = \{(a + b) - 2ax - 3bx^2 : a, b \in R\}$.

56. First compute $T(\mathbf{u}) = \text{proj}_v\mathbf{u}$, for $\mathbf{u} = (x, y, z)$.

$$T(\mathbf{u}) = \text{proj}_v\mathbf{u} = \frac{(x, y, z) \cdot (3, 0, 4)}{(3, 0, 4) \cdot (3, 0, 4)}(3, 0, 4) = \frac{3x + 4z}{25}(3, 0, 4)$$

(a) Setting $T(\mathbf{u}) = \mathbf{0}$, you have $3x + 4z = 0$, and so $\text{nullity}(T) = 2$. So, $\text{rank}(T) = 3 - 2 = 1$.

(b) A basis for the kernel of T is obtained by solving $3x + 4z = 0$. Letting $t = z$ and $s = y$, you have

$x = \frac{1}{3}(-4z) = -\frac{4}{3}t$. So, a basis for the kernel of T is $\left\{(0, 1, 0), \left(-\frac{4}{3}, 0, 1\right)\right\}$.

58. $A = \begin{bmatrix} 1 & -2 & 1 & 0 \\ 0 & 1 & 2 & 3 \\ 0 & 0 & 0 & 1 \end{bmatrix} \Rightarrow \begin{bmatrix} 1 & 0 & 5 & 0 \\ 0 & 1 & 2 & 0 \\ 0 & 0 & 0 & 1 \end{bmatrix}$

(a) $\dim(R^4) = 4$

(b) $\dim(R^3) = 3$

(c) $x_1 + 5x_3 = 0 \rightarrow x_1 = -5x_3$

$x_2 + 2x_3 = 0 \rightarrow x_2 = -2x_3$

$x_4 = 0$

So, $\ker(T) = \{(-5x_3, -2x_3, x_3, 0)\}$ and

$\dim(\ker(T)) = 1$.

(d) T is not one-to-one since the $\ker(T) \neq \{\mathbf{0}\}$.

(e) $\text{rank}(T) = 3$

$= \dim(R^3)$

So, T is onto by Theorem 6.7.

(f) T is *not* an isomorphism since it is not one-to-one.

60. Theorem 6.9 tells you that if $M_{m,n}$ and $M_{j,k}$ are of the same dimension then they are isomorphic. So, you can conclude that $mn = jk$.

62. (a) False. A concept of a dimension of a linear transformation does not exist.

(b) True. See discussion on page 309 before Theorem 6.6.

(c) True. Because $\dim(P_1) = \dim(R^2) = 2$ and any two vector spaces of equal finite dimension are isomorphic (Theorem 6.9 on page 311).

64. From Theorem 6.5,

$\text{rank}(T) + \text{nullity}(T) = n = $ dimension of V. T is one-to-one if and only if $\text{nullity}(T) = 0$ if and only if $\text{rank}(T) = $ dimension of V.

66. $T^{-1}(U)$ is nonempty because $T(\mathbf{0}) = \mathbf{0} \in U \Rightarrow \mathbf{0} \in T^{-1}(U)$.

Let $\mathbf{v}_1, \mathbf{v}_2 \in T^{-1}(U) \Rightarrow T(\mathbf{v}_1) \in U$ and $T(\mathbf{v}_2) \in U$. Because U is a subspace of W,

$T(\mathbf{v}_1) + T(\mathbf{v}_2) = T(\mathbf{v}_1 + \mathbf{v}_2) \in U \Rightarrow \mathbf{v}_1 + \mathbf{v}_2 \in T^{-1}(U)$.

Let $\mathbf{v} \in T^{-1}(U)$ and $c \in R \Rightarrow T(\mathbf{v}) \in U$. Because U is a subspace of W, $cT(\mathbf{v}) = T(c\mathbf{v}) \in U \Rightarrow c\mathbf{v} \in T^{-1}(U)$.

If $U = \{\mathbf{0}\}$, then $T^{-1}(U)$ is the kernel of T.

Section 6.3   Matrices for Linear Transformations

2. Because

$$T\left(\begin{bmatrix} 1 \\ 0 \end{bmatrix}\right) = \begin{bmatrix} 2 \\ 1 \\ -4 \end{bmatrix} \quad \text{and} \quad T\left(\begin{bmatrix} 0 \\ 1 \end{bmatrix}\right) = \begin{bmatrix} -3 \\ 1 \\ 1 \end{bmatrix},$$

the standard matrix for T is $A = \begin{bmatrix} 2 & -3 \\ 1 & -1 \\ -4 & 1 \end{bmatrix}$.

4. Because

$$T\left(\begin{bmatrix} 1 \\ 0 \end{bmatrix}\right) = \begin{bmatrix} 4 \\ 0 \\ 2 \end{bmatrix} \quad \text{and} \quad T\left(\begin{bmatrix} 0 \\ 1 \end{bmatrix}\right) = \begin{bmatrix} 1 \\ 0 \\ -3 \end{bmatrix},$$

the standard matrix for T is

$$\begin{bmatrix} 4 & 1 \\ 0 & 0 \\ 2 & -3 \end{bmatrix}.$$

6. Because

$$T\left(\begin{bmatrix} 1 \\ 0 \\ 0 \\ 0 \end{bmatrix}\right) = \begin{bmatrix} 0 \\ 0 \\ 0 \\ 0 \end{bmatrix}, \quad T\left(\begin{bmatrix} 0 \\ 1 \\ 0 \\ 0 \end{bmatrix}\right) = \begin{bmatrix} 0 \\ 0 \\ 0 \\ 0 \end{bmatrix}, \quad T\left(\begin{bmatrix} 0 \\ 0 \\ 1 \\ 0 \end{bmatrix}\right) = \begin{bmatrix} 0 \\ 0 \\ 0 \\ 0 \end{bmatrix},$$

and $T\left(\begin{bmatrix} 0 \\ 0 \\ 0 \\ 1 \end{bmatrix}\right) = \begin{bmatrix} 0 \\ 0 \\ 0 \\ 0 \end{bmatrix}$,

the standard matrix for T is $A = \begin{bmatrix} 0 & 0 & 0 & 0 \\ 0 & 0 & 0 & 0 \\ 0 & 0 & 0 & 0 \\ 0 & 0 & 0 & 0 \end{bmatrix}$.

8. Because

$$T\left(\begin{bmatrix} 1 \\ 0 \end{bmatrix}\right) = \begin{bmatrix} 1 \\ 1 \\ 2 \\ 0 \end{bmatrix} \quad \text{and} \quad T\left(\begin{bmatrix} 0 \\ 1 \end{bmatrix}\right) = \begin{bmatrix} 1 \\ -1 \\ 0 \\ 2 \end{bmatrix},$$

the standard matrix for T is

$$A = \begin{bmatrix} 1 & 1 \\ 1 & -1 \\ 2 & 0 \\ 0 & 2 \end{bmatrix}.$$

So, $T(\mathbf{v}) = \begin{bmatrix} 1 & 1 \\ 1 & -1 \\ 2 & 0 \\ 0 & 2 \end{bmatrix} \begin{bmatrix} 3 \\ -3 \end{bmatrix} = \begin{bmatrix} 0 \\ 6 \\ 6 \\ -6 \end{bmatrix}$

and $T(3, -3) = (0, 6, 6, -6)$.

10. $T(x_1, x_2, x_3, x_4) = (x_1 - x_3, x_2 - x_4, x_3 - x_1, x_2 + x_4)$

The standard matrix is

$$A = \begin{bmatrix} 1 & 0 & -1 & 0 \\ 0 & 1 & 0 & -1 \\ -1 & 0 & 1 & 0 \\ 0 & 1 & 0 & 1 \end{bmatrix}.$$

The image of $\mathbf{v}$ is

$$A\mathbf{v} = \begin{bmatrix} 1 & 0 & -1 & 0 \\ 0 & 1 & 0 & -1 \\ -1 & 0 & 1 & 0 \\ 0 & 1 & 0 & 1 \end{bmatrix} \begin{bmatrix} 1 \\ 2 \\ 3 \\ -2 \end{bmatrix} = \begin{bmatrix} -2 \\ 4 \\ 2 \\ 0 \end{bmatrix}.$$

So, $T(\mathbf{v}) = (-2, 4, 2, 0)$.

12. (a) The matrix of a reflection in the line
$y = x$, $T(x, y) = (y, x)$, is given by

$$A = \begin{bmatrix} T(1, 0) \vdots T(0, 1) \end{bmatrix} = \begin{bmatrix} 0 & 1 \\ 1 & 0 \end{bmatrix}.$$

(b) The image of **v** = (3, 4) is given by

$$A\mathbf{v} = \begin{bmatrix} 0 & 1 \\ 1 & 0 \end{bmatrix}\begin{bmatrix} 3 \\ 4 \end{bmatrix} = \begin{bmatrix} 4 \\ 3 \end{bmatrix}.$$

So, $T(3, 4) = (4, 3)$.

(c)

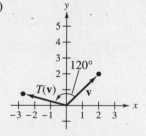

14. (a) The matrix of a reflection in the x-axis,
$T(x, y) = (x, -y)$, is given by

$$A = \begin{bmatrix} T(1, 0) \vdots T(0, 1) \end{bmatrix} = \begin{bmatrix} 1 & 0 \\ 0 & -1 \end{bmatrix}.$$

(b) The image of **v** = (4, -1) is given by

$$A\mathbf{v} = \begin{bmatrix} 1 & 0 \\ 0 & -1 \end{bmatrix}\begin{bmatrix} 4 \\ -1 \end{bmatrix} = \begin{bmatrix} 4 \\ 1 \end{bmatrix}.$$

So, $T(4, -1) = (4, 1)$.

(c)

16. (a) The counterclockwise rotation of 120° is given by

$$T(x, y) = \big(\cos(120)x - \sin(120)y, \sin(120)x + \cos(120)y\big)$$

$$= \left(-\frac{1}{2}x - \frac{\sqrt{3}}{2}y, \frac{\sqrt{3}}{2}x - \frac{1}{2}y\right).$$

So, the matrix is

$$A = \begin{bmatrix} T(1, 0) \vdots T(0, 1) \end{bmatrix} = \begin{bmatrix} -\dfrac{1}{2} & -\dfrac{\sqrt{3}}{2} \\ \dfrac{\sqrt{3}}{2} & -\dfrac{1}{2} \end{bmatrix}.$$

(b) The image of **v** = (2, 2) is given by

$$A\mathbf{v} = \begin{bmatrix} -\dfrac{1}{2} & -\dfrac{\sqrt{3}}{2} \\ \dfrac{\sqrt{3}}{2} & -\dfrac{1}{2} \end{bmatrix}\begin{bmatrix} 2 \\ 2 \end{bmatrix} = \begin{bmatrix} -1 - \sqrt{3} \\ \sqrt{3} - 1 \end{bmatrix}.$$

So, $T(2, 2) = \left(-1 - \sqrt{3}, \sqrt{3} - 1\right)$.

(c)

18. (a) The clockwise rotation of $30°$ is given by

$$T(x, y) = \left(\cos(-30)x - \sin(-30)y, \sin(-30)x + \cos(-30)y\right)$$

$$= \left(\frac{\sqrt{3}}{2}x + \frac{1}{2}y, -\frac{1}{2}x + \frac{\sqrt{3}}{2}y\right).$$

So, the matrix is

$$A = \left[T(1, 0) \vdots T(0, 1)\right] = \begin{bmatrix} \frac{\sqrt{3}}{2} & \frac{1}{2} \\ -\frac{1}{2} & \frac{\sqrt{3}}{2} \end{bmatrix}.$$

(b) The image of $\mathbf{v} = (2, 1)$ is given by

$$A\mathbf{v} = \begin{bmatrix} \frac{\sqrt{3}}{2} & \frac{1}{2} \\ -\frac{1}{2} & \frac{\sqrt{3}}{2} \end{bmatrix}\begin{bmatrix} 2 \\ 1 \end{bmatrix} = \begin{bmatrix} \sqrt{3} + \frac{1}{2} \\ -1 + \frac{\sqrt{3}}{2} \end{bmatrix}.$$

So, $T(2, 1) = \left(\sqrt{3} + \frac{1}{2}, -1 + \frac{\sqrt{3}}{2}\right).$

(c)

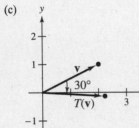

20. (a) The matrix of a reflection through the yz-coordinate plane is given by

$$A = \left[T(1, 0, 0) \vdots T(0, 1, 0) \vdots T(0, 0, 1)\right] = \begin{bmatrix} -1 & 0 & 0 \\ 0 & 1 & 0 \\ 0 & 0 & 1 \end{bmatrix}.$$

(b) The image of $\mathbf{v} = (2, 3, 4)$ is given by

$$A\mathbf{v} = \begin{bmatrix} -1 & 0 & 0 \\ 0 & 1 & 0 \\ 0 & 0 & 1 \end{bmatrix}\begin{bmatrix} 2 \\ 3 \\ 4 \end{bmatrix} = \begin{bmatrix} -2 \\ 3 \\ 4 \end{bmatrix}.$$

So, $T(2, 3, 4) = (-2, 3, 4).$

(c)

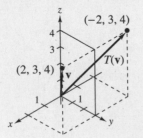

22. (a) The reflection of a vector **v** through **w** is given by

$$T(\mathbf{v}) = 2\,\text{proj}_\mathbf{w}\mathbf{v} - \mathbf{v}$$

$$T(x, y) = 2\,\frac{3x + y}{10}(3, 1) - (x, y)$$

$$= \left(\frac{4}{5}x + \frac{3}{5}y, \frac{3}{5}x - \frac{4}{5}y\right).$$

The standard matrix for T is

$$A = \left[\,T(1, 0) \vdots T(0, 1)\,\right] = \begin{bmatrix} \dfrac{4}{5} & \dfrac{3}{5} \\[2mm] \dfrac{3}{5} & -\dfrac{4}{5} \end{bmatrix}.$$

(b) The image of $\mathbf{v} = (1, 4)$ is

$$A\mathbf{v} = \begin{bmatrix} \dfrac{4}{5} & \dfrac{3}{5} \\[2mm] \dfrac{3}{5} & -\dfrac{4}{5} \end{bmatrix}\begin{bmatrix} 1 \\ 4 \end{bmatrix} = \begin{bmatrix} \dfrac{16}{5} \\[2mm] -\dfrac{13}{5} \end{bmatrix}.$$

So, $T(1, 4) = \left(\dfrac{16}{5}, \dfrac{13}{5}\right).$

(c)

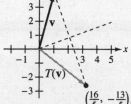

24. (a) The standard matrix for T is

$$A = \begin{bmatrix} 3 & -2 & 1 \\ 2 & -3 & 0 \\ 0 & 1 & -4 \end{bmatrix}.$$

(b) The image of $\mathbf{v} = (2, -1, -1)$ is

$$A\mathbf{v} = \begin{bmatrix} 3 & -2 & 1 \\ 2 & -3 & 0 \\ 0 & 1 & -4 \end{bmatrix}\begin{bmatrix} 2 \\ -1 \\ -1 \end{bmatrix} = \begin{bmatrix} 7 \\ 7 \\ 3 \end{bmatrix}.$$

So, $T(2, -1, -1)$ is $(7, 7, 3)$.

(c) Using a graphing utility or a computer software program to perform the multiplication in part (b) gives the same result.

26. (a) The standard matrix for T is

$$A = \begin{bmatrix} 1 & 2 & 0 & 0 \\ -1 & 1 & 0 & 0 \\ 0 & 0 & 2 & -1 \\ 1 & 0 & 0 & 0 \end{bmatrix}.$$

(b) The image of $\mathbf{v} = (0, 1, -1, 1)$ is

$$A\mathbf{v} = \begin{bmatrix} 1 & 2 & 0 & 0 \\ -1 & 1 & 0 & 0 \\ 0 & 0 & 2 & -1 \\ 1 & 0 & 0 & 0 \end{bmatrix}\begin{bmatrix} 0 \\ 1 \\ -1 \\ 1 \end{bmatrix} = \begin{bmatrix} 2 \\ 1 \\ -3 \\ 0 \end{bmatrix}.$$

So, $T(0, 1, -1, 1) = (2, 1, -3, 0)$.

(c) Using a graphing utility or a computer software program to perform the multiplication in part (b) gives the same result.

28. The standard matrices for T_1 and T_2 are

$$A_1 = \begin{bmatrix} 1 & 0 & 0 \\ 0 & 1 & 0 \\ 0 & 0 & 1 \end{bmatrix} \quad \text{and} \quad A_2 = \begin{bmatrix} 0 & 0 & 0 \\ 1 & 0 & 0 \\ 0 & 0 & 0 \end{bmatrix}.$$

The standard matrix for $T = T_2 \circ T_1$ is

$$A = A_2 A_1 = \begin{bmatrix} 0 & 0 & 0 \\ 1 & 0 & 0 \\ 0 & 0 & 0 \end{bmatrix}\begin{bmatrix} 1 & 0 & 0 \\ 0 & 1 & 0 \\ 0 & 0 & 1 \end{bmatrix} = \begin{bmatrix} 0 & 0 & 0 \\ 1 & 0 & 0 \\ 0 & 0 & 0 \end{bmatrix} = A_2$$

and the standard matrix for $T' = T_1 \circ T_2$ is

$$A' = A_1 A_2 = \begin{bmatrix} 1 & 0 & 0 \\ 0 & 1 & 0 \\ 0 & 0 & 1 \end{bmatrix}\begin{bmatrix} 0 & 0 & 0 \\ 1 & 0 & 0 \\ 0 & 0 & 0 \end{bmatrix} = \begin{bmatrix} 0 & 0 & 0 \\ 1 & 0 & 0 \\ 0 & 0 & 0 \end{bmatrix} = A_2.$$

30. The standard matrices for T_1 and T_2 are

$$A_1 = \begin{bmatrix} 1 & 0 \\ 0 & 1 \\ 0 & 1 \end{bmatrix} \quad \text{and} \quad A_2 = \begin{bmatrix} 0 & 1 & 0 \\ 0 & 0 & 1 \end{bmatrix}.$$

The standard matrix for $T = T_2 \circ T_1$ is

$$A_2 A_1 = \begin{bmatrix} 0 & 1 & 0 \\ 0 & 0 & 1 \end{bmatrix}\begin{bmatrix} 1 & 0 \\ 0 & 1 \\ 0 & 1 \end{bmatrix} = \begin{bmatrix} 0 & 1 \\ 0 & 1 \end{bmatrix}$$

and the standard matrix for $T' = T_1 \circ T_2$ is

$$A_1 A_2 = \begin{bmatrix} 1 & 0 \\ 0 & 1 \\ 0 & 1 \end{bmatrix}\begin{bmatrix} 0 & 1 & 0 \\ 0 & 0 & 1 \end{bmatrix} = \begin{bmatrix} 0 & 1 & 0 \\ 0 & 0 & 1 \\ 0 & 0 & 1 \end{bmatrix}.$$

32. The standard matrix for T is

$$A = \begin{bmatrix} 2 & 0 \\ 0 & 0 \end{bmatrix}.$$

Because $|A| = 0$, A is not invertible, and so T is not invertible.

34. The standard matrix for T is

$$A = \begin{bmatrix} 1 & 1 \\ 1 & -1 \end{bmatrix}.$$

Because $|A| = -2 \neq 0$, A is invertible.

$$A^{-1} = -\frac{1}{2}\begin{bmatrix} -1 & -1 \\ -1 & 1 \end{bmatrix} = \begin{bmatrix} \frac{1}{2} & \frac{1}{2} \\ \frac{1}{2} & -\frac{1}{2} \end{bmatrix}$$

So, $T^{-1}(x, y) = \left(\frac{1}{2}x + \frac{1}{2}y, \frac{1}{2}x - \frac{1}{2}y\right)$.

38. (a) The standard matrix for T is

$$A' = \begin{bmatrix} 1 & -1 & 0 \\ 0 & 1 & -1 \end{bmatrix}$$

and the image of $\mathbf{v}$ under T is

$$A'\mathbf{v} = \begin{bmatrix} 1 & -1 & 0 \\ 0 & 1 & -1 \end{bmatrix}\begin{bmatrix} 1 \\ 2 \\ 3 \end{bmatrix} = \begin{bmatrix} -1 \\ -1 \end{bmatrix}.$$

So, $T(\mathbf{v}) = (-1, -1)$.

(b) The image of each vector in B is as follows.

$$T(1, 1, 1) = (0, 0) = 0(1, 2) + 0(1, 1)$$

$$T(1, 1, 0) = (0, 1) = (1, 2) - (1, 1)$$

$$T(0, 1, 1) = (-1, 0) = (1, 2) - 2(1, 1)$$

So, $\left[T(1, 1, 1)\right]_{B'} = \begin{bmatrix} 0 \\ 0 \end{bmatrix}$, $\left[T(1, 1, 0)\right]_{B'} = \begin{bmatrix} -1 \\ 1 \end{bmatrix}$, and $\left[T(0, 1, 1)\right]_{B'} = \begin{bmatrix} 1 \\ -2 \end{bmatrix}$,

which implies that $A = \begin{bmatrix} 0 & 1 & 1 \\ 0 & -1 & -2 \end{bmatrix}$.

Then, because $[\mathbf{v}]_B = \begin{bmatrix} 2 \\ -1 \\ 1 \end{bmatrix}$, $[T(\mathbf{v})]_{B'} = A[\mathbf{v}]_B = \begin{bmatrix} 0 & 1 & 1 \\ 0 & -1 & -2 \end{bmatrix}\begin{bmatrix} 2 \\ -1 \\ 1 \end{bmatrix} = \begin{bmatrix} 0 \\ -1 \end{bmatrix}$.

So, $T(\mathbf{v}) = 0(1, 2) - (1, 1) = (-1, -1)$.

36. The standard matrix for T is

$$A = \begin{bmatrix} 1 & -2 & 0 & 0 \\ 0 & 1 & 0 & 0 \\ 0 & 0 & 1 & 1 \\ 0 & 0 & 1 & 0 \end{bmatrix}.$$

Because $|A| = -1 \neq 0$, A is invertible. Calculate A^{-1} by Gauss-Jordan elimination

$$A^{-1} = \begin{bmatrix} 1 & 2 & 0 & 0 \\ 0 & 1 & 0 & 0 \\ 0 & 0 & 0 & 1 \\ 0 & 0 & 1 & -1 \end{bmatrix}$$

and conclude that

$$T^{-1}(x_1, x_2, x_3, x_4) = (x_1 + 2x_2, x_2, x_4, x_3 - x_4).$$

40. (a) The standard matrix for T is

$$A' = \begin{bmatrix} 1 & 1 & 1 & 1 \\ -1 & 0 & 0 & 1 \end{bmatrix}$$

and the image of $\mathbf{v} = (4, -3, 1, 1)$ under T is

$$A'\mathbf{v} = \begin{bmatrix} 1 & 1 & 1 & 1 \\ -1 & 0 & 0 & 1 \end{bmatrix}\begin{bmatrix} 4 \\ -3 \\ 1 \\ 1 \end{bmatrix} = \begin{bmatrix} 3 \\ -3 \end{bmatrix} \Rightarrow T(\mathbf{v}) = (3, -3).$$

(b) Because

$$T(1, 0, 0, 1) = (2, 0) \;\; = 0(1, 1) + (2, 0)$$
$$T(0, 1, 0, 1) = (2, 1) \;\; = (1, 1) + \tfrac{1}{2}(2, 0)$$
$$T(1, 0, 1, 0) = (2, -1) = -(1, 1) + \tfrac{3}{2}(2, 0)$$
$$T(1, 1, 0, 0) = (2, -1) = -(1, 1) + \tfrac{3}{2}(2, 0),$$

the matrix for T relative to B and B' is $A = \begin{bmatrix} 0 & 1 & -1 & -1 \\ 1 & \frac{1}{2} & \frac{3}{2} & \frac{3}{2} \end{bmatrix}$.

Because $\mathbf{v} = (4, -3, 1, 1) = \tfrac{7}{2}(1, 0, 0, 1) - \tfrac{5}{2}(0, 1, 0, 1) + (1, 0, 1, 0) - \tfrac{1}{2}(1, 1, 0, 0)$, you have

$$\big[T(\mathbf{v})\big]_{B'} = A[\mathbf{v}]_B = \begin{bmatrix} 0 & 1 & -1 & -1 \\ 1 & \frac{1}{2} & \frac{3}{2} & \frac{3}{2} \end{bmatrix}\begin{bmatrix} \frac{7}{2} \\ -\frac{5}{2} \\ 1 \\ -\frac{1}{2} \end{bmatrix} = \begin{bmatrix} -3 \\ 3 \end{bmatrix}.$$

So, $T(\mathbf{v}) = -3(1, 1) + 3(2, 0) = (3, -3)$.

42. (a) The standard matrix for T is $A' = \begin{bmatrix} 2 & -12 \\ 1 & -5 \end{bmatrix}$ and the image of $\mathbf{v} = (10, 5)$ under T is

$$A'\mathbf{v} = \begin{bmatrix} 2 & -12 \\ 1 & -5 \end{bmatrix}\begin{bmatrix} 10 \\ 5 \end{bmatrix} = \begin{bmatrix} -40 \\ -15 \end{bmatrix} \Rightarrow T(\mathbf{v}) = (-40, -15).$$

(b) Because

$$T(4, 1) = (-4, -1) = -(4, 1)$$
$$T(3, 1) = (-6, -2) = -2(3, 1),$$

the matrix for T relative to B and B' is $A = \begin{bmatrix} -1 & 0 \\ 0 & -2 \end{bmatrix}$.

Because $\mathbf{v} = (10, 5) = -5(4, 1) + 10(3, 1)$, you have $\big[T(\mathbf{v})\big]_{B'} = A[\mathbf{v}]_B = \begin{bmatrix} -1 & 0 \\ 0 & -2 \end{bmatrix}\begin{bmatrix} -5 \\ 10 \end{bmatrix} = \begin{bmatrix} 5 \\ -20 \end{bmatrix}$.

So, $T(\mathbf{v}) = 5(4, 1) - 20(3, 1) = (-40, -15)$.

44. The image of each vector in B is as follows $T(1) = x^2, T(x) = x^3, T(x^2) = x^4$.

So, the matrix of T relative to B and B' is $A = \begin{bmatrix} 0 & 0 & 0 \\ 0 & 0 & 0 \\ 1 & 0 & 0 \\ 0 & 1 & 0 \\ 0 & 0 & 1 \end{bmatrix}$.

46. The image of each vector in B is as follows.

$$D\left(e^{2x}\right) = 2e^{2x}$$

$$D\left(xe^{2x}\right) = e^{2x} + 2xe^{2x}$$

$$D\left(x^2e^{2x}\right) = 2xe^{2x} + 2x^2e^{2x}$$

So, the matrix of T relative to B is $A = \begin{bmatrix} 2 & 1 & 0 \\ 0 & 2 & 2 \\ 0 & 0 & 2 \end{bmatrix}$.

48. Because $5e^{2x} - 3xe^{2x} + x^2e^{2x} = 5\left(e^{2x}\right) - 3\left(xe^{2x}\right) + 1\left(x^2e^{2x}\right)$,

$$A[\mathbf{v}]_B = \begin{bmatrix} 2 & 1 & 0 \\ 0 & 2 & 2 \\ 0 & 0 & 2 \end{bmatrix}\begin{bmatrix} 5 \\ -3 \\ 1 \end{bmatrix} = \begin{bmatrix} 7 \\ -4 \\ 2 \end{bmatrix} \Rightarrow D_x\left(5e^{2x} - 3xe^{2x} + x^2e^{2x}\right) = 7e^{2x} - 4xe^{2x} + 2x^2e^{2x}.$$

50. (a) Let $T : R^n \to R^m$ be a linear transformation such that, for the standard basis vectors e_i of R^n,

$$T(\mathbf{e}_1) = \begin{bmatrix} a_{11} \\ a_{21} \\ \vdots \\ a_{m1} \end{bmatrix}, T(\mathbf{e}_2) = \begin{bmatrix} a_{12} \\ a_{22} \\ \vdots \\ a_{m2} \end{bmatrix}, \ldots, T(\mathbf{e}_n) = \begin{bmatrix} a_{1n} \\ a_{2n} \\ \vdots \\ a_{mn} \end{bmatrix}.$$

Then the $m \times n$ matrix whose n columns correspond to $T(e_i)$

$$A = \begin{bmatrix} a_{11} & a_{12} & \cdots & a_{1n} \\ a_{21} & a_{22} & \cdots & a_{2n} \\ \vdots & \vdots & & \vdots \\ a_{m1} & a_{m2} & \cdots & a_{mn} \end{bmatrix}$$

is such that $T(\mathbf{v}) = A\mathbf{v}$ for every $\mathbf{v}$ in R^n. A is called the standard matrix of T.

(b) Let $T_1 : R^n \to R^m$ and $T_2 : R^m \to R^p$ be linear transformations with standard matrices A_1 and A_2, respectively. The composition $T : R^n \to R^p$, defined by $T(\mathbf{v}) = T_2\left(T_1(\mathbf{v})\right)$, is a linear transformation. Moreover, the standard matrix A for T is given by the matrix product $A = A_2 A_1$.

(c) To find the inverse of a linear transformation T, first find the standard matrix A of T. Then find the inverse of A using the techniques shown in Section 2.3.

(d) To find the transformation matrix relative to nonstandard basis, first find $T(\mathbf{v}_1), T(\mathbf{v}_2), \ldots, T(\mathbf{v}_n)$. Then determine the coordinate matrices relative to B'. Finally, form the matrix T relative to B and B' by using the coordinate matrices as columns to produce $A = \begin{bmatrix} a_{11} & a_{12} & \cdots & a_{1n} \\ a_{21} & a_{22} & \cdots & a_{2n} \\ \vdots & \vdots & & \vdots \\ a_{n1} & a_{m2} & \cdots & a_{mn} \end{bmatrix}$.

52. Because $T(\mathbf{v}) = k\mathbf{v}$ for all $\mathbf{v} \in R^n$, the standard matrix for T is the $n \times n$ diagonal matrix

$$\begin{bmatrix} k & 0 & \cdots & 0 \\ 0 & k & & \vdots \\ \vdots & & k & 0 \\ 0 & \cdots & 0 & k \end{bmatrix}.$$

54. (a) True. See discussion, under "Composition of Linear Transformations," pages 317–318.

(b) False. See Example 3, page 318.

(c) False. See Theorem 6.12, page 319.

56. $(1 \Rightarrow 2)$: Let T be invertible. If $T(\mathbf{v}_1) = T(\mathbf{v}_2)$, then $T^{-1}(T(\mathbf{v}_1)) = T^{-1}(T(\mathbf{v}_2))$ and $\mathbf{v}_1 = \mathbf{v}_2$, so T is one-to-one. T is onto because for any $\mathbf{w} \in R^n, T^{-1}(\mathbf{w}) = \mathbf{v}$ satisfies $T(\mathbf{v}) = \mathbf{w}$.

$(2 \Rightarrow 1)$: Let T be an isomorphism. Define T^{-1} as follows: Because T is onto, for any $\mathbf{w} \in R^n$, there exists $\mathbf{v} \in R^n$ such that $T(\mathbf{v}) = \mathbf{w}$. Because T is one-to-one, this $\mathbf{v}$ is unique. So, define the inverse of T by $T^{-1}(\mathbf{w}) = \mathbf{v}$ if and only if $T(\mathbf{v}) = \mathbf{w}$. Finally, the corollaries to Theorems 6.3 and 6.4 show that 2 and 3 are equivalent.

If T is invertible, $T(\mathbf{x}) = A\mathbf{x}$ implies that $T^{-1}(T(\mathbf{x})) = \mathbf{x} = A^{-1}(A\mathbf{x})$ and the standard matrix of T^{-1} is A^{-1}.

58. $\mathbf{b}$ is in the range of the linear transformation $T: R^n \to R^m$ given by $T(\mathbf{x}) = A\mathbf{x}$ if and only if $\mathbf{b}$ is in the column space of A.

Section 6.4 Transition Matrices and Similarity

2. The standard matrix for T is $A = \begin{bmatrix} 2 & 1 \\ 1 & -2 \end{bmatrix}$. Furthermore, the transition matrix P from B' to the standard basis B, and its

inverse are $P = \begin{bmatrix} 1 & 0 \\ 2 & 4 \end{bmatrix}$ and $P^{-1} = \begin{bmatrix} 1 & 0 \\ -\frac{1}{2} & \frac{1}{4} \end{bmatrix}$. Therefore, the matrix for T relative to B' is

$$A' = P^{-1}AP = \begin{bmatrix} 1 & 0 \\ -\frac{1}{2} & \frac{1}{4} \end{bmatrix}\begin{bmatrix} 2 & 1 \\ 1 & -2 \end{bmatrix}\begin{bmatrix} 1 & 0 \\ 2 & 4 \end{bmatrix} = \begin{bmatrix} 4 & 4 \\ -\frac{11}{4} & -4 \end{bmatrix}$$

4. The standard matrix for T is $A = \begin{bmatrix} 1 & -2 \\ 4 & 0 \end{bmatrix}$. Furthermore, the transition matrix P from B' to the standard basis B, and its

inverse, are $P = \begin{bmatrix} -2 & -1 \\ 1 & 1 \end{bmatrix}$ and $P^{-1} = \begin{bmatrix} -1 & -1 \\ 1 & 2 \end{bmatrix}$. Therefore, the matrix for T relative to B' is

$$A' = P^{-1}AP = \begin{bmatrix} -1 & -1 \\ 1 & 2 \end{bmatrix}\begin{bmatrix} 1 & -2 \\ 4 & 0 \end{bmatrix}\begin{bmatrix} -2 & -1 \\ 1 & 1 \end{bmatrix} = \begin{bmatrix} 12 & 7 \\ -20 & -11 \end{bmatrix}$$

6. The standard matrix for T is $A = \begin{bmatrix} 0 & 0 & 0 \\ 0 & 0 & 0 \\ 0 & 0 & 0 \end{bmatrix}$. Furthermore, the transition matrix P from B' to the standard basis B, and its

inverse, are $P = \begin{bmatrix} 1 & 1 & 0 \\ 1 & 0 & 1 \\ 0 & 1 & 1 \end{bmatrix}$ and $P^{-1} = \frac{1}{2}\begin{bmatrix} 1 & 1 & -1 \\ 1 & -1 & 1 \\ -1 & 1 & 1 \end{bmatrix}$. Therefore, the matrix for T relative to B' is

$$A' = P^{-1}AP = \begin{bmatrix} 0 & 0 & 0 \\ 0 & 0 & 0 \\ 0 & 0 & 0 \end{bmatrix}.$$

8. The standard matrix for T is $A = \begin{bmatrix} 1 & 0 & 0 \\ 1 & 2 & 0 \\ 1 & 1 & 3 \end{bmatrix}$. Furthermore, the transition matrix P from B' to the standard basis B, and

its inverse, are $P = \begin{bmatrix} 1 & 0 & 0 \\ -1 & 0 & 1 \\ 0 & 1 & -1 \end{bmatrix}$ and $P^{-1} = \begin{bmatrix} 1 & 0 & 0 \\ 1 & 1 & 1 \\ 1 & 1 & 0 \end{bmatrix}$. Therefore, the matrix for T relative to B' is

$$A' = P^{-1}AP = \begin{bmatrix} 1 & 0 & 0 \\ 1 & 1 & 1 \\ 1 & 1 & 0 \end{bmatrix}\begin{bmatrix} 1 & 0 & 0 \\ 1 & 2 & 0 \\ 1 & 1 & 3 \end{bmatrix}\begin{bmatrix} 1 & 0 & 0 \\ -1 & 0 & 1 \\ 0 & 1 & -1 \end{bmatrix} = \begin{bmatrix} 1 & 0 & 0 \\ 0 & 3 & 0 \\ 0 & 0 & 2 \end{bmatrix}.$$

10. (a) The transition matrix P from B' to B is found by row-reducing $\begin{bmatrix} B \vdots B' \end{bmatrix}$ to $\begin{bmatrix} I \vdots P \end{bmatrix}$.

$$\begin{bmatrix} B \vdots B' \end{bmatrix} = \begin{bmatrix} 1 & -2 & \vdots & 1 & 0 \\ 1 & 3 & \vdots & -1 & 1 \end{bmatrix} \Rightarrow \begin{bmatrix} I \vdots P \end{bmatrix} = \begin{bmatrix} 1 & 0 & \vdots & \frac{1}{5} & \frac{2}{5} \\ 0 & 1 & \vdots & -\frac{2}{5} & \frac{1}{5} \end{bmatrix}$$

So, $P = \begin{bmatrix} \frac{1}{5} & \frac{2}{5} \\ -\frac{2}{5} & \frac{1}{5} \end{bmatrix}$.

(b) The coordinate matrix for $\mathbf{v}$ relative to B is $[\mathbf{v}]_B = P[\mathbf{v}]_{B'} = \begin{bmatrix} \frac{1}{5} & \frac{2}{5} \\ -\frac{2}{5} & \frac{1}{5} \end{bmatrix}\begin{bmatrix} 1 \\ -3 \end{bmatrix} = \begin{bmatrix} -1 \\ -1 \end{bmatrix}$.

Furthermore, the image of $\mathbf{v}$ under T relative to B is $[T(\mathbf{v})]_B = A[\mathbf{v}]_B = \begin{bmatrix} 3 & 2 \\ 0 & 4 \end{bmatrix}\begin{bmatrix} -1 \\ -1 \end{bmatrix} = \begin{bmatrix} -5 \\ -4 \end{bmatrix}$.

(c) The matrix of T relative to B' is $A' = P^{-1}AP = \begin{bmatrix} 1 & -2 \\ 2 & 1 \end{bmatrix}\begin{bmatrix} 3 & 2 \\ 0 & 4 \end{bmatrix}\begin{bmatrix} \frac{1}{5} & \frac{2}{5} \\ -\frac{2}{5} & \frac{1}{5} \end{bmatrix} = \begin{bmatrix} 3 & 0 \\ -2 & 4 \end{bmatrix}$.

(d) The image of $\mathbf{v}$ under T relative to B' is $P^{-1}[T(\mathbf{v})]_B = \begin{bmatrix} 1 & -2 \\ 2 & 1 \end{bmatrix}\begin{bmatrix} -5 \\ -4 \end{bmatrix} = \begin{bmatrix} 3 \\ -14 \end{bmatrix}$.

You can also find the image of $\mathbf{v}$ under T relative to B' by $A'[\mathbf{v}]_{B'} = \begin{bmatrix} 3 & 0 \\ -2 & 4 \end{bmatrix}\begin{bmatrix} 1 \\ -3 \end{bmatrix} = \begin{bmatrix} 3 \\ -14 \end{bmatrix}$.

12. (a) The transition matrix P from B' to B is found by row-reducing $\begin{bmatrix} B \vdots B' \end{bmatrix}$ to $\begin{bmatrix} I \vdots P \end{bmatrix}$.

$$P = \begin{bmatrix} -1 & -5 \\ 0 & -3 \end{bmatrix}$$

(b) The coordinate matrix for $\mathbf{v}$ relative to B is $[\mathbf{v}]_B = P[\mathbf{v}]_{B'} = \begin{bmatrix} -1 & -5 \\ 0 & -3 \end{bmatrix}\begin{bmatrix} 1 \\ -4 \end{bmatrix} = \begin{bmatrix} 19 \\ 12 \end{bmatrix}$.

Furthermore, the image of $\mathbf{v}$ under T relative to B is $[T(\mathbf{v})]_B = A[\mathbf{v}]_B = \begin{bmatrix} 2 & 1 \\ 0 & -1 \end{bmatrix}\begin{bmatrix} 19 \\ 12 \end{bmatrix} = \begin{bmatrix} 50 \\ -12 \end{bmatrix}$.

(c) The matrix of T relative to B' is $A' = P^{-1}AP = \begin{bmatrix} -1 & \frac{5}{3} \\ 0 & -\frac{1}{3} \end{bmatrix}\begin{bmatrix} 2 & 1 \\ 0 & -1 \end{bmatrix}\begin{bmatrix} -1 & -5 \\ 0 & -3 \end{bmatrix} = \begin{bmatrix} 2 & 18 \\ 0 & -1 \end{bmatrix}$.

(d) The image of $\mathbf{v}$ under T relative to B' is $P^{-1}[T(\mathbf{v})]_B = \begin{bmatrix} -1 & \frac{5}{3} \\ 0 & -\frac{1}{3} \end{bmatrix}\begin{bmatrix} 50 \\ -12 \end{bmatrix} = \begin{bmatrix} -70 \\ 4 \end{bmatrix}$.

You can also find the image of $\mathbf{v}$ under T relative to B' by $A'[\mathbf{v}]_{B'} = \begin{bmatrix} 2 & 18 \\ 0 & -1 \end{bmatrix}\begin{bmatrix} 1 \\ -4 \end{bmatrix} = \begin{bmatrix} -70 \\ 4 \end{bmatrix}$.

14. (a) The transition matrix P from B' to B is found by row-reducing $\begin{bmatrix} B & B' \end{bmatrix}$ to $\begin{bmatrix} I & P \end{bmatrix}$.

$$\begin{bmatrix} B & B' \end{bmatrix} = \begin{bmatrix} 1 & 1 & -1 & 1 & 0 & 0 \\ 1 & -1 & 1 & 0 & 1 & 0 \\ -1 & 1 & 1 & 0 & 0 & 1 \end{bmatrix} \Rightarrow \begin{bmatrix} 1 & 0 & 0 & \frac{1}{2} & \frac{1}{2} & 0 \\ 0 & 1 & 0 & \frac{1}{2} & 0 & \frac{1}{2} \\ 0 & 0 & 1 & 0 & \frac{1}{2} & \frac{1}{2} \end{bmatrix} = \begin{bmatrix} I & P \end{bmatrix}$$

So, $P = \begin{bmatrix} \frac{1}{2} & \frac{1}{2} & 0 \\ \frac{1}{2} & 0 & \frac{1}{2} \\ 0 & \frac{1}{2} & \frac{1}{2} \end{bmatrix}$

(b) The coordinate matrix for $\mathbf{v}$ relative to B is $\begin{bmatrix} \mathbf{v} \end{bmatrix}_B = P\begin{bmatrix} \mathbf{v} \end{bmatrix}_{B'} = \begin{bmatrix} \frac{1}{2} & \frac{1}{2} & 0 \\ \frac{1}{2} & 0 & \frac{1}{2} \\ 0 & \frac{1}{2} & \frac{1}{2} \end{bmatrix}\begin{bmatrix} 2 \\ 1 \\ 1 \end{bmatrix} = \begin{bmatrix} \frac{3}{2} \\ \frac{3}{2} \\ 1 \end{bmatrix}$.

Furthermore, the image of $\mathbf{v}$ under T relative to B is

$$\begin{bmatrix} T(\mathbf{v}) \end{bmatrix}_B = A\begin{bmatrix} \mathbf{v} \end{bmatrix}_B = \begin{bmatrix} \frac{3}{2} & -1 & -\frac{1}{2} \\ -\frac{1}{2} & 2 & \frac{1}{2} \\ \frac{1}{2} & 1 & \frac{5}{2} \end{bmatrix}\begin{bmatrix} \frac{3}{2} \\ \frac{3}{2} \\ 1 \end{bmatrix} = \begin{bmatrix} \frac{1}{4} \\ \frac{11}{4} \\ \frac{19}{4} \end{bmatrix}.$$

(c) The matrix of T relative to B' is $A' = P^{-1}AP$.

$$A' = P^{-1}AP = \begin{bmatrix} 1 & 1 & -1 \\ 1 & -1 & 1 \\ -1 & 1 & 1 \end{bmatrix}\begin{bmatrix} \frac{3}{2} & -1 & -\frac{1}{2} \\ -\frac{1}{2} & 2 & \frac{1}{2} \\ \frac{1}{2} & 1 & \frac{5}{2} \end{bmatrix}\begin{bmatrix} \frac{1}{2} & \frac{1}{2} & 0 \\ \frac{1}{2} & 0 & \frac{1}{2} \\ 0 & \frac{1}{2} & \frac{1}{2} \end{bmatrix} = \begin{bmatrix} \frac{1}{4} & -1 & -\frac{5}{4} \\ \frac{1}{4} & 2 & -\frac{1}{4} \\ \frac{5}{4} & 1 & \frac{15}{4} \end{bmatrix}$$

(d) The image of $\mathbf{v}$ under T relative to B' is

$$P^{-1}\begin{bmatrix} T(\mathbf{v}) \end{bmatrix}_B = \begin{bmatrix} 1 & 1 & -1 \\ 1 & -1 & 1 \\ -1 & 1 & 1 \end{bmatrix}\begin{bmatrix} \frac{3}{2} \\ \frac{3}{2} \\ 1 \end{bmatrix} = \begin{bmatrix} 2 \\ 1 \\ 1 \end{bmatrix}.$$

You can also find the image of $\mathbf{v}$ under T relative to B^1 by

$$A'\begin{bmatrix} \mathbf{v} \end{bmatrix}_{B'} = \begin{bmatrix} \frac{1}{4} & -1 & -\frac{5}{4} \\ \frac{1}{4} & 2 & -\frac{1}{4} \\ \frac{5}{4} & 1 & \frac{15}{4} \end{bmatrix}\begin{bmatrix} 2 \\ 1 \\ 1 \end{bmatrix} = \begin{bmatrix} -\frac{7}{4} \\ \frac{9}{4} \\ \frac{29}{4} \end{bmatrix}.$$

16. A is similar to A' since

$$A' = P^{-1}AP = \begin{bmatrix} 1 & -4 \\ 0 & 1 \end{bmatrix}\begin{bmatrix} 1 & 4 \\ 0 & 1 \end{bmatrix}\begin{bmatrix} 1 & 4 \\ 0 & 1 \end{bmatrix} = \begin{bmatrix} 1 & 4 \\ 0 & 1 \end{bmatrix}.$$

18. A is similar to A' since

$$A' = P^{-1}AP = \begin{bmatrix} 1 & 0 & 0 \\ -1 & 1 & 0 \\ 0 & -1 & 1 \end{bmatrix}\begin{bmatrix} 2 & 0 & 0 \\ 0 & 1 & 0 \\ 0 & 0 & 3 \end{bmatrix}\begin{bmatrix} 1 & 0 & 0 \\ 1 & 1 & 0 \\ 1 & 1 & 1 \end{bmatrix} = \begin{bmatrix} 2 & 0 & 0 \\ -1 & 1 & 0 \\ 2 & 2 & 3 \end{bmatrix}.$$

20. The transition matrix from B' to the standard matrix has columns consisting of the vectors in B'.

$$P = \begin{bmatrix} 1 & 1 & -1 \\ 1 & -1 & 1 \\ -1 & 1 & 1 \end{bmatrix}$$

and it follows that

$$P^{-1} = \begin{bmatrix} \frac{1}{2} & \frac{1}{2} & 0 \\ \frac{1}{2} & 0 & \frac{1}{2} \\ 0 & \frac{1}{2} & \frac{1}{2} \end{bmatrix}.$$

So, the matrix for T relative to B' is

$$A' = P^{-1}AP$$

$$= \begin{bmatrix} \frac{1}{2} & \frac{1}{2} & 0 \\ \frac{1}{2} & 0 & \frac{1}{2} \\ 0 & \frac{1}{2} & \frac{1}{2} \end{bmatrix} \begin{bmatrix} \frac{3}{2} & -1 & -\frac{1}{2} \\ -\frac{1}{2} & 2 & \frac{1}{2} \\ \frac{1}{2} & 1 & \frac{5}{2} \end{bmatrix} \begin{bmatrix} 1 & 1 & -1 \\ 1 & -1 & 1 \\ -1 & 1 & 1 \end{bmatrix}$$

$$= \begin{bmatrix} 1 & 0 & 0 \\ 0 & 2 & 0 \\ 0 & 0 & 3 \end{bmatrix}.$$

22. First, note that A and B are similar.

$$P^{-1}AP = \begin{bmatrix} -1 & -1 & 2 \\ 0 & -1 & 2 \\ 1 & 2 & -3 \end{bmatrix} \begin{bmatrix} 1 & 0 & 0 \\ 0 & -2 & 0 \\ 0 & 0 & 3 \end{bmatrix} \begin{bmatrix} -1 & 1 & 0 \\ 2 & 1 & 2 \\ 1 & 1 & 1 \end{bmatrix}$$

$$= \begin{bmatrix} 11 & 7 & 10 \\ 10 & 8 & 10 \\ -18 & -12 & -17 \end{bmatrix}$$

Now,

$$|B| = \begin{vmatrix} 11 & 7 & 10 \\ 10 & 8 & 10 \\ -18 & -12 & -17 \end{vmatrix}$$

$$= 11(-16) - 7(10) + 10(24)$$

$$= -6 = |A|.$$

24. Because

$B = P^{-1}AP$, and $A^4 = \begin{bmatrix} 1 & 0 \\ 0 & 2 \end{bmatrix}^4 = \begin{bmatrix} 1 & 0 \\ 0 & 16 \end{bmatrix}$, you have

$$B^4 = P^{-1}A^4P$$

$$= \begin{bmatrix} 3 & -5 \\ -1 & 2 \end{bmatrix} \begin{bmatrix} 1 & 0 \\ 0 & 16 \end{bmatrix} \begin{bmatrix} 2 & 5 \\ 1 & 3 \end{bmatrix}$$

$$= \begin{bmatrix} -74 & -225 \\ 30 & 91 \end{bmatrix}.$$

26. If $B = P^{-1}AP$ and A is idempotent, then

$$B^2 = \left(P^{-1}AP\right)^2$$

$$= \left(P^{-1}AP\right)\left(P^{-1}AP\right)$$

$$= P^{-1}A^2P$$

$$= P^{-1}AP$$

$$= B,$$

which shows that B is idempotent.

28. If $A\mathbf{x} = \mathbf{x}$ and $B = P^{-1}AP$, then $PB = AP$ and $PBP^{-1} = A$. So, $PBP^{-1}\mathbf{x} = A\mathbf{x} = \mathbf{x}$.

30. Because A and B are similar, they represent the same linear transformation with respect to different bases. So, the range is the same, and so is the rank.

32. If A is nonsingular, then so is $P^{-1}AP = B$, and

$$B = P^{-1}AP$$

$$B^{-1} = \left(P^{-1}AP\right)^{-1} = P^{-1}A^{-1}\left(P^{-1}\right)^{-1} = P^{-1}A^{-1}P$$

which shows that A^{-1} and B^{-1} are similar.

34. Because $B = P^{-1}AP$, you have $AP = PB$, as follows.

$$\begin{bmatrix} a_{11} & \cdots & a_{1n} \\ \vdots & & \vdots \\ a_{n1} & \cdots & a_{nn} \end{bmatrix} \begin{bmatrix} p_{11} & \cdots & p_{1n} \\ \vdots & & \vdots \\ p_{n1} & \cdots & p_{nn} \end{bmatrix} = \begin{bmatrix} p_{11} & \cdots & p_{1n} \\ \vdots & & \vdots \\ p_{n1} & \cdots & p_{nn} \end{bmatrix} \begin{bmatrix} b_{11} & \cdots & 0 \\ \vdots & & \vdots \\ 0 & \cdots & b_{nn} \end{bmatrix}$$

So,

$$\begin{bmatrix} a_{11} & \cdots & a_{1n} \\ \vdots & & \vdots \\ a_{n1} & \cdots & a_{nn} \end{bmatrix} \begin{bmatrix} p_{1i} \\ \vdots \\ p_{ni} \end{bmatrix} = b_{ii} \begin{bmatrix} p_{1i} \\ \vdots \\ p_{ni} \end{bmatrix}$$

for $i = 1, 2, \ldots, n$.

36. (a) There are two ways to get from the coordinate matrix $[\mathbf{v}]_{B'}$ to the coordinate matrix $\left[T(\mathbf{v})\right]_{B'}$. One way is direct, using the matrix A' to obtain $A'[\mathbf{v}]_{B'} = \left[T(\mathbf{v})\right]_{B'}$. The second way is indirect, using the matrices P, A, and P^{-1} to obtain

$$P^{-1}AP[\mathbf{v}]_{B'} = \left[T(\mathbf{v})\right]_{B'}.$$

(b) To determine if two square matrices A and A' are similar, the equation $A' = P^{-1}AP$ must hold true for some invertible matrix P.

38. (a) True. See discussion, page 324, and note that $A' = P^{-1}AP \Rightarrow PA'P^{-1} = PP^{-1}APP^{-1} = A$.

(b) False. Unless it is a diagonal matrix, see Example 5, page 327.

Section 6.5   Applications of Linear Transformations

2. The standard matrix for T is $A = \begin{bmatrix} -1 & 0 \\ 0 & 1 \end{bmatrix}$.

(a) $\begin{bmatrix} -1 & 0 \\ 0 & 1 \end{bmatrix}\begin{bmatrix} 2 \\ 5 \end{bmatrix} = \begin{bmatrix} -2 \\ 5 \end{bmatrix} \Rightarrow T(2, 5) = (-2, 5)$

(b) $\begin{bmatrix} -1 & 0 \\ 0 & 1 \end{bmatrix}\begin{bmatrix} -4 \\ -1 \end{bmatrix} = \begin{bmatrix} 4 \\ -1 \end{bmatrix} \Rightarrow T(-4, -1) = (4, -1)$

(c) $\begin{bmatrix} -1 & 0 \\ 0 & 1 \end{bmatrix}\begin{bmatrix} a \\ 0 \end{bmatrix} = \begin{bmatrix} -a \\ 0 \end{bmatrix} \Rightarrow T(a, 0) = (-a, 0)$

(d) $\begin{bmatrix} -1 & 0 \\ 0 & 1 \end{bmatrix}\begin{bmatrix} 0 \\ b \end{bmatrix} = \begin{bmatrix} 0 \\ b \end{bmatrix} \Rightarrow T(0, b) = (0, b)$

(e) $\begin{bmatrix} -1 & 0 \\ 0 & 1 \end{bmatrix}\begin{bmatrix} c \\ -d \end{bmatrix} = \begin{bmatrix} -c \\ -d \end{bmatrix} \Rightarrow T(c, -d) = (-c, -d)$

(f) $\begin{bmatrix} -1 & 0 \\ 0 & 1 \end{bmatrix}\begin{bmatrix} f \\ g \end{bmatrix} = \begin{bmatrix} -f \\ g \end{bmatrix} \Rightarrow T(f, g) = (-f, g)$

4. The standard matrix for T is $A = \begin{bmatrix} 0 & -1 \\ -1 & 0 \end{bmatrix}$.

(a) $\begin{bmatrix} 0 & -1 \\ -1 & 0 \end{bmatrix}\begin{bmatrix} -1 \\ 2 \end{bmatrix} = \begin{bmatrix} -2 \\ 1 \end{bmatrix} \Rightarrow T(-1, 2) = (-2, 1)$

(b) $\begin{bmatrix} 0 & -1 \\ -1 & 0 \end{bmatrix}\begin{bmatrix} 2 \\ 3 \end{bmatrix} = \begin{bmatrix} -3 \\ -2 \end{bmatrix} \Rightarrow T(2, 3) = (-3, -2)$

(c) $\begin{bmatrix} 0 & -1 \\ -1 & 0 \end{bmatrix}\begin{bmatrix} a \\ 0 \end{bmatrix} = \begin{bmatrix} 0 \\ -a \end{bmatrix} \Rightarrow T(a, 0) = (0, -a)$

(d) $\begin{bmatrix} 0 & -1 \\ -1 & 0 \end{bmatrix}\begin{bmatrix} 0 \\ b \end{bmatrix} = \begin{bmatrix} -b \\ 0 \end{bmatrix} \Rightarrow T(0, b) = (-b, 0)$

(e) $\begin{bmatrix} 0 & -1 \\ -1 & 0 \end{bmatrix}\begin{bmatrix} e \\ -d \end{bmatrix} = \begin{bmatrix} d \\ -e \end{bmatrix} \Rightarrow T(e, -d) = (d, -e)$

(f) $\begin{bmatrix} 0 & -1 \\ -1 & 0 \end{bmatrix}\begin{bmatrix} -f \\ g \end{bmatrix} = \begin{bmatrix} -g \\ f \end{bmatrix} \Rightarrow T(-f, g) = (-g, f)$

6. (a) $T(x, y) = xT(1, 0) + yT(0, 1)$
$= x(1, 1) + y(0, 1)$
$= (x, x + y)$

(b) T is vertical shear.

8. $T(x, y) = \left(\dfrac{x}{4}, y\right)$

(a) Identify T as a horizontal contraction from its standard matrix $A = \begin{bmatrix} \dfrac{1}{4} & 0 \\ 0 & 1 \end{bmatrix}$.

(b)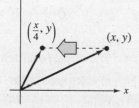

10. (a) Identify T as a vertical expansion from its standard matrix $A = \begin{bmatrix} 1 & 0 \\ 0 & 3 \end{bmatrix}$.

(b)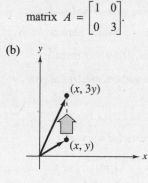

12. $T(x, y) = (x + 4y, y)$

(a) Identify T as a horizontal shear from its standard

matrix $A = \begin{bmatrix} 1 & 4 \\ 0 & 1 \end{bmatrix}$.

(b)

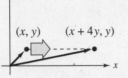

14. $T(x, y) = (x, 4x + y)$

(a) Identify T as a vertical shear from its matrix

$A = \begin{bmatrix} 1 & 0 \\ 4 & 1 \end{bmatrix}$.

(b)

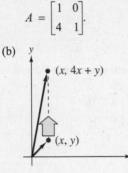

16. The reflection in the x-axis is given by
$T(x, y) = (x, -y)$. If (x, y) is a fixed point, then
$T(x, y) = (x, y) = (x, -y)$ which implies that
$y = 0$. So, the set of fixed points is $\{(t, 0) : t \text{ is real}\}$

18. The reflection in the line $y = -x$ is given by
$T(x, y) = (y, -x)$. If (x, y) is a fixed point then
$T(x, y) = (x, y) = (y, -x)$ which implies $-x = y$. So,
the set of fixed points is $\{(t, -t) : t \text{ is real}\}$

20. A horizontal expansion has the standard matrix
$\begin{bmatrix} k & 0 \\ 0 & 1 \end{bmatrix}$ where $k > 1$.

A fixed point of T satisfies the equation

$T(\mathbf{v}) = \begin{bmatrix} k & 0 \\ 0 & 1 \end{bmatrix}\begin{bmatrix} v_1 \\ v_2 \end{bmatrix} = \begin{bmatrix} kv_1 \\ v_2 \end{bmatrix} = \begin{bmatrix} v_1 \\ v_2 \end{bmatrix} = \mathbf{v}$

So the fixed points of T are
$\{\mathbf{v} = (0, t): t \text{ is a real number}\}$.

22. A vertical shear has the form $T(x, y) = (x, y + kx)$. If
(x, y) is a fixed point, then
$T(x, y) = (x, y) = (x, y + kx)$ which implies that
$x = 0$. So the set of fixed points is $\{(0, t) : t \text{ is real}\}$.

24. Find the image of each vertex under $T(x, y) = (y, x)$.

$T(0, 0) = (0, 0), \quad T(1, 0) = (0, 1),$
$T(1, 1) = (1, 1), \quad T(0, 1) = (1, 0)$

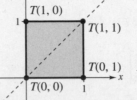

26. Find the image of each vertex under $T(x, y) = (x, 3y)$.

$T(0, 0) = (0, 0), \quad T(1, 0) = (1, 0),$
$T(1, 1) = (1, 3), \quad T(0, 1) = (0, 3)$

The image of the unit square under T is shown in the
following figure.

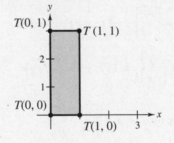

28. Find the image of each vertex under
$T(x, y) = (x, y + 3x)$.

$T(0, 0) = (0, 0), \quad T(1, 0) = (1, 3),$
$T(1, 1) = (1, 4), \quad T(0, 1) = (0, 1)$

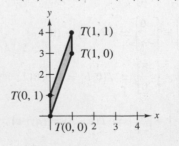

30. Find the image of each vertex under $T(x, y) = (y, x)$.

$T(0, 0) = (0, 0), \quad T(0, 2) = (2, 0),$

$T(1, 2) = (2, 1), \quad T(1, 0) = (0, 1)$

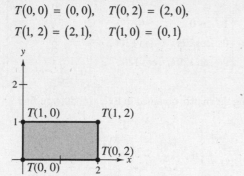

32. Find the image of each vertex under $T(x, y) = (2x, y)$.

$T(0, 0) = (0, 0), \quad T(0, 2) = (0, 2),$

$T(1, 2) = (2, 2), \quad T(1, 0) = (2, 0)$

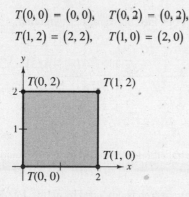

34. Find the image of each vertex under

$T(x, y) = (x, y + 2x)$.

$T(0, 0) = (0, 0), \quad T(0, 2) = (0, 2),$

$T(1, 2) = (1, 4), \quad T(1, 0) = (1, 2)$

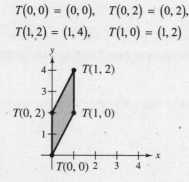

36. Find the image of each vertex under

$T(x, y) = (x, x + y)$.

(a) $T(0, 0) = (0, 0) \quad T(1, 2) = (1, 3) \quad T(3, 6) = (3, 9)$

$T(5, 2) = (5, 7) \quad T(6, 0) = (6, 6)$

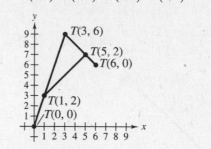

(b) $T(0, 0) = (0, 0) \quad T(0, 6) = (0, 6)$

$T(6, 6) = (6, 12) \quad T(6, 0) = (6, 6)$

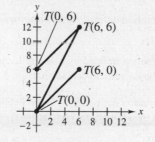

38. Find the image of each vertex under

$T(x, y) = \left(\tfrac{1}{2}x, 2y\right)$.

(a) $T(0, 0) = (0, 0) \quad T(1, 2) = \left(\tfrac{1}{2}, 4\right)$

$T(3, 6) = \left(\tfrac{3}{2}, 12\right) \quad T(5, 2) = \left(\tfrac{5}{2}, 4\right)$

$T(6, 0) = (3, 0)$

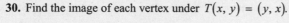

(b) $T(0, 0) = (0, 0) \quad T(0, 6) = (0, 12)$

$T(6, 6) = (3, 12) \quad T(6, 0) = (3, 0)$

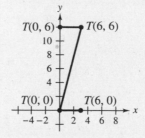

40. The images of the given vectors are as follows.

$$A\begin{bmatrix} 1 \\ 0 \end{bmatrix} = \begin{bmatrix} 3 & 0 \\ 0 & 3 \end{bmatrix}\begin{bmatrix} 1 \\ 0 \end{bmatrix} = \begin{bmatrix} 3 \\ 0 \end{bmatrix} \Rightarrow T(1, 0) = (3, 0)$$

$$A\begin{bmatrix} 0 \\ 1 \end{bmatrix} = \begin{bmatrix} 3 & 0 \\ 0 & 3 \end{bmatrix}\begin{bmatrix} 0 \\ 1 \end{bmatrix} = \begin{bmatrix} 0 \\ 3 \end{bmatrix} \Rightarrow T(0, 1) = (0, 3)$$

$$A\begin{bmatrix} 2 \\ 2 \end{bmatrix} = \begin{bmatrix} 3 & 0 \\ 0 & 3 \end{bmatrix}\begin{bmatrix} 2 \\ 2 \end{bmatrix} = \begin{bmatrix} 6 \\ 6 \end{bmatrix} \Rightarrow T(2, 2) = (6, 6)$$

42. The linear transformation defined by A is a vertical shear.

44. The linear transformation defined by A is a reflection in the x-axis followed by a vertical contraction.

46. The linear transformation defined by A is a reflection in the y-axis followed by a horizontal contraction.

48. Because $\begin{bmatrix} 1 & 0 \\ 0 & 3 \end{bmatrix}$ represents a vertical expansion, and

$\begin{bmatrix} 0 & 1 \\ 1 & 0 \end{bmatrix}$ represents a reflection in the line $x = y$, A is a

vertical expansion *followed* by a reflection in the line $x = y$.

50. A rotation of $60°$ about the x-axis is given by the matrix

$$A = \begin{bmatrix} 1 & 0 & 0 \\ 0 & \cos 60° & -\sin 60° \\ 0 & \sin 60° & \cos 60° \end{bmatrix} = \begin{bmatrix} 1 & 0 & 0 \\ 0 & \dfrac{1}{2} & -\dfrac{\sqrt{3}}{2} \\ 0 & \dfrac{\sqrt{3}}{2} & \dfrac{1}{2} \end{bmatrix}.$$

52. A rotation of $120°$ about the x-axis is given by the matrix

$$A = \begin{bmatrix} 1 & -0 & 0 \\ 0 & \cos 120° & -\sin 120° \\ 0 & \sin 120° & \cos 120° \end{bmatrix} = \begin{bmatrix} 1 & 0 & 0 \\ 0 & -\dfrac{1}{2} & -\dfrac{\sqrt{3}}{2} \\ 0 & \dfrac{\sqrt{3}}{2} & -\dfrac{1}{2} \end{bmatrix}.$$

54. Using the matrix obtained in Exercise 50, you find

$$T(1, 1, 1) = \begin{bmatrix} 1 & 0 & 0 \\ 0 & \dfrac{1}{2} & -\dfrac{\sqrt{3}}{2} \\ 0 & \dfrac{\sqrt{3}}{2} & \dfrac{1}{2} \end{bmatrix}\begin{bmatrix} 1 \\ 1 \\ 1 \end{bmatrix} = \begin{bmatrix} 1 \\ \dfrac{\left(1 - \sqrt{3}\right)}{2} \\ \dfrac{\left(1 + \sqrt{3}\right)}{2} \end{bmatrix}.$$

56. Using the matrix obtained in Exercise 52, you find

$$T(1, 1, 1) = \begin{bmatrix} 1 & 0 & 0 \\ 0 & -\dfrac{1}{2} & -\dfrac{\sqrt{3}}{2} \\ 0 & \dfrac{\sqrt{3}}{2} & -\dfrac{1}{2} \end{bmatrix}\begin{bmatrix} 1 \\ 1 \\ 1 \end{bmatrix} = \begin{bmatrix} 1 \\ \dfrac{\left(-1 - \sqrt{3}\right)}{2} \\ \dfrac{\left(-1 + \sqrt{3}\right)}{2} \end{bmatrix}.$$

58. The indicated tetrahedron is produced by a $-90°$ rotation about the z-axis.

60. The indicated tetrahedron is produced by a $180°$ rotation about the z-axis.

62. The indicated tetrahedron is produced by a $180°$ rotation about the x-axis.

64. A rotation of $45°$ about the y-axis is given by $A_1 = \begin{bmatrix} \cos 45° & 0 & \sin 45° \\ 0 & 1 & 0 \\ -\sin 45° & 0 & \cos 45° \end{bmatrix} = \begin{bmatrix} \frac{\sqrt{2}}{2} & 0 & \frac{\sqrt{2}}{2} \\ 0 & 1 & 0 \\ -\frac{\sqrt{2}}{2} & 0 & \frac{\sqrt{2}}{2} \end{bmatrix}$

while a rotation of $90°$ about the z-axis is given by $A_2 = \begin{bmatrix} \cos 90° & -\sin 90° & 0 \\ \sin 90° & \cos 90° & 0 \\ 0 & 0 & 1 \end{bmatrix} = \begin{bmatrix} 0 & -1 & 0 \\ 1 & 0 & 0 \\ 0 & 0 & 1 \end{bmatrix}$.

So, the desired matrix is $A = A_2 A_1 = \begin{bmatrix} 0 & -1 & 0 \\ 1 & 0 & 0 \\ 0 & 0 & 1 \end{bmatrix} \begin{bmatrix} \frac{\sqrt{2}}{2} & 0 & \frac{\sqrt{2}}{2} \\ 0 & 1 & 0 \\ -\frac{\sqrt{2}}{2} & 0 & \frac{\sqrt{2}}{2} \end{bmatrix} = \begin{bmatrix} 0 & -1 & 0 \\ \frac{\sqrt{2}}{2} & 0 & \frac{\sqrt{2}}{2} \\ -\frac{\sqrt{2}}{2} & 0 & \frac{\sqrt{2}}{2} \end{bmatrix}$.

The image of $(1, 1, 1)$ is obtained by computing

$$\begin{bmatrix} 0 & -1 & 0 \\ \frac{\sqrt{2}}{2} & -1 & \frac{\sqrt{2}}{2} \\ -\frac{\sqrt{2}}{2} & 0 & \frac{\sqrt{2}}{2} \end{bmatrix} \begin{bmatrix} 1 \\ 1 \\ 1 \end{bmatrix} = \begin{bmatrix} -1 \\ \sqrt{2} \\ 0 \end{bmatrix}$$

66. A rotation of $45°$ about the z-axis is given by $A_1 = \begin{bmatrix} \cos 45° & -\sin 45° & 0 \\ \sin 45° & \cos 45° & 0 \\ 0 & 0 & 1 \end{bmatrix} = \begin{bmatrix} \frac{\sqrt{2}}{2} & -\frac{\sqrt{2}}{2} & 0 \\ \frac{\sqrt{2}}{2} & \frac{\sqrt{2}}{2} & 0 \\ 0 & 0 & 1 \end{bmatrix}$

while a rotation of $135°$ about the x-axis is given by $A_2 = \begin{bmatrix} 1 & 0 & 0 \\ 0 & \cos 135° & -\sin 135° \\ 0 & \sin 135° & \cos 135° \end{bmatrix} = \begin{bmatrix} 1 & 0 & 0 \\ 0 & -\frac{\sqrt{2}}{2} & -\frac{\sqrt{2}}{2} \\ 0 & \frac{\sqrt{2}}{2} & -\frac{\sqrt{2}}{2} \end{bmatrix}$

So, the desired matrix is

$$A = A_2 A_1 = \begin{bmatrix} 1 & 0 & 0 \\ 0 & -\frac{\sqrt{2}}{2} & -\frac{\sqrt{2}}{2} \\ 0 & \frac{\sqrt{2}}{2} & -\frac{\sqrt{2}}{2} \end{bmatrix} \begin{bmatrix} \frac{\sqrt{2}}{2} & -\frac{\sqrt{2}}{2} & 0 \\ \frac{\sqrt{2}}{2} & \frac{\sqrt{2}}{2} & 0 \\ 0 & 0 & 1 \end{bmatrix} = \begin{bmatrix} \frac{\sqrt{2}}{2} & -\frac{\sqrt{2}}{2} & 0 \\ -\frac{1}{2} & -\frac{1}{2} & -\frac{\sqrt{2}}{2} \\ \frac{1}{2} & \frac{1}{2} & -\frac{\sqrt{2}}{2} \end{bmatrix}.$$

The image of $(1, 1, 1)$ is obtained by computing

$$\begin{bmatrix} \frac{\sqrt{2}}{2} & -\frac{\sqrt{2}}{2} & 0 \\ -\frac{1}{2} & -\frac{1}{2} & -\frac{\sqrt{2}}{2} \\ \frac{1}{2} & \frac{1}{2} & -\frac{\sqrt{2}}{2} \end{bmatrix} \begin{bmatrix} 1 \\ 1 \\ 1 \end{bmatrix} = \begin{bmatrix} 0 \\ \frac{(-2 - \sqrt{2})}{2} \\ \frac{(2 - \sqrt{2})}{2} \end{bmatrix}.$$

68. (a) The linear transformation of $\begin{bmatrix} -1 & 0 \\ 0 & 1 \end{bmatrix}$ represents a reflection in the *y*-axis.

   (b) The linear transformation of $\begin{bmatrix} 1 & 0 \\ 0 & -1 \end{bmatrix}$ represents a reflection in the *x*-axis.

   (c) The linear transformation of $\begin{bmatrix} 0 & 1 \\ 1 & 0 \end{bmatrix}$ represents a reflection in the line $y = x$.

   (d) The linear transformation of $\begin{bmatrix} k & 0 \\ 0 & 1 \end{bmatrix}$, where $k > 1$, represents a horizontal expansion.

   (e) The linear transformation of $\begin{bmatrix} k & 0 \\ 0 & 1 \end{bmatrix}$, where $0 < k < 1$, represents a horizontal contraction.

   (f) The linear transformation of $\begin{bmatrix} 1 & 0 \\ 0 & k \end{bmatrix}$, where $k > 1$, represents a vertical expansion.

   (g) The linear transformation of $\begin{bmatrix} 1 & 0 \\ 0 & k \end{bmatrix}$, where $0 < k < 1$, is represented by a vertical contraction.

   (h) The linear transformation of $\begin{bmatrix} 1 & k \\ 0 & 1 \end{bmatrix}$ represents a horizontal shear.

   (i) The linear transformation of $\begin{bmatrix} 1 & 0 \\ k & 1 \end{bmatrix}$ represents a vertical shear.

   (j) The linear transformation of $\begin{bmatrix} 1 & 0 & 0 \\ 0 & \cos\theta & -\sin\theta \\ 0 & \sin\theta & \cos\theta \end{bmatrix}$ represents a rotation about the *x*-axis.

   (k) The linear transformation of $\begin{bmatrix} \cos\theta & 0 & \sin\theta \\ 0 & 1 & 0 \\ -\sin\theta & 0 & \cos\theta \end{bmatrix}$ represents a rotation about the *y*-axis.

   (l) The linear transformation of $\begin{bmatrix} \cos\theta & -\sin\theta & 0 \\ \sin\theta & \cos\theta & 0 \\ 0 & 0 & 1 \end{bmatrix}$ represents a rotation about the *z*-axis.

Review Exercises for Chapter 6

2. (a) $T(\mathbf{v}) = T(4, -1) = (3, -2)$

   (b) $T(v_1, v_2) = (v_1 + v_2, 2v_2) = (8, 4)$

   $$v_1 + v_2 = 8$$
   $$2v_2 = 4$$
   $$v_1 = 6, v_2 = 2$$

   Preimage of **w** is $(6, 2)$.

4. (a) $T(\mathbf{v}) = T(-2, 1, 2) = (-1, 3, 2)$

   (b) $T(v_1, v_2, v_3) = (v_1 + v_2, v_2 + v_3, v_3) = (0, 1, 2)$

   $$v_1 + v_2 = 0$$
   $$v_2 + v_3 = 1$$
   $$v_3 = 2$$
   $$v_2 = -1, v_1 = 1$$

   Preimage of **w** is $(1, -1, 2)$.

6. T does not preserve addition or scalar multiplication, and hence, T is *not* a linear transformation. A counterexample is

$$T(1,1) + T(1,0) = (4,1) + (4,0)$$
$$= (8,1) \neq (5,1) = T(2,1).$$

8. $T(x, y) = (x + y, y)$

$$T(x_1, y_1) + T(x_2, y_2) = (x_1 + y_1, y_1) + (x_2 + y_2, y_2)$$
$$= x_1 + y_1 + x_2 + y_2, y_1 + y_2$$
$$= (x_1 + x_2) + (y_1 + y_2), y_1 + y_2$$

So, T preserves addition.

$$cT(x, y) = c(x + y, y) = cx + cy, cy = T(cx, cy)$$

So, T preserves scalar multiplication.

So, T is a linear transformation with standard matrix

$$A = \begin{bmatrix} 1 & 1 \\ 0 & 1 \end{bmatrix}.$$

10. T does not preserve addition or scalar multiplication, and so, T is *not* a linear transformation. A counterexample is

$$-2T(3,-3) = -2(|3|, |-3|) = (-6,-6) \neq (6,6)$$
$$= T(-6,6) = T(-2(3), -2(-3)).$$

12. T preserves addition.

$$T(x_1, y_1, z_1) + T(x_2, y_2, z_2) = (z_1, y_1, x_1) + (z_2, y_2, x_2)$$
$$= (z_1 + z_2, y_1 + y_2, x_1 + x_2)$$
$$= T(x_1 + x_2, y_1 + y_2, z_1 + z_2)$$

T preserves scalar multiplication.

$$cT(x, y, z) = c(z, y, x) = (cz, cy, cx) = T(cx, cy, cz)$$

So, T is a linear transformation with standard matrix

$$A = \begin{bmatrix} 0 & 0 & 1 \\ 0 & 1 & 0 \\ 1 & 0 & 0 \end{bmatrix}.$$

14. Because $(0,1,1) = (1,1,1) - (1,0,0)$, you have

$$T(0,1,1) = T(1,1,1) - T(1,0,0)$$
$$= 1 - 3$$
$$= -2.$$

16. Because $(2,4) = 2(1,-1) + 3(0,2)$, you have

$$T(2,4) = 2T(1,-1) + 3T(0,2)$$
$$= 2(2,-3) + 3(0,8)$$
$$= (4,-6) + (0,24)$$
$$= (4,18).$$

18. (a) Because A is a 2×3 matrix, it maps R^3 into $R^2, (n = 3, m = 2)$.

(b) Because $T(\mathbf{v}) = A\mathbf{v}$ and

$$A\mathbf{v} = \begin{bmatrix} 1 & 2 & -1 \\ 1 & 0 & 1 \end{bmatrix} \begin{bmatrix} 5 \\ 2 \\ 2 \end{bmatrix} = \begin{bmatrix} 7 \\ 7 \end{bmatrix},$$

it follows that $T(5, 2, 2) = (7, 7)$.

(c) The preimage of $\mathbf{w}$ is given by the solution to the equation $T(v_1, v_2, v_3) = \mathbf{w} = (4, 2)$.

The equivalent system of linear equations

$$v_1 + 2v_2 - v_3 = 4$$
$$v_1 \quad\quad + v_3 = 2$$

has the solution

$$\{(2 - t, 1 + t, t) : t \text{ is a real number}\}.$$

20. (a) Because A is a 1×2 matrix, it maps R^2 into R^1 $(n = 2, m = 1)$.

(b) Because $T(\mathbf{v}) = A\mathbf{v}$ and

$$A\mathbf{v} = \begin{bmatrix} 2, -1 \end{bmatrix} \begin{bmatrix} 1 \\ 2 \end{bmatrix} = [0], \text{ it follows } T(1, 2) = 0.$$

(c) The preimage of $\mathbf{w}$ is given by the solution to the equation $T(v_1, v_2) = \mathbf{w} = (-1)$.

The equivalent system of linear equations is
$$2v_1 - v_2 = -1, \text{ which has the solution}$$

$$\left\{ \left(\frac{t}{2} - \frac{1}{2}, t \right) : t \text{ is a real number} \right\}.$$

22. (a) Because A is a 2×2 matrix, it maps R^2 into R^2 $(n = 2, m = 2)$.

(b) Because $T(\mathbf{v}) = A\mathbf{v}$ and

$$A\mathbf{v} = \begin{bmatrix} 2 & 1 \\ 0 & 1 \end{bmatrix} \begin{bmatrix} 8 \\ 4 \end{bmatrix} = \begin{bmatrix} 20 \\ 4 \end{bmatrix}, \text{ it follows that}$$

$$T(8, 4) = (20, 4).$$

(c) The preimage of $\mathbf{w}$ is given by the solution to the equation $T(v_1, v_2) = \mathbf{w} = (5, 2)$.

The equivalent system of linear equations
$$2v_1 + v_2 = 5$$
$$v_2 = 2, v_1 = \frac{3}{2}$$

has the solution $\left(\frac{3}{2}, 2 \right)$.

24. (a) Because A is a 3×2 matrix, it maps R^2 into R^3 $(n = 2, m = 3)$.

(b) Because $T(\mathbf{v}) = A\mathbf{v}$ and

$$A\mathbf{v} = \begin{bmatrix} 1 & 0 \\ 0 & -1 \\ 1 & 2 \end{bmatrix} \begin{bmatrix} 1 \\ 2 \end{bmatrix} = \begin{bmatrix} 1 \\ -2 \\ 5 \end{bmatrix}, \text{ it follows that}$$

$T(1, 2) = (1, -2, 5)$.

(c) The preimage of $\mathbf{w}$ is given by the solution to the equation $T(v_1, v_2) = \mathbf{w} = (2, -5, 12)$.

The equivalent system of linear equations

$$\begin{aligned} v_1 &= 2 \\ -v_2 &= -5 \\ v_1 + 2v_2 &= 12 \end{aligned}$$

has the solution $v_1 = 2$ and $v_2 = 5$. So, the preimage is $(2, 5)$.

26. If you translate the vertex $(5, 3)$ back to the origin $(0, 0)$, then the other vertices $(3, 5)$ and $(3, 0)$ are translated to $(-2, 2)$ and $(-2, -3)$, respectively. The rotation of $90°$ is given by the matrix in Exercise 51, and you have

$$\begin{bmatrix} 0 & -1 \\ 1 & 0 \end{bmatrix} \begin{bmatrix} -2 \\ 2 \end{bmatrix} = \begin{bmatrix} -2 \\ -2 \end{bmatrix} \qquad \begin{bmatrix} 0 & -1 \\ 1 & 0 \end{bmatrix} \begin{bmatrix} -2 \\ -3 \end{bmatrix} = \begin{bmatrix} 3 \\ -2 \end{bmatrix}.$$

Translating back to the original coordinate system, the new vertices are $(5, 3), (3, 1)$ and $(8, 1)$.

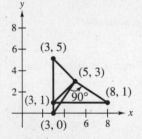

28. (a) The standard matrix for T is

$$A = \begin{bmatrix} 1 & 2 & 0 \\ 0 & 1 & 2 \\ 2 & 0 & 1 \end{bmatrix}.$$

Solving $A\mathbf{v} = \mathbf{0}$ yields the solution $\mathbf{v} = \mathbf{0}$. So, $\ker(T)$ consists of the zero vector, $\ker(T) = \{(0, 0, 0)\}$.

(b) Because $\ker(T)$ is dimension 0, $\text{range}(T)$ must be all of R^3. So, a basis for the range is $\{(1, 0, 0), (0, 1, 0), (0, 0, 1)\}$.

30. (a) The standard matrix for T is

$$A = \begin{bmatrix} 1 & 1 & 0 \\ 0 & 1 & 1 \\ 1 & 0 & -1 \end{bmatrix}.$$

Solving $A\mathbf{v} = \mathbf{0}$ yields the solution $\{(t, -t, t) : t \in R\}$. So, a basis for $\ker(T)$ is $\{(1, -1, 1)\}$.

(b) Use Gauss-Jordan elimination to reduce A^T as follows.

$$A^T = \begin{bmatrix} 1 & 0 & 1 \\ 1 & 1 & 0 \\ 0 & 1 & -1 \end{bmatrix} \Rightarrow \begin{bmatrix} 1 & 0 & 1 \\ 0 & 1 & -1 \\ 0 & 0 & 0 \end{bmatrix}$$

The nonzero row vectors form a basis for the range of T, $\{(1, 0, 1), (0, 1, -1)\}$.

32. $A = \begin{bmatrix} 1 & 1 \\ 0 & -1 \\ 2 & 1 \end{bmatrix} \Rightarrow \begin{bmatrix} 1 & 0 \\ 0 & 1 \\ 0 & 0 \end{bmatrix}$

(a) $\ker(T) = \{(0, 0)\}$

(b) $\dim(\ker(T)) = \text{nullity}(T) = 0$

(c) $A^T = \begin{bmatrix} 1 & 0 & 2 \\ 1 & -1 & 1 \end{bmatrix} \Rightarrow \begin{bmatrix} 1 & 0 & 2 \\ 0 & 1 & 1 \end{bmatrix}$

$\text{range}(T)$ is span $\{(1, 0, 2), (0, 1, 1)\}$.

(d) $\dim(\text{range}(T)) = \text{rank}(T) = 2$

34. $A = \begin{bmatrix} 1 & 1 & -1 \\ 1 & 2 & 1 \\ 0 & 1 & 0 \end{bmatrix} \Rightarrow \begin{bmatrix} 1 & 0 & 0 \\ 0 & 1 & 0 \\ 0 & 0 & 1 \end{bmatrix}$

(a) $\ker(T) = \{(0, 0, 0)\}$

(b) $\dim(\ker(T)) = \text{nullity}(T) = 0$

(c) $A^T = \begin{bmatrix} 1 & 1 & 0 \\ 1 & 2 & 1 \\ -1 & 1 & 0 \end{bmatrix} \Rightarrow \begin{bmatrix} 1 & 0 & 0 \\ 0 & 1 & 0 \\ 0 & 0 & 1 \end{bmatrix}$

$\text{range}(T)$ is span $\{(1, 0, 0), (0, 1, 0) (0, 0, 1)\}$

(d) $\dim(\text{range}(T)) = 3$

36. $\text{Rank}(T) = \dim P_5 - \text{nullity}(T) = 6 - 4 = 2$

38. $\text{nullity}(T) = \dim(M_{2,2}) - \text{rank}(T) = 4 - 3 = 1$

40. The standard matrix for T is

$$A = \begin{bmatrix} 1 & 0 & 0 \\ 0 & 1 & 0 \\ 0 & 0 & 0 \end{bmatrix}.$$

Therefore, you have

$$A^2 = \begin{bmatrix} 1 & 0 & 0 \\ 0 & 1 & 0 \\ 0 & 0 & 0 \end{bmatrix}\begin{bmatrix} 1 & 0 & 0 \\ 0 & 1 & 0 \\ 0 & 0 & 0 \end{bmatrix} = \begin{bmatrix} 1 & 0 & 0 \\ 0 & 1 & 0 \\ 0 & 0 & 0 \end{bmatrix} = A.$$

42. The standard matrix for T, relative to $B = \{1, x, x^2, x^3\}$, is

$$A = \begin{bmatrix} 0 & 1 & 0 & 0 \\ 0 & 0 & 2 & 0 \\ 0 & 0 & 0 & 3 \\ 0 & 0 & 0 & 0 \end{bmatrix}$$

Therefore, you have

$$A^2 = \begin{bmatrix} 0 & 1 & 0 & 0 \\ 0 & 0 & 2 & 0 \\ 0 & 0 & 0 & 3 \\ 0 & 0 & 0 & 0 \end{bmatrix}\begin{bmatrix} 0 & 1 & 0 & 0 \\ 0 & 0 & 2 & 0 \\ 0 & 0 & 0 & 3 \\ 0 & 0 & 0 & 0 \end{bmatrix} = \begin{bmatrix} 0 & 0 & 2 & 0 \\ 0 & 0 & 0 & 6 \\ 0 & 0 & 0 & 0 \\ 0 & 0 & 0 & 0 \end{bmatrix}.$$

44. The standard matrices for T_1 and T_2 are

$$A_1 = \begin{bmatrix} 1 \\ 3 \end{bmatrix} \quad \text{and} \quad A_2 = \begin{bmatrix} 2 & 1 \end{bmatrix}.$$

The standard matrix for $T = T_1 \circ T_2$ is

$$A = A_1 A_2 = \begin{bmatrix} 1 \\ 3 \end{bmatrix}\begin{bmatrix} 2 & 1 \end{bmatrix} = \begin{bmatrix} 2 & 1 \\ 6 & 3 \end{bmatrix}$$

and the standard matrix for $T' = T_2 \circ T_1$ is

$$A' = A_2 A_1 = \begin{bmatrix} 2 & 1 \end{bmatrix}\begin{bmatrix} 1 \\ 3 \end{bmatrix} = \begin{bmatrix} 5 \end{bmatrix}.$$

46. The standard matrix for T is

$$A = \begin{bmatrix} \cos\theta & -\sin\theta \\ \sin\theta & \cos\theta \end{bmatrix}.$$

A is invertible and its inverse is given by

$$A^{-1} = \begin{bmatrix} \cos\theta & \sin\theta \\ -\sin\theta & \cos\theta \end{bmatrix}.$$

48. The standard matrix for T is

$$A = \begin{bmatrix} 1 & 1 & 0 \\ 0 & 1 & -1 \end{bmatrix}.$$

Because A is *not* invertible, T has no inverse.

50. (a) Because $|A| = 1 \neq 0$, $\ker(T) = \{(0,0)\}$ and T is one-to-one.

(b) Because $\text{rank}(A) = 2$, T is onto.

(c) The transformation is one-to-one and onto, and is, therefore, invertible.

52. (a) Because $|A| = 40 \neq 0$, $\ker(T) = \{(0,0,0)\}$, and T is one-to-one.

(b) Because $\text{rank}(A) = 3$, T is onto.

(c) The transformation is one-to-one and onto, and therefore invertible.

54. (a) The standard matrix for T is

$$A = \begin{bmatrix} 0 & 2 \\ 0 & 0 \end{bmatrix}$$

so it follows that

$$A\mathbf{v} = \begin{bmatrix} 0 & 2 \\ 0 & 0 \end{bmatrix}\begin{bmatrix} -1 \\ 3 \end{bmatrix} = \begin{bmatrix} 6 \\ 0 \end{bmatrix} \Rightarrow T(\mathbf{v}) = (6, 0).$$

(b) The image of each vector in B is as follows.

$T(2,1) = (2,0) = -2(-1,0) + 0(2,2)$

$T(-1,0) = (0,0) = 0(-1,0) + 0(2,2)$

Therefore, the matrix for T relative to B and B' is

$$A' = \begin{bmatrix} -2 & 0 \\ 0 & 0 \end{bmatrix}.$$

Because $\mathbf{v} = (-1,3) = 3(2,1) + 7(-1,0)$,

$$[\mathbf{v}]_B = \begin{bmatrix} 3 \\ 7 \end{bmatrix} \quad \text{and} \quad A'[\mathbf{v}]_B = \begin{bmatrix} -2 & 0 \\ 0 & 0 \end{bmatrix}\begin{bmatrix} 3 \\ 7 \end{bmatrix} = \begin{bmatrix} -6 \\ 0 \end{bmatrix}.$$

So, $T(\mathbf{v}) = -6(-1,0) + 0(2,2) = (6,0)$.

56. The standard matrix for T is

$$A = \begin{bmatrix} 1 & 3 & 0 \\ 3 & 1 & 0 \\ 0 & 0 & -2 \end{bmatrix}.$$

The transition matrix from B' to B, the standard matrix, is P

$$P = \begin{bmatrix} 1 & 1 & 0 \\ 1 & -1 & 0 \\ 0 & 0 & 1 \end{bmatrix} \quad P^{-1} = \begin{bmatrix} \frac{1}{2} & \frac{1}{2} & 0 \\ \frac{1}{2} & -\frac{1}{2} & 0 \\ 0 & 0 & 1 \end{bmatrix}.$$

The matrix A' for T relative to B' is

$A' = P^{-1}AP$

$$= \begin{bmatrix} \frac{1}{2} & \frac{1}{2} & 0 \\ \frac{1}{2} & -\frac{1}{2} & 0 \\ 0 & 0 & 1 \end{bmatrix}\begin{bmatrix} 1 & 3 & 0 \\ 3 & 1 & 0 \\ 0 & 0 & -2 \end{bmatrix}\begin{bmatrix} 1 & 1 & 0 \\ 1 & -1 & 0 \\ 0 & 0 & 1 \end{bmatrix}$$

$$= \begin{bmatrix} 4 & 0 & 0 \\ 0 & -2 & 0 \\ 0 & 0 & -2 \end{bmatrix}.$$

Because, $A' = P^{-1}AP$, it follows that A and A' are similar.

58. Since $A' = P^{-1}AP$

$$= \begin{bmatrix} 0 & 0 & 1 \\ \frac{1}{2} & 0 & -\frac{1}{2} \\ \frac{1}{2} & -1 & -\frac{1}{2} \end{bmatrix} \begin{bmatrix} 1 & 0 & 1 \\ -1 & 3 & 1 \\ 0 & 0 & 2 \end{bmatrix} \begin{bmatrix} 1 & 2 & 0 \\ 0 & 1 & -1 \\ 1 & 0 & 0 \end{bmatrix}$$

$$= \begin{bmatrix} 2 & 0 & 0 \\ 0 & 1 & 0 \\ 0 & 0 & 3 \end{bmatrix}$$

A and A' are similar.

60. (a) Because $T(\mathbf{v}) = \text{proj}_{\mathbf{u}}\mathbf{v}$ where $\mathbf{u} = (4, 3)$, you have

$$T(\mathbf{v}) = \frac{4x + 3y}{25}(4, 3).$$

So,

$$T(1, 0) = \left(\frac{16}{25}, \frac{12}{25}\right) \quad \text{and} \quad T(0, 1) = \left(\frac{12}{25}, \frac{9}{25}\right)$$

and the standard matrix for T is

$$A = \frac{1}{25}\begin{bmatrix} 16 & 12 \\ 12 & 9 \end{bmatrix}.$$

(b) $(I - A)^2 = \left(\frac{1}{25}\begin{bmatrix} 9 & -12 \\ -12 & 16 \end{bmatrix}\right)^2$

$$= \frac{1}{25}\begin{bmatrix} 9 & -12 \\ -12 & 16 \end{bmatrix} = I - A.$$

(c) $A\mathbf{v} = \frac{1}{25}\begin{bmatrix} 16 & 12 \\ 12 & 9 \end{bmatrix}\begin{bmatrix} 5 \\ 0 \end{bmatrix} = \begin{bmatrix} \frac{16}{5} \\ \frac{12}{5} \end{bmatrix}$

$(I - A)\mathbf{v} = \frac{1}{25}\begin{bmatrix} 9 & -12 \\ -12 & 16 \end{bmatrix}\begin{bmatrix} 5 \\ 0 \end{bmatrix} = \begin{bmatrix} \frac{9}{5} \\ -\frac{12}{5} \end{bmatrix}$

(d)

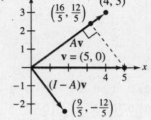

62. Suppose $\mathbf{b} = \mathbf{0}$. Then $T(\mathbf{v}) = A\mathbf{v}$. $T(\mathbf{u} + \mathbf{v}) = A(\mathbf{u} + \mathbf{v}) = A\mathbf{u} + A\mathbf{v} = T(\mathbf{u}) + T(\mathbf{v})$

$cT(\mathbf{v}) = c(A\mathbf{v}) = (cA)\mathbf{v} = T(c\mathbf{v})$

So, $T : R^2 \to R^2$ is a linear transformation.

Suppose T is a linear transformation. Then $T(\mathbf{u} + \mathbf{v}) = A(\mathbf{u} + \mathbf{v}) + \mathbf{b}$ and $T(\mathbf{u}) + T(\mathbf{v}) = (A\mathbf{u} + \mathbf{b}) + (A\mathbf{v} + \mathbf{b})$.

$$T(\mathbf{u} + \mathbf{v}) = T(\mathbf{u}) + T(\mathbf{v})$$

$$A(\mathbf{u} + \mathbf{v}) + \mathbf{b} = (A\mathbf{u} + \mathbf{b}) + (A\mathbf{v} + \mathbf{b})$$

$$A\mathbf{u} + A\mathbf{v} + \mathbf{b} = A\mathbf{u} + A\mathbf{v} + 2\mathbf{b}$$

$$\mathbf{b} = 2\mathbf{b}$$

$$\mathbf{0} = \mathbf{b}$$

64. (a) Let $S = \begin{bmatrix} 1 & 0 \\ 0 & 0 \end{bmatrix}$ and $T = \begin{bmatrix} 0 & 0 \\ 0 & 1 \end{bmatrix}$.

Then $S + T = \begin{bmatrix} 1 & 0 \\ 0 & 1 \end{bmatrix}$ and $\text{rank}(S + T)$

$$= \text{rank}(S) + \text{rank}(T).$$

(b) Let $S = T = \begin{bmatrix} 1 & 0 \\ 0 & 0 \end{bmatrix}$.

Then $S + T = \begin{bmatrix} 2 & 0 \\ 0 & 0 \end{bmatrix}$ and $\text{rank}(S + T)$

$$= 1 < 2 = \text{rank}(S) + \text{rank}(T).$$

66. (a) Let $\mathbf{v} \in \text{kernel}(T)$, which implies that $T(\mathbf{v}) = \mathbf{0}$.

Clearly $(S \circ T)(\mathbf{v}) = \mathbf{0}$ as well, which shows that

$\mathbf{v} \in \text{kernel}(S \circ T)$.

(b) Let $\mathbf{w} \in W$. Because $S \circ T$ is onto, there exists

$\mathbf{v} \in V$ such that $(S \circ T)(\mathbf{v}) = \mathbf{w}$. So,

$S(T(\mathbf{v})) = \mathbf{w}$, and S is onto.

68. Compute the images of the basis vectors under D_x.

$$D_x(1) = 0$$

$$D_x(x) = 1$$

$$D_x(\sin x) = \cos x$$

$$D_x(\cos x) = -\sin x$$

So, the matrix of D_x relative to this basis is

$$\begin{bmatrix} 0 & 1 & 0 & 0 \\ 0 & 0 & 0 & 0 \\ 0 & 0 & 0 & -1 \\ 0 & 0 & 1 & 0 \end{bmatrix}.$$

The range of D_x is spanned by $\{x, \sin x, \cos x\}$, whereas the kernel is spanned by $\{1\}$.

70. First compute the effect of T on the basis $\{1, x, x^2, x^3\}$.

$$T(1) = 1$$
$$T(x) = 1 + x$$
$$T(x^2) = 2x + x^2$$
$$T(x^3) = 3x^2 + x^3$$

The standard matrix for T is

$$A = \begin{bmatrix} 1 & 1 & 0 & 0 \\ 0 & 1 & 2 & 0 \\ 0 & 0 & 1 & 3 \\ 0 & 0 & 0 & 1 \end{bmatrix}.$$

Because the $\text{rank}(A) = 4$, the $\text{rank}(T) = 4$ and $\text{nullity}(T) = 0$.

72. (a) T is a horizontal shear.

(b)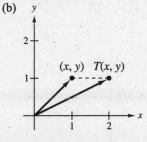

74. (a) T is a horizontal expansion.

(b)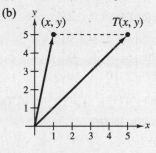

76. (a) T is a vertical shear.

(b)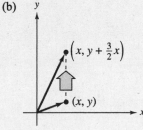

78. The image of each vertex is $T(0,0) = (0,0)$, $T(1,0) = (2,0), T(0,1) = (0,1)$. A sketch of the triangle and its image follows.

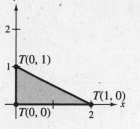

80. The image of each vertex is $T(0,0) = (0,0), T(1,0) = (1,2), T(0,1) = (0,1)$. A sketch of the triangle and its image follows.

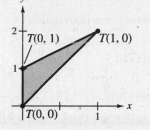

82. The transformation is a vertical shear $\begin{bmatrix} 1 & 0 \\ 3 & 1 \end{bmatrix}$ followed by a vertical expansion $\begin{bmatrix} 1 & 0 \\ 0 & 2 \end{bmatrix}$.

84. A rotation of $90°$ about the x-axis is given by

$$A = \begin{bmatrix} 1 & 0 & 0 \\ 0 & \cos 90° & -\sin 90° \\ 0 & \sin 90° & \cos 90° \end{bmatrix} = \begin{bmatrix} 1 & 0 & 0 \\ 0 & 0 & -1 \\ 0 & 1 & 0 \end{bmatrix}.$$

Because $A\mathbf{v} = \begin{bmatrix} 1 & 0 & 0 \\ 0 & 0 & -1 \\ 0 & 1 & 0 \end{bmatrix} \begin{bmatrix} 1 \\ -1 \\ 1 \end{bmatrix} = \begin{bmatrix} 1 \\ -1 \\ -1 \end{bmatrix}$,

the image of $(1, -1, 1)$ is $(1, -1, -1)$.

86. A rotation of 30° about the *y*-axis is given by

$$A = \begin{bmatrix} \cos 30° & 0 & \sin 30° \\ 0 & 1 & 0 \\ -\sin 30° & 0 & \cos 30° \end{bmatrix} = \begin{bmatrix} \dfrac{\sqrt{3}}{2} & 0 & \dfrac{1}{2} \\ 0 & 1 & 0 \\ -\dfrac{1}{2} & 0 & \dfrac{\sqrt{3}}{2} \end{bmatrix}.$$

Because

$$A\mathbf{v} = \begin{bmatrix} \dfrac{\sqrt{3}}{2} & 0 & \dfrac{1}{2} \\ 0 & 1 & 0 \\ -\dfrac{1}{2} & 0 & \dfrac{\sqrt{3}}{2} \end{bmatrix} \begin{bmatrix} 1 \\ -1 \\ 1 \end{bmatrix} = \begin{bmatrix} \dfrac{\sqrt{3}}{2} + \dfrac{1}{2} \\ -1 \\ -\dfrac{1}{2} + \dfrac{\sqrt{3}}{2} \end{bmatrix},$$

the image of $(1, -1, 1)$ is $\left(\dfrac{\sqrt{3}}{2} + \dfrac{1}{2}, -1, -\dfrac{1}{2} + \dfrac{\sqrt{3}}{2} \right)$.

88. A rotation of 120° about the *y*-axis is given by

$$A_1 = \begin{bmatrix} \cos 120° & 0 & \sin 120° \\ 0 & 1 & 0 \\ -\sin 120° & 0 & \cos 120° \end{bmatrix} = \begin{bmatrix} -\dfrac{1}{2} & 0 & \dfrac{\sqrt{3}}{2} \\ 0 & 1 & 0 \\ -\dfrac{\sqrt{3}}{2} & 0 & -\dfrac{1}{2} \end{bmatrix}$$

while a rotation of 45° about the *z*-axis is given by

$$A_2 = \begin{bmatrix} \cos 45° & -\sin 45° & 0 \\ \sin 45° & \cos 45° & 0 \\ 0 & 0 & 1 \end{bmatrix} = \begin{bmatrix} \dfrac{\sqrt{2}}{2} & -\dfrac{\sqrt{2}}{2} & 0 \\ \dfrac{\sqrt{2}}{2} & \dfrac{\sqrt{2}}{2} & 0 \\ 0 & 0 & 1 \end{bmatrix}.$$

So, the pair of rotations is given by

$$A_2 A_1 = \begin{bmatrix} \dfrac{\sqrt{2}}{2} & -\dfrac{\sqrt{2}}{2} & 0 \\ \dfrac{\sqrt{2}}{2} & \dfrac{\sqrt{2}}{2} & 0 \\ 0 & 0 & 1 \end{bmatrix} \begin{bmatrix} -\dfrac{1}{2} & 0 & \dfrac{\sqrt{3}}{2} \\ 0 & 1 & 0 \\ -\dfrac{\sqrt{3}}{2} & 0 & -\dfrac{1}{2} \end{bmatrix}$$

$$= \begin{bmatrix} -\dfrac{\sqrt{2}}{4} & -\dfrac{\sqrt{2}}{2} & \dfrac{\sqrt{6}}{4} \\ -\dfrac{\sqrt{2}}{4} & \dfrac{\sqrt{2}}{2} & \dfrac{\sqrt{6}}{4} \\ -\dfrac{\sqrt{3}}{2} & 0 & -\dfrac{1}{2} \end{bmatrix}.$$

90. A rotation of 60° about the *x*-axis is given by

$$A_1 = \begin{bmatrix} 1 & 0 & 0 \\ 0 & \cos 60° & -\sin 60° \\ 0 & \sin 60° & \cos 60° \end{bmatrix} = \begin{bmatrix} 1 & 0 & 0 \\ 0 & \dfrac{1}{2} & -\dfrac{\sqrt{3}}{2} \\ 0 & \dfrac{\sqrt{3}}{2} & \dfrac{1}{2} \end{bmatrix}$$

while a rotation of 60° about the *z*-axis is given by

$$A_2 = \begin{bmatrix} \cos 60° & -\sin 60° & 0 \\ \sin 60° & \cos 60° & 0 \\ 0 & 0 & 1 \end{bmatrix} = \begin{bmatrix} \dfrac{1}{2} & -\dfrac{\sqrt{3}}{2} & 0 \\ \dfrac{\sqrt{3}}{2} & \dfrac{1}{2} & 0 \\ 0 & 0 & 1 \end{bmatrix}.$$

So, the pair of rotations is given by

$$A_2 A_1 = \begin{bmatrix} \dfrac{1}{2} & -\dfrac{\sqrt{3}}{2} & 0 \\ \dfrac{\sqrt{3}}{2} & \dfrac{1}{2} & 0 \\ 0 & 0 & 1 \end{bmatrix} \begin{bmatrix} 1 & 0 & 0 \\ 0 & \dfrac{1}{2} & -\dfrac{\sqrt{3}}{2} \\ 0 & \dfrac{\sqrt{3}}{2} & \dfrac{1}{2} \end{bmatrix}$$

$$= \begin{bmatrix} \dfrac{1}{2} & \dfrac{\sqrt{3}}{4} & \dfrac{3}{4} \\ \dfrac{\sqrt{3}}{2} & \dfrac{1}{4} & -\dfrac{\sqrt{3}}{4} \\ 0 & \dfrac{\sqrt{3}}{2} & \dfrac{1}{2} \end{bmatrix}.$$

92. The standard matrix for *T* is

$$\begin{bmatrix} 1 & 0 & 0 \\ 0 & \cos 90° & -\sin 90° \\ 0 & \sin 90° & \cos 90° \end{bmatrix} = \begin{bmatrix} 1 & 0 & 0 \\ 0 & 0 & -1 \\ 0 & 1 & 0 \end{bmatrix}.$$

Therefore, *T* is given by $T(x, y, z) = (x, -z, y)$. The image of each vertex is as follows.

$T(0, 0, 0) = (0, 0, 0)$

$T(1, 1, 0) = (1, 0, 1)$

$T(0, 0, 1) = (0, -1, 0)$

$T(1, 1, 1) = (1, -1, 1)$

$T(1, 0, 0) = (1, 0, 0)$

$T(0, 1, 0) = (0, 0, 1)$

$T(1, 0, 1) = (1, -1, 0)$

$T(0, 1, 1) = (0, -1, 1)$

94. The standard matrix for T is

$$\begin{bmatrix} \cos 120° & -\sin 120° & 0 \\ \sin 120° & \cos 120° & 0 \\ 0 & 0 & 1 \end{bmatrix} = \begin{bmatrix} -\dfrac{1}{2} & -\dfrac{\sqrt{3}}{2} & 0 \\ \dfrac{\sqrt{3}}{2} & -\dfrac{1}{2} & 0 \\ 0 & 0 & 1 \end{bmatrix}.$$

Therefore, T is given by

$$T(x, y, z) = \left(-\frac{1}{2}x - \frac{\sqrt{3}}{2}y, \frac{\sqrt{3}}{2}x - \frac{1}{2}y, z\right).$$ The image

of each vertex is as follows.

$T(0, 0, 0) = (0, 0, 0)$

$T(1, 0, 0) = \left(-\dfrac{1}{2}, \dfrac{\sqrt{3}}{2}, 0\right)$

$T(1, 1, 0) = \left(-\dfrac{1}{2} - \dfrac{\sqrt{3}}{2}, \dfrac{\sqrt{3}}{2} - \dfrac{1}{2}, 0\right)$

$T(0, 1, 0) = \left(-\dfrac{\sqrt{3}}{2}, -\dfrac{1}{2}, 0\right)$

$T(0, 0, 1) = (0, 0, 1)$

$T(1, 0, 1) = \left(-\dfrac{1}{2}, \dfrac{\sqrt{3}}{2}, 1\right)$

$T(1, 1, 1) = \left(-\dfrac{1}{2} - \dfrac{\sqrt{3}}{2}, \dfrac{\sqrt{3}}{2} - \dfrac{1}{2}, 1\right)$

$T(0, 1, 1) = \left(-\dfrac{\sqrt{3}}{2}, -\dfrac{1}{2}, 1\right)$

96. (a) True. The statement is true because if T is a reflection $T(x, y) = (x, -y)$, then the standard matrix is

$$\begin{bmatrix} 1 & 0 \\ 0 & -1 \end{bmatrix}.$$

(b) True. The statement is true because the linear transformation $T(x, y) = (x, ky)$ has the standard matrix.

$$\begin{bmatrix} 1 & 0 \\ 0 & k \end{bmatrix}.$$

(c) True. The statement is true because the matrix

$$\begin{bmatrix} \cos(\theta) & 0 & \sin(\theta) \\ 0 & 1 & 0 \\ -\sin(\theta) & 0 & \cos(\theta) \end{bmatrix}$$

will rotate a point θ degrees. If $\theta = 30$ degrees, you obtain the matrix in the statement.

98. (a) True. D_x is a linear transformation because it preserves addition and scalar multiplication. Further, $D_x(P_n) = P_{n-1}$ because for all natural numbers $i \geq 1$, $D_x(x^i) = ix^{i-1}$.

(b) False. If T is a linear transformation $V \to W$, then kernel of T is defined to be a set of $\mathbf{v} \in V$, such that $T(\mathbf{v}) = \mathbf{0}_W$.

(c) True. If $T = T_2 \circ T_1$ and A_i is the standard matrix for T_i, $i = 1, 2$, then the standard matrix for T is equal $A_2 A_1$ by Theorem 6.11 on page 317.

Project Solutions for Chapter 6

1 Reflections in the Plane-I

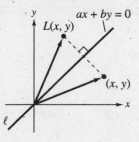

1.

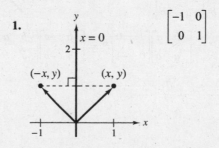

2. $\begin{bmatrix} 1 & 0 \\ 0 & -1 \end{bmatrix}$

3. $\begin{bmatrix} 0 & 1 \\ 1 & 0 \end{bmatrix}$

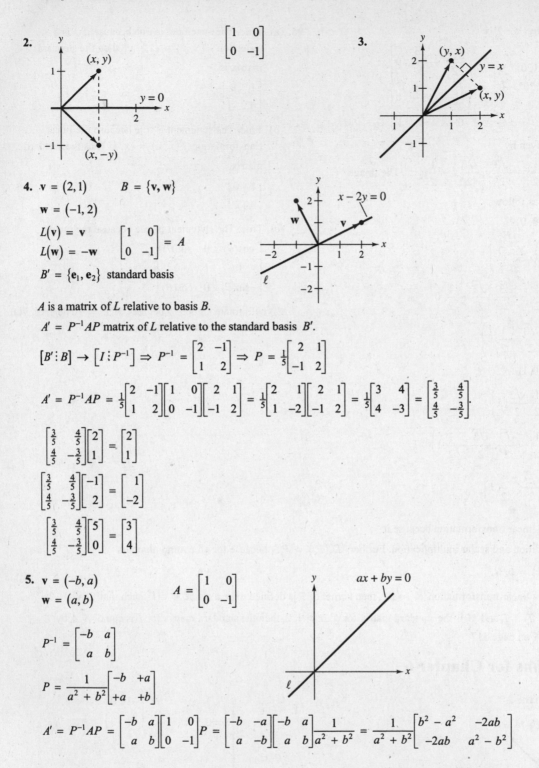

4. $\mathbf{v} = (2, 1)$ $B = \{\mathbf{v}, \mathbf{w}\}$

$\mathbf{w} = (-1, 2)$

$L(\mathbf{v}) = \mathbf{v}$ $\begin{bmatrix} 1 & 0 \\ 0 & -1 \end{bmatrix} = A$

$L(\mathbf{w}) = -\mathbf{w}$

$B' = \{\mathbf{e}_1, \mathbf{e}_2\}$ standard basis

A is a matrix of L relative to basis B.

$A' = P^{-1}AP$ matrix of L relative to the standard basis B'.

$[B' \vdots B] \rightarrow [I \vdots P^{-1}] \Rightarrow P^{-1} = \begin{bmatrix} 2 & -1 \\ 1 & 2 \end{bmatrix} \Rightarrow P = \frac{1}{5}\begin{bmatrix} 2 & 1 \\ -1 & 2 \end{bmatrix}$

$A' = P^{-1}AP = \frac{1}{5}\begin{bmatrix} 2 & -1 \\ 1 & 2 \end{bmatrix}\begin{bmatrix} 1 & 0 \\ 0 & -1 \end{bmatrix}\begin{bmatrix} 2 & 1 \\ -1 & 2 \end{bmatrix} = \frac{1}{5}\begin{bmatrix} 2 & 1 \\ 1 & -2 \end{bmatrix}\begin{bmatrix} 2 & 1 \\ -1 & 2 \end{bmatrix} = \frac{1}{5}\begin{bmatrix} 3 & 4 \\ 4 & -3 \end{bmatrix} = \begin{bmatrix} \frac{3}{5} & \frac{4}{5} \\ \frac{4}{5} & -\frac{3}{5} \end{bmatrix}$

$\begin{bmatrix} \frac{3}{5} & \frac{4}{5} \\ \frac{4}{5} & -\frac{3}{5} \end{bmatrix}\begin{bmatrix} 2 \\ 1 \end{bmatrix} = \begin{bmatrix} 2 \\ 1 \end{bmatrix}$

$\begin{bmatrix} \frac{3}{5} & \frac{4}{5} \\ \frac{4}{5} & -\frac{3}{5} \end{bmatrix}\begin{bmatrix} -1 \\ 2 \end{bmatrix} = \begin{bmatrix} 1 \\ -2 \end{bmatrix}$

$\begin{bmatrix} \frac{3}{5} & \frac{4}{5} \\ \frac{4}{5} & -\frac{3}{5} \end{bmatrix}\begin{bmatrix} 5 \\ 0 \end{bmatrix} = \begin{bmatrix} 3 \\ 4 \end{bmatrix}$

5. $\mathbf{v} = (-b, a)$ $A = \begin{bmatrix} 1 & 0 \\ 0 & -1 \end{bmatrix}$

$\mathbf{w} = (a, b)$

$P^{-1} = \begin{bmatrix} -b & a \\ a & b \end{bmatrix}$

$P = \frac{1}{a^2 + b^2}\begin{bmatrix} -b & +a \\ +a & +b \end{bmatrix}$

$A' = P^{-1}AP = \begin{bmatrix} -b & a \\ a & b \end{bmatrix}\begin{bmatrix} 1 & 0 \\ 0 & -1 \end{bmatrix}P = \begin{bmatrix} -b & -a \\ a & -b \end{bmatrix}\begin{bmatrix} -b & a \\ a & b \end{bmatrix}\frac{1}{a^2 + b^2} = \frac{1}{a^2 + b^2}\begin{bmatrix} b^2 - a^2 & -2ab \\ -2ab & a^2 - b^2 \end{bmatrix}$

6. $3x + 4y = 0$ $A' = \dfrac{1}{3^2 + 4^2}\begin{bmatrix} 7 & -24 \\ -24 & -7 \end{bmatrix}$

$$\frac{1}{25}\begin{bmatrix} 7 & -24 \\ -24 & -7 \end{bmatrix}\begin{bmatrix} 3 \\ 4 \end{bmatrix} = \frac{1}{25}\begin{bmatrix} -75 \\ -100 \end{bmatrix} = \begin{bmatrix} -3 \\ -4 \end{bmatrix}$$

$$\frac{1}{25}\begin{bmatrix} 7 & -24 \\ -24 & -7 \end{bmatrix}\begin{bmatrix} -4 \\ 3 \end{bmatrix} = \frac{1}{25}\begin{bmatrix} -100 \\ 75 \end{bmatrix} = \begin{bmatrix} -4 \\ 3 \end{bmatrix}$$

$$\frac{1}{25}\begin{bmatrix} 7 & -24 \\ -24 & -7 \end{bmatrix}\begin{bmatrix} 0 \\ 5 \end{bmatrix} = \frac{1}{25}\begin{bmatrix} -24 \cdot 5 \\ -7 \cdot 5 \end{bmatrix} = \begin{bmatrix} -\dfrac{24}{5} \\ -\dfrac{7}{5} \end{bmatrix}$$

2 Reflections in the Plane-II

1. $\mathbf{v} = (0, 1)$ $\begin{bmatrix} 0 & 0 \\ 0 & 1 \end{bmatrix}$

2. $\mathbf{v} = (1, 0)$ $\begin{bmatrix} 1 & 0 \\ 0 & 0 \end{bmatrix}$

3. $\mathbf{v} = (2, 1)$ $B = \{\mathbf{v}, \mathbf{w}\}$
$\mathbf{w} = (-1, 2)$

$\left.\begin{array}{l} \text{proj}_{\mathbf{v}}\mathbf{v} = \mathbf{v} \\ \text{proj}_{\mathbf{v}}\mathbf{w} = \mathbf{0} \end{array}\right\}$ $A = \begin{bmatrix} 1 & 0 \\ 0 & 0 \end{bmatrix}$

$P^{-1} = \begin{bmatrix} 2 & -1 \\ 1 & 2 \end{bmatrix}$, $P = \frac{1}{5}\begin{bmatrix} 2 & 1 \\ -1 & 2 \end{bmatrix}$

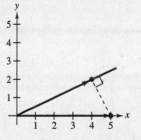

$A' = P^{-1}AP = $ matrix of L relative to standard basis.

$$= \begin{bmatrix} 2 & -1 \\ 1 & 2 \end{bmatrix}\begin{bmatrix} 1 & 0 \\ 0 & 0 \end{bmatrix}P = \begin{bmatrix} 2 & 0 \\ 1 & 0 \end{bmatrix}\begin{bmatrix} 2 & 1 \\ -1 & 2 \end{bmatrix}\frac{1}{5} = \begin{bmatrix} \frac{4}{5} & \frac{2}{5} \\ \frac{2}{5} & \frac{1}{5} \end{bmatrix}$$

$\begin{bmatrix} \frac{4}{5} & \frac{2}{5} \\ \frac{2}{5} & \frac{1}{5} \end{bmatrix}\begin{bmatrix} 2 \\ 1 \end{bmatrix} = \begin{bmatrix} 2 \\ 1 \end{bmatrix}$, $\begin{bmatrix} \frac{4}{5} & \frac{2}{5} \\ \frac{2}{5} & \frac{1}{5} \end{bmatrix}\begin{bmatrix} -1 \\ 2 \end{bmatrix} = \begin{bmatrix} 0 \\ 0 \end{bmatrix}$

$\begin{bmatrix} \frac{4}{5} & \frac{2}{5} \\ \frac{2}{5} & \frac{1}{5} \end{bmatrix}\begin{bmatrix} 5 \\ 0 \end{bmatrix} = \begin{bmatrix} 4 \\ 2 \end{bmatrix}$

4. $\mathbf{v} = (-b, a)$

$\mathbf{w} = (a, b)$
$\qquad A = \begin{bmatrix} 1 & 0 \\ 0 & 0 \end{bmatrix}$

$$P^{-1} = \begin{bmatrix} -b & a \\ a & b \end{bmatrix} \qquad P = \frac{1}{a^2 + b^2} \begin{bmatrix} -b & a \\ a & b \end{bmatrix}$$

$$A' = P^{-1}AP = \frac{1}{a^2 + b^2} \begin{bmatrix} b^2 & -ab \\ -ab & a^2 \end{bmatrix}$$

5. $\text{proj}_\mathbf{v}\mathbf{u} = \dfrac{1}{2}\big(\mathbf{u} + L(\mathbf{u})\big) \quad \Rightarrow \quad L(\mathbf{u}) = 2\text{proj}_\mathbf{v}\mathbf{u} - \mathbf{u}$

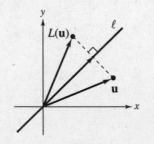

$L = 2\,\text{proj}_\mathbf{v} - I$

$\quad = 2\dfrac{1}{a^2 + b^2}\begin{bmatrix} b^2 & -ab \\ -ab & a^2 \end{bmatrix} - \begin{bmatrix} 1 & 0 \\ 0 & 1 \end{bmatrix}$

$\quad = \dfrac{1}{a^2 + b^2}\left(\begin{bmatrix} 2b^2 & -2ab \\ -2ab & 2a^2 \end{bmatrix} - \begin{bmatrix} a^2 + b^2 & 0 \\ 0 & a^2 + b^2 \end{bmatrix}\right)$

$\quad = \dfrac{1}{a^2 + b^2}\begin{bmatrix} b^2 - a^2 & -2ab \\ -2ab & a^2 - b^2 \end{bmatrix}$

CHAPTER 7
Eigenvalues and Eigenvectors

C H A P T E R 7
Eigenvalues and Eigenvectors

Section 7.1 Eigenvalues and Eigenvectors

2. $A\mathbf{x}_1 = \begin{bmatrix} 4 & -5 \\ 2 & -3 \end{bmatrix}\begin{bmatrix} 1 \\ 1 \end{bmatrix} = \begin{bmatrix} -1 \\ -1 \end{bmatrix} = -1\begin{bmatrix} 1 \\ 1 \end{bmatrix} = \lambda_1\mathbf{x}_1$

$A\mathbf{x}_2 = \begin{bmatrix} 4 & -5 \\ 2 & -3 \end{bmatrix}\begin{bmatrix} 5 \\ 2 \end{bmatrix} = \begin{bmatrix} 10 \\ 4 \end{bmatrix} = 2\begin{bmatrix} 5 \\ 2 \end{bmatrix} = \lambda_2\mathbf{x}_2$

4. $A\mathbf{x}_1 = \begin{bmatrix} -2 & 4 \\ 1 & 1 \end{bmatrix}\begin{bmatrix} 1 \\ 1 \end{bmatrix} = \begin{bmatrix} 2 \\ 2 \end{bmatrix} = 2\begin{bmatrix} 1 \\ 1 \end{bmatrix} = \lambda_1\mathbf{x}_1$

$A\mathbf{x}_2 = \begin{bmatrix} -2 & 4 \\ 1 & 1 \end{bmatrix}\begin{bmatrix} -4 \\ 1 \end{bmatrix} = \begin{bmatrix} 12 \\ -3 \end{bmatrix} = -3\begin{bmatrix} -4 \\ 1 \end{bmatrix} = \lambda_2\mathbf{x}_2$

6. $A\mathbf{x}_1 = \begin{bmatrix} -2 & 2 & -3 \\ 2 & 1 & -6 \\ -1 & -2 & 0 \end{bmatrix}\begin{bmatrix} 1 \\ 2 \\ -1 \end{bmatrix} = \begin{bmatrix} 5 \\ 10 \\ -5 \end{bmatrix} = 5\begin{bmatrix} 1 \\ 2 \\ -1 \end{bmatrix} = \lambda_1\mathbf{x}_1$

$A\mathbf{x}_2 = \begin{bmatrix} -2 & 2 & -3 \\ 2 & 1 & -6 \\ -1 & -2 & 0 \end{bmatrix}\begin{bmatrix} -2 \\ 1 \\ 0 \end{bmatrix} = \begin{bmatrix} 6 \\ -3 \\ 0 \end{bmatrix} = -3\begin{bmatrix} -2 \\ 1 \\ 0 \end{bmatrix} = \lambda_2\mathbf{x}_2$

$A\mathbf{x}_3 = \begin{bmatrix} -2 & 2 & -3 \\ 2 & 1 & -6 \\ -1 & -2 & 0 \end{bmatrix}\begin{bmatrix} 3 \\ 0 \\ 1 \end{bmatrix} = \begin{bmatrix} -9 \\ 0 \\ -3 \end{bmatrix} = -3\begin{bmatrix} 3 \\ 0 \\ 1 \end{bmatrix} = \lambda_3\mathbf{x}_3$

8. $A\mathbf{x}_1 = \begin{bmatrix} 4 & -1 & 3 \\ 0 & 2 & 1 \\ 0 & 0 & 3 \end{bmatrix}\begin{bmatrix} 1 \\ 0 \\ 0 \end{bmatrix} = \begin{bmatrix} 4 \\ 0 \\ 0 \end{bmatrix} = 4\begin{bmatrix} 1 \\ 0 \\ 0 \end{bmatrix} = \lambda_1\mathbf{x}_1$

$A\mathbf{x}_2 = \begin{bmatrix} 4 & -1 & 3 \\ 0 & 2 & 1 \\ 0 & 0 & 3 \end{bmatrix}\begin{bmatrix} 1 \\ 2 \\ 0 \end{bmatrix} = \begin{bmatrix} 2 \\ 4 \\ 0 \end{bmatrix} = 2\begin{bmatrix} 1 \\ 2 \\ 0 \end{bmatrix} = \lambda_2\mathbf{x}_2$

$A\mathbf{x}_3 = \begin{bmatrix} 4 & -1 & 3 \\ 0 & 2 & 1 \\ 0 & 0 & 3 \end{bmatrix}\begin{bmatrix} -2 \\ 1 \\ 1 \end{bmatrix} = \begin{bmatrix} -6 \\ 3 \\ 3 \end{bmatrix} = 3\begin{bmatrix} -2 \\ 1 \\ 1 \end{bmatrix} = \lambda_3\mathbf{x}_3$

10. (a) $A(c\mathbf{x}_1) = \begin{bmatrix} 2 & 3 & 1 \\ 0 & -1 & 2 \\ 0 & 0 & 3 \end{bmatrix}\begin{bmatrix} c \\ 0 \\ 0 \end{bmatrix} = \begin{bmatrix} 2c \\ 0 \\ 0 \end{bmatrix} = 2\begin{bmatrix} c \\ 0 \\ 0 \end{bmatrix} = 2(c\mathbf{x}_1)$

(b) $A(c\mathbf{x}_2) = \begin{bmatrix} 2 & 3 & 1 \\ 0 & -1 & 2 \\ 0 & 0 & 3 \end{bmatrix}\begin{bmatrix} c \\ -c \\ 0 \end{bmatrix}$

$= \begin{bmatrix} -c \\ c \\ 0 \end{bmatrix} = -1\begin{bmatrix} c \\ -c \\ 0 \end{bmatrix} = -(c\mathbf{x}_2)$

(c) $A(c\mathbf{x}_3) = \begin{bmatrix} 2 & 3 & 1 \\ 0 & -1 & 2 \\ 0 & 0 & 3 \end{bmatrix}\begin{bmatrix} 5c \\ c \\ 2c \end{bmatrix}$

$= \begin{bmatrix} 15c \\ 3c \\ 6c \end{bmatrix} = 3\begin{bmatrix} 5c \\ c \\ 2c \end{bmatrix} = 3(c\mathbf{x}_3)$

12. (a) Because

$$A\mathbf{x} = \begin{bmatrix} -3 & 10 \\ 5 & 2 \end{bmatrix}\begin{bmatrix} 4 \\ 4 \end{bmatrix} = \begin{bmatrix} 28 \\ 28 \end{bmatrix} = 7\begin{bmatrix} 4 \\ 4 \end{bmatrix}$$

$\mathbf{x}$ *is* an eigenvector of A (with corresponding eigenvalue 7).

(b) Because

$$A\mathbf{x} = \begin{bmatrix} -3 & 10 \\ 5 & 2 \end{bmatrix}\begin{bmatrix} -8 \\ 4 \end{bmatrix} = \begin{bmatrix} 64 \\ -32 \end{bmatrix} = -8\begin{bmatrix} -8 \\ 4 \end{bmatrix}$$

$\mathbf{x}$ *is* an eigenvector of A (with corresponding eigenvalue -8).

(c) Because

$$A\mathbf{x} = \begin{bmatrix} -3 & 10 \\ 5 & 2 \end{bmatrix}\begin{bmatrix} -4 \\ 8 \end{bmatrix} = \begin{bmatrix} 92 \\ -4 \end{bmatrix} \neq \lambda\begin{bmatrix} -4 \\ 8 \end{bmatrix}$$

$\mathbf{x}$ is *not* an eigenvector of A.

(d) Because

$$A\mathbf{x} = \begin{bmatrix} -3 & 10 \\ 5 & 2 \end{bmatrix}\begin{bmatrix} 5 \\ -3 \end{bmatrix} = \begin{bmatrix} -45 \\ 19 \end{bmatrix} \neq \lambda\begin{bmatrix} 5 \\ -3 \end{bmatrix}$$

$\mathbf{x}$ is *not* an eigenvector of A.

14. (a) Because $A\mathbf{x} = \begin{bmatrix} 1 & 0 & 5 \\ 0 & -2 & 4 \\ 1 & -2 & 9 \end{bmatrix} \begin{bmatrix} 1 \\ 1 \\ 0 \end{bmatrix} = \begin{bmatrix} 1 \\ -2 \\ -1 \end{bmatrix} \neq \lambda \begin{bmatrix} 1 \\ 1 \\ 0 \end{bmatrix}$, $\mathbf{x}$ is *not* an eigenvector of A.

(b) Because $A\mathbf{x} = \begin{bmatrix} 1 & 0 & 5 \\ 0 & -2 & 4 \\ 1 & -2 & 9 \end{bmatrix} \begin{bmatrix} -5 \\ 2 \\ 1 \end{bmatrix} = \begin{bmatrix} 0 \\ 0 \\ 0 \end{bmatrix} = 0 \begin{bmatrix} -5 \\ 2 \\ 1 \end{bmatrix}$, $\mathbf{x}$ *is* an eigenvector (with corresponding eigenvalue 0).

(c) The zero vector is never an eigenvector.

(d) Because $A\mathbf{x} = \begin{bmatrix} 1 & 0 & 5 \\ 0 & -2 & 4 \\ 1 & -2 & 9 \end{bmatrix} \begin{bmatrix} 2\sqrt{6} - 3 \\ -2\sqrt{6} + 6 \\ 3 \end{bmatrix} = \begin{bmatrix} 12 + 2\sqrt{6} \\ 4\sqrt{6} \\ 6\sqrt{6} + 12 \end{bmatrix} = \left(4 + 2\sqrt{6} \right) \begin{bmatrix} 2\sqrt{6} - 3 \\ -2\sqrt{6} + 6 \\ 3 \end{bmatrix}$,

$\mathbf{x}$ *is* an eigenvector of A $\left(\text{with corresponding eigenvalue } 4 + 2\sqrt{6}\right)$.

16. Geometrically, multiplying a vector in R^2 by A corresponds to a horizontal shear.

$$\begin{bmatrix} 1 & k \\ 0 & 1 \end{bmatrix} \begin{bmatrix} x \\ y \end{bmatrix} = \begin{bmatrix} x + ky \\ y \end{bmatrix}$$

The only vectors mapped onto scalar multiples of themselves are those lying on the x axis.

$$\begin{bmatrix} 1 & k \\ 0 & 1 \end{bmatrix} \begin{bmatrix} x \\ 0 \end{bmatrix} = \begin{bmatrix} x \\ 0 \end{bmatrix} = 1 \begin{bmatrix} x \\ 0 \end{bmatrix}$$

So, the only eigenvalue is 1, and the corresponding eigenspace is the x-axis.

18. (a) The characteristic equation is

$$|\lambda I - A| = \begin{vmatrix} \lambda - 1 & 4 \\ 2 & \lambda - 8 \end{vmatrix} = \lambda^2 - 9\lambda = \lambda(\lambda - 9) = 0.$$

(b) The eigenvalues are $\lambda_1 = 0$ and $\lambda_2 = 9$.

For $\lambda_1 = 0$, $\begin{bmatrix} \lambda_1 - 1 & 4 \\ 2 & \lambda_1 - 8 \end{bmatrix} \begin{bmatrix} x_1 \\ x_2 \end{bmatrix} = \begin{bmatrix} 0 \\ 0 \end{bmatrix} \Rightarrow \begin{bmatrix} 1 & -4 \\ 0 & 0 \end{bmatrix} \begin{bmatrix} x_1 \\ x_2 \end{bmatrix} = \begin{bmatrix} 0 \\ 0 \end{bmatrix}$.

The solution is $\{(4t, t) : t \in R\}$. So, an eigenvector corresponding to $\lambda_1 = 0$ is $(4, 1)$.

For $\lambda_2 = 9$, $\begin{bmatrix} \lambda_2 - 1 & 4 \\ 2 & \lambda_2 - 8 \end{bmatrix} \begin{bmatrix} x_1 \\ x_2 \end{bmatrix} = \begin{bmatrix} 0 \\ 0 \end{bmatrix} \Rightarrow \begin{bmatrix} 2 & 1 \\ 0 & 0 \end{bmatrix} \begin{bmatrix} x_1 \\ x_2 \end{bmatrix} = \begin{bmatrix} 0 \\ 0 \end{bmatrix}$.

The solution is $\{(-t, 2t) : t \in R\}$. So, an eigenvector corresponding to $\lambda_2 = 9$ is $(-1, 2)$.

20. (a) The characteristic equation is

$$|\lambda I - A| = \begin{vmatrix} \lambda - \frac{1}{4} & -\frac{1}{4} \\ -\frac{1}{2} & \lambda \end{vmatrix} = \lambda^2 - \frac{1}{4}\lambda - \frac{1}{8} = \left(\lambda - \frac{1}{2}\right)\left(\lambda + \frac{1}{4}\right) = 0.$$

(b) The eigenvalues are $\lambda_1 = \frac{1}{2}$ and $\lambda_2 = -\frac{1}{4}$.

For $\lambda_1 = \frac{1}{2}$, $\begin{bmatrix} \lambda_1 - \frac{1}{4} & -\frac{1}{4} \\ -\frac{1}{2} & \lambda_1 \end{bmatrix} \begin{bmatrix} x_1 \\ x_2 \end{bmatrix} = \begin{bmatrix} 0 \\ 0 \end{bmatrix} \Rightarrow \begin{bmatrix} 1 & -1 \\ 0 & 0 \end{bmatrix} \begin{bmatrix} x_1 \\ x_2 \end{bmatrix} = \begin{bmatrix} 0 \\ 0 \end{bmatrix}$.

The solution is $\{(t, t) : t \in R\}$. So, an eigenvector corresponding to $\lambda_1 = \frac{1}{2}$ is $(1, 1)$.

For $\lambda_2 = -\frac{1}{4}$, $\begin{bmatrix} \lambda_2 - \frac{1}{4} & -\frac{1}{4} \\ -\frac{1}{2} & \lambda_2 \end{bmatrix} \begin{bmatrix} x_1 \\ x_2 \end{bmatrix} = \begin{bmatrix} 0 \\ 0 \end{bmatrix} \Rightarrow \begin{bmatrix} 1 & \frac{1}{2} \\ 0 & 0 \end{bmatrix} \begin{bmatrix} x_1 \\ x_2 \end{bmatrix} = \begin{bmatrix} 0 \\ 0 \end{bmatrix}$.

The solution is $\{(t, -2t) : t \in R\}$. So, an eigenvector corresponding to $\lambda_2 = -\frac{1}{4}$ is $(1, -2)$.

22. (a) The characteristic equation is $|\lambda I - A| = \begin{vmatrix} \lambda - 3 & -2 & -1 \\ 0 & \lambda & -2 \\ 0 & -2 & \lambda \end{vmatrix} = (\lambda - 3)(\lambda^2 - 4) = 0.$

(b) The eigenvalues are $\lambda_1 = -2, \lambda_2 = 2,$ and $\lambda_3 = 3.$

For $\lambda_1 = -2,$ $\begin{bmatrix} \lambda_1 - 3 & -2 & -1 \\ 0 & \lambda_1 & -2 \\ 0 & -2 & \lambda_1 \end{bmatrix}\begin{bmatrix} x_1 \\ x_2 \\ x_3 \end{bmatrix} = \begin{bmatrix} 0 \\ 0 \\ 0 \end{bmatrix} \Rightarrow \begin{bmatrix} -5 & -2 & -1 \\ 0 & -2 & -2 \\ 0 & -2 & -2 \end{bmatrix}\begin{bmatrix} x_1 \\ x_2 \\ x_3 \end{bmatrix} = \begin{bmatrix} 0 \\ 0 \\ 0 \end{bmatrix}.$

The solution is $\{(t, -5t, 5t) : t \in R\}.$ So, an eigenvector corresponding to $\lambda_1 = -2$ is $(1, -5, 5).$

For $\lambda_2 = 2,$ $\begin{bmatrix} \lambda_2 - 3 & -2 & -1 \\ 0 & \lambda_2 & -2 \\ 0 & -2 & \lambda_2 \end{bmatrix}\begin{bmatrix} x_1 \\ x_2 \\ x_3 \end{bmatrix} = \begin{bmatrix} 0 \\ 0 \\ 0 \end{bmatrix} \Rightarrow \begin{bmatrix} -1 & -2 & -1 \\ 0 & 2 & -2 \\ 0 & -2 & 2 \end{bmatrix}\begin{bmatrix} x_1 \\ x_2 \\ x_3 \end{bmatrix} = \begin{bmatrix} 0 \\ 0 \\ 0 \end{bmatrix}.$

The solution is $\{(-3t, t, t) : t \in R\}.$ So, an eigenvector corresponding to $\lambda_2 = 2$ is $(-3, 1, 1).$

For $\lambda_3 = 3,$ $\begin{bmatrix} \lambda_3 - 3 & -2 & -1 \\ 0 & \lambda_3 & -2 \\ 0 & -2 & \lambda_3 \end{bmatrix}\begin{bmatrix} x_1 \\ x_2 \\ x_3 \end{bmatrix} = \begin{bmatrix} 0 \\ 0 \\ 0 \end{bmatrix} \Rightarrow \begin{bmatrix} 0 & -2 & -1 \\ 0 & 3 & -2 \\ 0 & -2 & 3 \end{bmatrix}\begin{bmatrix} x_1 \\ x_2 \\ x_3 \end{bmatrix} = \begin{bmatrix} 0 \\ 0 \\ 0 \end{bmatrix}.$

The solution is $\{(t, 0, 0) : t \in R\}.$ So, an eigenvector corresponding to $\lambda_3 = 3$ is $(1, 0, 0).$

24. (a) The characteristic equation is $|\lambda I - A| = \begin{vmatrix} \lambda - 3 & -2 & 3 \\ 3 & \lambda + 4 & -9 \\ 1 & 2 & \lambda - 5 \end{vmatrix} = \lambda^3 - 4\lambda^2 + 4\lambda = \lambda(\lambda - 2)^2 = 0.$

(b) The eigenvalues are $\lambda_1 = 0, \lambda_2 = 2$ (repeated).

For $\lambda_1 = 0,$ $\begin{bmatrix} \lambda_1 - 3 & -2 & 3 \\ 3 & \lambda_1 + 4 & -9 \\ 1 & 2 & \lambda_1 - 5 \end{bmatrix}\begin{bmatrix} x_1 \\ x_2 \\ x_3 \end{bmatrix} = \begin{bmatrix} 0 \\ 0 \\ 0 \end{bmatrix} \Rightarrow \begin{bmatrix} 1 & 0 & 1 \\ 0 & 1 & -3 \\ 0 & 0 & 0 \end{bmatrix}\begin{bmatrix} x_1 \\ x_2 \\ x_3 \end{bmatrix} = \begin{bmatrix} 0 \\ 0 \\ 0 \end{bmatrix}.$

The solution is $\{(-t, 3t, t) : t \in R\}.$ So, an eigenvector corresponding to $\lambda_1 = 0$ is $(-1, 3, 1).$

For $\lambda_2 = 2,$ $\begin{bmatrix} \lambda_2 - 3 & -2 & 3 \\ 3 & \lambda_2 + 4 & -9 \\ 1 & 2 & \lambda_2 - 5 \end{bmatrix}\begin{bmatrix} x_1 \\ x_2 \\ x_3 \end{bmatrix} = \begin{bmatrix} 0 \\ 0 \\ 0 \end{bmatrix} \Rightarrow \begin{bmatrix} 1 & 2 & -3 \\ 0 & 0 & 0 \\ 0 & 0 & 0 \end{bmatrix}\begin{bmatrix} x_1 \\ x_2 \\ x_3 \end{bmatrix} = \begin{bmatrix} 0 \\ 0 \\ 0 \end{bmatrix}.$

The solution is $\{(-2s + 3t, s, t) : s, t \in R\}.$ So, two independent eigenvectors corresponding to $\lambda_2 = 2$ are $(-2, 1, 0)$ and $(3, 0, 1).$

26. (a) The characteristic equation is $|\lambda I - A| = \begin{vmatrix} \lambda - 1 & \frac{3}{2} & -\frac{5}{2} \\ 2 & \lambda - \frac{13}{2} & 10 \\ -\frac{3}{2} & \frac{9}{2} & \lambda - 8 \end{vmatrix} = \left(\lambda - \frac{29}{2} \right)\left(\lambda - \frac{1}{2} \right)^2 = 0.$

(b) The eigenvalues are $\lambda_1 = \frac{29}{2}, \lambda_2 = \frac{1}{2}$ (repeated).

For $\lambda_1 = \frac{29}{2}$, $\begin{bmatrix} \lambda_1 - 1 & \frac{3}{2} & -\frac{5}{2} \\ 2 & \lambda_1 - \frac{13}{2} & 10 \\ -\frac{3}{2} & \frac{9}{2} & \lambda_1 - 8 \end{bmatrix} \begin{bmatrix} x_1 \\ x_2 \\ x_3 \end{bmatrix} = \begin{bmatrix} 0 \\ 0 \\ 0 \end{bmatrix} \Rightarrow \begin{bmatrix} 3 & 0 & -1 \\ 0 & 3 & 4 \\ 0 & 0 & 0 \end{bmatrix} \begin{bmatrix} x_1 \\ x_2 \\ x_3 \end{bmatrix} = \begin{bmatrix} 0 \\ 0 \\ 0 \end{bmatrix}.$

The solution is $\{(t, -4t, 3t) : t \in R\}$. So, an eigenvector corresponding to $\lambda_1 = \frac{29}{2}$ is $(1, -4, 3)$.

For $\lambda_2 = \frac{1}{2}$, $\begin{bmatrix} \lambda_2 - 1 & \frac{3}{2} & -\frac{5}{2} \\ 2 & \lambda_2 - \frac{13}{2} & 10 \\ -\frac{3}{2} & \frac{9}{2} & \lambda_2 - 8 \end{bmatrix} \begin{bmatrix} x_1 \\ x_2 \\ x_3 \end{bmatrix} = \begin{bmatrix} 0 \\ 0 \\ 0 \end{bmatrix} \Rightarrow \begin{bmatrix} 1 & -3 & 5 \\ 0 & 0 & 0 \\ 0 & 0 & 0 \end{bmatrix} \begin{bmatrix} x_1 \\ x_2 \\ x_3 \end{bmatrix} = \begin{bmatrix} 0 \\ 0 \\ 0 \end{bmatrix}.$

The solution is $\{(3s - 5t, s, t) : s, t \in R\}$. So, two eigenvectors corresponding to $\lambda_2 = \frac{1}{2}$ are $(3, 1, 0)$ and $(-5, 0, 1)$.

28. (a) The characteristic equation is $|\lambda I - A| = \begin{vmatrix} \lambda - 3 & 0 & 0 & 0 \\ -4 & \lambda - 1 & 0 & 0 \\ 0 & 0 & \lambda - 2 & -1 \\ 0 & 0 & 0 & \lambda - 2 \end{vmatrix} = (\lambda - 3)(\lambda - 1)(\lambda - 2)^2 = 0.$

(b) The eigenvalues are $\lambda_1 = 3, \lambda_2 = 1, \lambda_3 = 2$ (repeated).

For $\lambda_1 = 3$, $\begin{bmatrix} 0 & 0 & 0 & 0 \\ -4 & 2 & 0 & 0 \\ 0 & 0 & 1 & -1 \\ 0 & 0 & 0 & 1 \end{bmatrix} \begin{bmatrix} x_1 \\ x_2 \\ x_3 \\ x_4 \end{bmatrix} = \begin{bmatrix} 0 \\ 0 \\ 0 \\ 0 \end{bmatrix} \Rightarrow \begin{bmatrix} 1 & -\frac{1}{2} & 0 & 0 \\ 0 & 0 & 0 & 0 \\ 0 & 0 & 1 & 1 \\ 0 & 0 & 0 & 0 \end{bmatrix} \begin{bmatrix} x_1 \\ x_2 \\ x_3 \\ x_4 \end{bmatrix} = \begin{bmatrix} 0 \\ 0 \\ 0 \\ 0 \end{bmatrix}.$

The solution is $\left\{ \left(\frac{1}{2}t, t, 0, 0 \right) : t \in R \right\}$. So, an eigenvector corresponding to $\lambda_1 = 3$ is $(1, 2, 0, 0)$.

For $\lambda_2 = 1$, $\begin{bmatrix} 2 & 0 & 0 & 0 \\ -4 & 0 & 0 & 0 \\ 0 & 0 & -1 & -1 \\ 0 & 0 & 0 & -1 \end{bmatrix} \begin{bmatrix} x_1 \\ x_2 \\ x_3 \\ x_4 \end{bmatrix} = \begin{bmatrix} 0 \\ 0 \\ 0 \\ 0 \end{bmatrix} \Rightarrow \begin{bmatrix} 1 & 0 & 0 & 0 \\ 0 & 0 & 1 & 0 \\ 0 & 0 & 0 & 1 \\ 0 & 0 & 0 & 0 \end{bmatrix} \begin{bmatrix} x_1 \\ x_2 \\ x_3 \\ x_4 \end{bmatrix} = \begin{bmatrix} 0 \\ 0 \\ 0 \\ 0 \end{bmatrix}.$

The solution is $\{(0, t, 0, 0) : t \in R\}$. So, an eigenvector corresponding to $\lambda_2 = 1$ is $(0, 1, 0, 0)$.

For $\lambda_3 = 2$, $\begin{bmatrix} -1 & 0 & 0 & 0 \\ -4 & 1 & 0 & 0 \\ 0 & 0 & 0 & -1 \\ 0 & 0 & 0 & 0 \end{bmatrix} \begin{bmatrix} x_1 \\ x_2 \\ x_3 \\ x_4 \end{bmatrix} = \begin{bmatrix} 0 \\ 0 \\ 0 \\ 0 \end{bmatrix} \Rightarrow \begin{bmatrix} 1 & 0 & 0 & 0 \\ 0 & 1 & 0 & 0 \\ 0 & 0 & 0 & 1 \\ 0 & 0 & 0 & 0 \end{bmatrix} \begin{bmatrix} x_1 \\ x_2 \\ x_3 \\ x_4 \end{bmatrix} = \begin{bmatrix} 0 \\ 0 \\ 0 \\ 0 \end{bmatrix}.$

The solution is $\{(0, 0, t, 0) : t \in R\}$. So, an eigenvector corresponding to $\lambda_3 = 2$ is $(0, 0, 1, 0)$.

30. Using a graphing utility: $\lambda = -7, 3$

32. Using a graphing utility: $\lambda = \frac{1}{5}, \frac{1}{2}, 3$

34. Using a graphing utility: $\lambda = 0, 1, 2$

36. Using a graphing utility: $\lambda = 0, 0, 3, 5$

38. Using a graphing utility: $\lambda = 0, 1, 1, 4$

40. The eigenvalues are the entries on the main diagonal, $-5, 7,$ and 3.

42. The eigenvalues are the entries on the main diagonal, $\frac{1}{2}, \frac{5}{4}, 0,$ and $\frac{3}{4}$.

44. (a) The characteristic equation is

$$|\lambda I - A| = \begin{vmatrix} \lambda + 6 & -2 \\ -3 & \lambda + 1 \end{vmatrix} = \lambda^2 + 7\lambda = \lambda(\lambda + 7).$$

The eigenvalues are $\lambda_1 = 0$ and $\lambda_2 = -7$.

(b) For $\lambda_1 = 0$, $\begin{bmatrix} -6 & 2 \\ 3 & -1 \end{bmatrix}\begin{bmatrix} x_1 \\ x_2 \end{bmatrix} = \begin{bmatrix} 0 \\ 0 \end{bmatrix} \Rightarrow \begin{bmatrix} 3 & -1 \\ 0 & 0 \end{bmatrix}\begin{bmatrix} x_1 \\ x_2 \end{bmatrix} = \begin{bmatrix} 0 \\ 0 \end{bmatrix}.$

The solution is $\{(t, 3t) : t \in R\}$. So, a basis for the eigenspace is $B_1 = \{(1, 3)\}$.

For $\lambda_2 = -7$, $\begin{bmatrix} -1 & -2 \\ -3 & -6 \end{bmatrix}\begin{bmatrix} x_1 \\ x_2 \end{bmatrix} = \begin{bmatrix} 0 \\ 0 \end{bmatrix} \Rightarrow \begin{bmatrix} 1 & 2 \\ 0 & 0 \end{bmatrix}\begin{bmatrix} x_1 \\ x_2 \end{bmatrix} = \begin{bmatrix} 0 \\ 0 \end{bmatrix}.$

The solution is $\{(-2t, t) : t \in R\}$. So, a basis for the eigenspace is $B_2 = \{(-2, 1)\}$.

(c) $A' = \begin{bmatrix} 0 & 0 \\ 0 & -7 \end{bmatrix}$

46. (a) The characteristic equation is $|\lambda I - A| = \begin{vmatrix} \lambda - 3 & -1 & -4 \\ -2 & \lambda - 4 & 0 \\ -5 & -5 & \lambda - 6 \end{vmatrix} = \lambda^3 - 13\lambda^2 + 32\lambda - 20$

$$= (\lambda - 1)(\lambda - 2)(\lambda - 10).$$

The eigenvalues are $\lambda_1 = 1$, $\lambda_2 = 2$, and $\lambda_3 = 10$.

(b) For $\lambda_1 = 1$, $\begin{bmatrix} -2 & -1 & -4 \\ -2 & -3 & 0 \\ -5 & -5 & -5 \end{bmatrix}\begin{bmatrix} x_1 \\ x_2 \\ x_3 \end{bmatrix} = \begin{bmatrix} 0 \\ 0 \\ 0 \end{bmatrix} \Rightarrow \begin{bmatrix} 1 & 0 & 3 \\ 0 & 1 & -2 \\ 0 & 0 & 0 \end{bmatrix}\begin{bmatrix} x_1 \\ x_2 \\ x_3 \end{bmatrix} = \begin{bmatrix} 0 \\ 0 \\ 0 \end{bmatrix}.$

The solution is $\{(-3t, 2t, t) : t \in R\}$. So, a basis for the eigenspace is $B_1 = \{(-3, 2, 1)\}$.

For $\lambda_2 = 2$, $\begin{bmatrix} -1 & -1 & -4 \\ -2 & -2 & 0 \\ -5 & -5 & -4 \end{bmatrix}\begin{bmatrix} x_1 \\ x_2 \\ x_3 \end{bmatrix} = \begin{bmatrix} 0 \\ 0 \\ 0 \end{bmatrix} \Rightarrow \begin{bmatrix} 1 & 1 & 0 \\ 0 & 0 & 1 \\ 0 & 0 & 0 \end{bmatrix}\begin{bmatrix} x_1 \\ x_2 \\ x_3 \end{bmatrix} = \begin{bmatrix} 0 \\ 0 \\ 0 \end{bmatrix}.$

The solution is $\{(t, -t, 0) : t \in R\}$. So, a basis for the eigenspace is $B_2 = \{(1, -1, 0)\}$.

For $\lambda_3 = 10$, $\begin{bmatrix} 7 & -1 & -4 \\ -2 & 6 & 0 \\ -5 & -5 & 4 \end{bmatrix}\begin{bmatrix} x_1 \\ x_2 \\ x_3 \end{bmatrix} = \begin{bmatrix} 0 \\ 0 \\ 0 \end{bmatrix} \Rightarrow \begin{bmatrix} 1 & -3 & 0 \\ 0 & 5 & -1 \\ 0 & 0 & 0 \end{bmatrix}\begin{bmatrix} x_1 \\ x_2 \\ x_3 \end{bmatrix} = \begin{bmatrix} 0 \\ 0 \\ 0 \end{bmatrix}.$

The solution is $\{(3t, t, 5t) : t \in R\}$. So, a basis for the eigenspace is $B_3 = \{(3, 1, 5)\}$.

(c) $A' = \begin{bmatrix} 1 & 0 & 0 \\ 0 & 2 & 0 \\ 0 & 0 & 10 \end{bmatrix}$

48. The characteristic equation is

$$|\lambda I - A| = \begin{vmatrix} \lambda - 6 & 1 \\ -1 & \lambda - 5 \end{vmatrix} = \lambda^2 - 11\lambda + 31 = 0.$$

Because

$$A^2 - 11A + 31I = \begin{bmatrix} 6 & -1 \\ 1 & 5 \end{bmatrix}^2 - 11\begin{bmatrix} 6 & -1 \\ 1 & 5 \end{bmatrix} + 31\begin{bmatrix} 1 & 0 \\ 0 & 1 \end{bmatrix} = \begin{bmatrix} 35 & -11 \\ 11 & 24 \end{bmatrix} - \begin{bmatrix} 66 & -11 \\ 11 & 55 \end{bmatrix} + \begin{bmatrix} 31 & 0 \\ 0 & 31 \end{bmatrix} = \begin{bmatrix} 0 & 0 \\ 0 & 0 \end{bmatrix}$$

the theorem holds for this matrix.

50. The characteristic equation is

$$|\lambda I - A| = \begin{vmatrix} \lambda + 3 & -1 & 0 \\ 1 & \lambda - 3 & -2 \\ 0 & -4 & \lambda - 3 \end{vmatrix} = \lambda^3 - 3\lambda^2 - 16\lambda = 0.$$

Because

$$A^3 - 3A^2 - 16A = \begin{bmatrix} -3 & 1 & 0 \\ -1 & 3 & 2 \\ 0 & 4 & 3 \end{bmatrix}^3 - 3\begin{bmatrix} -3 & 1 & 0 \\ -1 & 3 & 2 \\ 0 & 4 & 3 \end{bmatrix}^2 - 16\begin{bmatrix} -3 & 1 & 0 \\ -1 & 3 & 2 \\ 0 & 4 & 3 \end{bmatrix}$$

$$= \begin{bmatrix} -24 & 16 & 6 \\ -16 & 96 & 68 \\ -12 & 136 & 99 \end{bmatrix} - 3\begin{bmatrix} 8 & 0 & 2 \\ 0 & 16 & 12 \\ -4 & 24 & 17 \end{bmatrix} - 16\begin{bmatrix} -3 & 1 & 0 \\ -1 & 3 & 2 \\ 0 & 4 & 0 \end{bmatrix} = \begin{bmatrix} 0 & 0 & 0 \\ 0 & 0 & 0 \\ 0 & 0 & 0 \end{bmatrix}$$

the theorem holds for this matrix.

52. For the $n \times n$ matrix $A = \begin{bmatrix} a_{ij} \end{bmatrix}$, the sum of the diagonal entries, or the trace, of A is given by $\sum_{i=1}^{n} a_{ii}$.

Exercise 16: $\lambda_1 = 0, \lambda_2 = 9$

(a) $\sum_{i=1}^{2} \lambda_i = 9 = \sum_{i=1}^{2} a_{ii}$

(b) $|A| = \begin{vmatrix} 1 & -4 \\ -2 & 8 \end{vmatrix} = 0 = 0 \cdot 9 = \lambda_1 \cdot \lambda_2$

Exercise 18: $\lambda_1 = \frac{1}{2}, \lambda_2 = -\frac{1}{4}$

(a) $\sum_{i=1}^{2} \lambda_i = \frac{1}{4} = \sum_{i=1}^{2} a_{ii}$

(b) $|A| = \begin{vmatrix} \frac{1}{4} & \frac{1}{4} \\ \frac{1}{2} & 0 \end{vmatrix} = -\frac{1}{8} = \frac{1}{2}\left(-\frac{1}{4}\right) = \lambda_1 \cdot \lambda_2$

Exercise 20: $\lambda_1 = -5, \lambda_2 = 7, \lambda_3 = 3$

(a) $\sum_{i=1}^{3} \lambda_i = 5 = \sum_{i=1}^{3} a_{ii}$

(b) $|A| = \begin{vmatrix} -5 & 0 & 0 \\ 3 & 7 & 0 \\ 4 & -2 & 3 \end{vmatrix} = -105 = -5 \cdot 7 \cdot 3 = \lambda_1 \cdot \lambda_2 \cdot \lambda_3$

Exercise 22: $\lambda_1 = -2, \lambda_2 = 2, \lambda_3 = 3$

(a) $\sum_{i=1}^{3} \lambda_i = 3 = \sum_{i=1}^{3} a_{ii}$

(b) $|A| = \begin{vmatrix} 3 & 2 & 1 \\ 0 & 0 & 2 \\ 0 & 2 & 0 \end{vmatrix} = -12 = -2 \cdot 2 \cdot 3 = \lambda_1 \cdot \lambda_2 \cdot \lambda_3$

Exercise 24: $\lambda_1 = 0, \lambda_2 = 2, \lambda_3 = 2$

(a) $\sum_{i=1}^{3} \lambda_i = 4 = \sum_{i=1}^{3} a_{ii}$

(b) $|A| = \begin{vmatrix} 3 & 2 & -3 \\ -3 & -4 & 9 \\ -1 & -2 & 5 \end{vmatrix} = 0 = 0 \cdot 2 \cdot 2 = \lambda_1 \cdot \lambda_2 \cdot \lambda_3$

Exercise 26: $\lambda_1 = \frac{29}{2}, \lambda_2 = \frac{1}{2}, \lambda_3 = \frac{1}{2}$

(a) $\sum_{i=1}^{3} \lambda_i = \frac{31}{2} = \sum_{i=1}^{3} a_{ii}$

(b) $|A| = \begin{vmatrix} 1 & -\frac{3}{2} & \frac{5}{2} \\ -2 & \frac{13}{2} & -10 \\ \frac{3}{2} & -\frac{9}{2} & 8 \end{vmatrix} = \frac{29}{8} = \frac{29}{2} \cdot \frac{1}{2} \cdot \frac{1}{2} = \lambda_1 \cdot \lambda_2 \cdot \lambda_3$

Exercise 28: $\lambda_1 = 3, \lambda_2 = 1, \lambda_3 = 2, \lambda_4 = 2$

(a) $\sum_{i=1}^{4} \lambda_i = 8 = \sum_{i=1}^{4} a_{ii}$

(b) $|A| = \begin{vmatrix} 3 & 0 & 0 & 0 \\ 4 & 1 & 0 & 0 \\ 0 & 0 & 2 & 1 \\ 0 & 0 & 0 & 2 \end{vmatrix} = 12 = 3 \cdot 1 \cdot 2 \cdot 2 = \lambda_1 \cdot \lambda_2 \cdot \lambda_3 \cdot \lambda_4$

54. $\lambda = 0$ is an eigenvalue of $A \Leftrightarrow |0I - A| = 0 \Leftrightarrow |A| = 0$.

56. Observe that $|\lambda I - A^T| = |(\lambda I - A)^T| = |\lambda I - A|$. Because the characteristic equations of A and A^T are the same, A and A^T must have the same eigenvalues. However, the eigenspaces are not the same.

58. Let $\mathbf{u} = (u_1, u_2)$ be the fixed vector in R^2, and $\mathbf{v} = (v_1, v_2)$. Then $\text{proj}_\mathbf{u}\mathbf{v} = \frac{u_1 v_1 + u_2 v_2}{u_1^2 + u_2^2}(u_1, u_2)$.

Because $T(1, 0) = \frac{u_1}{u_1^2 + u_2^2}(u_1, u_2)$ and $T(0, 1) = \frac{u_2}{u_1^2 + u_2^2}(u_1, u_2)$,

the standard matrix A of T is $A = \frac{1}{u_1^2 + u_2^2}\begin{bmatrix} u_1^2 & u_1 u_2 \\ u_1 u_2 & u_2^2 \end{bmatrix}$.

Now,

$A\mathbf{u} = \frac{1}{u_1^2 + u_2^2}\begin{bmatrix} u_1^2 & u_1 u_2 \\ u_1 u_2 & u_2^2 \end{bmatrix}\begin{bmatrix} u_1 \\ u_2 \end{bmatrix} = \frac{1}{u_1^2 + u_2^2}\begin{bmatrix} u_1^3 + u_1 u_2^2 \\ u_1^2 u_2 + u_2^3 \end{bmatrix} = \frac{1}{u_1^2 + u_2^2}\begin{bmatrix} u_1(u_1^2 + u_2^2) \\ u_2(u_1^2 + u_2^2) \end{bmatrix} = \frac{u_1^2 + u_2^2}{u_1^2 + u_2^2}\begin{bmatrix} u_1 \\ u_2 \end{bmatrix} = 1\mathbf{u}$

and

$A\begin{bmatrix} u_2 \\ -u_1 \end{bmatrix} = \frac{1}{u_1^2 + u_2^2}\begin{bmatrix} u_1^2 & u_1 u_2 \\ u_1 u_2 & u_2^2 \end{bmatrix}\begin{bmatrix} u_2 \\ -u_1 \end{bmatrix} = \frac{1}{u_1^2 + u_2^2}\begin{bmatrix} u_1^2 u_2 - u_1^2 u_2 \\ u_1 u_2^2 - u_1 u_2^2 \end{bmatrix} = \frac{1}{u_1^2 + u_2^2}\begin{bmatrix} 0 \\ 0 \end{bmatrix} = 0\begin{bmatrix} u_2 \\ -u_1 \end{bmatrix}$.

So, $\lambda = 1$ and $\lambda_2 = 0$ are the eigenvalues of A.

60. Let $A^2 = O$ and consider $A\mathbf{x} = \lambda\mathbf{x}$. Then $O = A^2\mathbf{x} = A(\lambda\mathbf{x}) = \lambda A\mathbf{x} = \lambda^2\mathbf{x}$ which implies $\lambda = 0$.

62. (a) $-2, 1, 3$ (repeated)

(b) There are four roots of the characteristic equation, so A has order 4.

(c) When $\lambda = -2, 1$, or 3, $\lambda I - A$ is singular.

(d) No. Zero is not an eigenvalue of A, so A is nonsingular.

64. The characteristic equation of A is $|\lambda I - A| = \begin{vmatrix} \lambda & -1 \\ 1 & \lambda \end{vmatrix} = \lambda^2 + 1 = 0$ which has no real solution.

66. (a) True. By definition of eigenvalue space, $A\mathbf{x} = \lambda\mathbf{x}$ and $\lambda\mathbf{x}$ is parallel to $\mathbf{x}$ for any real number λ.

    (b) False. The set of eigenvectors corresponding to λ together with the zero vector (which is never an eigenvector for any eigenvalue) forms a subspace of R^n. **(Theorem 7.1 on page 344).**

68. Substituting the value $\lambda = 3$ yields the system

$$\begin{bmatrix} \lambda - 3 & -1 & 0 \\ 0 & \lambda - 3 & 0 \\ 0 & 0 & \lambda - 3 \end{bmatrix}\begin{bmatrix} x_1 \\ x_2 \\ x_3 \end{bmatrix} = \begin{bmatrix} 0 \\ 0 \\ 0 \end{bmatrix} \Rightarrow \begin{bmatrix} 0 & 1 & 0 \\ 0 & 0 & 0 \\ 0 & 0 & 0 \end{bmatrix}\begin{bmatrix} x_1 \\ x_2 \\ x_3 \end{bmatrix} = \begin{bmatrix} 0 \\ 0 \\ 0 \end{bmatrix}.$$

So, 3 has two linearly independent eigenvectors and the dimension of the eigenspace is 2.

70. Substituting the value $\lambda = 3$ yields the system

$$\begin{bmatrix} \lambda - 3 & -1 & -1 \\ 0 & \lambda - 3 & -1 \\ 0 & 0 & \lambda - 3 \end{bmatrix}\begin{bmatrix} x_1 \\ x_2 \\ x_3 \end{bmatrix} = \begin{bmatrix} 0 \\ 0 \\ 0 \end{bmatrix} \Rightarrow \begin{bmatrix} 0 & 1 & 0 \\ 0 & 0 & 1 \\ 0 & 0 & 0 \end{bmatrix}\begin{bmatrix} x_1 \\ x_2 \\ x_3 \end{bmatrix} = \begin{bmatrix} 0 \\ 0 \\ 0 \end{bmatrix}.$$

So, 3 has one linearly independent eigenvector, and the dimension of the eigenspace is 1.

72. Because $T\left(e^{-2x}\right) = \dfrac{d}{dx}\left[e^{-2x}\right] = -2e^{-2x}$, the eigenvalue corresponding to $f(x) = e^{-2x}$ is -2.

74. The standard matrix for T is

$$A = \begin{bmatrix} 2 & 1 & -1 \\ 0 & -1 & 2 \\ 0 & 0 & -1 \end{bmatrix}.$$

The characteristic equation of A is

$$|\lambda I - A| = \begin{vmatrix} \lambda - 2 & -1 & 1 \\ 0 & \lambda + 1 & -2 \\ 0 & 0 & \lambda + 1 \end{vmatrix} = (\lambda - 2)(\lambda + 1)^2.$$

The eigenvalues are $\lambda_1 = 2$ and $\lambda_2 = -1$ (repeated). The corresponding eigenvectors are found by solving

$$\begin{vmatrix} \lambda_i - 2 & -1 & 1 \\ 0 & \lambda_i + 1 & -2 \\ 0 & 0 & \lambda_i + 1 \end{vmatrix}\begin{bmatrix} a_0 \\ a_1 \\ a_2 \end{bmatrix} = \begin{bmatrix} 0 \\ 0 \\ 0 \end{bmatrix}$$

for each λ_i. So, $p_1(x) = 1$ corresponds to $\lambda_1 = 2$, and $p_2(x) = 1 - 3x$ corresponds to $\lambda_2 = -1$.

76. The characteristic equation of A is

$$\begin{vmatrix} \lambda - \cos\theta & \sin\theta \\ -\sin\theta & \lambda - \cos\theta \end{vmatrix} = \lambda^2 - 2\cos\theta\,\lambda + \left(\cos^2\theta + \sin^2\theta\right) = \lambda^2 - 2\cos\theta\,\lambda + 1.$$

There are real eigenvalues if the discriminant of this quadratic equation in λ is nonnegative:

$$b^2 - 4ac = 4\cos^2\theta - 4 = 4\left(\cos^2\theta - 1\right) \geq 0 \Rightarrow \cos^2\theta = 1 \Rightarrow \theta = 0, \pi.$$

The only rotations that send vectors to multiples of themselves are the identity $(\theta = 0)$ and the $180°$-rotation $(\theta = \pi)$.

78. 0 is the only eigenvalue of a nilpotent matrix. For if $A\mathbf{x} = \lambda\mathbf{x}$, then $A^2\mathbf{x} = A\lambda\mathbf{x} = \lambda^2\mathbf{x}$.

So,

$$A^k\mathbf{x} = \lambda^k\mathbf{x} = \mathbf{0} \quad \Rightarrow \quad \lambda^k = 0 \Rightarrow \lambda = 0.$$

Section 7.2 Diagonalization

2. (b) $\lambda = 2, 4$

4. (b) $\lambda = -1, 2$

6. (b) $\lambda = 1, 0.8, 0.7, 0.7$

8. The eigenvalues of A are $\lambda_1 = \frac{1}{2}$ and $\lambda_2 = -\frac{1}{2}$ (see Exercise 19, Section 7.1). The corresponding eigenvectors $(3, 1)$ and $(1, 1)$ are used to form the columns of P. So,

$$P = \begin{bmatrix} 3 & 1 \\ 1 & 1 \end{bmatrix} \Rightarrow P^{-1} = \begin{bmatrix} \frac{1}{2} & -\frac{1}{2} \\ -\frac{1}{2} & \frac{3}{2} \end{bmatrix}$$

and

$$P^{-1}AP = \begin{bmatrix} \frac{1}{2} & -\frac{1}{2} \\ -\frac{1}{2} & \frac{3}{2} \end{bmatrix} \begin{bmatrix} 1 & -\frac{3}{2} \\ \frac{1}{2} & -1 \end{bmatrix} \begin{bmatrix} 3 & 1 \\ 1 & 1 \end{bmatrix} = \begin{bmatrix} \frac{1}{2} & 0 \\ 0 & -\frac{1}{2} \end{bmatrix}.$$

10. The eigenvalues of A are $\lambda_1 = -2$, $\lambda_2 = 2$, $\lambda_3 = 3$. From Exercise 22, Section 7.1, the corresponding eigenvectors $(1, -5, 5)$, $(-3, 1, 1)$ and $(1, 0, 0)$ are used to form the columns of P. So,

$$P = \begin{bmatrix} 1 & -3 & 1 \\ -5 & 1 & 0 \\ 5 & 1 & 0 \end{bmatrix} \Rightarrow P^{-1} = \begin{bmatrix} 0 & -0.1 & 0.1 \\ 0 & 0.5 & 0.5 \\ 1 & 1.6 & 1.4 \end{bmatrix}$$

and

$$P^{-1}AP = \begin{bmatrix} 0 & -0.1 & 0.1 \\ 0 & 0.5 & 0.5 \\ 1 & 1.6 & 1.4 \end{bmatrix} \begin{bmatrix} 3 & 2 & 1 \\ 0 & 0 & 2 \\ 0 & 2 & 0 \end{bmatrix} \begin{bmatrix} 1 & -3 & 1 \\ -5 & 1 & 0 \\ 5 & 1 & 0 \end{bmatrix}$$

$$= \begin{bmatrix} -2 & 0 & 0 \\ 0 & 2 & 0 \\ 0 & 0 & 3 \end{bmatrix}.$$

12. The eigenvalues of A are $\lambda_1 = 0$ and $\lambda_2 = 2$ (repeated). From Exercise 24, Section 7.1, the corresponding eigenvectors $(-1, 3, 1)$, $(3, 0, 1)$ and $(-2, 1, 0)$ are used to form the columns of P. So,

$$P = \begin{bmatrix} -1 & 3 & -2 \\ 3 & 0 & 1 \\ 1 & 1 & 0 \end{bmatrix} \Rightarrow P^{-1} = \begin{bmatrix} \frac{1}{2} & 1 & -\frac{3}{2} \\ -\frac{1}{2} & -1 & \frac{5}{2} \\ -\frac{3}{2} & -2 & \frac{9}{2} \end{bmatrix}, \text{ and}$$

$$P^{-1}AP = \begin{bmatrix} \frac{1}{2} & 1 & -\frac{3}{2} \\ -\frac{1}{2} & -1 & \frac{5}{2} \\ -\frac{3}{2} & -2 & \frac{9}{2} \end{bmatrix} \begin{bmatrix} 3 & 2 & -3 \\ -3 & -4 & 9 \\ -1 & -2 & 5 \end{bmatrix} \begin{bmatrix} -1 & 3 & -2 \\ 3 & 0 & 1 \\ 1 & 1 & 0 \end{bmatrix} = \begin{bmatrix} 0 & 0 & 0 \\ 0 & 2 & 0 \\ 0 & 0 & 2 \end{bmatrix}.$$

14. The eigenvalues of A are $\lambda_1 = 4$ and $\lambda_2 = 2$ (repeated). Furthermore, there are just two linearly independent eigenvectors of A, $\mathbf{x}_1 = (1, 1, 1)$ and $\mathbf{x}_2 = (0, 0, 1)$. So, A is not diagonalizable.

16. The matrix A has only one eigenvalue, $\lambda = 0$, and a basis for the eigenspace is $\{(1, -2)\}$. So, A does not satisfy Theorem 7.5 and is not diagonalizable.

18. A is triangular, so the eigenvalues are simply the entries on the main diagonal. So, the only eigenvalue is $\lambda = 1$, and a basis for the eigenspace is $\{(0, 1)\}$.

    Because A does not have two linearly independent eigenvectors, it does not satisfy Theorem 7.5 and it is not diagonalizable.

20. The characteristic equation of A is $(\lambda - 2)(\lambda + 1)^2 = 0$. For eigenvalue $\lambda_1 = 2$ you find the eigenvector $(1, 0, 0)$. The eigenvector corresponding to $\lambda_2 = -1$ (repeated) is $(1, -3, 0)$. So, A has only two linearly independent eigenvectors. So, A does not satisfy Theorem 7.5 and is not diagonalizable.

22. From Exercise 38, Section 7.1, you know that A has only three linearly independent eigenvectors. So, A does not satisfy Theorem 7.5 and is not diagonalizable.

24. The eigenvalue of A is $\lambda = 2$ (repeated). Because A does not have two *distinct* eigenvalues, Theorem 7.6 does not guarantee that A is diagonalizable.

26. The eigenvalues of A are $\lambda_1 = 4$, $\lambda_2 = 1$, $\lambda_3 = -2$. Because A has three *distinct* eigenvalues, it is diagonalizable by Theorem 7.6.

28. The standard matrix for T is

$$A = \begin{bmatrix} -2 & 2 & -3 \\ 2 & 1 & -6 \\ -1 & -2 & 0 \end{bmatrix}$$

which has eigenvalues $\lambda_1 = 5$, $\lambda_2 = -3$ (repeated), and corresponding eigenvectors $(1, 2, -1)$, $(3, 0, 1)$ and $(-2, 1, 0)$. Let $B = \{(1, 2, -1), (3, 0, 1), (-2, 1, 0)\}$ and the matrix of T relative to this basis is

$$A' = \begin{bmatrix} 5 & 0 & 0 \\ 0 & -3 & 0 \\ 0 & 0 & -3 \end{bmatrix}.$$

30. The standard matrix for T is

$$A = \begin{bmatrix} 2 & 0 & 1 \\ 0 & 3 & 4 \\ 0 & 0 & 1 \end{bmatrix}$$

which has eigenvalues $\lambda_1 = 2$, $\lambda_2 = 3$ and $\lambda_3 = 1$, and corresponding eigenvectors $(1, 0, 0)$, $(0, 1, 0)$, and $(-1, -2, 1)$. Let $B = \{(1, x, -1 - 2x + x^2)\}$ and the matrix of T relative to this basis is

$$A' = \begin{bmatrix} 2 & 0 & 0 \\ 0 & 3 & 0 \\ 0 & 0 & 1 \end{bmatrix}.$$

32. Let P be the matrix of eigenvectors corresponding to the n distinct eigenvalues $\lambda_1, \cdots, \lambda_n$. Then $P^{-1}AP = D$ is a diagonal matrix $\Rightarrow A = PDP^{-1}$. From Exercise 39, $A^k = PD^kP^{-1}$, which show that the eigenvalues of A^k are $\lambda_1^k, \lambda_2^k, \cdots, \lambda_n^k$.

34. The eigenvalues and corresponding eigenvectors of A are $\lambda_1 = 3$, $\lambda_2 = -2$ and $\mathbf{x}_1 = (3, 2)$ and $\mathbf{x}_2 = (-1, 1)$. Construct a nonsingular matrix P from the eigenvectors of A,

$$P = \begin{bmatrix} 3 & -1 \\ 2 & 1 \end{bmatrix}$$

and find a diagonal matrix B similar to A.

$$B = P^{-1}AP = \begin{bmatrix} \frac{1}{5} & \frac{1}{5} \\ -\frac{2}{5} & \frac{3}{5} \end{bmatrix}\begin{bmatrix} 1 & 3 \\ 2 & 0 \end{bmatrix}\begin{bmatrix} 3 & -1 \\ 2 & 1 \end{bmatrix} = \begin{bmatrix} 3 & 0 \\ 0 & -2 \end{bmatrix}$$

Then,

$$A^7 = PB^7P^{-1}$$

$$= \begin{bmatrix} 3 & -1 \\ 2 & 1 \end{bmatrix}\begin{bmatrix} 3^7 & 0 \\ 0 & (-2)^7 \end{bmatrix}\begin{bmatrix} \frac{1}{5} & \frac{1}{5} \\ -\frac{2}{5} & \frac{3}{5} \end{bmatrix}$$

$$= \begin{bmatrix} 1261 & 1389 \\ 926 & 798 \end{bmatrix}$$

36. The eigenvalues and corresponding eigenvectors of A are $\lambda_1 = -1$, $\lambda_2 = 0$, $\lambda_3 = 2$, $\mathbf{x}_1 = (2, 2, 3)$, $\mathbf{x}_2 = (1, 1, 1)$ and $\mathbf{x}_3 = (0, 1, 0)$. Construct a nonsingular matrix P from the eigenvectors of A,

$$P = \begin{bmatrix} 2 & 1 & 0 \\ 2 & 1 & 1 \\ 3 & 1 & 0 \end{bmatrix}$$

and find a diagonal matrix B similar to A.

$$B = P^{-1}AP$$

$$= \begin{bmatrix} -1 & 0 & 1 \\ 3 & 0 & -2 \\ -1 & 1 & 0 \end{bmatrix}\begin{bmatrix} 2 & 0 & -2 \\ 0 & 2 & -2 \\ 3 & 0 & -3 \end{bmatrix}\begin{bmatrix} 2 & 1 & 0 \\ 2 & 1 & 1 \\ 3 & 1 & 0 \end{bmatrix}$$

$$= \begin{bmatrix} -1 & 0 & 0 \\ 0 & 0 & 0 \\ 0 & 0 & 2 \end{bmatrix}$$

Then,

$$A^5 = PB^5P^{-1} = P\begin{bmatrix} -1 & 0 & 0 \\ 0 & 0 & 0 \\ 0 & 0 & 32 \end{bmatrix}P^{-1} = \begin{bmatrix} 2 & 0 & -2 \\ -30 & 32 & -2 \\ 3 & 0 & -3 \end{bmatrix}.$$

38. (a) True. See Theorem 7.5 on page 354.

(b) False. Matrix

$$\begin{bmatrix} 2 & 0 \\ 0 & 2 \end{bmatrix}$$

is diagonalizable (it is already diagonal) but it has only one eigenvalue $\lambda = 2$ (repeated).

40. (a) $X = \begin{bmatrix} 1 & 0 \\ 0 & 1 \end{bmatrix} \Rightarrow e^X = I + I + \dfrac{I}{2!} + \dfrac{I}{3!} + \cdots = \begin{bmatrix} 1 + 1 + \dfrac{1}{2!} + \dfrac{1}{3!} + \cdots & 0 \\ 0 & 1 + 1 + \dfrac{1}{2!} + \dfrac{1}{3!} + \cdots \end{bmatrix} = \begin{bmatrix} e & 0 \\ 0 & e \end{bmatrix}$

(b) $X = \begin{bmatrix} 1 & 0 \\ 1 & 0 \end{bmatrix} \Rightarrow e^X = I + \begin{bmatrix} 1 & 0 \\ 1 & 0 \end{bmatrix} + \dfrac{1}{2!}\begin{bmatrix} 1 & 0 \\ 1 & 0 \end{bmatrix} + \dfrac{1}{3!}\begin{bmatrix} 1 & 0 \\ 1 & 0 \end{bmatrix} + \cdots = \begin{bmatrix} e & 0 \\ e - 1 & 1 \end{bmatrix}$

(c) $X = \begin{bmatrix} 0 & 1 \\ 1 & 0 \end{bmatrix} \Rightarrow e^X = I + \begin{bmatrix} 0 & 1 \\ 1 & 0 \end{bmatrix} + \dfrac{1}{2!}\begin{bmatrix} 1 & 0 \\ 0 & 1 \end{bmatrix} + \dfrac{1}{3!}\begin{bmatrix} 0 & 1 \\ 1 & 0 \end{bmatrix} + \dfrac{1}{4!}\begin{bmatrix} 1 & 0 \\ 0 & 1 \end{bmatrix} + \cdots$

Because $e = 1 + 1 + \dfrac{1}{2} + \dfrac{1}{3!} + \dfrac{1}{4!}$ and $e^{-1} = 1 - 1 + \dfrac{1}{2} - \dfrac{1}{3!} + \dfrac{1}{4!} - \cdots$, you see that $e^X = \dfrac{1}{2}\begin{bmatrix} e + e^{-1} & e - e^{-1} \\ e - e^{-1} & e + e^{-1} \end{bmatrix}$.

(d) $X = \begin{bmatrix} 2 & 0 \\ 0 & -2 \end{bmatrix} \Rightarrow e^X = I + \begin{bmatrix} 2 & 0 \\ 0 & -2 \end{bmatrix} + \dfrac{1}{2!}\begin{bmatrix} 2^2 & 0 \\ 0 & 2^2 \end{bmatrix} + \dfrac{1}{3!}\begin{bmatrix} 2^3 & 0 \\ 0 & -2^3 \end{bmatrix} + \cdots = \begin{bmatrix} e^2 & 0 \\ 0 & e^{-2} \end{bmatrix}$.

42. Assume that A is diagonalizable, $P^{-1}AP = D$, where D is diagonal. Then

$$D^T = \left(P^{-1}AP\right)^T = P^T A^T \left(P^{-1}\right)^T = P^T A^T \left(P^T\right)^{-1}$$

is diagonal, which shows that A^T is diagonalizable.

44. Consider the characteristic equation $\left|\lambda I - A\right| = \begin{vmatrix} \lambda - a & -b \\ -c & \lambda - d \end{vmatrix} = \lambda^2 - (a + d)\lambda + (ad - bc) = 0$.

This equation has real and unequal roots if and only if $(a + d)^2 - 4(ad - bc) > 0$, which is equivalent
to $(a - d)^2 > -4bc$. So, A is diagonalizable if $-4bc < (a - d)^2$, and not diagonalizable if $-4bc > (a - d)^2$.

46. From Exercise 78, Section 7.1, you know that zero is the only eigenvalue of the nilpotent matrix A. If A were diagonalizable, then there would exist an invertible matrix P, such that $P^{-1}AP = D$, where D is the zero matrix. So, $A = PDP^{-1} = O$, which is impossible.

48. (a) A is diagonalizable when it is similar to a diagonal matrix D.

(b) A is diagonalizable when it has n linearly independent eigenvectors.

(c) A is diagonalizable when it has n distinct eigenvalues.

50. The only eigenvalue is $\lambda = 0$, and a basis for the eigenspace is $\{(0, 1)\}$. Since the matrix does not have two linearly independent eigenvectors, the matrix is not diagonalizable.

Section 7.3 Symmetric Matrices and Orthogonal Diagonalization

2. Because

$$A^T = \begin{bmatrix} 6 & -2 \\ -2 & 1 \end{bmatrix}^T = \begin{bmatrix} 6 & -2 \\ -2 & 1 \end{bmatrix} = A$$

the matrix is symmetric.

4. Because

$$\begin{bmatrix} 1 & -5 & 4 \\ -5 & 3 & 6 \\ -4 & 6 & 2 \end{bmatrix}^T \neq \begin{bmatrix} 1 & -5 & -4 \\ -5 & 3 & 6 \\ 4 & 6 & 2 \end{bmatrix}$$

the matrix is *not* symmetric.

6. Because

$$\begin{bmatrix} 2 & 0 & 3 & 5 \\ 0 & 11 & 0 & -2 \\ 3 & 0 & 5 & 0 \\ 5 & -2 & 0 & 1 \end{bmatrix}^T = \begin{bmatrix} 2 & 0 & 3 & 5 \\ 0 & 11 & 0 & -2 \\ 3 & 0 & 5 & 0 \\ 5 & -2 & 0 & 1 \end{bmatrix}$$

the matrix *is* symmetric.

8. The characteristic equation of A is

$$|\lambda I - A| = \begin{vmatrix} \lambda & -a & 0 \\ -a & \lambda & -a \\ 0 & -a & \lambda \end{vmatrix} = \lambda\left(\lambda - a\sqrt{2}\right)\left(\lambda + a\sqrt{2}\right).$$

The eigenvalues are $\lambda_1 = -a\sqrt{2}$, $\lambda_2 = 0$, and $\lambda_3 = a\sqrt{2}$. Since the eigenvalues are real, A is diagonalizable. The corresponding eigenvectors are $\left(1, -\sqrt{2}, 1\right)$, $(1, 0, -1)$, and $\left(1, \sqrt{2}, 1\right)$, respectively. So,

$$P = \begin{bmatrix} 1 & 1 & 1 \\ -\sqrt{2} & 0 & \sqrt{2} \\ 1 & -1 & 1 \end{bmatrix} \text{ and}$$

$$P^{-1}AP = \begin{bmatrix} \frac{1}{4} & -\frac{\sqrt{2}}{4} & \frac{1}{4} \\ \frac{1}{2} & 0 & -\frac{1}{2} \\ \frac{1}{4} & \frac{\sqrt{2}}{4} & \frac{1}{4} \end{bmatrix} \begin{bmatrix} 0 & a & 0 \\ a & 0 & a \\ 0 & a & 0 \end{bmatrix} \begin{bmatrix} 1 & 1 & 1 \\ -\sqrt{2} & 0 & \sqrt{2} \\ 1 & -1 & 1 \end{bmatrix} = \begin{bmatrix} -a\sqrt{2} & 0 & 0 \\ 0 & 0 & 0 \\ 0 & 0 & a\sqrt{2} \end{bmatrix}.$$

10. The characteristic equation of A is

$$|\lambda I - A| = \begin{vmatrix} \lambda - a & -a & -a \\ -a & \lambda - a & -a \\ -a & -a & \lambda - a \end{vmatrix} = \lambda^2(\lambda - 3a).$$

The eigenvalues are $\lambda_1 = 0$ and $\lambda_2 = 3a$. Since the eigenvalues are real, A is diagonalizable. The corresponding eigenvectors are $(-1, 1, 0)$ and $(-1, 0, 1)$ for λ_1 and $(1, 1, 1)$ for λ_2. So,

$$P = \begin{bmatrix} -1 & -1 & 1 \\ 1 & 0 & 1 \\ 0 & 1 & 1 \end{bmatrix} \text{ and}$$

$$P^{-1}AP = \begin{bmatrix} -\frac{1}{3} & \frac{2}{3} & -\frac{1}{3} \\ -\frac{1}{3} & -\frac{1}{3} & \frac{2}{3} \\ \frac{1}{3} & \frac{1}{3} & \frac{1}{3} \end{bmatrix} \begin{bmatrix} a & a & a \\ a & a & a \\ a & a & a \end{bmatrix} \begin{bmatrix} -1 & -1 & 1 \\ 1 & 0 & 1 \\ 0 & 1 & 1 \end{bmatrix} = \begin{bmatrix} 0 & 0 & 0 \\ 0 & 0 & 0 \\ 0 & 0 & 3a \end{bmatrix}.$$

12. The characteristic equation of A is

$$|\lambda I - A| = \begin{vmatrix} \lambda - 2 & 0 \\ 0 & \lambda - 2 \end{vmatrix} = (\lambda - 2)^2 = 0.$$

Therefore, the eigenvalue is $\lambda = 2$. The multiplicity of $\lambda = 2$ is 2, so the dimension of the corresponding eigenspace is 2 (by Theorem 7.7).

14. The characteristic equation of A is

$$|\lambda I - A| = \begin{vmatrix} \lambda - 2 & -1 & -1 \\ -1 & \lambda - 2 & -1 \\ -1 & -1 & \lambda - 2 \end{vmatrix}$$

$$= (\lambda - 1)^2(\lambda - 4) = 0.$$

Therefore, the eigenvalues are $\lambda_1 = 1$ and $\lambda_2 = 4$. The multiplicity of $\lambda_1 = 1$ is 2, so the dimension of the corresponding eigenspace is 2 (by Theorem 7.7). The dimension of the eigenspace corresponding to $\lambda_2 = 4$ is 1.

16. The characteristic equation of A is

$$|\lambda I - A| = \begin{vmatrix} \lambda & -4 & -4 \\ -4 & \lambda - 2 & 0 \\ -4 & 0 & \lambda + 2 \end{vmatrix}$$

$$= (\lambda - 6)(\lambda + 6)\lambda = 0.$$

Therefore, the eigenvalues are $\lambda_1 = 6$, $\lambda_2 = -6$ and $\lambda_3 = 0$. The dimension of the eigenspace corresponding of each eigenvalue is 1.

18. The characteristic equation of A is

$$|\lambda I - A| = \begin{vmatrix} \lambda - 2 & 1 & 1 \\ 1 & \lambda - 2 & 1 \\ 1 & 1 & \lambda - 2 \end{vmatrix} = \lambda(\lambda - 3)^2 = 0.$$

Therefore, the eigenvalues are $\lambda_1 = 0$ and $\lambda_2 = 3$. The dimension of the eigenspace corresponding to $\lambda_1 = 0$ is 1. The multiplicity of $\lambda_2 = 3$ is 2, so the dimension of the corresponding eigenspace is 2 (by Theorem 7.7).

20. The characteristic equation of A is

$$|\lambda I - A| = \begin{vmatrix} \lambda + 1 & -2 & 0 & 0 \\ -2 & \lambda + 1 & 0 & 0 \\ 0 & 0 & \lambda + 1 & -2 \\ 0 & 0 & -2 & \lambda + 1 \end{vmatrix}$$

$$= (\lambda - 1)^2 (\lambda + 3)^2.$$

The eigenvalues are $\lambda_1 = 1$ and $\lambda_2 = -3$. The dimension of the corresponding eigenspace of each eigenvalue is 2 (by Theorem 7.7).

22. The characteristic equation of A is

$$|\lambda I - A| = \begin{vmatrix} \lambda - 1 & 1 & 0 & 0 & 0 \\ 1 & \lambda - 1 & 0 & 0 & 0 \\ 0 & 0 & \lambda - 1 & 0 & 0 \\ 0 & 0 & 0 & \lambda - 1 & 1 \\ 0 & 0 & 0 & 1 & \lambda - 1 \end{vmatrix}$$

$$= \lambda^2 (\lambda - 2)^2 (\lambda - 1).$$

The eigenvalues are $\lambda_1 = 0$, $\lambda_2 = 2$, and $\lambda_3 = 1$. The dimensions of the corresponding eigenspaces are 2, 2, and 1, respectively (by Theorem 7.7).

28. Because $PP^T = \begin{bmatrix} 4 & -1 & -4 \\ -1 & 0 & -17 \\ 1 & 4 & -1 \end{bmatrix} \begin{bmatrix} 4 & -1 & 1 \\ -1 & 0 & 4 \\ -4 & -17 & -1 \end{bmatrix} = \begin{bmatrix} 33 & 64 & 4 \\ 64 & 290 & 16 \\ 4 & 16 & 18 \end{bmatrix} \neq I_3,$

P is not orthogonal.

30. Because $PP^T = \begin{bmatrix} \dfrac{\sqrt{2}}{3} & 0 & \dfrac{\sqrt{5}}{2} \\ 0 & \dfrac{2\sqrt{5}}{5} & 0 \\ -\dfrac{\sqrt{2}}{6} & -\dfrac{\sqrt{5}}{5} & \dfrac{1}{2} \end{bmatrix} \begin{bmatrix} \dfrac{\sqrt{2}}{3} & 0 & -\dfrac{\sqrt{2}}{6} \\ 0 & \dfrac{2\sqrt{5}}{5} & -\dfrac{\sqrt{5}}{5} \\ \dfrac{\sqrt{5}}{2} & 0 & \dfrac{1}{2} \end{bmatrix} = \begin{bmatrix} \dfrac{53}{36} & 0 & \dfrac{9\sqrt{5} - 4}{36} \\ 0 & \dfrac{4}{5} & -\dfrac{2}{5} \\ \dfrac{9\sqrt{5} - 4}{36} & \dfrac{2}{5} & \dfrac{91}{180} \end{bmatrix} \neq I_3,$

P is not orthogonal.

32. Because $PP^T = \begin{bmatrix} \dfrac{1}{10}\sqrt{10} & 0 & 0 & -\dfrac{3}{10}\sqrt{10} \\ 0 & 0 & 1 & 0 \\ 0 & 1 & 0 & 0 \\ \dfrac{3}{10}\sqrt{10} & 0 & 0 & \dfrac{1}{10}\sqrt{10} \end{bmatrix} \begin{bmatrix} \dfrac{1}{10}\sqrt{10} & 0 & 0 & \dfrac{3}{10}\sqrt{10} \\ 0 & 0 & 1 & 0 \\ 0 & 1 & 0 & 0 \\ -\dfrac{3}{10}\sqrt{10} & 0 & 0 & \dfrac{1}{10}\sqrt{10} \end{bmatrix} = I_4,$ $P^T = P^{-1}$ and P is orthogonal. Letting

$$p_1 = \begin{bmatrix} \dfrac{1}{10}\sqrt{10} \\ 0 \\ 0 \\ \dfrac{3}{10}\sqrt{10} \end{bmatrix}, p_2 = \begin{bmatrix} 0 \\ 0 \\ 1 \\ 0 \end{bmatrix}, p_3 = \begin{bmatrix} 0 \\ 1 \\ 0 \\ 0 \end{bmatrix}, \text{ and } p_4 = \begin{bmatrix} -\dfrac{3}{10}\sqrt{10} \\ 0 \\ 0 \\ \dfrac{1}{10}\sqrt{10} \end{bmatrix} \text{ produces}$$

$p_1 \cdot p_2 = p_1 \cdot p_3 = p_1 \cdot p_4 = p_2 \cdot p_3 = p_2 \cdot p_4 = p_3 \cdot p_4 = 0$ and $\|p_1\| = \|p_2\| = \|p_3\| = \|p_4\| = 1.$ So $\{p_1, p_2, p_3, p_4\}$ is an orthonormal set.

24. Because $PP^T = \begin{bmatrix} \dfrac{2}{3} & -\dfrac{2}{3} \\ \dfrac{2}{3} & \dfrac{1}{3} \end{bmatrix} \begin{bmatrix} \dfrac{2}{3} & \dfrac{2}{3} \\ -\dfrac{2}{3} & \dfrac{1}{3} \end{bmatrix} = \begin{bmatrix} \dfrac{8}{9} & \dfrac{2}{9} \\ \dfrac{2}{9} & \dfrac{5}{9} \end{bmatrix} \neq I_2, P$ is not orthogonal.

26. Because

$$PP^T = \begin{bmatrix} -\dfrac{4}{5} & 0 & \dfrac{3}{5} \\ 0 & 1 & 0 \\ \dfrac{3}{5} & 0 & \dfrac{4}{5} \end{bmatrix} \begin{bmatrix} -\dfrac{4}{5} & 0 & \dfrac{3}{5} \\ 0 & 1 & 0 \\ \dfrac{3}{5} & 0 & \dfrac{4}{5} \end{bmatrix} = I_3, P^T = P^{-1} \text{ and}$$

P is orthogonal. Letting $p_1 = \begin{bmatrix} -\dfrac{4}{5} \\ 0 \\ \dfrac{3}{5} \end{bmatrix}, p_2 = \begin{bmatrix} 0 \\ 1 \\ 0 \end{bmatrix}$, and

$p_3 = \begin{bmatrix} \dfrac{3}{5} \\ 0 \\ \dfrac{4}{5} \end{bmatrix}$ produces

$p_1 \cdot p_2 = p_1 \cdot p_3 = p_2 \cdot p_3 = 0$ and $\|p_1\| = \|p_2\| = \|p_3\| = 1.$ So, $\{p_1, p_2, p_3\}$ is an orthonormal set.

34. The characteristic polynomial of A is

$$|\lambda I - A| = \begin{vmatrix} \lambda + 1 & 2 \\ 2 & \lambda - 2 \end{vmatrix} = (\lambda + 2)(\lambda - 3).$$

The eigenvalues are $\lambda_1 = -2$ and $\lambda_2 = 3$. Every eigenvector corresponding to $\lambda_1 = -2$ is of the form $x_1 = (2t, t)$, and every eigenvector corresponding to $\lambda_2 = 3$ is of the form $x_2 = (s, -2s)$.

$$x_1 \cdot x_2 = 2st - 2st = 0$$

So, x_1 and x_2 are orthogonal.

36. The matrix is diagonal, so the eigenvalues are $\lambda_1 = 3$, $\lambda_2 = -3$, and $\lambda_3 = 2$. Every eigenvector corresponding to $\lambda_1 = 3$ is of the form $x_1 = (t, 0, 0)$, every eigenvector corresponding to $\lambda_2 = -3$ is of the form $x_2 = (0, s, 0)$, and every eigenvector corresponding to $\lambda_3 = 2$ is of the form $x_3 = (0, 0, u)$.

$$x_1 \cdot x_2 = x_1 \cdot x_3 = x_2 \cdot x_3 = 0$$

So, $\{x_1, x_2, x_3\}$ is an orthogonal set.

38. The characteristic polynomial of A is

$$|\lambda I - A| = \begin{vmatrix} \lambda - 1 & 0 & -1 \\ 0 & \lambda - 1 & 0 \\ -1 & 0 & \lambda + 1 \end{vmatrix} = \lambda^2(\lambda - 1).$$

The eigenvalues are $\lambda_1 = 0$ and $\lambda_2 = 1$. Every eigenvector corresponding to $\lambda_1 = 0$ is of the form $x_1 = (0, 0, 0)$ and $x_2 = (0, 0, 0)$, and every eigenvector corresponding to $\lambda_1 = 1$ is of the form $x_3 = (0, t, 0)$.

$$x_1 \cdot x_2 = x_1 \cdot x_3 = x_2 \cdot x_3 = 0$$

So, $\{x_1, x_2, x_3\}$ is an orthogonal set.

40. The matrix is not symmetric, so it is not orthogonally diagonalizable.

42. The matrix is symmetric, so it is orthogonally diagonalizable.

44. The eigenvalues of A are $\lambda_1 = 2$ and $\lambda_2 = 6$, with corresponding eigenvectors $(1, -1)$ and $(1, 1)$, respectively. Normalize each eigenvector to form the columns of P. Then

$$P = \begin{bmatrix} \dfrac{\sqrt{2}}{2} & \dfrac{\sqrt{2}}{2} \\ -\dfrac{\sqrt{2}}{2} & \dfrac{\sqrt{2}}{2} \end{bmatrix} \text{ and } P^T A P = \begin{bmatrix} \dfrac{\sqrt{2}}{2} & -\dfrac{\sqrt{2}}{2} \\ \dfrac{\sqrt{2}}{2} & \dfrac{\sqrt{2}}{2} \end{bmatrix} \begin{bmatrix} 4 & 2 \\ 2 & 4 \end{bmatrix} \begin{bmatrix} \dfrac{\sqrt{2}}{2} & \dfrac{\sqrt{2}}{2} \\ -\dfrac{\sqrt{2}}{2} & \dfrac{\sqrt{2}}{2} \end{bmatrix} = \begin{bmatrix} 2 & 0 \\ 0 & 6 \end{bmatrix}.$$

46. The eigenvalues of A are $\lambda_1 = -1$ (repeated) and $\lambda_2 = 2$, with corresponding eigenvectors $(-1, 0, 1), (-1, 1, 0)$ and $(1, 1, 1)$, respectively. Use Gram–Schmidt Orthonormalization process to orthonormalize the two eigenvectors corresponding to $\lambda_1 = -1$.

$$(-1, 0, 1) \rightarrow \left(-\frac{1}{\sqrt{2}}, 0, \frac{1}{\sqrt{2}}\right)$$

$$(-1, 1, 0) - \frac{1}{2}(-1, 0, 1) = \left(-\frac{1}{2}, 1, -\frac{1}{2}\right) \rightarrow \left(\frac{1}{\sqrt{6}}, -\frac{2}{\sqrt{6}}, \frac{1}{\sqrt{6}}\right)$$

Normalizing the third eigenvector corresponding to $\lambda_2 = 2$, you can form the columns of P. So,

$$P = \begin{bmatrix} \dfrac{1}{\sqrt{3}} & -\dfrac{1}{\sqrt{2}} & \dfrac{1}{\sqrt{6}} \\[2mm] \dfrac{1}{\sqrt{3}} & 0 & -\dfrac{2}{\sqrt{6}} \\[2mm] \dfrac{1}{\sqrt{3}} & \dfrac{1}{\sqrt{2}} & \dfrac{1}{\sqrt{6}} \end{bmatrix}$$

and

$$P^T A P = \begin{bmatrix} \dfrac{1}{\sqrt{3}} & \dfrac{1}{\sqrt{3}} & \dfrac{1}{\sqrt{3}} \\[2mm] -\dfrac{1}{\sqrt{2}} & 0 & \dfrac{1}{\sqrt{2}} \\[2mm] \dfrac{1}{\sqrt{6}} & -\dfrac{2}{\sqrt{6}} & \dfrac{1}{\sqrt{6}} \end{bmatrix} \begin{bmatrix} 0 & 1 & 1 \\ 1 & 0 & 1 \\ 1 & 1 & 0 \end{bmatrix} \begin{bmatrix} \dfrac{1}{\sqrt{3}} & -\dfrac{1}{\sqrt{2}} & \dfrac{1}{\sqrt{6}} \\[2mm] \dfrac{1}{\sqrt{3}} & 0 & -\dfrac{2}{\sqrt{6}} \\[2mm] \dfrac{1}{\sqrt{3}} & \dfrac{1}{\sqrt{2}} & \dfrac{1}{\sqrt{6}} \end{bmatrix} = \begin{bmatrix} 2 & 0 & 0 \\ 0 & -1 & 0 \\ 0 & 0 & -1 \end{bmatrix}.$$

48. The eigenvalues of A are $\lambda_1 = 5$, $\lambda_2 = 0$, $\lambda_3 = -5$, with corresponding eigenvectors $(3, 5, 4)$, $(-4, 0, 3)$ and $(3, -5, 4)$ respectively. Normalize each eigenvector to form the columns of P. Then

$$P = \frac{1}{10}\begin{bmatrix} 3\sqrt{2} & -8 & 3\sqrt{2} \\ 5\sqrt{2} & 0 & -5\sqrt{2} \\ 4\sqrt{2} & 6 & 4\sqrt{2} \end{bmatrix}$$

and

$$P^T A P = \frac{1}{10}\begin{bmatrix} 3\sqrt{2} & 5\sqrt{2} & 4\sqrt{2} \\ -8 & 0 & 6 \\ 3\sqrt{2} & -5\sqrt{2} & 4\sqrt{2} \end{bmatrix} \begin{bmatrix} 0 & 3 & 0 \\ 3 & 0 & 4 \\ 0 & 4 & 0 \end{bmatrix} \frac{1}{10}\begin{bmatrix} 3\sqrt{2} & -8 & 3\sqrt{2} \\ 5\sqrt{2} & 0 & -5\sqrt{2} \\ 4\sqrt{2} & 6 & 4\sqrt{2} \end{bmatrix} = \begin{bmatrix} 5 & 0 & 0 \\ 0 & 0 & 0 \\ 0 & 0 & -5 \end{bmatrix}.$$

50. The characteristic polynomial of A, $|\lambda I - A| = (\lambda - 8)(\lambda + 4)^2$, yields the eigenvalues $\lambda_1 = 8$ and $\lambda_2 = -4$. λ_1 has a multiplicity of 1 and λ_2 has a multiplicity of 2. An eigenvector for λ_1 is $\mathbf{v}_1 = (1, 1, 2)$, which normalizes to

$$\mathbf{u}_1 = \frac{\mathbf{v}_1}{\|\mathbf{v}_1\|} = \left(\frac{\sqrt{6}}{6}, \frac{\sqrt{6}}{6}, \frac{\sqrt{6}}{3}\right).$$

Two eigenvectors for λ_2 are $\mathbf{v}_2 = (-1, 1, 0)$ and $\mathbf{v}_3 = (-2, 0, 1)$. Note that $\mathbf{v}_1$ is orthogonal to $\mathbf{v}_2$ and $\mathbf{v}_3$, as guaranteed by Theorem 7.9. The eigenvectors $\mathbf{v}_2$ and $\mathbf{v}_3$, however, are not orthogonal to each other. To find two orthonormal eigenvectors for λ_2, use the Gram-Schmidt process as follows.

$$\mathbf{w}_2 = \mathbf{v}_2 = (-1, 1, 0)$$

$$\mathbf{w}_3 = \mathbf{v}_3 - \left(\frac{\mathbf{v}_3 \cdot \mathbf{w}_2}{\mathbf{w}_2 \cdot \mathbf{w}_2}\right)\mathbf{w}_2 = (-1, -1, 1)$$

These vectors normalize to

$$\mathbf{u}_2 = \frac{\mathbf{w}_2}{\|\mathbf{w}_2\|} = \left(-\frac{\sqrt{2}}{2}, \frac{\sqrt{2}}{2}, 0\right)$$

$$\mathbf{u}_3 = \frac{\mathbf{w}_3}{\|\mathbf{w}_3\|} = \left(-\frac{\sqrt{3}}{3}, -\frac{\sqrt{3}}{3}, \frac{\sqrt{3}}{3}\right).$$

The matrix P has $\mathbf{u}_1, \mathbf{u}_2,$ and $\mathbf{u}_3$ as its column vectors.

$$P = \begin{bmatrix} \dfrac{\sqrt{6}}{6} & -\dfrac{\sqrt{2}}{2} & -\dfrac{\sqrt{3}}{3} \\ \dfrac{\sqrt{6}}{6} & \dfrac{\sqrt{2}}{2} & -\dfrac{\sqrt{3}}{3} \\ \dfrac{\sqrt{6}}{3} & 0 & \dfrac{\sqrt{3}}{3} \end{bmatrix}$$

and

$$P^T A P = \begin{bmatrix} \dfrac{\sqrt{6}}{6} & \dfrac{\sqrt{6}}{6} & \dfrac{\sqrt{6}}{3} \\ -\dfrac{\sqrt{2}}{2} & \dfrac{\sqrt{2}}{2} & 0 \\ -\dfrac{\sqrt{3}}{3} & -\dfrac{\sqrt{3}}{3} & \dfrac{\sqrt{3}}{3} \end{bmatrix} \begin{bmatrix} -2 & 2 & 4 \\ 2 & -2 & 4 \\ 4 & 4 & 4 \end{bmatrix} \begin{bmatrix} \dfrac{\sqrt{6}}{6} & -\dfrac{\sqrt{2}}{2} & -\dfrac{\sqrt{3}}{3} \\ \dfrac{\sqrt{6}}{6} & \dfrac{\sqrt{2}}{2} & -\dfrac{\sqrt{3}}{3} \\ \dfrac{\sqrt{6}}{3} & 0 & \dfrac{\sqrt{3}}{3} \end{bmatrix} = \begin{bmatrix} 8 & 0 & 0 \\ 0 & -4 & 0 \\ 0 & 0 & -4 \end{bmatrix}.$$

52. The eigenvalues of A are $\lambda_1 = 0$ (repeated) and $\lambda_2 = 2$ (repeated). The eigenvectors corresponding to $\lambda_1 = 0$ are $(1, -1, 0, 0)$ and $(0, 0, 1, -1)$, while those corresponding to $\lambda_2 = 2$ are $(1, 1, 0, 0)$ and $(0, 0, 1, 1)$. Normalizing these eigenvectors to form P, you have

$$
P = \begin{bmatrix} \dfrac{\sqrt{2}}{2} & 0 & \dfrac{\sqrt{2}}{2} & 0 \\[6pt] -\dfrac{\sqrt{2}}{2} & 0 & \dfrac{\sqrt{2}}{2} & 0 \\[6pt] 0 & \dfrac{\sqrt{2}}{2} & 0 & \dfrac{\sqrt{2}}{2} \\[6pt] 0 & -\dfrac{\sqrt{2}}{2} & 0 & \dfrac{\sqrt{2}}{2} \end{bmatrix}
$$

and

$$
P^T A P = \begin{bmatrix} \dfrac{\sqrt{2}}{2} & -\dfrac{\sqrt{2}}{2} & 0 & 0 \\[6pt] 0 & 0 & \dfrac{\sqrt{2}}{2} & -\dfrac{\sqrt{2}}{2} \\[6pt] \dfrac{\sqrt{2}}{2} & \dfrac{\sqrt{2}}{2} & 0 & 0 \\[6pt] 0 & 0 & \dfrac{\sqrt{2}}{2} & \dfrac{\sqrt{2}}{2} \end{bmatrix} \begin{bmatrix} 1 & 1 & 0 & 0 \\ 1 & 1 & 0 & 0 \\ 0 & 0 & 1 & 1 \\ 0 & 0 & 1 & 1 \end{bmatrix} \begin{bmatrix} \dfrac{\sqrt{2}}{2} & 0 & \dfrac{\sqrt{2}}{2} & 0 \\[6pt] -\dfrac{\sqrt{2}}{2} & 0 & \dfrac{\sqrt{2}}{2} & 0 \\[6pt] 0 & \dfrac{\sqrt{2}}{2} & 0 & \dfrac{\sqrt{2}}{2} \\[6pt] 0 & -\dfrac{\sqrt{2}}{2} & 0 & \dfrac{\sqrt{2}}{2} \end{bmatrix} = \begin{bmatrix} 0 & 0 & 0 & 0 \\ 0 & 0 & 0 & 0 \\ 0 & 0 & 2 & 0 \\ 0 & 0 & 0 & 2 \end{bmatrix}.
$$

54. (a) False. The fact that a matrix P is invertible does *not* imply $P^{-1} = P^T$, only that P^{-1} exists. The definition of orthogonal matrix (page 364) requires that a matrix P is invertible *and* $P^{-1} = P^T$. For example,

$$
\begin{bmatrix} 1 & 3 \\ 3 & 4 \end{bmatrix}
$$

is invertible $\left(|A| \neq 0\right)$ but $A^{-1} \neq A^T$.

(b) True. See Theorem 7.10 on page 367.

56. Suppose $P^{-1}AP = D$ is diagonal, with λ the only eigenvalue. Then

$$
A = PDP^{-1} = P(\lambda I)P^{-1} = \lambda I.
$$

58. (a) Yes. $A = A^T$

(b) and (c) Yes, by Theorem 7.7.

(d) The multiplicity of each eigenvalue is 1, so the dimensions of the corresponding eigenspaces are 1.

(e) No. The columns do not form an orthonormal set.

(f) Yes, by Theorem 7.9.

(g) Yes, by Theorem 7.10.

Section 7.4 Applications of Eigenvalues and Eigenvectors

2. $\mathbf{x}_2 = A\mathbf{x}_1 = \begin{bmatrix} 0 & 4 \\ \frac{1}{16} & 0 \end{bmatrix}\begin{bmatrix} 160 \\ 160 \end{bmatrix} = \begin{bmatrix} 640 \\ 10 \end{bmatrix}$

$\mathbf{x}_3 = A\mathbf{x}_2 = \begin{bmatrix} 0 & 4 \\ \frac{1}{16} & 0 \end{bmatrix}\begin{bmatrix} 640 \\ 10 \end{bmatrix} = \begin{bmatrix} 40 \\ 40 \end{bmatrix}$

4. $x_2 = Ax_1 = \begin{bmatrix} 0 & 2 & 0 \\ \frac{1}{2} & 0 & 0 \\ 0 & \frac{1}{2} & 0 \end{bmatrix}\begin{bmatrix} 8 \\ 8 \\ 8 \end{bmatrix} = \begin{bmatrix} 16 \\ 4 \\ 4 \end{bmatrix}$

$x_3 = Ax_2 = \begin{bmatrix} 0 & 2 & 0 \\ \frac{1}{2} & 0 & 0 \\ 0 & \frac{1}{2} & 0 \end{bmatrix}\begin{bmatrix} 16 \\ 4 \\ 4 \end{bmatrix} = \begin{bmatrix} 8 \\ 8 \\ 2 \end{bmatrix}$

6. $x_2 = Ax_1 = \begin{bmatrix} 0 & 6 & 4 & 0 & 0 \\ \frac{1}{2} & 0 & 0 & 0 & 0 \\ 0 & 1 & 0 & 0 & 0 \\ 0 & 0 & \frac{1}{2} & 0 & 0 \\ 0 & 0 & 0 & \frac{1}{2} & 0 \end{bmatrix}\begin{bmatrix} 24 \\ 24 \\ 24 \\ 24 \\ 24 \end{bmatrix} = \begin{bmatrix} 240 \\ 12 \\ 24 \\ 12 \\ 12 \end{bmatrix}$

$x_3 = Ax_2 = \begin{bmatrix} 0 & 6 & 4 & 0 & 0 \\ \frac{1}{2} & 0 & 0 & 0 & 0 \\ 0 & 1 & 0 & 0 & 0 \\ 0 & 0 & \frac{1}{2} & 0 & 0 \\ 0 & 0 & 0 & \frac{1}{2} & 0 \end{bmatrix}\begin{bmatrix} 240 \\ 12 \\ 24 \\ 12 \\ 12 \end{bmatrix} = \begin{bmatrix} 168 \\ 120 \\ 12 \\ 12 \\ 6 \end{bmatrix}$

8. The eigenvalues are $\frac{1}{2}$ and $-\frac{1}{2}$. Choosing the positive eigenvalue, $\lambda = \frac{1}{2}$, you find the corresponding eigenvector by row-reducing $\lambda I - A = \frac{1}{2}I - A$.

$$\begin{bmatrix} \frac{1}{2} & -4 \\ -\frac{1}{16} & \frac{1}{2} \end{bmatrix} \Rightarrow \begin{bmatrix} 1 & -8 \\ 0 & 0 \end{bmatrix}$$

So, an eigenvector is $(8, 1)$, and the stable age distribution vector is $\mathbf{x} = t\begin{bmatrix} 8 \\ 1 \end{bmatrix}$.

10. The eigenvalues of A are $0, 1$, and -1. Choosing the positive eigenvalue, let $\lambda = 1$. A corresponding eigenvector is found by row-reducing $1I - A$.

$$\begin{bmatrix} 1 & -2 & 0 \\ -\frac{1}{2} & 1 & 0 \\ 0 & -\frac{1}{2} & 1 \end{bmatrix} \Rightarrow \begin{bmatrix} 1 & 0 & -4 \\ 0 & 1 & -2 \\ 0 & 0 & 0 \end{bmatrix}$$

So, an eigenvector is $(4, 2, 1)$ and a stable age distribution vector is $x = t\begin{bmatrix} 4 \\ 2 \\ 1 \end{bmatrix}$.

12. The eigenvalues of A are $-1, 0$, and 2. Choosing the positive eigenvalue, let $\lambda = 2$. A corresponding eigenvector is found by row-reducing $2I - A$.

$$\begin{bmatrix} 2 & -6 & -4 & 0 & 0 \\ -\frac{1}{2} & 2 & 0 & 0 & 0 \\ 0 & -1 & 2 & 0 & 0 \\ 0 & 0 & -\frac{1}{2} & 2 & 0 \\ 0 & 0 & 0 & \frac{1}{2} & 2 \end{bmatrix} \Rightarrow \begin{bmatrix} 1 & 0 & 0 & 0 & -128 \\ 0 & 1 & 0 & 0 & -32 \\ 0 & 0 & 1 & 0 & -16 \\ 0 & 0 & 0 & 1 & -4 \\ 0 & 0 & 0 & 0 & 0 \end{bmatrix}$$

So, an eigenvector is $(128, 32, 16, 4, 1)$ and a stable age distribution vector is

$$x = t\begin{bmatrix} 128 \\ 32 \\ 16 \\ 4 \\ 1 \end{bmatrix}.$$

14. Construct the age transition matrix.

$$A = \begin{bmatrix} 3 & 6 & 3 \\ 0.8 & 0 & 0 \\ 0 & 0.25 & 0 \end{bmatrix}.$$

The current age distribution vector is

$$x_1 = \begin{bmatrix} 120 \\ 120 \\ 120 \end{bmatrix}.$$

In 1 year, the age distribution vector will be

$$x_2 = Ax_1 = \begin{bmatrix} 3 & 6 & 3 \\ 0.8 & 0 & 0 \\ 0 & 0.25 & 0 \end{bmatrix}\begin{bmatrix} 120 \\ 120 \\ 120 \end{bmatrix} = \begin{bmatrix} 1440 \\ 96 \\ 30 \end{bmatrix}.$$

In 2 years, the age distribution vector will be

$$x_3 = Ax_2 = \begin{bmatrix} 3 & 6 & 3 \\ 0.8 & 0 & 0 \\ 0 & 0.25 & 0 \end{bmatrix}\begin{bmatrix} 1440 \\ 96 \\ 30 \end{bmatrix} = \begin{bmatrix} 4986 \\ 1152 \\ 24 \end{bmatrix}.$$

16. The eigenvalues of A are $\lambda_1 = 1$ and $\lambda_2 = -1$, with corresponding eigenvector $(2, 1)$ and $(-2, 1)$, respectively. Then A can be diagonalized as follows

$$P^{-1}AP = \begin{bmatrix} \frac{1}{4} & \frac{1}{2} \\ -\frac{1}{4} & \frac{1}{2} \end{bmatrix}\begin{bmatrix} 0 & 2 \\ \frac{1}{2} & 0 \end{bmatrix}\begin{bmatrix} 2 & -2 \\ 1 & 1 \end{bmatrix} = \begin{bmatrix} 1 & 0 \\ 0 & -1 \end{bmatrix} = D.$$

So, $A = PDP^{-1}$ and $A^n = PD^nP^{-1}$.

If n is even, $D^n = I$ and $A^n = I$. If n is odd,

$$D^n = D \text{ and } A^n = PDP^{-1} = \begin{bmatrix} 0 & 2 \\ \frac{1}{2} & 0 \end{bmatrix} = A. \text{ So,}$$

$A^n x_1$ does not approach a limit as n approaches infinity.

18. The solution to the differential equation $y' = ky$ is $y = Ce^{kt}$. So, $y_1 = C_1e^{-5t}$ and $y_2 = C_2e^{4t}$.

20. The solution to the differential equation $y' = ky$ is $y = Ce^{kt}$. So, $y_1 = C_1e^{1/2t}$ and $y_2 = C_2e^{1/8t}$.

22. The solution to the differential equation $y' = ky$ is $y = Ce^{kt}$. So, $y_1 = C_1e^{5t}$, $y_2 = C_2e^{-2t}$, and $y_3 = C_3e^{-3t}$.

24. The solution to the differential equation $y' = ky$ is $y = Ce^{kt}$. So, $y_1 = C_1e^{-2/3t}$, $y_2 = C_2e^{-3/5t}$, and $y_3 = C_3e^{-8t}$.

26. The solution to the differential equation $y' = ky$ is $y = Ce^{kt}$. So, $y_1 = C_1e^{\pi t}$, $y_2 = C_2e^{-\pi t}$, and $y_3 = C_3e^{\pi^2 t}$.

28. The solution to the differential equation $y' = ky$ is $y = Ce^{kt}$. So, $y_1 = C_1e^{-0.1t}$, $y_2 = C_2e^{-\frac{7}{4}t}$, $y_3 = C_3e^{-2\pi t}$, and $y_4 = C_4e^{\sqrt{5}t}$.

30. This system has the matrix form

$$\mathbf{y'} = \begin{bmatrix} y_1' \\ y_2' \end{bmatrix} = \begin{bmatrix} 1 & -4 \\ -2 & 8 \end{bmatrix}\begin{bmatrix} y_1 \\ y_2 \end{bmatrix} = A\mathbf{y}.$$

The eigenvalues of A are $\lambda_1 = 0$ and $\lambda_2 = 9$, with corresponding eigenvectors $(4, 1)$ and $(-1, 2)$, respectively. So, you can diagonalize A using a matrix P whose columns are the eigenvectors of A.

$$P = \begin{bmatrix} 4 & -1 \\ 1 & 2 \end{bmatrix} \quad \text{and} \quad P^{-1}AP = \begin{bmatrix} 0 & 0 \\ 0 & 9 \end{bmatrix}$$

The solution of the system $\mathbf{w'} = P^{-1}AP\mathbf{w}$ is

$w_1 = C_1$ and $w_2 = C_2 e^{9t}$. Return to the original system by applying the substitution $\mathbf{y} = P\mathbf{w}$.

$$\mathbf{y} = \begin{bmatrix} y_1 \\ y_2 \end{bmatrix} = \begin{bmatrix} 4 & -1 \\ 1 & 2 \end{bmatrix}\begin{bmatrix} w_1 \\ w_2 \end{bmatrix} = \begin{bmatrix} 4w_1 - w_2 \\ w_1 + 2w_2 \end{bmatrix}$$

So, the solution is

$y_1 = 4C_1 - C_2 e^{9t}$

$y_2 = C_1 + 2C_2 e^{9t}.$

32. This system has the matrix form

$$\mathbf{y'} = \begin{bmatrix} y_1' \\ y_2' \end{bmatrix} = \begin{bmatrix} 1 & -1 \\ 2 & 4 \end{bmatrix}\begin{bmatrix} y_1 \\ y_2 \end{bmatrix} = A\mathbf{y}.$$

The eigenvalues of A are $\lambda_1 = 2$ and $\lambda_2 = 3$, with corresponding eigenvectors $(1, -1)$ and $(-1, 2)$, respectively. So, you can diagonalize A using a matrix P whose columns are the eigenvectors of A.

$$P = \begin{bmatrix} 1 & -1 \\ -1 & 2 \end{bmatrix} \quad \text{and} \quad P^{-1}AP = \begin{bmatrix} 2 & 0 \\ 0 & 3 \end{bmatrix}$$

The solution of the system $\mathbf{w'} = P^{-1}AP\mathbf{w}$ is

$w_1 = C_1 e^{2t}$ and $w_2 = C_2 e^{3t}$. Return to the original system by applying the substitution $\mathbf{y} = P\mathbf{w}$.

$$\mathbf{y} = \begin{bmatrix} y_1 \\ y_2 \end{bmatrix} = \begin{bmatrix} 1 & -1 \\ -1 & 2 \end{bmatrix}\begin{bmatrix} w_1 \\ w_2 \end{bmatrix} = \begin{bmatrix} w_1 - w_2 \\ -w_1 + 2w_2 \end{bmatrix}$$

So, the solution is

$y_1 = C_1 e^{2t} - C_2 e^{3t}$

$y_2 = -C_1 e^{2t} + 2C_2 e^{3t}.$

34. This system has the matrix form

$$\mathbf{y'} = \begin{bmatrix} y_1' \\ y_2' \\ y_3' \end{bmatrix} = \begin{bmatrix} -2 & 0 & 1 \\ 0 & 3 & 4 \\ 0 & 0 & 1 \end{bmatrix}\begin{bmatrix} y_1 \\ y_2 \\ y_3 \end{bmatrix} = A\mathbf{y}.$$

The eigenvalues of A are $\lambda_1 = -2$, $\lambda_2 = 3$ and $\lambda_3 = 1$, with corresponding eigenvectors $(1, 0, 0)$, $(0, 1, 0)$ and $(1, -6, 3)$, respectively. So, you can diagonalize A using a matrix P whose columns are the eigenvectors of A.

$$P = \begin{bmatrix} 1 & 0 & 1 \\ 0 & 1 & -6 \\ 0 & 0 & 3 \end{bmatrix} \quad \text{and} \quad P^{-1}AP = \begin{bmatrix} -2 & 0 & 0 \\ 0 & 3 & 0 \\ 0 & 0 & 1 \end{bmatrix}$$

The solution of the system $\mathbf{w'} = P^{-1}AP\mathbf{w}$ is

$w_1 = C_1 e^{-2t}$, $w_2 = C_2 e^{3t}$ and $w_3 = C_3 e^{t}$. Return to the original system by applying the substitution $\mathbf{y} = P\mathbf{w}$.

$$\mathbf{y} = \begin{bmatrix} y_1 \\ y_2 \\ y_3 \end{bmatrix} = \begin{bmatrix} 1 & 0 & 1 \\ 0 & 1 & -6 \\ 0 & 0 & 3 \end{bmatrix}\begin{bmatrix} w_1 \\ w_2 \\ w_3 \end{bmatrix} = \begin{bmatrix} w + w_3 \\ w_2 - 6w_3 \\ 3w_3 \end{bmatrix}$$

So, the solution is

$y_1 = C_1 e^{-2t} \qquad\qquad + C_3 e^{t}$

$y_2 = \qquad\quad C_2 e^{3t} - 6C_3 e^{t}$

$y_3 = \qquad\qquad\qquad\qquad 3C_3 e^{t}.$

36. This system has the matrix form

$$\mathbf{y'} = \begin{bmatrix} y_1' \\ y_2' \\ y_3' \end{bmatrix} = \begin{bmatrix} 2 & 1 & 1 \\ 1 & 1 & 0 \\ 1 & 0 & 1 \end{bmatrix}\begin{bmatrix} y_1 \\ y_2 \\ y_3 \end{bmatrix} = A\mathbf{y}.$$

The eigenvalues of A are $\lambda_1 = 0$, $\lambda_2 = 1$ and $\lambda_3 = 3$, with corresponding eigenvectors $(-1, 1, 1)$, $(0, 1, -1)$ and $(2, 1, 1)$, respectively. So, you can diagonalize A using a matrix P whose columns are the eigenvectors.

$$P = \begin{bmatrix} -1 & 0 & 2 \\ 1 & 1 & 1 \\ 1 & -1 & 1 \end{bmatrix} \quad \text{and} \quad P^{-1}AP = \begin{bmatrix} 0 & 0 & 0 \\ 0 & 1 & 0 \\ 0 & 0 & 3 \end{bmatrix}$$

The solution of the system $\mathbf{w'} = P^{-1}AP\mathbf{w}$ is

$w_1 = C_1$, $w_2 = C_2 e^{t}$ and $w_3 = C_3 e^{3t}$. Return to the original system by applying the substitution $\mathbf{y} = P\mathbf{w}$.

$$\mathbf{y} = \begin{bmatrix} y_1 \\ y_2 \\ y_3 \end{bmatrix} = \begin{bmatrix} -1 & 0 & 2 \\ 1 & 1 & 1 \\ 1 & -1 & 1 \end{bmatrix}\begin{bmatrix} w_1 \\ w_2 \\ w_3 \end{bmatrix} = \begin{bmatrix} -w_1 + 2w_3 \\ w_1 + w_2 + w_3 \\ w_1 + w_2 + w_3 \end{bmatrix}$$

So, the solution is

$y_1 = -C_1 \qquad\qquad + 2C_3 e^{3t}$

$y_2 = C_1 + C_2 e^{t} + C_3 e^{3t}$

$y_3 = C_1 - C_2 e^{t} + C_3 e^{3t}.$

38. Because

$$\mathbf{y}' = \begin{bmatrix} y_1' \\ y_2' \end{bmatrix} = \begin{bmatrix} 1 & -1 \\ 1 & 1 \end{bmatrix} \begin{bmatrix} y_1 \\ y_2 \end{bmatrix} = A\mathbf{y}$$

the system represented by $\mathbf{y}' = A\mathbf{y}$ is

$$y_1' = y_1 - y_2$$
$$y_2' = y_1 + y_2.$$

Note that

$$y_1' = C_1 e^t \cos t - C_1 e^t \sin t + C_2 e^t \sin t + C_2 e^t \cos t = y_1 - y_2$$

and

$$y_2' = -C_2 e^t \cos t + C_2 e^t \sin t + C_1 e^t \sin t + C_1 e^t \cos t = y_1 + y_2.$$

40. Because

$$\mathbf{y}' = \begin{bmatrix} y_1' \\ y_2' \\ y_3' \end{bmatrix} = \begin{bmatrix} 0 & 1 & 0 \\ 0 & 0 & 1 \\ 1 & -3 & 3 \end{bmatrix} \begin{bmatrix} y_1 \\ y_2 \\ y_3 \end{bmatrix} = A\mathbf{y}$$

the system represented by $\mathbf{y}' = A\mathbf{y}$ is

$$y_1' = y_2$$
$$y_2' = y_3$$
$$y_3' = y_1 - 3y_2 + 3y_3.$$

Note that

$$y_1' = C_1 e^t + C_2 t e^t + C_2 e^t + C_3 t^2 e^t + 2C_3 t e^t = y_2$$

$$y_2' = (C_1 + C_2)e^t + (C_2 + 2C_3)t e^t + (C_2 + 2C_3)e^t + C_3 t^2 e^t + 2C_3 t e^t = y_3$$

$$y_3' = (C_1 + 2C_2 + 2C_3)e^t + (C_2 + 4C_3)t e^t + (C_2 + 4C_3)e^t + C_3 t^2 e^t + 2C_3 t e^t$$

$$= \left(C_1 e^t + C_2 t e^t + C_3 t^2 e^t\right) - 3\left((C_1 + C_2)e^t + (C_2 + 2C_3)t e^t + C_3 t^2 e^t\right)$$

$$+ 3\left((C_1 + 2C_2 + 2C_3)e^t + (C_2 + 4C_3)t e^t + C_3 t^2 e^t\right)$$

$$= y_1 - 3y_2 + 3y_3.$$

42. The matrix of the quadratic form is

$$A = \begin{bmatrix} a & \dfrac{b}{2} \\ \dfrac{b}{2} & c \end{bmatrix} = \begin{bmatrix} 1 & -2 \\ -2 & 1 \end{bmatrix}.$$

44. The matrix of the quadratic form is

$$A = \begin{bmatrix} a & \dfrac{b}{2} \\ \dfrac{b}{2} & c \end{bmatrix} = \begin{bmatrix} 12 & -\dfrac{5}{2} \\ -\dfrac{5}{2} & 0 \end{bmatrix}.$$

46. The matrix of the quadratic form is

$$A = \begin{bmatrix} a & \dfrac{b}{2} \\ \dfrac{b}{2} & c \end{bmatrix} = \begin{bmatrix} 16 & -2 \\ -2 & 20 \end{bmatrix}.$$

48. The matrix of the quadratic form is

$$A = \begin{bmatrix} a & \dfrac{b}{2} \\ \dfrac{b}{2} & c \end{bmatrix} = \begin{bmatrix} 5 & -1 \\ -1 & 5 \end{bmatrix}.$$

The eigenvalues of A are $\lambda_1 = 4$ and $\lambda_2 = 6$, with corresponding eigenvectors $\mathbf{x}_1 = (1, 1)$ and $\mathbf{x}_2 = (-1, 1)$, respectively. Using unit vectors in the direction of $\mathbf{x}_1$ and $\mathbf{x}_2$ to form the columns of P, you have

$$P = \begin{bmatrix} \dfrac{\sqrt{2}}{2} & -\dfrac{\sqrt{2}}{2} \\ \dfrac{\sqrt{2}}{2} & \dfrac{\sqrt{2}}{2} \end{bmatrix} \quad \text{and} \quad P^T A P = \begin{bmatrix} 4 & 0 \\ 0 & 6 \end{bmatrix}.$$

50. The matrix of the quadratic form is

$$A = \begin{bmatrix} a & \dfrac{b}{2} \\ \dfrac{b}{2} & c \end{bmatrix} = \begin{bmatrix} 3 & -\sqrt{3} \\ -\sqrt{3} & 1 \end{bmatrix}.$$

The eigenvalues of A are $\lambda_1 = 0$ and $\lambda_2 = 4$, with corresponding eigenvectors $\mathbf{x}_1 = \left(1, \sqrt{3}\right)$ and $\mathbf{x}_2 = \left(-\sqrt{3}, 1\right)$, respectively. Using unit vectors in the direction of $\mathbf{x}_1$ and $\mathbf{x}_2$ to form the columns of P, you have

$$P = \begin{bmatrix} \dfrac{1}{2} & -\dfrac{\sqrt{3}}{2} \\ \dfrac{\sqrt{3}}{2} & \dfrac{1}{2} \end{bmatrix} \quad \text{and} \quad P^T A P = \begin{bmatrix} 0 & 0 \\ 0 & 4 \end{bmatrix}.$$

52. The matrix of the quadratic form is

$$A = \begin{bmatrix} a & \dfrac{b}{2} \\ \dfrac{b}{2} & c \end{bmatrix} = \begin{bmatrix} 17 & 16 \\ 16 & -7 \end{bmatrix}.$$

The eigenvalues of A are $\lambda_1 = -15$ and $\lambda_2 = 25$, with corresponding eigenvectors $\mathbf{x}_1 = \left(1, -2\right)$ and $\mathbf{x}_2 = (2, 1)$, respectively. Using unit vectors in the direction of $\mathbf{x}_1$ and $\mathbf{x}_2$ to form the columns of P, you have

$$P = \begin{bmatrix} \dfrac{1}{\sqrt{5}} & \dfrac{2}{\sqrt{5}} \\ -\dfrac{2}{\sqrt{5}} & \dfrac{1}{\sqrt{5}} \end{bmatrix} \quad \text{and} \quad P^T A P = \begin{bmatrix} -15 & 0 \\ 0 & 25 \end{bmatrix}.$$

54. The matrix of the quadratic form is

$$A = \begin{bmatrix} a & \dfrac{b}{2} \\ \dfrac{b}{2} & c \end{bmatrix} = \begin{bmatrix} 1 & 2 \\ 2 & 1 \end{bmatrix}.$$

This matrix has eigenvalues of -1 and 3, and corresponding unit eigenvectors $\left(\dfrac{1}{\sqrt{2}}, -\dfrac{1}{\sqrt{2}}\right)$ and $\left(\dfrac{1}{\sqrt{2}}, \dfrac{1}{\sqrt{2}}\right)$, respectively.

So, let

$$P = \begin{bmatrix} \dfrac{1}{\sqrt{2}} & \dfrac{1}{\sqrt{2}} \\ -\dfrac{1}{\sqrt{2}} & \dfrac{1}{\sqrt{2}} \end{bmatrix} \quad \text{and} \quad P^T A P = \begin{bmatrix} -1 & 0 \\ 0 & 3 \end{bmatrix}.$$

This implies that the rotated conic is a hyperbola with equation $-(x')^2 + 3(y')^2 = 9$.

56. The matrix of the quadratic form is $A = \begin{bmatrix} a & \dfrac{b}{2} \\ \dfrac{b}{2} & c \end{bmatrix} = \begin{bmatrix} 7 & 16 \\ 16 & -17 \end{bmatrix}.$

This matrix has eigenvalues of -25 and 15, with corresponding unit eigenvectors $\left(\dfrac{1}{\sqrt{5}}, -\dfrac{2}{\sqrt{5}}\right)$ and $\left(\dfrac{2}{\sqrt{5}}, \dfrac{1}{\sqrt{5}}\right)$ respectively.

Let $P = \begin{bmatrix} \dfrac{1}{\sqrt{5}} & \dfrac{2}{\sqrt{5}} \\ -\dfrac{2}{\sqrt{5}} & \dfrac{1}{\sqrt{5}} \end{bmatrix} \quad \text{and} \quad P^T A P = \begin{bmatrix} -25 & 0 \\ 0 & 15 \end{bmatrix}.$

This implies that the rotated conic is a hyperbola with equation $-25(x')^2 + 15(y')^2 - 50 = 0$.

58. The matrix of the quadratic form is

$$A = \begin{bmatrix} a & \dfrac{b}{2} \\ \dfrac{b}{2} & c \end{bmatrix} = \begin{bmatrix} 8 & 4 \\ 4 & 8 \end{bmatrix}.$$

This matrix has eigenvalues of 4 and 12, and corresponding unit eigenvectors $\left(\dfrac{1}{\sqrt{2}}, -\dfrac{1}{\sqrt{2}}\right)$ and $\left(\dfrac{1}{\sqrt{2}}, \dfrac{1}{\sqrt{2}}\right)$, respectively.

So, let

$$P = \begin{bmatrix} \dfrac{1}{\sqrt{2}} & \dfrac{1}{\sqrt{2}} \\ -\dfrac{1}{\sqrt{2}} & \dfrac{1}{\sqrt{2}} \end{bmatrix} \quad \text{and} \quad P^T AP = \begin{bmatrix} 4 & 0 \\ 0 & 12 \end{bmatrix}.$$

This implies that the rotated conic is an ellipse. Furthermore,

$$[d \quad e]P = \begin{bmatrix} 10\sqrt{2} & 26\sqrt{2} \end{bmatrix} \begin{bmatrix} \dfrac{1}{\sqrt{2}} & \dfrac{1}{\sqrt{2}} \\ -\dfrac{1}{\sqrt{2}} & \dfrac{1}{\sqrt{2}} \end{bmatrix} = \begin{bmatrix} -16 & 36 \end{bmatrix} = [d' \quad e'],$$

so the equation in the $x'y'$ coordinate system is

$$4(x')^2 + 12(y')^2 - 16x' + 36y' + 31 = 0.$$

60. The matrix of the quadratic form is $A = \begin{bmatrix} a & \dfrac{b}{2} \\ \dfrac{b}{2} & c \end{bmatrix} = \begin{bmatrix} 5 & -1 \\ -1 & 5 \end{bmatrix}.$

The eigenvalues of A are 4 and 6, with corresponding unit eigenvectors $\left(\dfrac{1}{\sqrt{2}}, \dfrac{1}{\sqrt{2}}\right)$ and $\left(-\dfrac{1}{\sqrt{2}}, \dfrac{1}{\sqrt{2}}\right)$, respectively.

So, let

$$P = \begin{bmatrix} \dfrac{1}{\sqrt{2}} & -\dfrac{1}{\sqrt{2}} \\ \dfrac{1}{\sqrt{2}} & \dfrac{1}{\sqrt{2}} \end{bmatrix} \quad \text{and} \quad P^T AP = \begin{bmatrix} 4 & 0 \\ 0 & 6 \end{bmatrix}.$$

This implies that the rotated conic is an ellipse. Furthermore, $[d \quad e]P = \begin{bmatrix} 10\sqrt{2} & 0 \end{bmatrix} \begin{bmatrix} \dfrac{1}{\sqrt{2}} & -\dfrac{1}{\sqrt{2}} \\ \dfrac{1}{\sqrt{2}} & \dfrac{1}{\sqrt{2}} \end{bmatrix} = \begin{bmatrix} 10 & -10 \end{bmatrix} = [d' \quad e'],$

so the equation in the $x'y'$-coordinate system is $4(x')^2 + 6(y')^2 + 10x' + 10y' = 0.$

62. The matrix of the quadratic form is $A = \begin{bmatrix} 2 & 1 & 1 \\ 1 & 2 & 1 \\ 1 & 1 & 2 \end{bmatrix}$.

The eigenvalues of A are 1, 1 and 4, with corresponding unit eigenvectors $\left(\frac{1}{\sqrt{6}}, \frac{1}{\sqrt{6}}, -\frac{2}{\sqrt{6}} \right), \left(-\frac{1}{\sqrt{2}}, \frac{1}{\sqrt{2}}, 0 \right)$ and

$\left(\frac{1}{\sqrt{3}}, \frac{1}{\sqrt{3}}, \frac{1}{\sqrt{3}} \right)$, respectively. Then let

$$P = \begin{bmatrix} \dfrac{1}{\sqrt{6}} & -\dfrac{1}{\sqrt{2}} & \dfrac{1}{\sqrt{3}} \\ \dfrac{1}{\sqrt{6}} & \dfrac{1}{\sqrt{2}} & \dfrac{1}{\sqrt{3}} \\ -\dfrac{2}{\sqrt{6}} & 0 & \dfrac{1}{\sqrt{3}} \end{bmatrix} \quad \text{and} \quad P^T A P = \begin{bmatrix} 1 & 0 & 0 \\ 0 & 1 & 0 \\ 0 & 0 & 4 \end{bmatrix}.$$

So, the equation of the rotated quadratic surface is $(x')^2 + (y')^2 + 4(z')^2 - 1 = 0$ (ellipsoid).

64. The matrix of the quadratic form is $A = \begin{bmatrix} 1 & 1 & 0 \\ 1 & 1 & 0 \\ 0 & 0 & 1 \end{bmatrix}$.

The eigenvalues of A are 0, 1, and 2, with corresponding eigenvectors $(-1, 1, 0), (0, 0, 1)$, and $(1, 1, 0)$, respectively.

Then let

$$P = \begin{bmatrix} -\dfrac{\sqrt{2}}{2} & 0 & \dfrac{\sqrt{2}}{2} \\ \dfrac{\sqrt{2}}{2} & 0 & \dfrac{\sqrt{2}}{2} \\ 0 & 1 & 0 \end{bmatrix} \quad \text{and} \quad P^T A P = \begin{bmatrix} 0 & 0 & 0 \\ 0 & 1 & 0 \\ 0 & 0 & 2 \end{bmatrix}.$$

So, the equation of the rotated quadratic surface is $(y')^2 + 2(z')^2 - 8 = 0$.

66. (a) To model population growth, use the average number of offspring for each age class and the probabilities of surviving to the next age class to form the age transition matrix A. The initial age distribution vector $\mathbf{x}_1$ is used to find $\mathbf{x}_2$ by the formula $\mathbf{x}_n = A\mathbf{x}_{n-1}$. An eigenvector corresponding to a positive eigenvalue of A is a stable age distribution vector.

(b) To solve a system of first order linear differential equations find the coefficient matrix A for the system, then find a matrix P that diagonalizes A. Solve the system $\mathbf{w}' = P^{-1}AP_{\mathbf{w}}$ to find $\mathbf{w}$, and then $P_{\mathbf{w}}$ is the solution of the original system.

(c) To use the Principal Axes Theorem to perform a rotation of axes, find the matrix A of the quadratic form of the conic or quadric surface. The eigenvalues of A are the coefficients of the squared terms in the rotated system.

Review Exercises for Chapter 7

2. (a) The characteristic equation of A is given by

$$|\lambda I - A| = \begin{vmatrix} \lambda - 2 & -1 \\ 4 & \lambda + 2 \end{vmatrix} = \lambda^2 = 0.$$

(b) The eigenvalue of A is $\lambda = 0$ (repeated).

(c) To find the eigenvectors corresponding to $\lambda = 0$, solve the matrix equation $(\lambda I - A)\mathbf{x} = \mathbf{0}$. Row reducing the augmented matrix,

$$\begin{bmatrix} -2 & -1 & : & 0 \\ 4 & 2 & : & 0 \end{bmatrix} \Rightarrow \begin{bmatrix} 2 & 1 & : & 0 \\ 0 & 0 & : & 0 \end{bmatrix}$$

you see that a basis for the eigenspace is $\{(-1, 2)\}$.

4. (a) The characteristic equation of A is given by

$$|\lambda I - A| = \begin{vmatrix} \lambda + 4 & -1 & -2 \\ 0 & \lambda - 1 & -1 \\ 0 & 0 & \lambda - 3 \end{vmatrix}$$

$$= (\lambda + 4)(\lambda - 1)(\lambda - 3) = 0.$$

(b) The eigenvalues of A are $\lambda_1 = -4$, $\lambda_2 = 1$, and $\lambda_3 = 3$.

(c) To find the eigenvectors corresponding to $\lambda_1 = -4$, solve the matrix equation $(\lambda_1 I - A)\mathbf{x} = \mathbf{0}$. Row reducing the augmented matrix,

$$\begin{bmatrix} 0 & -1 & -2 & \vdots & 0 \\ 0 & -5 & -1 & \vdots & 0 \\ 0 & 0 & -7 & \vdots & 0 \end{bmatrix} \Rightarrow \begin{bmatrix} 0 & 1 & 0 & \vdots & 0 \\ 0 & 0 & 1 & \vdots & 0 \\ 0 & 0 & 0 & \vdots & 0 \end{bmatrix}$$

you see that a basis for the eigenspace $\lambda_1 = -4$ is $\{(1, 0, 0)\}$. Similarly, solve $(\lambda_2 I - A)\mathbf{x} = \mathbf{0}$ for $\lambda_2 = 1$, and see that $\{(1, 5, 0)\}$ is a basis for the eigenspace of $\lambda_2 = 1$. Finally, solve $(\lambda_3 I - A)\mathbf{x} = \mathbf{0}$ for $\lambda_3 = 3$, and determine that $\{(5, 7, 14)\}$ is a basis for its eigenspace.

6. (a) The characteristic equation of A is given by

$$|\lambda I - A| = \begin{vmatrix} \lambda - 1 & 0 & -4 \\ 0 & \lambda - 1 & 2 \\ -1 & 0 & \lambda + 2 \end{vmatrix}$$

$$= (\lambda + 3)(\lambda - 1)(\lambda - 2) = 0.$$

(b) The eigenvalues of A are $\lambda_1 = -3$, $\lambda_2 = 1$, and $\lambda_3 = 2$.

(c) To find the eigenvector corresponding to $\lambda_1 = -3$, solve the matrix equation $(\lambda_1 I - A)\mathbf{x} = \mathbf{0}$.

Row-reducing the augmented matrix,

$$\begin{bmatrix} -4 & 0 & -4 & \vdots & 0 \\ 0 & -4 & 2 & \vdots & 0 \\ -1 & 0 & -1 & \vdots & 0 \end{bmatrix} \Rightarrow \begin{bmatrix} 1 & 0 & 1 & \vdots & 0 \\ 0 & 1 & -\frac{1}{2} & \vdots & 0 \\ 0 & 0 & 0 & \vdots & 0 \end{bmatrix}$$

you can see that a basis for the eigenspace of $\lambda_1 = -3$ is $\{(-2, 1, 2)\}$.

Similarly, solve $(\lambda_2 I - A)\mathbf{x} = \mathbf{0}$ for $\lambda_2 = 1$, and see that $\{(0, 1, 0)\}$ is a basis for the eigenspace of $\lambda_2 = 1$. Finally, solve $(\lambda_3 I - A)\mathbf{x} = \mathbf{0}$ for $\lambda_3 = 2$, and see that $\{(4, -2, 1)\}$ is a basis for its eigenspace.

8. (a) $|\lambda I - A| = (\lambda - 1)(\lambda - 2)(\lambda - 4)^2 = 0$

(b) $\lambda_1 = 1$, $\lambda_2 = 2$, $\lambda_3 = 4$ (repeated)

(c) A basis for the eigenspace of $\lambda_1 = 1$ is $\{(-1, 0, 1, 0)\}$.

A basis for the eigenspace of $\lambda_2 = 2$ is $\{(-2, 1, 1, 0)\}$.

A basis for the eigenspace of $\lambda_3 = 4$ is

$$\{(2, 3, 1, 0), (0, 0, 0, 1)\}.$$

10. The eigenvalues of A are $\lambda_1 = \frac{1}{2}$ and $\lambda_2 = \frac{1}{4}$. From Exercise 20, Section 7.1, the corresponding eigenvectors $(1, 1)$ and $(1, -2)$ are used to form the column of P. So,

$$P = \begin{bmatrix} 1 & 1 \\ 1 & -2 \end{bmatrix} \Rightarrow P^{-1} = \begin{bmatrix} \frac{2}{3} & \frac{1}{3} \\ \frac{1}{3} & -\frac{1}{3} \end{bmatrix}, \text{ and}$$

$$P^{-1}AP = \begin{bmatrix} \frac{2}{3} & \frac{1}{3} \\ \frac{1}{3} & -\frac{1}{3} \end{bmatrix}\begin{bmatrix} \frac{1}{4} & \frac{1}{4} \\ \frac{1}{2} & 0 \end{bmatrix}\begin{bmatrix} 1 & 1 \\ 1 & -2 \end{bmatrix} = \begin{bmatrix} \frac{1}{2} & 0 \\ 0 & -\frac{1}{4} \end{bmatrix}.$$

12. The eigenvalues of A are the solutions of

$$|\lambda I - A| = \begin{vmatrix} \lambda - 3 & 2 & -2 \\ 2 & \lambda & 1 \\ -2 & 1 & \lambda \end{vmatrix} = (\lambda + 1)^2(\lambda - 5) = 0.$$

Therefore, the eigenvalues are -1 (repeated) and 5. The corresponding eigenvectors are solutions of $(\lambda I - A)\mathbf{x} = \mathbf{0}$.

So, $(1, 1, -1)$ and $(2, 5, 1)$ are eigenvectors corresponding to $\lambda_1 = -1$, while $(2, -1, 1)$ corresponds to $\lambda_2 = 5$. Now form P from these eigenvectors and note that

$$P = \begin{bmatrix} 1 & 2 & 2 \\ 1 & 5 & -1 \\ -1 & 1 & 1 \end{bmatrix} \text{ and } P^{-1}AP = \begin{bmatrix} -1 & 0 & 0 \\ 0 & -1 & 0 \\ 0 & 0 & 5 \end{bmatrix}.$$

14. The eigenvalues of A are the solutions of

$$|\lambda I - A| = \begin{vmatrix} \lambda - 2 & 1 & -1 \\ 2 & \lambda - 3 & 2 \\ 1 & -1 & \lambda \end{vmatrix}$$

$$= (\lambda - 1)^2(\lambda - 3) = 0.$$

Therefore, the eigenvalues are $\lambda_1 = 1$ (repeated) and $\lambda_2 = 3$. The corresponding eigenvectors are solutions of $(\lambda I - A)\mathbf{x} = \mathbf{0}$. So, $(-1, 0, 1)$ and $(1, 1, 0)$ are eigenvectors corresponding to $\lambda_1 = 1$, while $(-1, 2, 1)$ corresponds to $\lambda_2 = 3$. Now form P from these eigenvectors and note that

$$P = \begin{bmatrix} -1 & 1 & -1 \\ 0 & 1 & 2 \\ 1 & 0 & 1 \end{bmatrix} \text{ and } P^{-1}AP = \begin{bmatrix} 1 & 0 & 0 \\ 0 & 1 & 0 \\ 0 & 0 & 3 \end{bmatrix}.$$

16. Consider the characteristic equation $|\lambda I - A| = \begin{vmatrix} \lambda - \cos\theta & \sin\theta \\ -\sin\theta & \lambda - \cos\theta \end{vmatrix} = \lambda^2 - 2\cos\theta \cdot \lambda + 1 = 0.$

The discriminant of this quadratic equation in λ is $b^2 - 4ac = 4\cos^2\theta - 4 = -4\sin^2\theta.$

Because $0 < \theta < \pi$, this discriminant is always negative, and the characteristic equation has no real roots.

18. The eigenvalue is $\lambda = -1$ (repeated). To find its corresponding eigenspace, solve $(\lambda I - A)\mathbf{x} = \mathbf{0}$ with $\lambda = -1.$

$$\begin{bmatrix} \lambda + 1 & -2 & \vdots & 0 \\ 0 & \lambda + 1 & \vdots & 0 \end{bmatrix} = \begin{bmatrix} 0 & -2 & \vdots & 0 \\ 0 & 0 & \vdots & 0 \end{bmatrix} \Rightarrow \begin{bmatrix} 0 & 1 & \vdots & 0 \\ 0 & 0 & \vdots & 0 \end{bmatrix}$$

Because the eigenspace is only one-dimensional, the matrix A is not diagonalizable.

20. The eigenvalues are $\lambda = -2$ (repeated) and $\lambda = 4.$ Because the eigenspace corresponding to $\lambda = -2$ is only one-dimensional, the matrix is not diagonalizable.

22. The eigenvalues of B are 5 and 3 with corresponding eigenvectors $(-1, 1)$ and $(-1, 2)$, respectively. Form the columns of P from the eigenvectors of B. So,

$$P = \begin{bmatrix} -1 & -1 \\ 1 & 2 \end{bmatrix} \text{ and}$$

$$P^{-1}BP = \begin{bmatrix} -2 & -1 \\ 1 & 1 \end{bmatrix}\begin{bmatrix} 7 & 2 \\ -4 & 1 \end{bmatrix}\begin{bmatrix} -1 & -1 \\ 1 & 2 \end{bmatrix} = \begin{bmatrix} 5 & 0 \\ 0 & 3 \end{bmatrix} = A.$$

Therefore, A and B are similar.

24. The eigenvalues of B are 1 and -2 (repeated) with corresponding eigenvectors $(-1, -1, 1), (1, 1, 0),$ and $(1, 0, 1)$, respectively. Form the columns of P from the eigenvectors of B. So,

$$P = \begin{bmatrix} -1 & 1 & 1 \\ -1 & 1 & 0 \\ 1 & 0 & 1 \end{bmatrix} \text{ and}$$

$$P^{-1}BP = \begin{bmatrix} -1 & 1 & 1 \\ -1 & 2 & 1 \\ 1 & -1 & 0 \end{bmatrix}\begin{bmatrix} 1 & -3 & -3 \\ 3 & -5 & -3 \\ -3 & 3 & 1 \end{bmatrix}\begin{bmatrix} -1 & 1 & 1 \\ -1 & 1 & 0 \\ 1 & 0 & 1 \end{bmatrix} = \begin{bmatrix} 1 & 0 & 0 \\ 0 & -2 & 0 \\ 0 & 0 & -2 \end{bmatrix} = A.$$

Therefore, A and B are similar.

26. Because

$$A^T = \begin{bmatrix} \dfrac{2\sqrt{5}}{5} & \dfrac{\sqrt{5}}{5} \\ \dfrac{\sqrt{5}}{5} & -\dfrac{2\sqrt{5}}{5} \end{bmatrix} = A$$

A is symmetric. Furthermore, the column vectors of A form an orthonormal set. So, A is both symmetric and orthogonal.

28. Because

$$A^T = \begin{bmatrix} \dfrac{4}{5} & 0 & -\dfrac{3}{5} \\ 0 & 1 & 0 \\ \dfrac{3}{5} & 0 & \dfrac{4}{5} \end{bmatrix} \neq A$$

A is *not* symmetric. However, the column vectors form an orthonormal set, so A *is* orthogonal.

30. Because

$$A^T = \begin{bmatrix} \dfrac{\sqrt{3}}{3} & \dfrac{\sqrt{3}}{3} & \dfrac{\sqrt{3}}{3} \\ \dfrac{\sqrt{3}}{3} & \dfrac{2\sqrt{3}}{3} & 0 \\ \dfrac{\sqrt{3}}{3} & 0 & \dfrac{\sqrt{3}}{3} \end{bmatrix} = A$$

A is symmetric. Because the column vectors of A do not form an orthonormal set, A is not orthogonal.

32. The characteristic polynomial of A is

$$|\lambda I - A| = \begin{vmatrix} \lambda - 4 & 2 \\ 2 & \lambda - 1 \end{vmatrix} = \lambda(\lambda - 5).$$

The eigenvalues are $\lambda_1 = 0$ and $\lambda_2 = 5$. Every eigenvector corresponding to $\lambda_1 = 0$ is of the form $x_1 = (t, 2t)$, and every eigenvector corresponding to $\lambda_2 = 5$ is of the form $x_2 = (2s, -s)$.

$$x_1 \cdot x_2 = 2st - 2st = 0$$

So, x_1 and x_2 are orthogonal.

34. The matrix is diagonal, so the eigenvalues are $\lambda_1 = 2$ and $\lambda_2 = 5$. Every eigenvector corresponding to $\lambda_1 = 2$ is of the form $x_1 = (t_1, t_2, 0)$, and every eigenvector corresponding to $\lambda_2 = 5$ is of the form $x_2 = (0, 0, s)$.

$$x_1 \cdot x_2 = 0$$

So, x_1 and x_2 are othogonal.

36. The matrix is not symmetric, so it is not orthogonally diagonalizable.

38. The eigenvalues of A are 17 and -17, with corresponding unit eigenvectors $\left(\dfrac{5}{\sqrt{34}}, \dfrac{3}{\sqrt{34}}\right)$ and $\left(-\dfrac{3}{\sqrt{34}}, \dfrac{5}{\sqrt{34}}\right)$, respectively.

Form the columns of P from the eigenvectors of A.

$$P = \begin{bmatrix} \dfrac{5}{\sqrt{34}} & -\dfrac{3}{\sqrt{34}} \\ \dfrac{3}{\sqrt{34}} & \dfrac{5}{\sqrt{34}} \end{bmatrix}$$

$$P^T A P = \begin{bmatrix} \dfrac{5}{\sqrt{34}} & \dfrac{3}{\sqrt{34}} \\ -\dfrac{3}{\sqrt{34}} & \dfrac{5}{\sqrt{34}} \end{bmatrix} \begin{bmatrix} 8 & 15 \\ 15 & -8 \end{bmatrix} \begin{bmatrix} \dfrac{5}{\sqrt{34}} & -\dfrac{3}{\sqrt{34}} \\ \dfrac{3}{\sqrt{34}} & \dfrac{5}{\sqrt{34}} \end{bmatrix} = \begin{bmatrix} 17 & 0 \\ 0 & -17 \end{bmatrix}$$

40. The eigenvalues of A are -3, 0, and b, with corresponding unit eigenvectors $(0, 1, 0)$, $\left(\dfrac{1}{\sqrt{2}}, 0, \dfrac{1}{\sqrt{2}}\right)$, and

$\left(\dfrac{1}{\sqrt{2}}, 0, -\dfrac{1}{\sqrt{2}}\right)$. Form the columns of P from the eigenvectors of A.

$$P = \begin{bmatrix} 0 & \dfrac{1}{\sqrt{2}} & \dfrac{1}{\sqrt{2}} \\ 1 & 0 & 0 \\ 0 & \dfrac{1}{\sqrt{2}} & -\dfrac{1}{\sqrt{2}} \end{bmatrix}$$

$$P^T A P = \begin{bmatrix} 0 & 1 & 0 \\ \dfrac{1}{\sqrt{2}} & 0 & \dfrac{1}{\sqrt{2}} \\ \dfrac{1}{\sqrt{2}} & 0 & -\dfrac{1}{\sqrt{2}} \end{bmatrix} \begin{bmatrix} 3 & 0 & -3 \\ 0 & -3 & 0 \\ -3 & 0 & 3 \end{bmatrix} \begin{bmatrix} 0 & \dfrac{1}{\sqrt{2}} & \dfrac{1}{\sqrt{2}} \\ 1 & 0 & 0 \\ 0 & \dfrac{1}{\sqrt{2}} & -\dfrac{1}{\sqrt{2}} \end{bmatrix} = \begin{bmatrix} -3 & 0 & 0 \\ 0 & 0 & 0 \\ 0 & 0 & 6 \end{bmatrix}$$

42. The eigenvalues of A are $3, -1$, and 5, with corresponding eigenvectors

$$\left(\frac{1}{\sqrt{2}}, \frac{1}{\sqrt{2}}, 0\right), \left(\frac{1}{\sqrt{2}}, -\frac{1}{\sqrt{2}}, 0\right), (0, 0, 1).$$

Form the columns of P from the eigenvectors of A

$$P = \begin{bmatrix} \frac{1}{\sqrt{2}} & \frac{1}{\sqrt{2}} & 0 \\ \frac{1}{\sqrt{2}} & -\frac{1}{\sqrt{2}} & 0 \\ 0 & 0 & 1 \end{bmatrix}$$

$$P^T AP = \begin{bmatrix} \frac{1}{\sqrt{2}} & \frac{1}{\sqrt{2}} & 0 \\ \frac{1}{\sqrt{2}} & -\frac{1}{\sqrt{2}} & 0 \\ 0 & 0 & 1 \end{bmatrix} \begin{bmatrix} 1 & 2 & 0 \\ 2 & 1 & 0 \\ 0 & 0 & 5 \end{bmatrix} \begin{bmatrix} \frac{1}{\sqrt{2}} & \frac{1}{\sqrt{2}} & 0 \\ \frac{1}{\sqrt{2}} & -\frac{1}{\sqrt{2}} & 0 \\ 0 & 0 & 1 \end{bmatrix}$$

$$= \begin{bmatrix} 3 & 0 & 0 \\ 0 & -1 & 0 \\ 0 & 0 & 5 \end{bmatrix}$$

44. The eigenvalues of A are $-\frac{1}{2}$ and 1. The eigenvectors corresponding to $\lambda = 1$ are $\mathbf{x} = t(2, 1)$. By choosing $t = \frac{1}{3}$, you find the steady state probability vector for A to be $\mathbf{v} = \left(\frac{2}{3}, \frac{1}{3}\right)$. Note that

$$A\mathbf{v} = \begin{bmatrix} \frac{1}{2} & 1 \\ \frac{1}{2} & 0 \end{bmatrix} \begin{bmatrix} \frac{2}{3} \\ \frac{1}{3} \end{bmatrix} = \begin{bmatrix} \frac{2}{3} \\ \frac{1}{3} \end{bmatrix} = \mathbf{v}.$$

46. The eigenvalues of A are $\frac{1}{5}$ and 1. The eigenvectors corresponding to $\lambda = 1$ are $\mathbf{x} = t(1, 3)$. By choosing $t = \frac{1}{4}$, you can find the steady state probability vector for A to be $\mathbf{v} = \left(\frac{1}{4}, \frac{3}{4}\right)$. Note that

$$A\mathbf{v} = \begin{bmatrix} 0.4 & 0.2 \\ 0.6 & 0.8 \end{bmatrix} \begin{bmatrix} \frac{1}{4} \\ \frac{3}{4} \end{bmatrix} = \begin{bmatrix} \frac{1}{4} \\ \frac{3}{4} \end{bmatrix} = \mathbf{v}.$$

48. The eigenvalues of A are $-0.2060, 0.5393$ and 1. The eigenvectors corresponding to $\lambda = 1$ are $\mathbf{x} = t(2, 1, 2)$. By choosing $t = \frac{1}{5}$, find the steady state probability vector for A to be $\mathbf{v} = \left(\frac{2}{5}, \frac{1}{5}, \frac{2}{5}\right)$. Note that

$$A\mathbf{v} = \begin{bmatrix} \frac{1}{3} & \frac{2}{3} & \frac{1}{3} \\ \frac{1}{3} & \frac{1}{3} & 0 \\ \frac{1}{3} & 0 & \frac{2}{3} \end{bmatrix} \begin{bmatrix} \frac{2}{5} \\ \frac{1}{5} \\ \frac{2}{5} \end{bmatrix} = \begin{bmatrix} \frac{2}{5} \\ \frac{1}{5} \\ \frac{2}{5} \end{bmatrix} = \mathbf{v}.$$

50. The eigenvalues of A are $\frac{1}{10}, \frac{1}{5}$, and 1. The eigenvectors corresponding to $\lambda = 1$ are $\mathbf{x} = t(3, 1, 5)$. By choosing $t = \frac{1}{9}$, you can find the steady state probability vector for A to be $\mathbf{v} = \left(\frac{1}{3}, \frac{1}{9}, \frac{5}{9}\right)$. Note that

$$A\mathbf{v} = \begin{bmatrix} 0.3 & 0.1 & 0.4 \\ 0.2 & 0.4 & 0.0 \\ 0.5 & 0.5 & 0.6 \end{bmatrix} \begin{bmatrix} \frac{1}{3} \\ \frac{1}{9} \\ \frac{5}{9} \end{bmatrix} = \begin{bmatrix} \frac{1}{3} \\ \frac{1}{9} \\ \frac{5}{9} \end{bmatrix} = \mathbf{v}.$$

52. For the sake of simplicity, assume $a_n = 1$, and observe that the following proof holds for any nonzero a_n. First show by induction that for the $n \times n$ matrix C_n,

$$|C_n| = \begin{vmatrix} \lambda & -1 & 0 & \cdots & 0 \\ 0 & \lambda & -1 & \cdots & 0 \\ \vdots & \vdots & \vdots & & -1 \\ b_0 & b_1 & b_2 & \cdots & b_{n-1} \end{vmatrix} = b_{n-1}\lambda^{n-1} + \cdots + b_1\lambda + b_0.$$

For $n = 1$, $|C_1| = b_0$, and for $n = 2$,

$$|C_2| = \begin{vmatrix} \lambda & -1 \\ b_0 & b_1 \end{vmatrix} = b_1\lambda + b_0.$$

Assuming the property for n, you see that

$$|C_{n+1}| = \begin{vmatrix} \lambda & -1 & 0 & \cdots & 0 \\ 0 & \lambda & -1 & \cdots & 0 \\ \vdots & \vdots & \vdots & \vdots & -1 \\ b_0 & b_1 & b_2 & \cdots & b_n \end{vmatrix} = b_n\lambda^n + |C_n| = b_n\lambda^n + b_{n-1}\lambda^{n-1} + b_1\lambda + b_0.$$

So, showing the property is valid for $n + 1$. You can now evaluate the characteristic equation of A as follows.

$$|\lambda I - A| = \begin{vmatrix} \lambda & -1 & 0 & \cdots & 0 \\ 0 & \lambda & -1 & \cdots & 0 \\ \vdots & \vdots & \vdots & & \vdots \\ 0 & 0 & 0 & \vdots & -1 \\ a_0 & a_1 & a_2 & \vdots & \lambda + a_{n-1} \end{vmatrix} = (\lambda + a_{n-1})\lambda^{n-1} + |C_{n-2}| = \lambda^n + a_{n-1}\lambda^{n-1} + a_{n-2}\lambda^{n-2} + \ldots + a_1\lambda + a_0.$$

54. From the form $p(\lambda) = a_0 + a_1\lambda + a_2\lambda^2 + a_3\lambda^3$, you have $a_0 = 189$, $a_1 = -120$, $a_2 = -7$ and $a_3 = 2$. This implies that the companion matrix of p is

$$A = \begin{bmatrix} 0 & 1 & 0 \\ 0 & 0 & 1 \\ -\frac{189}{2} & 60 & \frac{7}{2} \end{bmatrix}.$$

The eigenvalues of A are $\frac{3}{2}$, 9, and -7, the zeros of p.

56. The characteristic equation of A is $|\lambda I - A| = \lambda^3 - 20\lambda^2 + 128\lambda - 256 = 0$.

Because $A^3 - 20A^2 + 128A - 256I = O$, you have $A^2 = \begin{bmatrix} 9 & 4 & -3 \\ -2 & 0 & 6 \\ -1 & -4 & 11 \end{bmatrix}\begin{bmatrix} 9 & 4 & -3 \\ -2 & 0 & 6 \\ -1 & -4 & 11 \end{bmatrix} = \begin{bmatrix} 76 & 48 & -36 \\ -24 & -32 & 72 \\ -12 & -48 & 100 \end{bmatrix}$

and

$$A^3 = 20A^2 - 128A + 256I = 20\begin{bmatrix} 76 & 48 & -32 \\ -24 & -32 & 72 \\ -12 & -48 & 100 \end{bmatrix} - 128\begin{bmatrix} 9 & 4 & -3 \\ -2 & 0 & 6 \\ -1 & -4 & 11 \end{bmatrix} + 256\begin{bmatrix} 1 & 0 & 0 \\ 0 & 1 & 0 \\ 0 & 0 & 1 \end{bmatrix} = \begin{bmatrix} 624 & 448 & -336 \\ -224 & -384 & 672 \\ -112 & -448 & 848 \end{bmatrix}.$$

58. $(A + cI)\mathbf{x} = A\mathbf{x} + cI\mathbf{x} = \lambda\mathbf{x} + c\mathbf{x} = (\lambda + c)\mathbf{x}$. So, $\mathbf{x}$ is an eigenvector of $(A + cI)$ with eigenvalue $(\lambda + c)$.

60. (a) The eigenvalues of A are 3 and 1, with corresponding eigenvectors $(1, 1)$ and $(1, -1)$. Letting these eigenvectors form the columns of P, you can diagonalize A.

$$P = \begin{bmatrix} 1 & 1 \\ 1 & -1 \end{bmatrix} \text{ and } P^{-1}AP = \begin{bmatrix} 3 & 0 \\ 0 & 1 \end{bmatrix} = D$$

So, $A = PDP^{-1} = P\begin{bmatrix} 3 & 0 \\ 0 & 1 \end{bmatrix}P^{-1}$. Letting $B = P\begin{bmatrix} \sqrt{3} & 0 \\ 0 & 1 \end{bmatrix}P^{-1} = \frac{1}{2}\begin{bmatrix} \sqrt{3}+1 & \sqrt{3}-1 \\ \sqrt{3}-1 & \sqrt{3}+1 \end{bmatrix}$

you have $B = \left(P\begin{bmatrix} \sqrt{3} & 0 \\ 0 & 1 \end{bmatrix}P^{-1}\right)^2 = P\begin{bmatrix} \sqrt{3} & 0 \\ 0 & 1 \end{bmatrix}^2 P^{-1} = P\begin{bmatrix} 3 & 0 \\ 0 & 1 \end{bmatrix}P^{-1} = A.$

(b) In general, let $A = PDP^{-1}$, D diagonal with positive eigenvalues on the diagonal. Let D' be the diagonal matrix consisting of the square roots of the diagonal entries of D. Then if $B = PD'P^{-1}$,

$$B^2 = (PD'P^{-1})(PD'P^{-1}) = P(D')^2P^{-1} = PDP^{-1} = A.$$

62. Because $A\mathbf{x} = A^2\mathbf{x}$ and
$A^2\mathbf{x} = A(A\mathbf{x}) = A(\lambda\mathbf{x}) = \lambda^2\mathbf{x}$, you see that
$\lambda\mathbf{x} = \lambda^2\mathbf{x}$, or $\lambda = \lambda^2 \Rightarrow \lambda = 0$ or 1.

64. If A is symmetric and has 0 as its only eigenvalue, then $P^TAP = \mathbf{0}$, the zero matrix, which implies that $A = \mathbf{0}$.

66. (a) True. See Theorem 7.2 on page 426.

(b) False. See remark after the "Definitions of Eigenvalue and Eigenvector" on page 422. If $\mathbf{x} = \mathbf{0}$ is allowed to be an eigenvector, then the definition of eigenvalue would be meaningless, because $A\mathbf{0} = \lambda\mathbf{0}$ for *all* real numbers λ.

(c) True. See page 453.

68. The population after one transition is

$$\mathbf{x}_2 = \begin{bmatrix} 0 & 1 \\ \frac{3}{4} & 0 \end{bmatrix}\begin{bmatrix} 32 \\ 32 \end{bmatrix} = \begin{bmatrix} 32 \\ 24 \end{bmatrix}$$

and after two transitions is

$$\mathbf{x}_3 = \begin{bmatrix} 0 & 1 \\ \frac{3}{4} & 0 \end{bmatrix}\begin{bmatrix} 32 \\ 24 \end{bmatrix} = \begin{bmatrix} 24 \\ 24 \end{bmatrix}.$$

The eigenvalues of A are $\pm\frac{\sqrt{3}}{2}$. Choose the positive eigenvalue and find the corresponding eigenvector to be $(2, \sqrt{3})$, and the stable age distribution vector is

$$\mathbf{x} = t\begin{bmatrix} 2 \\ \sqrt{3} \end{bmatrix}$$

70. The population after one transition is

$$\mathbf{x}_2 = \begin{bmatrix} 0 & 2 & 2 \\ \frac{1}{2} & 0 & 0 \\ 0 & 0 & 0 \end{bmatrix} \begin{bmatrix} 240 \\ 240 \\ 240 \end{bmatrix} = \begin{bmatrix} 960 \\ 120 \\ 0 \end{bmatrix}$$

and after two transitions is

$$\mathbf{x}_3 = \begin{bmatrix} 0 & 2 & 2 \\ \frac{1}{2} & 0 & 0 \\ 0 & 0 & 0 \end{bmatrix} \begin{bmatrix} 960 \\ 120 \\ 0 \end{bmatrix} = \begin{bmatrix} 240 \\ 480 \\ 0 \end{bmatrix}.$$

The positive eigenvalue 1 has corresponding eigenvector

$(2, 1, 0)$, and the stable distribution vector is $\mathbf{x} = t\begin{bmatrix} 2 \\ 1 \\ 0 \end{bmatrix}$.

72. Construct the age transition matrix.

$$A = \begin{bmatrix} 4 & 8 & 2 \\ 0.75 & 0 & 0 \\ 0 & 0.6 & 0 \end{bmatrix}$$

The current age distribution vector is $\mathbf{x}_1 = \begin{bmatrix} 120 \\ 120 \\ 120 \end{bmatrix}$.

In one year, the age distribution vector will be

$$\mathbf{x}_2 = A\mathbf{x}_1 = \begin{bmatrix} 4 & 8 & 2 \\ 0.75 & 0 & 0 \\ 0 & 0.6 & 0 \end{bmatrix} \begin{bmatrix} 120 \\ 120 \\ 120 \end{bmatrix} = \begin{bmatrix} 1680 \\ 90 \\ 72 \end{bmatrix}.$$

In two years, the age distribution vector will be

$$\mathbf{x}_3 = A\mathbf{x}_2 = \begin{bmatrix} 4 & 8 & 2 \\ 0.75 & 0 & 0 \\ 0 & 0.6 & 0 \end{bmatrix} \begin{bmatrix} 1680 \\ 90 \\ 72 \end{bmatrix} = \begin{bmatrix} 7584 \\ 1260 \\ 54 \end{bmatrix}.$$

74. The solution of the differential equation $y' = ky$ is
$y = Ce^{kt}$. So, $y_1 = C_1 e^{10t}$, $y_2 = C_2 e^{-0.1t}$,

$y_3 = C_3 e^{\sqrt{2}t}$, and $y_4 = C_4 e^{3/4t}$.

76. The matrix corresponds to the system $\mathbf{y}' = A\mathbf{y}$ is

$$A = \begin{bmatrix} 3 & 0 \\ 1 & -1 \end{bmatrix}.$$

This matrix has eigenvalues 3 and -1, with
corresponding eigenvectors $(4, 1)$ and $(0, 1)$. So, a matrix
P that diagonalizes A is

$$P = \begin{bmatrix} 4 & 0 \\ 1 & 1 \end{bmatrix} \quad \text{and} \quad P^{-1}AP = \begin{bmatrix} 3 & 0 \\ 0 & -1 \end{bmatrix}.$$

The system represented by $\mathbf{w}' = P^{-1}AP\mathbf{w}$ has solutions
$w_1 = C_1 e^{3t}$ and $w_2 = c_2 e^{-t}$. Substitute $\mathbf{y} = P\mathbf{w}$ and
obtain

$$\begin{bmatrix} y_1 \\ y_2 \end{bmatrix} = \begin{bmatrix} 4 & 0 \\ 1 & 1 \end{bmatrix} \begin{bmatrix} w_1 \\ w_2 \end{bmatrix} = \begin{bmatrix} 4w_1 \\ w_1 + w_2 \end{bmatrix}$$

which yields the solution

$$y_1 = 4C_1 e^{3t}$$
$$y_2 = C_1 e^{3t} + C_2 e^{-t}.$$

78. The matrix corresponding to the system $\mathbf{y}' = A\mathbf{y}$ is

$$A = \begin{bmatrix} 6 & -1 & 2 \\ 0 & 3 & -1 \\ 0 & 0 & 1 \end{bmatrix}.$$

The eigenvalues of A are 6, 3, and 1, with corresponding
eigenvectors $(1, 0, 0), (1, 3, 0)$, and $(-3, 5, 10)$. So, you
can diagonalize A by forming P.

$$P = \begin{bmatrix} 1 & 1 & -3 \\ 0 & 3 & 5 \\ 0 & 0 & 10 \end{bmatrix} \quad \text{and} \quad P^{-1}AP = \begin{bmatrix} 6 & 0 & 0 \\ 0 & 3 & 0 \\ 0 & 0 & 1 \end{bmatrix}.$$

The system represented by $\mathbf{w}' = P^{-1}AP\mathbf{w}$ has solutions
$w_1 = C_1 e^{6t}$, $w_2 = C_2 e^{3t}$, and $w_3 = C_3 e^{t}$. Substitute
$\mathbf{y} = P\mathbf{w}$ and obtain

$$\begin{bmatrix} y_1 \\ y_2 \\ y_3 \end{bmatrix} = \begin{bmatrix} 1 & 1 & -3 \\ 0 & 3 & 5 \\ 0 & 0 & 10 \end{bmatrix} \begin{bmatrix} w_1 \\ w_2 \\ w_3 \end{bmatrix} = \begin{bmatrix} w_1 + w_2 - 3w_3 \\ 3w_2 + 5w_3 \\ 10w_3 \end{bmatrix}$$

which yields the solution

$$y_1 = C_1 e^{6t} + C_2 e^{3t} - 3C_3 e^{t}$$
$$y_2 = 3C_2 e^{3t} + 5C_3 e^{t}$$
$$y_3 = 10C_3 e^{t}.$$

80. (a) The matrix of the quadratic form is

$$A = \begin{bmatrix} a & \dfrac{b}{2} \\ \dfrac{b}{2} & c \end{bmatrix} = \begin{bmatrix} 1 & -\dfrac{\sqrt{3}}{2} \\ -\dfrac{\sqrt{3}}{2} & 2 \end{bmatrix}.$$

(b) The eigenvalues are $\dfrac{1}{2}$ and $\dfrac{5}{2}$, with corresponding unit eigenvectors $\left(\dfrac{\sqrt{3}}{2}, \dfrac{1}{2}\right)$ and $\left(-\dfrac{1}{2}, \dfrac{\sqrt{3}}{2}\right)$.

Use these eigenvectors to form the columns of P.

$$P = \begin{bmatrix} \dfrac{\sqrt{3}}{2} & -\dfrac{1}{2} \\ \dfrac{1}{2} & \dfrac{\sqrt{3}}{2} \end{bmatrix} \quad \text{and} \quad P^{T}AP = \begin{bmatrix} \dfrac{1}{2} & 0 \\ 0 & \dfrac{5}{2} \end{bmatrix}$$

(c) This implies that the equation of the rotated conic is

$$\frac{1}{2}(x')^2 + \frac{5}{2}(y')^2 = 10, \text{ an ellipse.}$$

(d)

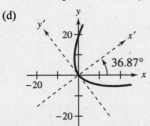

82. (a) The matrix of the quadratic form is

$$A = \begin{bmatrix} 1 & \dfrac{b}{2} \\ \dfrac{b}{2} & c \end{bmatrix} = \begin{bmatrix} 9 & -12 \\ -12 & 16 \end{bmatrix}.$$

(b) The eigenvalues are 0 and 25, with corresponding unit eigenvectors $\left(\dfrac{4}{5}, \dfrac{3}{5}\right)$ and $\left(-\dfrac{3}{5}, \dfrac{4}{5}\right)$. Use these

eigenvectors to form the columns of P.

$$P = \begin{bmatrix} \dfrac{4}{5} & -\dfrac{3}{5} \\ \dfrac{3}{5} & \dfrac{4}{5} \end{bmatrix} \quad \text{and} \quad P^{T}AP = \begin{bmatrix} 0 & 0 \\ 0 & 25 \end{bmatrix}$$

This implies that the equation of the rotated conic is a parabola.

(c) Furthermore,

$$[d \quad e]P = [-400 \quad -300]\begin{bmatrix} \dfrac{4}{5} & -\dfrac{3}{5} \\ \dfrac{3}{5} & \dfrac{4}{5} \end{bmatrix} = [-500 \quad 0] = [d' \quad e']$$

so the equation in the $x'y'$-coordinate system is $25(y')^2 - 500x' = 0$.

(d)

Project Solutions for Chapter 7

1 Population Growth and Dynamical Systems (I)

1. $A = \begin{bmatrix} 0.5 & 0.6 \\ -0.4 & 3.0 \end{bmatrix}$, $\lambda_1 = 0.6, \mathbf{w}_1 = \begin{bmatrix} 6 \\ 1 \end{bmatrix}$

$$\lambda_2 = 2.9, \mathbf{w}_2 = \begin{bmatrix} 1 \\ 4 \end{bmatrix}$$

$$P = \begin{bmatrix} 6 & 1 \\ 1 & 4 \end{bmatrix}, \quad P^{-1} = \frac{1}{23}\begin{bmatrix} 4 & -1 \\ -1 & 6 \end{bmatrix}, \quad P^{-1}AP = \begin{bmatrix} 0.6 & 0 \\ 0 & 2.9 \end{bmatrix}$$

$$\mathbf{w}_1 = C_1 e^{0.6t}, \quad \mathbf{w}_2 = C_2 e^{2.9t}, \quad \mathbf{y} = P\mathbf{w}$$

$$\begin{bmatrix} y_1 \\ y_2 \end{bmatrix} = \begin{bmatrix} 6 & 1 \\ 1 & 4 \end{bmatrix}\begin{bmatrix} C_1 e^{0.6t} \\ C_2 e^{2.9t} \end{bmatrix} = \begin{bmatrix} 6C_1 e^{0.6t} + C_2 e^{2.9t} \\ C_1 e^{0.6t} + 4C_2 e^{2.9t} \end{bmatrix}$$

$$\left. \begin{array}{l} y_1(0) = 36 \Rightarrow 6C_1 + C_2 = 36 \\ y_2(0) = 121 \Rightarrow C_1 + 4C_2 = 121 \end{array} \right\}$$

So, $C_1 = 1, C_2 = 30$ and

$$y_1 = 6e^{0.6t} + 30e^{2.9t}$$
$$y_2 = e^{0.6t} + 120e^{2.9t}.$$

2. No, neither species disappears. As $t \to \infty$, $y_1 \to 30e^{2.9t}$ and $y_2 \to 120e^{2.9t}$.

3.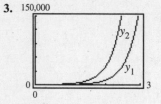

4. As $t \to \infty$, $y_1 \to 30e^{2.9t}$, $y_2 \to 120e^{2.9t}$, and $\dfrac{y_2}{y_1} = 4$.

5. The population y_2 ultimately disappears around $t = 1.6$.

2 The Fibonacci Sequence

1.

$x_1 = 1$	$x_4 = 3$	$x_7 = 13$	$x_{10} = 55$
$x_2 = 1$	$x_5 = 5$	$x_8 = 21$	$x_{11} = 89$
$x_3 = 2$	$x_6 = 8$	$x_9 = 34$	$x_{12} = 144$

2. $\begin{bmatrix} 1 & 1 \\ 1 & 0 \end{bmatrix}\begin{bmatrix} x_{n-1} \\ x_{n-2} \end{bmatrix} = \begin{bmatrix} x_{n-1} + x_{n-2} \\ x_{n-1} \end{bmatrix} = \begin{bmatrix} x_n \\ x_{n-1} \end{bmatrix}$. x_n generated from $\begin{bmatrix} x_{n-1} \\ x_{n-2} \end{bmatrix}$

3. $A\begin{bmatrix} 1 \\ 1 \end{bmatrix} = A\begin{bmatrix} x_2 \\ x_1 \end{bmatrix} = \begin{bmatrix} x_3 \\ x_2 \end{bmatrix} = \begin{bmatrix} 2 \\ 1 \end{bmatrix}$

$A^2\begin{bmatrix} 1 \\ 1 \end{bmatrix} = \begin{bmatrix} 3 \\ 2 \end{bmatrix} = \begin{bmatrix} x_4 \\ x_3 \end{bmatrix}$

In general, $A^n\begin{bmatrix} 1 \\ 1 \end{bmatrix} = \begin{bmatrix} x_{n+2} \\ x_{n+1} \end{bmatrix}$ or $A^{n-2}\begin{bmatrix} 1 \\ 1 \end{bmatrix} = \begin{bmatrix} x_n \\ x_{n-1} \end{bmatrix}$.

4. $\begin{vmatrix} \lambda - 1 & -1 \\ -1 & \lambda \end{vmatrix} = \lambda^2 - \lambda - 1 = 0 \quad \Rightarrow \quad \lambda = \dfrac{1 \pm \sqrt{5}}{2}$

$\lambda_1 = \dfrac{1 + \sqrt{5}}{2}$ eigenvector: $\begin{bmatrix} 2 \\ -1 + \sqrt{5} \end{bmatrix}$

$\lambda_2 = \dfrac{1 - \sqrt{5}}{2}$ eigenvector: $\begin{bmatrix} 2 \\ -1 - \sqrt{5} \end{bmatrix}$

$P = \begin{bmatrix} 2 & 2 \\ -1 + \sqrt{5} & -1 - \sqrt{5} \end{bmatrix}$

$P^{-1} = \dfrac{1}{4\sqrt{5}} \begin{bmatrix} 1 + \sqrt{5} & 2 \\ -1 + \sqrt{5} & -2 \end{bmatrix}$

$P^{-1}AP = \begin{bmatrix} \lambda_1 & 0 \\ 0 & \lambda_2 \end{bmatrix}$

5. $P^{-1}AP = D$

$P^{-1}A^{n-2}P = D^{n-2}$

$A^{n-2} = PD^{n-2}P^{-1}$

$= \dfrac{1}{4\sqrt{5}} \begin{bmatrix} 2 & 2 \\ -1 + \sqrt{5} & -1 - \sqrt{5} \end{bmatrix} \begin{bmatrix} \left(\dfrac{1 + \sqrt{5}}{2}\right)^{n-2} & 0 \\ 0 & \left(\dfrac{1 - \sqrt{5}}{2}\right)^{n-2} \end{bmatrix} \begin{bmatrix} 1 + \sqrt{5} & 2 \\ -1 + \sqrt{5} & -2 \end{bmatrix}$

$= \dfrac{1}{4\sqrt{5}} \begin{bmatrix} 2(\lambda_1)^{n-2} & 2(\lambda_2)^{n-2} \\ (-1 + \sqrt{5})(\lambda_1)^{n-2} & (-1 - \sqrt{5})(\lambda_2)^{n-2} \end{bmatrix} \begin{bmatrix} 1 + \sqrt{5} & 2 \\ -1 + \sqrt{5} & -2 \end{bmatrix}$

$= \dfrac{1}{4\sqrt{5}} \begin{bmatrix} 2(1 + \sqrt{5})(\lambda_1)^{n-2} + 2(-1 + \sqrt{5})(\lambda_2)^{n-2} & 4(\lambda_1)^{n-2} - 4\lambda_2^{n-2} \\ +4\lambda_1^{n-2} - 4\lambda_2^{n-2} & 2(-1 + \sqrt{5})\lambda_1^{n-2} + 2(1 + \sqrt{5})\lambda_2^{n-2} \end{bmatrix}$

$A^{n-2}\begin{bmatrix} 1 \\ 1 \end{bmatrix} = \begin{bmatrix} x_n \\ x_{n-1} \end{bmatrix} \Rightarrow$

$x_n = \dfrac{1}{4\sqrt{5}}\left[2(1 + \sqrt{5})\lambda_1^{n-2} + 2(-1 + \sqrt{5})\lambda_2^{n-2} + 4\lambda_1^{n-2} - 4\lambda_2^{n-2}\right]$

$= \dfrac{1}{\sqrt{5}}\left[\lambda_1^n - \lambda_2^n\right]$

$x_n = \dfrac{1}{\sqrt{5}}\left[\left(\dfrac{1 + \sqrt{5}}{2}\right)^n - \left(\dfrac{1 - \sqrt{5}}{2}\right)^n\right]$

$x_1 = \dfrac{1}{\sqrt{5}}(\sqrt{5}) = 1$

$x_2 = \dfrac{1}{\sqrt{5}}\left[\dfrac{6 + 2\sqrt{5}}{4} - \dfrac{6 - 2\sqrt{5}}{4}\right] = 1$

$x_3 = \dfrac{1}{\sqrt{5}}\left[\dfrac{6 + 2\sqrt{5}}{4} \cdot \dfrac{1 + \sqrt{5}}{2} - \dfrac{6 - 2\sqrt{5}}{4} \cdot \dfrac{1 - \sqrt{5}}{2}\right] = \dfrac{1}{\sqrt{5}}\left[\dfrac{16 + 8\sqrt{5}}{8} - \dfrac{16 - 8\sqrt{5}}{8}\right] = 2$

6. $x_{10} = 55$, $x_{20} = 6765$

7. For example, $\dfrac{x_{20}}{x_{19}} = \dfrac{6765}{4181} = 1.618\ldots.$

The quotients seem to be approaching a fixed value near 1.618.

8. Let the limit be $\dfrac{x_n}{x_{n-1}} = b$. Then for large n, $n \rightarrow \infty$.

$$b \approx \frac{x_n}{x_{n-1}} = \frac{x_{n-1} + x_{n-2}}{x_{n-1}} \approx 1 + \frac{1}{b} \quad \Rightarrow \quad b^2 - b - 1 = 0 \quad \Rightarrow \quad b = \frac{1 \pm \sqrt{5}}{2}$$

Taking the positive value, $b = \dfrac{1 + \sqrt{5}}{2} \approx 1.618$.